The Beekay
Guide to
1500
British
and
European
Carp Waters

**Compiled by
Kevin Maddocks
and
Peter Mohan**

Acknowledgements

Beekay Publishers would like to thank all those people from many parts of the country who have so readily agreed to provide information to help with the compilation of this book.

We are especially grateful to John Wilson, the well-known angler and tackle dealer, of John's Tackle Den, 16 Bridewell Alley, Norwich, Norfolk, for permission to publish details based on his excellent book *Where to Fish in Norfolk and Suffolk*, published by Jarrold and Sons Ltd of Norwich, to Steve Bowers of 12 Machin Road, Erdington, Birmingham, and his friends of the Central Specimen Group who helped in connection with waters in the West Midlands, to Kevin Gulliford of Ebbw Vale who assisted with waters in Wales, and to Mr Beedom of Doncaster, Steve Francis, Neville Fickling, Len Gurd, Ann Pillinger, John Callaghan, Steve Cole, Bill Turner, Roger Emmet, Rupe Attwood, Adam Joste, Mick Sutton, Norman Smith, Peter Stone, Mick Ellingworth, John Baron, Rory, of Southend Angling Centre and Mike of Bleak Hall Sports, Kempston, Bedford. We also thank all those who we hope will write to us in the future with corrections, amendments and additions for our fifth edition.

*   County Maps
Please note that these maps are not to scale, nor are the locations indicated the exact geographical position of the place concerned. They are only intended to be a rough guide when the reader does not have a proper map to hand.

**A
Waters which have the letter 'A' beside them have some form of accommodation connected with them, and so are particularly suitable for holidays; many of them for family holidays.

Cover picture: John Baker
Index compiled by Ann Pillinger

ISBN 0 94767443 8

Design, production and advertisement sales: Dave Watson
20 Beaufort Gardens, Ascot, Berkshire SL5 8PG. Tel: 0344 23844

Introduction

It has been said that the last thing left to do in carp fishing is to publish a list of carp waters and their locations, and this is what BK Publishers have tried to do with this book. We feel that the publication of this material ushers in a new era in carp fishing; one which is long overdue. The time has passed for one of the major factors in carp fishing to be the excessive secrecy which was a characteristic of the sport in past years.

In 1969, when the British Carp Study Group, the world's first large national organisation for carp anglers was founded by Peter Mohan, there were probably about 250 specialist carp anglers in the whole country; now there are reliably estimated to be around 50,000, many of whom, when they take up the sport each year in their thousands, demand every type of information about baits, methods and rigs, and also about locations of carp waters.

Secrecy

The older and more secretive carp anglers, who don't like the idea of a book of this kind, should remember that they are very much in the minority; most of today's carp anglers will welcome a book of this sort. We feel, too, that so will most carp anglers once they read the contents of the book. We have been very careful to omit all waters we know to be 'secret'; we have left out any waters, club or otherwise, where there are 'no publicity' rules; and we have omitted all waters where membership cannot be obtained. We even asked many carp anglers which waters they wanted to be left out of the book, and we did not include those waters!

Most of the waters listed are those which anyone can fish, and which were already known to many anglers. We don't feel that a listing in this book will substantially increase the number fishing any particular water; in fact, the number fishing your water may actually be reduced when readers learn about other waters from this book and go to fish them, thus 'spreading the load' better on waters throughout the country.

We are not in the business of giving away anglers' secrets and this has been carefully avoided in the book as far as possible. This book, the first ever Guide to Carp Waters, will have its critics, but we feel that like anything new it has now been accepted and has become as natural a part of the carp scene as any book on carp methods and tactics, and that all carp anglers will want to own a copy. Obviously, the book will be particularly helpful to the many thousands of anglers who take up specialist carp fishing every year, but we feel it will also be especially helpful to more experienced carp anglers who wish to try other waters, and we are sure that it will be of great help to the many who write to well known carp anglers regularly asking them for the names of waters they can fish whilst they are on holiday in different parts of the country.

Carp Waters It must be noted by readers that many of the waters listed in this book are not really 'carp waters', if this is taken to mean waters containing mainly, or only, carp. In fact there are very few waters in the country which contain only carp, or where carp are very much in the majority. Most waters contain only some carp, and so many of these have been included in this book. We have listed many waters which contain few carp, because some carp anglers prefer to fish this type of water in the hope of big carp from an unrecognised water. So please don't expect most of the lakes listed to be packed with carp; they often aren't.

Quite a few of those 'secret' and 'no publicity' lakes which we have not been able to list in this book may come under the category of waters which contain mainly carp, and often big ones - which is the reason those who control the waters of this kind want to keep them quiet!

Organisation of the book Some angling guides we have examined are so complex that they are difficult to use, and to avoid this we kept the layout of the book as simple as possible. The waters are classified into counties, which are arranged in alphabetical order, and the waters under each county name are also arranged in alphabetical order, with an index at the back of the book. The categories are listed for each water, and there are no abbreviations so there is nothing to look up; all the information you will need will be under the entry for the venue concerned.

We don't feel it appropriate for a book of this kind to include instructional articles or 'tips' on carp fishing. If you want this kind of material, obtain copies of a carp magazine, or we can strongly recommend the following books also published by BK Publishers: *Carp Fever* by Kevin Maddocks, *Successful Angling Series* by Rob Maylin, and *Big Water Carp* by Jim Gibbinson. All the information about baits, methods, tackle, flavours, bait recipes and rigs will be found in these three books.

Research Readers (and reviewers!) should take careful note of the fact that is **absolutely impossible** for a guide of this kind to be completely accurate.

The present revision took six months work, followed by three months to prepare and print the book. During this time, it is inevitable that many of the details listed have changed; in fact, we were making 'corrections of corrections' right up to the last minute, but it was obviously impossible to make corrections after the book had gone to print - and it takes three months at least to print a book, during which time some of the information in the book is obviously out of date, as waters change hands, or owners change fishing costs.

In addition, in January this year we wrote over 300 letters to people many of whom controlled waters listed in this book and only 80 replies were received - had the other 220 answered our letter, the book would undoubtedly be even more accurate.

Even some of our critics were of little help; they told us where we were wrong, but many didn't bother to send us the correct information, so that we could put it right!

If **you** can help, please contact us as soon as possible, so that we can make further corrections for the next edition in two years time.

Because of the obvious problems mentioned above, the Publishers can take no responsibility for any mistakes or omissions which may have occurred - all of our information is published in good faith, but it would have taken us many years to visit all the waters listed, in which case the book would never have been published, and some of the information supplied by others, may not necessarily be accurate.

We have done our best to make the information as accurate as possible, but had we taken any longer to check it even more carefully, more details would have become out of date!

Some of the categories such as whether a water is easy, moderate or difficult are subjective, and some anglers may not agree with us; we can only enter in what our judgement is correct.

We shall be happy to hear from readers if they have any criticism of the information provided, and especially if they would like to add any waters to the book which they thinks should be included. Just write to Beekay Publishers at the address given at the beginning of the book, if you wish to comment on any of the information given, or to add anything to the new edition.

Information Please note the book is a 'guide' to carp waters. Exactly the same information is not included for every water, and any omissions are intentional. If you find that categories are omitted from some of the waters this was simply because we were not able to obtain the information in the case of that water to enable us to complete the category. If there was information which we were unable to obtain or which we weren't sure about, we simply left out that category.

In some cases we were able to find out very little about a water, but as long as we were able to give a rough idea of where it was, that it existed, and that it contained some carp, and that we could indicate in some way in which you could obtain permission to fish, then we thought it better to include the venue, and leave it to you to find out the rest of the information yourselves.

Revision

It is our intention to revise and up-date the book every two years, or sooner, so any information you can provide for future editions will be gratefully received by the Publishers, and will enable us to keep this guide up to date. (Please use the form at the back of this guide.)

Well-known Waters

Some readers may be surprised to find some of the well-known carp waters omitted from the list. As we have already said, we can see no point in listing waters which you cannot fish and other well-known waters have a publicity ban; there would be no point in including them, as this would only cause trouble for those lucky enough to be able to fish there. For this reason, some of the better known lakes have been left out.

Day Ticket Waters

In many cases, you can get permission to fish these waters in advance at the address given; if you can't, it might be worth going to the water and fishing. In many cases, there are bailiffs who will collect your money on the spot, although sometimes you may have to pay more if you buy a permit on the bank.

If it is stated that you must obtain a ticket in advance, it is advisable to do so, or you may be banned from fishing the water.

Club Waters

Clubs have some of the best carp waters in the country, but the carp anglers may well have to share the water with non-carp anglers. It pays to try to get on with other anglers, whatever you may think of them. If you upset them too much, you may well find that the clubs start to ban carp anglers; this has already happened in some cases. We are in a minority on waters of this kind, so we should be careful how we behave.

We are sorry that so few good club carp waters are included in this guide. We know of many good club waters but it has not been found possible to include them because most of the clubs seem to be very shy of publicity.

To give some idea of the problems of compiling a guide of this kind, we wrote to more than 100 of the major clubs which we know have good carp fisheries, most containing carp of over 20lbs; some of these were clubs which advertise in the angling press for more members from time to time.

Less than 10% replied.

Syndicate Waters

Most syndicate waters have not been included because in many cases it is impossible to obtain membership. Those that are included are on the request of those in charge of the water. We have not put syndicate waters in without permission, and since these are always on private property readers should not go to these waters without permission. We know of a number of cases where anglers have lost their chance of getting into a syndicate water by walking round that water before being given permission to do so! Syndicate water locations are deliberately omitted to avoid unwelcome visitors. Please remember that a syndicate leader is under no obligation to offer membership to anyone; he is likely to be very choosy.

Using the Information Contained in this Book

Please remember to use this book as the 'guide' it is intended to be. Read the information on the water concerned and then try and find out as much more about it as you can, which will help you to be successful with your fishing here.

Don't expect every bit of information to be exactly accurate, although, as we have already said, we have tried to be as careful as possible about accuracy. However, waters change, often rapidly, and what was the best bait or method at the time of compilation may not be so by the time you get to the water. This applies to prices, of course, which may be altered at any time. It may even apply to the ownership or control of the water, which may have changed during the compilation or printing of this book, which has taken about a year. So please don't blame us if you go to a water listed and find you can't fish it because control or other circumstances have changed since we listed it; just let us know how the circumstances have changed so that we can include the altered information in our next revision of this book. Club Secretaries change frequently, for example; those we have included were correct when we went to press.

Categories

Our categories are: Carp Only; Carp Water; Mixed Fishery; Few Carp. These are all self-explanatory, except perhaps the 'Carp Water' category, which in our judgement means that the water contains mainly carp.

BK Ratings	Our ratings are: Very Easy; Easy; Moderate; Fairly Hard; Difficult; Very Difficult; Super-Difficult.
	As we have said earlier, these ratings are only our opinion; if you disagree, please let us known.
Carp Anglers' Behaviour	We do feel that a note in connection with this subject is appropriate in a book of this kind, especially as many people who control waters have told us that the behaviour of some carp anglers is giving cause for concern.

Do not leave litter of any kind - take it home with you, and be especially careful not to leave monofilament nylon line at the waterside; it can damage birds and animals. Leave the bank clean and tidy, and do nothing in any way to upset or annoy other anglers, those who own the waters, or those who may visit them. At a time when angling is under attack by many people, most of whom know nothing about the subject, be conservation conscious, and try to be a good example of an angler. Do not harm waterbirds, either directly or indirectly, keep to bye-laws, especially those which have been introduced in connection with the use of lead weights, shut all gates and do nothing to damage the banks or vegetation on the waters you fish.

Long-stay carp fishing is already causing carp anglers to be banned from some waters; if the 'float angler' can never get a place to fish because all the swims are occupied by carp anglers who live in bivvies and hardly ever leave the water, which is happening in some places, it won't be long before those who control waters start to ban this type of fishing. You have only yourself to blame if this happens. There are others to consider apart from yourself; others who have as much right to be on the water as you have, and if you spoil their fishing, they may soon be at a club meeting voting out your type of fishing!

Leaving baits out for long periods whilst you are away is another thing which has been getting carp anglers a bad name in some quarters; all of these points will only give extra help to those who are against angling, and we would urge our readers to avoid these bad aspects of modern carp fishing.

Rod Licences   It is an offence not to have the appropriate rod licences, and you may also break the rules of the water you are fishing if you don't obtain them. Even if you are one of those people who don't approve of rod licences you will certainly find that for the sake of a few pounds you can avoid all the problems concerned with prosecution if you get caught.

Water Authority licences can be bought from most tackle shops and the name of the Authority concerned is listed with each water. All now come under the heading of the National Rivers Authority (NRA). The use of more than two rods is now banned in most areas.

In Conclusion

We hope you will find this book interesting and helpful. To help us keep up with changes which take place, we should be very interested to hear your comments and criticisms, or even occasionally a bit of praise if there is any due!

We also invite owners of commercial fisheries, day ticket or season ticket waters, or club waters, to send us details of their fisheries for inclusion in the next issue of this Guide; there is no charge for any insertion, although you may also take advertising space if you wish to do so - rates on application. You can ensure the opportunity to advertise by returning the advertisement enquiry form at the back of this guide. You will be contacted at the right time prior to production of the next edition.

We hope later editions of the 'BK Guide to Carp Waters' will eventually list every carp water in the country which can be fished by the general angling public; with your co-operation we are sure this can be achieved.

Good fishing, and we hope you enjoy your time spent in the beautiful British countryside - or even on the slightly less attractive town waters!

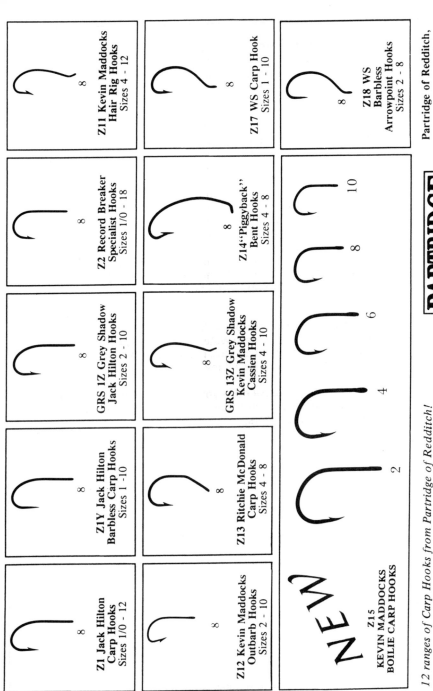

Z1 Jack Hilton
Carp Hooks
Sizes 1/0 - 12

Z1Y Jack Hilton
Barbless Carp Hooks
Sizes 1 -10

GRS 1Z Grey Shadow
Jack Hilton Hooks
Sizes 2 - 10

Z2 Record Breaker
Specialist Hooks
Sizes 1/0 - 18

Z11 Kevin Maddocks
Hair Rig Hooks
Sizes 4 - 12

Z12 Kevin Maddocks
Outbarb Hooks
Sizes 2 - 10

Z13 Ritchie McDonald
Carp Hooks
Sizes 4 - 8

GRS 13Z Grey Shadow
Kevin Maddocks
Cassien Hooks
Sizes 4 - 10

Z14 "Piggyback"
Bent Hooks
Sizes 4 - 8

Z17 WS Carp Hook
Sizes 1 - 10

Z18 WS
Barbless
Arrowpoint Hooks
Sizes 2 - 8

NEW

Z15
KEVIN MADDOCKS
BOILIE CARP HOOKS

12 ranges of Carp Hooks from Partridge of Redditch!
If you take sizes into account - over 60 different Hooks!!

Write for your free copy of our Carp Hook leaflet
and samples of some of the latest Hooks.

PARTRIDGE OF **REDDITCH**

Partridge of Redditch,
Mount Pleasant, Redditch,
Worcestershire. B97 4JE
Tel: (0527) 541380
Fax: (0527) 546956

11

COUNTY BOUNDARIES

1 TYNE AND WEAR
2 CLEVELAND
3 WEST YORKSHIRE
4 SOUTH YORKSHIRE
5 GREATER MANCHESTER
6 MERSEYSIDE
7 WEST MIDLANDS
8 BEDFORDSHIRE
9 BERKSHIRE
10 WEST GLAMORGAN
11 MID GLAMORGAN
12 SOUTH GLAMORGAN

NORTHUMBERLAND

DURHAM

CUMBRIA

ISLE OF MAN

NORTH YORKSHIRE

IRISH SEA

LANCASHIRE

HUMBERSIDE

GWYNEDD

CLWYD

ENGLAND

CHESHIRE   DERBY-   LINCOLNSHIRE
            SHIRE

NOTTINGHAM-SHIRE

STAFFORD-SHIRE

NORFOLK

SHROPSHIRE   LEICESTERSHIRE

WALES

POWYS   HEREFORD AND WORCESTER   WARWICK-SHIRE   NORTHAMPTON-SHIRE   CAMBRIDGE-SHIRE

SUFFOLK

DYFED

GLOUCESTER-SHIRE   OXFORD-SHIRE   BUCKINGHAM-SHIRE   HERTFORD-SHIRE   ESSEX

GWENT

GREATER LONDON

AVON   WILTSHIRE   SURREY   KENT

SOMERSET   HAMPSHIRE   WEST SUSSEX   EAST SUSSEX

DEVON   DORSET

ISLE OF WIGHT

CORNWALL

CONTENTS

The county designations used in this book are the most up to date: that is, those used since the boundary changes in 1974.

This means, for example, that there is now an East Sussex and a West Sussex, and that counties such as 'Middlesex' (now Greater London) and 'Worcestershire' (now Hereford and Worcester), no longer exist.

The waters in Ireland are all in the Irish Republic - we have not been able to track down an waters containing carp in Northern Ireland.

CARP BOOKS

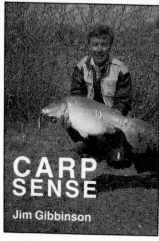

NEW

Hardback, 232 pages, 150
illustrations incl 22 in colour
£14.95

Hardback, 216 pages, 96
illustrations incl 32 in colour
£16.95

OTHER BEST-SELLING BOOKS

BIG-WATER CARP	JIM GIBBINSON	H/B	£14.95
CARP (SAS SERIES)	ROB MAYLIN	H/B	£10.95
CATFISH (SAS SERIES)	KEVIN MADDOCKS	H/B	£10.95
CARP FEVER, 10th issue	KEVIN MADDOCKS	S/B	£10.95
CASTING AT THE SUN	CHRIS YATES	S/B	£10.99
DEEPENING POOL	CHRIS YATES	H/B	£15.99
CATCH CARP	JOHN WILSON	H/B	£ 9.99
TIGER BAY	ROB MAYLIN	H/B	£16.95
IN PURSUIT OF CARP & CATFISH	KEVIN MADDOCKS	H/B	£15.95
RITCHIE ON CARP	RITCHIE McDONALD	H/B	£16.95
REDMIRE POOL	K. CLIFFORD & L. ARBERY	H/B	£16.95
5TH B.C.S.G. BOOK	VARIOUS	H/B	£16.50
CARP; NOW & THEN	ROD HUTCHINSON	S/B	£13.95
ROD HUTCHINSON'S BAIT BOOK	ROD HUTCHINSON	S/B	£ 2.95

AVON

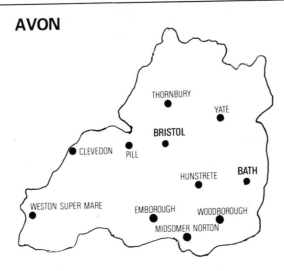

THORNBURY

YATE

BRISTOL

CLEVEDON PILL

HUNSTRETE **BATH**

WESTON SUPER MARE

EMBOROUGH WOODBOROUGH

MIDSOMER NORTON

Bitterwell Lake

Location:	Coalpit Heath, north Bristol
Type and Size:	2 acre pit
How to Find:	About one mile from recreation ground at Coalpit Heath
Carp Stock:	Heavily stocked, many small mirrors but occasional 20 caught
Category:	Mixed Fishery
Other Species:	Rudd, roach, tench, eels, small bream
Permits:	Caravan on site (Mrs Scully, The Chalet, Bitterwell Lake, Coalpit Heath, Bristol). Tel: 0454 778960
Cost:	£1.50 per rod per day
Baits/Methods:	Normal carp methods and bait plus float fishing
Control:	Council day and season ticket (Bristol Corporation)
Restrictions:	No night fishing although occasional night fishing permission can be obtained. No loose feeding
W/A:	NRA Wessex Region
BK Rating:	Moderate
Comments:	Hard fished 'town' water, often shoulder to shoulder at weekends

Emborough Pond

Location:	Ston Easton, near Midsomer Norton
Type and Size:	6 acre lake
How to Find:	Off the A37 south of Bristol
Carp Stock:	Some carp, mostly small commons
Category:	Few Carp
Other Species:	General coarse fish
Permits:	Day tickets on bank. Information from I. Crudgington, 37 Broad Street, Bath (tackle shop). Tel: 0225 466325
Cost:	On application
Control:	Knowle Angling Centre
W/A:	NRA Wessex Region
Comments:	'Public' lake in attractive surroundings

Fishponds Lido

Location:	Alcove Road, off Fishponds Road in the City of Bristol
Type and Size:	Deep old pit of about an acre or less
How to Find:	From the centre of Bristol find Fishponds Road and Alcove Road is less than a mile from the City Centre on the right. A path leads down to the lake.
Carp Stock:	Probably about 60 carp which were put in, in two stockings. Fish from the earlier stocking have reached upper double figure size and some 20s.
Category:	Mixed Fishery
Other Species:	Roach, tench and perch
Permits:	Season tickets from Fishponds Lido Angling Club, with a limited member ship and a waiting list. Details and cost from the Secretary, Mr R Hole, 70 Pound Road, Kingswood, Bristol or from Veals Tackle, Bristol.
Restrictions:	No night fishing
Control:	Club
W/A:	NRA Wessex Region
BK Rating:	Moderate
Comments:	A town water surrounded by houses and with a floating restaurant on it yet the water contains 20lb carp, which shows these can be caught within a city.

Ham Green Lake

Location:	Behind Ham Green Hospital, Pill, near Bristol
Type and Size:	Dammed estate lake in two parts, about an acre each
How to Find:	Take the A369 Bristol/Portishead road and turn right, signposted 'Ham Green and Pill'. Turn first right to Ham Green Hospital and continue down hill. Lake will be seen on the right.
Carp Stock:	Not large numbers, perhaps 50 fish in both lakes. Commons to about 11lbs. Mirrors to about 16lbs. A well authenticated fish of 20lbs was caught in 1991.
Category:	Mixed Fishery
Other Species:	Roach, rudd, tench, pike, eels
Permits:	On bank or Veals Tackle, Old Market, Bristol
Cost:	On application
Control:	Syndicate - Mr R Barnes, Withywood, Bristol
Baits/Methods:	Normal carp methods and baits. Some surface fishing
BK Rating:	Fairly Hard
W/A:	NRA Wessex Region
Comments:	Heavily weeded and full of lilies. Upper part best.

Henleaze Lake

Location:	Henleaze, Bristol, near the Downs
Type and Size:	15 acre town lake, used by a swimming club
Carp Stock:	Thought to contain crucians and small commons until summer 1991, when a catch of two commons weighing 29+ and 26+lbs was reported in an angling paper. The fish were caught on boilies amongst lilies. We have no proof that this catch was genuine and some local people doubt the weights
Category:	Few Carp?
Other Species:	Usual coarse fish

Permits:	On bank, or ask for information from Veals Fishing Tackle, Old Market Street or Southmead Tackle
BK Rating:	Very Difficult
W/A:	NRA Wessex Region

Hunstrete Lake

Location:	Village of Hunstrete, near Bath
Type and Size:	Dammed estate lake of about 5 acres
How to Find:	Take the main A4 Bath to Bristol road, and then the left fork (A368) at traffic lights at Newton St. Loe. After about 2 miles turn right towards Hunstrete and there is a path to the lake on the left, just before the village.
Carp Stock:	Probably only about 20—30 fish, most of which are doubles. Two twenties reported caught in 1985. There might be as many as four 20's in the lake, and possibly a near 30.
Category:	Few Carp
Other Species:	Tench, roach, bream
Permits:	Bathampton Angling Association; membership open at approximately £13.50 per season from the General Secretary, Dave Crookes, 25 Otago Terrace, Larkhall, Bath, Avon. Tel: Bath 27164. Limited tickets for Hunstrete Lake, details from Secretary.
Cost:	Approximately £13.50 per season
Restrictions:	No night fishing
Control:	Club
BK Rating:	Difficult
Baits/Methods:	Advanced carp fishing rigs and baits necessary
W/A:	NRA Wessex Region
Comments:	This is the lake named by Dick Walker in his literature as 'Lackey's Leap'. Fishing here with 'BB' Dick hooked one of the original commons, which now seem to have died out, and played it on very light tackle for an hour and 55 minutes, only to find it had the hook in its mouth and the line looped round a spine of the dorsal fin, which is perhaps why it fought so hard. Dick thought it was a 30, and the British record was then 26lbs; the fish actually weighed only 9¾lbs. There is a small syndicate on this water, details from the Secretary

Hutton Pond

Location:	Hutton Moor Road, Weston-super-Mare
Type and Size:	Ballast pit of about 1½ acres
How to Find:	Turn off the M5 motorway at the Weston-super-Mare exit and after about a mile find Hutton Moor Road on the left, shortly after the left hand Banwell turn. The pond will be found on the left after about 600 yards
Carp Stock:	A small number of mirrors most of which are lower doubles and are now quite old. Best known authenticated carp caught is 18¼lbs
Category:	Few Carp
Other Species:	Bream, roach, rudd, tench
Permits:	North Somerset Association of Anglers, permits approximately £12.50 as for Newtown Pond. Secretary: Mr R F Newton, 64 Clevedon Road, Tickenham, Clevedon, Avon. Club tickets also from local tackle dealers including Veals of Bristol, Old Market, Bristol
BK Rating:	Difficult, as there are not many carp

Baits/Methods:	Good specialist methods needed as these fish have been caught quite a lot over the years. Some may still be taken on floating crust after dark or in the early morning. Normal carp boilies etc best on the bottom. Bream a problem on soft baits, hard boilies such as Maestros work well
W/A:	NRA Wessex Region
Comments:	Not a very pleasant little place, with a road on one side, a railway line across the north end, and a 'factory' on the opposite side to the road. This bank is out of bounds as the 'factory' is a Government institution of some kind. The lake is long and narrow and nearly all carp are caught very close to the reeds on the 'factory' side; in fact, it is considered to be a waste of time anywhere but within a metre of this farther reed hedge

Newton Park

Location:	Newton St. Loe, near Bath
Type and Size:	3½ acre shallow lake
Carp Stock:	Recently stocked with 1,250lbs of carp - all small - from 4oz to 3lbs
Category:	Carp Water
Other Species:	Roach and perch
Permits:	A members only water of Bathampton AA - tickets from local tackle shops. Secretary: D Crookes, 25 Otago Terrace, Larkhall, Bath
Control:	Club
Restrictions:	Barbless hooks; no keepnets; possibly no night fishing
BK Rating:	Very Easy
W/A:	NRA Wessex Region

Woodborough Park Lake

Location:	Woodborough Court near Midsomer Norton
Type and Size:	Dammed estate lake of about 2 acres
How to Find:	Take the A367 Radstock road from Bath, and about two miles before Radstock you will see a left turn to Woodborough Court. Cars must be left in the car park on the right and it is about half a mile walk across fields to the lake.
Carp Stock:	Well stocked with mirrors many of which are under 10lbs, but there are some doubles and the best reported is about 15lbs.
Category:	Mixed Fishery
Other Species:	Tench, roach and perch
Permits:	This lake is on the same ticket as Hunstrete Lake, Bathampton Angling Association. Open membership from the General Secretary Dave Crookes, 25 Otago Terrace, Larkhall, Bath, Avon. Tel: 27164. In addition, only a few tickets are issued per day, and these must be obtained at a small extra cost from Crudgington Fishing Tackle, Bath or from Veals Fishing Tackle, Old Market, Bristol.
Cost:	Approximately £13.50 per season plus a small daily payment
Restrictions:	No night fishing; the dam is out of bounds
BK Rating:	Easy
Baits/Methods:	Normal carp fishing baits and methods
W/A:	NRA Wessex Region
Comments:	A very pleasant little water if you don't mind the walk. Since tickets are limited to four a day it can never get crowded. Bathampton AA now has another newly dug pond containing carp near Hunstrete; it is called

BEDFORDSHIRE

Airman Pit

Location:	On the A600 Bedford road, between Withy Pool and Shefford
Type and Size:	Brick pit of about 3½ acres
How to Find:	On the left hand side of the main A600 Hitchin to Bedford road between Kevin Maddocks' Withy Pool and the village of Shefford
Carp Stock:	Well stocked with small carp, a few doubles and one or two twenties
Category:	Carp Water
Other Species:	Roach, rudd, tench, pike, catfish, perch
Permits:	Seasonal from Shefford and District AA. Secretary: Mrs P Leath, 3 Ivel Close, Shefford. Tel: 0462 812323; or from Chris's Tackle Box, Henlow Camp, Beds
Cost:	£24 per season
Control:	Club
W/A:	NRA Anglian Region
BK Rating:	Easy
Comments:	There is another pit containing many carp on the same ticket

Arlesey Lake

Location:	Church End, Arlesey, near Hitchin
Type and Size:	Very deep, old brick pit of about 12 acres
How to Find:	Turn right going north on the A600 (Hitchin to Bedford road) at Henlow Camp, then right again at A507 junction - lake is alongside railway line on right.
Carp Stock:	About 100 carp to 30lbs. Plenty of upper doubles and some good twenties
Category:	Mixed Fishery
Other Species:	Perch, tench, roach, pike, catfish
Permits:	D Beatham, Etonbury Farm, Stotfold Road, Arlesey SG16 6XB. Tel: 0462 731709.
Cost:	On application
Control:	Syndicate
BK Rating:	Moderate
W/A:	NRA Anglian Region
Comments:	Famous as the lake where the late Richard Walker invented the Arlesey Bomb for fishing for the big perch at long range in 40ft of water. The lake is now being filled in and the fishing is not so pleasurable.

Beckerings Park Farm Reservoir

Location:	Steppingly, near Flitwick, just to the left of the A418 Flitwick - Millbrook road
Type and Size:	Small reservoir
Carp Stock:	Stocked in 1990 with 25 doubles including 7 carp over 20lbs
Category:	Mixed Fishery
Other Species:	Tench, roach and bream
Permits:	Members only water of Luton and District AC. Secretary: G Buss, 1 Easthill Road, Houghton Regis, Dunstable, Beds LU5 5EQ. Tel: Dunstable 862452. Permits can be obtained from local tackle shops, especially Leslie's of Luton.
Control:	Club
Restrictions:	Members only
BK Rating:	Moderate
W/A:	Anglian

Bedford Boating Lake

Location:	Alongside the River Great Ouse, Bedford Embankment
Type and Size:	Public town lake of about 2 acres
Carp Stock:	Occasional carp reported, including a 20lb common in July 1991
Category:	Few Carp
Other Species:	Roach, dace, bream, perch and pike
Permits:	None necessary - free fishing. Anglian licence required.
BK Rating:	Difficult
W/A:	NRA Anglian Region
Comments:	Busy town boating lake not known for its carp, but it does contain one or two good fish; lots of people and water birds. In August 1991 a famous match angler caught a 4lb terrapin here, which bit its captor - so anything could happen in this public lake.

New and best selling carp books from Beekay Publishers. See page 14

Blue Lagoon

Location:	On the Beds./Herts. border near Arlesey
Type and Size:	60 foot deep chalk pit of over 30 acres
Carp Stock:	Not many carp, but there are some big ones - a 37lb leather was caught in 1989 and at least one other 30 in 1990
Category:	Few Carp
Other Species:	Big pike, tench, bream, rudd, roach, perch and chub
Permits:	24 hour day tickets on bank, and also season tickets
Cost:	Day tickets about £2 per day
BK Rating:	Difficult
W/A:	NRA Anglian Region
Comments:	A true big fish water, with most fish caught in shallow water close in.

Blunham L-Shaped Lake

Location:	Blunham, between Sandy on the A1 and Bedford (A603)
Type and Size:	Long, narrow gravel pit of 5 acres
How to Find:	Turn off the A1 at Sandy and go to Blunham
Carp Stock:	Quite well stocked to upper twenties
Category:	Mixed Fishery
Other Species:	Tench, roach, rudd, bream, perch
Permits:	Season tickets from Blunham Angling Club, and local tackle shops.
Cost:	£15 per season
Control:	Club - Secretary: G Palmer, Tel: 02302 3959
BK Rating:	Difficult
W/A:	NRA Anglian Region

Blunham Pits

Location:	Blunham, just off the A1 at Sandy, near Biggleswade
Type and Size:	2 lakes of 6 and 7 acres, both gravel pits, and a stretch of the River Ivel
How to Find:	Turn off the A1 at Sandy, and the lakes will be seen near Blunham
Carp Stock:	Muddy Lake - good head of doubles and a few twenties to over 30lbs Clear Lake - good head of doubles and a few twenties.
Category:	Muddy - Carp Water; Clear - Mixed Fishery
Other Species:	Tench, roach, rudd, pike and perch
Permits:	Often vacancies from Mr Twell, Maperton Lodge, Station Road, Raunds, Northants. Tel: 0903 622007.
Cost:	Approximately £45 per person
Control:	Syndicate - try 0582 410277
BK Rating:	Moderate
W/A:	NRA Anglian Region
Comments:	Plenty of good carp in the River Ivel as well as in the pits.

Elstow Pits

Location:	Just off the A6 at Elstow near Bedford
Type and Size:	Brick pit of 30 acres plus
How to Find:	The pit will be seen on the right hand side of the A6 road going south from Bedford, near the village of Elstow
Carp Stock:	Well stocked with carp to 35lbs, with plenty of good doubles and 20's.
Category:	Carp Water

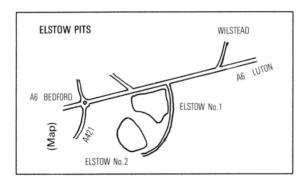

ELSTOW PITS

WILSTEAD

A6 LUTON

A6 BEDFORD

(Map)

A421

ELSTOW No.1

ELSTOW No.2

Other Species:	Roach, rudd, tench, bream, pike
Permits:	Syndicate only from Linear Fisheries, 2 Northcroft, Shenley Lodge, Milton Keynes MK5 7BE (Vacancies)
Cost:	Approximately £150 a season
Control:	Linear Fisheries. Tel: 0908 607577
BK Rating:	Moderate
Restrictions:	No day tickets - season (syndicate in advance only
W/A:	NRA Anglian Region
Comments:	One of the best upper doubles and 20's waters. A big water with good carp fishing, although the fish can be hard to find. Normal carp fishing methods and baits. Regulars estimate there are 50-100 twenties in this lake. Four 30's to 37lbs reported in 1991-92 season. There is a second large pit on the site, which is included in the membership. This contains a small number (perhaps only 20) really big fish, most of which are 20's, with the best caught a 33 pounder in 1991

Elstow Pit, Bedford a Linear Fisheries syndicate water which contains nearly 100 twenties

Felmersham Gravel Pits

Location:	Felmersham, off the A6 between Bedford and Rushden, and about 7 miles north of Bedford
Type and Size:	Two quite large gravel pits
Carp Stock:	Well stocked with carp to about 10lbs
Category:	Mixed Fishery
Other Species:	Tench
Permits:	Luton and District AA. Secretary: S R Branch, 3 Holmbrook Avenue, Luton, Beds. Members only.
Cost:	About £12.50 per season
Control:	Club
BK Rating:	Moderate
W/A:	Anglian

Fingers Lake

Location:	In the town of Bedford, off Goldington Road. next to Priory Lake
Type and Size:	Lake of about 5 acres
Carp Stock:	Some carp to 24lbs
Category:	Few Carp
Other Species:	Tench to 7lbs, bream, roach, rudd and pike
Permits:	Day tickets on bank at £1.50 for adults; 50p for under 12's. Season tickets £5 for OAP's; cost includes the larger Priory Lake
Control:	North Beds Borough Council. Tel: 0234 211182
Restrictions:	No night fishing; fishing from pegged swims only
BK Rating:	Moderate
W/A:	NRA Anglian Region

Green Lagoon

Location:	Beds/Herts border near Arlesey
Type and Size:	Three acre chalk pit, up to 30ft deep
Carp Stock:	Fairly well stocked with carp to low twenties
Category:	Mixed Fishery
Other Species:	Large bream, tench, perch, pike and roach
Permits:	24 hour day ticket on bank; season tickets
Cost:	About £2 per day
BK Rating:	Moderate
W/A:	Anglian
Comments:	Heavily fished, with difficult access.

Harrold-Odell Country Park

Location:	10 miles north west of Bedford
Type and Size:	Matured gravel pit of about 7 acres
How to Find:	The Country Park is signposted (5 miles) to the left of the A6 between Bedford and Rushden, shortly after the Falcon Inn
Carp Stock:	Some carp, numbers and size not known
Category:	Mixed Fishery
Other Species:	Pike, roach, rudd, perch, tench and bream

Permits:	The water is controlled by Harrold Working Mens AC. Tel: 0933 55696 (Cliff Roberts)
Control:	Club
Restrictions:	Members only. Probably no night fishing
W/A:	NRA Anglian Region
Comments:	A pleasant lake, but in a busy country park with Nature Reserve. Details, refreshments etc on site. There is another much larger lake opposite, where there are certainly fish, and possibly carp, and we understand that there may later be public fishing in this one also. For information contact Bedfordshire Leisure Services Dept, Beds County Council, County Hall, Cauldwell Street, Bedford. Tel: 0234 63222.

Houghton Regis Quarry

Location:	Houghton Road, Dunstable
Type and Size:	11 acre chalk pit
How to Find:	At the end of the main street in Dunstable going towards Leighton Buzzard; turn right at the roundabout towards Houghton Regis, and the pit is on the left.
Carp Stock:	About 200 carp; the best caught to date is 23lbs, plenty of low doubles, but most fish between 9 and 11lbs.
Category:	Mixed Fishery
Other Species:	Roach, bream, tench and pike
Permits:	Members only, Dunstable and District AC. Enquire in local tackle shops
Cost:	Low cost for season tickets
Control:	Club. Peter Garner. Tel: 0582 472067
Restrictions:	Special permission needed for night fishing; members only
BK Rating:	Moderate
W/A:	NRA Thames Region

Jones's Pit

Location:	Close to the A5 at Heath and Reach, between Dunstable and Bletchley
Type and Size:	Two clay pits, of 8 acres and 1 acre
Carp Stock:	Quite heavily stocked, mainly with doubles, with the occasional 20. Only a few carp in the small lake
Category:	Mixed Fishery
Other Species:	Catfish to 27lbs, roach, bream, pike and big crucians
Permits:	Season ticket water of Leisure Sport Angling, Thorpe Park, Staines Road, Chertsey, Surrey. Tel: Chertsey 87642
Cost:	About £15 per season
BK Rating:	Moderate
W/A:	NRA Anglian Region
Comments:	A famous catfish water, but with plenty of carp

Kempston Hardwick

Location:	Kempston Hardwick village, near Bedford
Type and Size:	4 pits, about 30 acres
How to Find:	Take the Ampthill road from Bedford, and the lake is opposite the Chimney Corner public house in Kempston Hardwick
Carp Stock:	This is a recently stocked water with a reasonable head of carp to lower doubles. Carp are reported to be growing well. Carp to 20lbs plus.
Category:	Mixed Fishery

Other Species: Tench, roach, bream, perch and pike
Permits: Enquire locally, or tackle shops in Bedford
Control: Not known at time of going to press
BK Rating: Moderate
W/A: Anglian
Comments: Also Brogborough Lake, carp to 24lbs.

Oldfield

Location: Arlesey, near Hitchin, alongside A507
Type and Size: Two gravel pits of 6 and 4 acres in quiet countryside
Carp Stock: Very heavily stocked with good looking fish to mid-twenties
Category: Mixed Fishery
Other Species: Bream, tench, roach, rudd and perch
Permits: Syndicate membership, enquire locally
Control: Private
BK Rating: Very Easy
W/A: Anglian
Comments: The main lake has been the setting for several carp videos, including Carp Fever I and Carp from the Start I, featuring Kevin Maddocks who caught many good fish here.

Priory Lake

Location: In the town of Bedford, off Goldington Road
Type and Size: 64 acre town lake, with a Visitors Centre and water sports
Carp Stock: Small number of carp to over 20lbs
Category: Few Carp
Other Species: Roach, perch, crucians and pike to 28lbs
Permits: Day tickets on bank
Cost: £1.50; 50p for under 12's. £5 per season for OAP's; also includes the smaller Fingers Lake
Control: Tel: 0234 211182; North Bedfordshire Borough Council
Restrictions: No night fishing. Fishing only from pegged swims. No livebait; no spinning
BK Rating: Very Difficult
W/A: NRA Anglian Region

Rackley Hills Pit

Location: Near the centre of Leighton Buzzard; Grovebury Road
Type and Size: Working sand pit of about 8 acres
How to Find: In Leighton Buzzard
Carp Stock: Small number of carp to 20lbs plus
Category: Few Carp
Other Species: Catfish to 35lbs
Permits: Seasonal from Leighton Buzzard Angling Club and selected tackle shops in the area. Secretary: B Smalley, 3 Isis Walk, Leighton Buzzard, Beds. Tel: 0525 852227.
Cost: £20 per season. Joint husband and wife £23. Juniors: £4. Senior citizens: £3.
Control: Club

BK Rating:	Very Difficult, very few fish
Restrictions:	Night fishing reserved for a selected few only
W/A:	NRA Anglian Region

Radwell Complex

Location:	Between Milton Ernest and Sharnbrook
Type and Size:	4 pits, two of which are quite large
How to Find:	These lakes can be seen from the A6, on the left hand side between Bedford and Rushden. Access is from a lane near the Swan public house in Radwell. To reach this village take a left turn off the A6 at Milton Ernest, cross the river and turn right just before the Swan
Carp Stock:	All the pits contain carp to about 10lbs
Category:	Mixed Fishery
Other Species:	Tench, bream, roach, perch and pike
Permits:	Vauxhall Motors AC. Season tickets from Leslie's of Luton, 89 Park Street, Luton. Tel: 0852 453542. Secretary: B Matthews, 88 Langford Drive, Luton Beds. Tel: Luton 419489.
Restrictions:	Members only - no day tickets
Control:	Club
BK Rating:	Moderate
W/A:	Anglian

Tingrith Manor Lake

Location:	Village of Tingrith, near Toddington, Dunstable
How to Find:	Leave the M1 at Toddington (junction 12) and take the road signposted 'Tingrith'
Type and Size:	Estate lake of 5 acres
Carp Stock:	Well stocked with commons to 10lbs. There are a few mirrors to upper doubles
Category:	Mixed Fishery
Other Species:	Perch, roach, rudd, pike and catfish
Permits:	Vauxhall Motors Angling Club. Season tickets from Leslie's Fishing Tackle, Luton. Secretary: B Matthews, 88 Langford Drive, Luton, Beds. Tel: Luton 419489.
Cost:	On application
Control:	Club
BK Rating:	Moderate
W/A:	Anglian
Baits/Methods:	Normal carp fishing methods and baits; floating baits sometimes work well.

Willington Lake

Location:	Near Great Barford Bridge, on the lane leading to Willington
Type and Size:	Gravel pit of about eight acres, dug in 1984
Carp Stock:	Restocked in 1990, with mostly mid-doubles to about 20lbs
Category:	Mixed Fishery
Other Species:	Big bream and pike; most other species
Permits:	Shefford and District AA. Secretary: Mrs P Leath, 3 Ivel Close, Shefford. Tel:0462 812323, or from Chris's Tackle Box, Henlow Camp

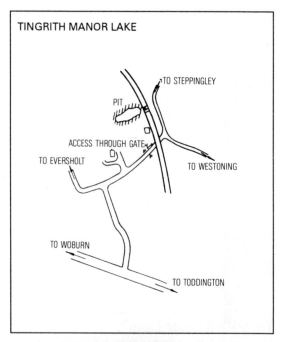

TINGRITH MANOR LAKE

TO STEPPINGLEY

PIT

ACCESS THROUGH GATE

TO EVERSHOLT

TO WESTONING

TO WOBURN

TO TODDINGTON

Peter Wilson
with the
Withy Pool lake
record of 41 pounds

Cost:	About £24 a season
Restrictions:	Club members only - no day tickets
BK Rating:	Easy
Comments:	On the same ticket as Airman Pit

Withy Pool

Location:	Bedford Road, Henlow Camp, Beds SG16 6EA
Type and Size:	Brick pit of 2½ acres and man-made lake of ¼ acre
How to Find:	Take the A600 Hitchin to Bedford road going north, and the lake is on the left about 300 yards after the roundabout at Lower Stondon, about 4 miles from Hitchin
Category:	Carp Water
Other Species:	Catfish to 20lbs; pike, perch, roach, tench, bream, grass carp, orfe and koi carp to 10lbs.

Kevin Maddocks caught this 35 pounder from Withy Pool in February 1990, only two weeks after his 40 from Northants. Both fish were caught on Maestro Boilies straight from the packet!

Cost:	On application
Permits:	Occasional vacancies in the small syndicate; no day tickets
Carp Stock:	On application
Restrictions:	No night fishing on main lake except for syndicate members
Control:	Private: contact Kevin Maddocks at the above address. Tel: 0462 816960
BK Rating:	Main lake - Difficult; small lake - Easy
W/A:	NRA Anglian Region
Comments:	Syndicate membership - waiting list. Small lake very heavily stocked with carp to over 20lbs, and lots of catfish. Brand new building incorporating separate ladies and gents toilets and shower.
	The main lake is a 100 year old clay pit which varies in depth from 4 to

Peter Mohan with
his personal best -
a 33½ caught in
August 1991 from
Withy Pool on a
KM Maestro
Bird Spice boilie

25 feet. It contained 20lb carp in the '50's. Dick Walker fished it and Jack Hilton caught his first doubles from the water, which was formerly known as Cafe Pool and Maylin's Pool. Since Kevin and Brenda Maddocks bought the property in 1985 it has become one of the best known small fisheries in the country for big carp - a fish under 20lbs from the main lake is very rare and more 30's are caught than 20's! In 1991 Withy Pool produced more than 20 thirty pound carp. The lake record currently stands at 41 pounds and gets beaten every year.NB Caravan holidays no longer available - syndicate only

A lovely 20 pound plus common from the small lake at Withy Pool

Woburn Sands

Location:	Woburn Sands village, near Woburn
Type and Size:	Brick pit of 10 acres
How to Find:	Take the A5 from Dunstable going north and turn off at Hockcliffe to Woburn Sands. Entrance is off the B557 road
Carp Stock:	About 40 carp to 20lbs plus
Category:	Mixed Fishery
Other Species:	Roach, bream, tench, rudd, pike, catfish
Permits:	Vauxhall Motors Angling Club. Season tickets only from Leslie's Tackle Shop, Luton. Secretary: B Matthews, 88 Langford Drive, Luton, Beds. Tel: Luton 419489
Cost:	About £12 per season
Control:	Club
BK Rating:	Fairly Difficult
W/A:	NRA Anglian Region

Woburn Sands Syndicate

Location:	Woburn Sands
Type and Size:	2 acre disused brick pit
Carp Stock:	About 40 doubles and a few low twenties
Category:	Carp Water
Other Species:	Catfish and roach
Permits:	Syndicate only — the Secretary, PO Box 885, Shenley Lodge, Milton Keynes MK5 7YU
Cost:	On application
BK Rating:	Moderate - the owner says that it's easy for good carp anglers, and difficult for those who are not so good! (I've only fished it once, and I had a blank, which shows what a useless carp angler I am! P.M.).
Restrictions:	No long stay fishing
Control:	Private
W/A:	Anglian
Comments:	A very pretty water, secluded and well protected; private property - do not visit without permission. Ideal for 'old fashioned' methods, such as stalking and float fishing.

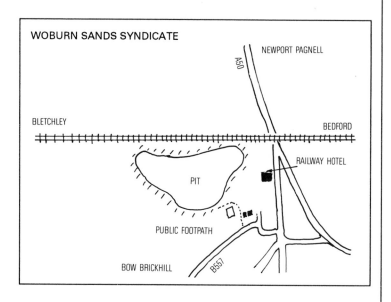

WOBURN SANDS SYNDICATE

BERKSHIRE

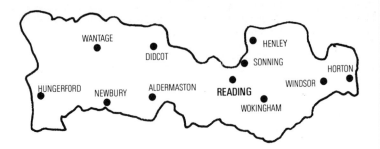

Aldermaston

Location:	Paices Hill, Aldermaston, near Reading
Type and Size:	7 lakes of an acre or less, and one lake, No 6,of 3.8 acres. Gravel pits
How to Find:	Take the M4 to the Theale turn off, and then A340 to Aldermaston. After Aldermaston the entrance is at the top of the hill on the right after the village.
Carp Stock:	The Leisure Sport Guide describes the carp as 'numerous' in Lake 6, but only to about 8lbs. Some doubles were introduced into Lakes 2 and 3 in 1982-83, and best reported to date is 25lbs.
Category:	Lake 6 - Carp Water. Other lakes are Mixed Fisheries
Permits:	This is an LSAC 'Special Venue'. Season tickets and day tickets. Apply to Leisure Sport for an application form for a Special Venue. Thorpe Park, Staines Road, Chertsey, Surrey. Tel: Chertsey 64872. A limited number of Coverall Permits are issued for all 31 LSA new venues including the Special Venue waters. Two passport photographs required to be sent with the application form. Day tickets on bank at £3
Cost:	£25 per season; juniors/OAP/disabled - £12.50; Coverall Permits (31 venues) - £120 (juniors/OAP/disabled - £60). Day tickets - £2 (dawn to dusk only).
Restrictions:	Usual rules - no camping, no fires, no radios. Night fishing allowed. Carp over 3lbs must not be retained.
BK Rating:	Lake 6 - Easy; others - Moderate
Control:	Leisure Sport. Tel: 0932 564872
W/A:	NRA Thames Region
Comments:	Day tickets from Youngs Garden Centre at site entrance.

Brimpton Lakes

Location:	Shalford Bridge, near Aldermaston
Type and Size:	Two large gravel pits
How to Find:	Off the Brimpton-Woolhampton road
Carp Stock:	Well stocked with carp, many of which are doubles
Category:	Mixed Fishery
Permits:	Reading and District AA. Secretary: D Capon, 61 Thame Road, Haddenham, Bucks HP17 8EP.
BK Rating:	Moderate
Control:	Club
W/A:	Thames

Burghfield

Location:	Pengewood Road, Pengewood, Burghfield
Type and Size:	Lake 1 - 94 acres; Lake 2 - 5 acres; Lake 3 - 3 acres. Gravel pits
How to Find:	Off the A4 from Reading to Southcote; Burghfield Road and the canal
Carp Stock:	Carp to over 30lbs reported
Category:	Few Carp
Other Species:	General coarse fish
Permits:	Leisure Sport Angling, Staines Road, Chertsey, Surrey. Tel: 0932 562633.
Cost:	£24
BK Rating:	Difficult
Control:	Leisure Sport Angling Club
Restrictions:	No bright lights
W/A:	NRA Thames Region
Comments:	Night fishing is allowed.

Countryside Club

Location:	Reading
Type and Size:	Some lake carp fishing, details not known
Carp Stock:	Well stocked with carp
Category:	Mixed Fishery
Other Species:	General coarse fish
Permits:	Countryside, 109 Upper Woodcote Road, Caversham Heights, Reading.
Control:	Private
BK Rating:	Not known
W/A:	NRA Thames Region

Horton

Location:	Stanwell Road, Horton, near Slough, Berks. Tel: 0753 684458
Type and Size:	Church Pool - 14 acres; Boat Pool - 6 acres; former gravel pits
How to Find:	Take junction 14 off the M25 and take the Poyle/Datchet road, and after roundabout take the first road on the left (Stanwell Road); the Horton Fishery entrance is on the left in one mile.
Carp Stock:	Church Lake is well stocked with very big carp to 44lbs. There were already carp in this lake, a former trout fishery, but in 1991 when Longfield (Staines), a famous carp water, was closed and netted 57 big carp, all of which were twenties and thirties, with some doubles and two forties, were transferred to Church Lake, Horton and a number of 30's and 40's have been caught since. Other big fish will be put into this water, which must now rank as one of the top carp fisheries in the country.
Category:	Mixed Fishery
Other Species:	Grass carp to 16lbs, bream to 11½lbs, tench to 834lbs, pike, roach, perch and eels
Permits:	Leisure Sport Angling, Thorpe Park, Staines Road, Chertsey, Surrey KT16 8PN. Tel: 0932 564872. This is an LSA 'Special Venue' and tickets may be hard to obtain.
Cost:	£200 per season
Restrictions:	Two rods only; 7 days stay only — after that you must leave for at least 24 hours. Members wishing to leave the fishery between 7am and 8pm are only allowed a 90 minute absence; no keepnets or sacks; no guests; 50 anglers only.

BK Rating:	Difficult
W/A:	NRA Thames Region
Comments:	There is a fisherman's lodge at Church Lake, open 24 hours a day, and two toilets in the car park. LSA rules and their bailiffs are very strict, and if you break the rules you will lose your membership. A 40½lb was caught in 1991.

Longmoor Lake

Location:	California Country Park, Nine Mile Ride, Finchampstead, Wokingham
Type and Size:	6 acre lake
Carp Stock:	Well stocked with carp to mid-twenties
Category:	Mixed Fishery
Other Species:	Pike, tench, perch, roach, rudd
Permits:	Day and season tickets sold on lakeside
Cost:	Adult Day - £2.00. Adult Season - £15.00.
Baits/Methods:	Normal carp fishing bait and methods
Control:	Council (Wokingham District Council)
Restrictions:	No nut baits, barbless hooks, night fishing through a syndicate only, no fishing on paved frontage.
BK Rating:	Moderate
W/A:	NRA Thames Region
Comments:	Plenty of good carp averaging 15lb in this picturesque lake with several islands and lily beds.

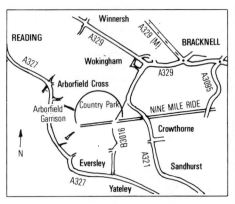

PAGO 36

Priory Water

Location:	Near Windsor
Type and Size:	Several gravel pits
How to Find:	Just off the Wraysbury junction of the M25
Carp Stock:	Priory - some good carp; Hythe Lagoon - some carp; Watts Pool - some carp
Category:	Mixed Fisheries
Other Species:	Mixed coarse fish
Permits:	Peter Howes. Tel: 0256 466343
Cost:	On application - about £12 per annum
BK Rating:	Insufficient information
Control:	Not known - try local tackle shops
W/A:	NRA Thames Region
Comments:	Priory also used for sailing.

Sonning Eye Pit

Location:	Off the A4155 Reading—Henley road at Sonning
Type and Size:	Huge gravel pit
Carp Stock:	Not many carp but said to be some big fish up to 40lbs
Category:	Few Carp
Permits:	Reading and District Angling Association. Secretary: D Capon, 61 Thame Road, Haddenham, Bucks HP17 8EP.
BK Rating:	Very Difficult
Restrictions:	No night fishing
Control:	Club
W/A:	NRA Thames Region

South Lake/Redlands Lake

Location:	Woodley, Reading
Type and Size:	Lake of 50 acres
How to Find:	Fairwater Road, behind The Thatchers public house
Carp Stock:	Well stocked with carp to 25lb
Category:	Mixed Fishery
Other Species:	Tench, roach and bream
Permits:	Mr Williams, South Lake Angling Society, 24 Duncan Road, Woodley, Reading
BK Rating:	Moderate
W/A:	NRA Thames Region
Restrictions:	Only open to those living within 3 miles of Woodley.

White Swan Lake

Location:	Dinton Pastures Country Park, Davis Street, Hurst, Wokingham
Type and Size:	Open gravel pit of about 24 acres
Carp Stock:	Well stocked with carp to upper twenties
Category:	Mixed Fishery
Other Species:	Pike, tench, perch, roach, rudd, chub, bream
Permits:	Day and season tickets sold on lakeside
Cost:	Adult Day - £2.00; Adult Season - £15.00.
Baits/Methods:	Normal carp fishing bait and methods
Control:	Council (Wokingham District Council)
Restrictions:	No nut baits, night fishing through a syndicate only
BK Rating:	Moderate to hard
W/A:	NRA Thames Region
Comments:	Well stocked with carp, also holds tench to over 11lbs and pike to 34lb.

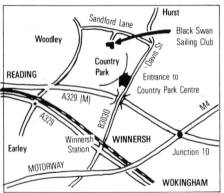

BUCKINGHAMSHIRE

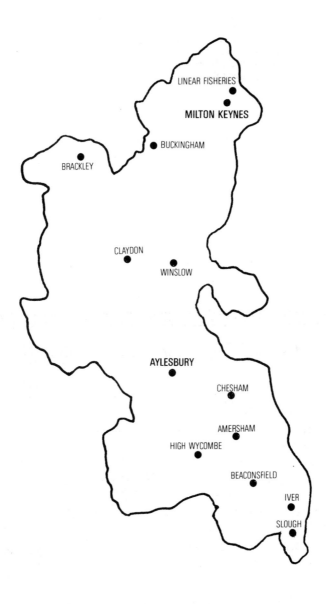

Linear Fisheries
Milton Keynes and Bedford

♦ Over 300 acres of lakes and river open to all anglers

♦ Heavily stocked with most species of coarse fish

♦ Carp syndicate waters with frequent vacancies:
Elstow Pits, Bedford: 30 acre lake containing nearly 100 twenties to over 30lbs, with second large lake containing some twenties to 30lbs
Redhouse Lake, Milton Keynes: 15 acre attractive lake, carp to 20lbs, low cost
Arboretum Lake, Milton Keynes: 3 acre lake, carp to upper twenties and specimen fish of other species
Gayhurst Lakes, near Milton Keynes: Two small estate lakes, carp to 20lbs

♦ Membership of Linear Fisheries Club, which includes Rocla Lake, with carp to 20lbs and several other lakes, and river, most of which contain good carp

♦ Day tickets and 24-hour tickets also available on all Linear waters, *except* syndicate lakes

♦ Big fish of most species caught regularly including carp to 32lbs, pike to over 30lbs, barbel and tench to double figures, bream to 8lbs and roach to 3lbs

♦ One of the most famous fisheries in the country, controlled and bailiffed by anglers, and with regular restocking. Frequent mentions in all angling journals and featured in a number of well known videos by the Original Video Company, PO Box 885, Shenley Lodge, Milton Keynes MK5 7YU.
Tel: 0908 691773

♦ Easy access – just 60 minutes from London and Birmingham

♦ All enquiries and tickets from:
The Secretary, Linear Fisheries, 2 Northcroft, Shenley Lodge, Milton Keynes, Bucks MK5 7BE. Tel: 0908 607577

♦ 48 page illustrated brochure – send two first class stamps to the Secretary

Alder Lake carp syndicate - a famous Linear Fisheries lake which produced 80 twenties in 1991

Alder and Poplar Lakes Carp Syndicate

Location: Linford Linear Fisheries, Little Linford Lane, Milton Keynes

Type and Size: Two gravel pits of 6 and 7 acres

How to Find: From junction 14 of the M1, turn right on the A409 towards Newport Pagnell, left at the first roundabout, right at the next roundabout and left again at the T-junction. In about 400 yards, turn right into Little Linford Lane. The entrance is on the left opposite the sailing club.

Carp Stock: Alder - mainly doubles to 30lbs; 100+ carp, 10% over 20lbs. Poplar - very heavily stocked with carp to 19lbs.

Category: Carp Waters

Other Species: Annual netting removes other species to maintain the lakes as carp waters

Permits: Linear Fisheries, Secretary: Len Gurd, Linear House, 2 Northcroft, Shenley Lodge, Milton Keynes, Bucks. Tel: 0908 607577. Syndicate season tickets only, no day tickets.

Cost: On application

BK Rating: Alder: Easy/Moderate. Poplar: Very Easy

Restrictions: No long stay fishing, 36 hour limit. Alternate Saturday and Sunday rotas. No sacking of carp. Bent hooks are banned.

Control: Linear Fisheries

W/A: NRA Anglian Region

Baits/Methods: Usual carp fishing baits and methods. Carp in Poplar easy to catch on all baits and rigs

Comments: This syndicate is already known as one of the country's best carp waters. Rules are strict so behaviour is good, and the waters are very well controlled by experienced carp anglers. These are two very pleasant mature lakes amid a big gravel pit complex. There are many trees and bushes on both lakes and also numerous islands, bays and gravel bars. No retaining of carp. Membership of the rest of Linford is also available by season or day tickets from Len Gurd. There are 5 other lakes on the complex stocked with large fish of most species, including carp, and 3 miles of the River Ouse is included containing large barbel and other species. Linear Fisheries also has Elstow Pit, near Bedford, a top carp fishery with many doubles and twenties to 30lbs. Syndicate only - vacancies now - enquire from Secretary. Tel: 0908 607577 (9am— 5pm). Both Poplar and Alder Lakes are featured in the 'Carp Fever' series of videos by Kevin Maddocks.

Gordon Owen with a 27-2 from one of the Linear Fisheries lakes at Linford

Amerden Pool

Location:	Amerden Grove, near Slough
Type and Size:	Small lake
How to Find:	Take the Taplow road from Slough and pass the Dumbell pub on your right. In 150 yds turn left at the garage, go under railway bridge, past sailing club, turn right and first right again, then follow track to lake.
Carp Stock:	A small number of carp to 16lbs
Category:	Few Carp
Other Species:	Crucians, tench, rudd, roach and perch
Permits:	Boyer Leisure, Trout Rd, West Drayton, Middx UB7 7DS. Tel: 0895 444707
Cost:	£30 per season
Control:	Boyer Leisure
Restrictions:	Barbless hooks; no keepnets or carp sacks; do not go through the house entrance; do not disturb livestock on the farmland.
BK Rating:	Difficult
W/A:	NRA Thames Region

New and best selling carp videos from Beekay Publishers. See page 19

Arboretum Carp Syndicate

Location:	Linford Linear Fisheries, Little Linford Lane, Milton Keynes
Type and Size:	Mature gravel pit of 3 acres, stream fed
How to Find:	As for Alder and Poplar Lakes, but pass the end of Little Linford Lane, go under the bridge and straight on at the mini-roundabout. Just after Linear Fisheries Rocla Lake, the entrance will be seen on the right. Car park is to the right of the entrance.
Carp Stock:	30+ fish from 10lbs to 30lbs, and some smaller fish
Category:	Mixed Fishery
Other Species:	Tench, bream, roach, rudd and a few catfish
Permits:	Linear Fisheries. Secretary: Len Gurd, Linear House, 2 Northcroft, Shenley Lodge. Milton Keynes, Bucks. Tel: 0908 607577. Syndicate only.
Cost:	On application
BK Rating:	Moderate
Control:	Linear Fisheries
Restrictions:	No long stay fishing, 36 hours maximum. Alternate Saturday and Sunday rota. No sacking of carp.
W/A:	NRA Anglian Region
Comments:	A most attractive lake with islands, backwaters, trees etc. Membership limited to 25, many of whom are not carp specialists

Aylesbury Arm Canal

Location:	Just outside Aylesbury
Type and Size:	Narrow disused canal
Carp Stock:	Well stocked with carp to doubles
Category:	Mixed Fishery
Other Species:	Usual coarse fish
Permits:	John MacDonald, Tel: 0296 29983
Control:	Club; Aylesbury DAF
BK Rating:	Moderate
W/A:	NRA Thames Region

Belcher's Farm

Location:	Just outside the attractive village of Aynho, near the railway line off the B4031 Aynho to Deddington road
Type and Size:	Two small farm ponds
Carp Stock:	Well stocked with carp to doubles
Category:	Carp Water
Other Species:	Some other coarse fish
Permits:	From the farm owners, Mr and Mrs Belcher on site
Cost:	About £3 per day
BK Rating:	Easy
W/A:	NRA Severn Trent Region

Black Horse Lake

Location:	Linford Linear Fisheries, Little Linford Lane, Milton Keynes
Type and Size:	Big open gravel pit of 25 acres
How to Find:	From junction 14 of the M1, turn right on the A409 towards Newport Pagnell, left at the first roundabout, right at the next roundabout and left again at the T-junction. Go under the bridge, straight on at the small

roundabout and turn right into the Linear Fisheries entrance. Car park on right.

Carp Stock: Holds some very large original carp caught to 32lbs. Stocked by Linear Fisheries with over 100 fast growing mirrors to double figures.

Category: Mixed Fishery

Other Species: Tench to 10lbs 3ozs; bream to 8lbs; pike to 30lbs; roach to 2½lbs; big eels

Permits: Season tickets (day only); day tickets; limited night syndicate vacancies. Linear Fisheries Secretary: Len Gurd, Linear House, 2 Northcroft, Shenley Lodge, Milton Keynes, Bucks. Tel: 0908 607577 or local tackle shops

Cost: £3 per rod per day; £4 for 24 hour permits; £26 per daytime season; £35 for 24 hour season. Reductions for juniors, OAP and disabled.

BK Rating: Moderate

Control: Linear Fisheries

Restrictions: No night fishing except for night syndicate. No sacking of carp

W/A: NRA Anglian Region

Comments: Large open gravel pit. Very rich water which produces big fish of all species. Carp stocked by Linear Fisheries put on 3lbs in the first year. Small number only of big original carp

Black Park

Location: Town of Iver

Type and Size: Park lake of about 7 acres

Carp Stock: Small number of carp to 28lbs

Category: Few Carp

Other Species: Pike and bream

Permits: Free fishing

Control: Council

BK Rating: Difficult

W/A: NRA Thames Region

Comments: Refreshments etc. available on site

Bowlers

Location: A stretch of the Grand Union Canal in Milton Keynes; good fishing between bridge 90 and 91 at Woughton Park; access from the Simpson roundabout or Netterfield roundabout

Type and Size: Shallow canal with some boat traffic

Carp Stock: Some carp to 20lbs

Category: Mixed Fishery

Other Species: Bream, roach, perch and gudgeon

Permits: Day tickets on bank

Cost: £3 for adults; £1.50 for juniors, OAP's and the disabled; tickets in advance from T Jeans, 107 Baccarra Grove, Bletchley, Milton Keynes

Control: Milton Keynes AA

Restrictions: Fishing from towpath only

BK Rating: Difficult

W/A: NRA Anglian Region

Calves Lane Lake

Location:	Love Hill Lane, off the B470 near Iver
Type and Size:	Small lake - 1½ acres
Carp Stock:	Stocked in 1990 with 250 carp to 7lbs
Category:	Mixed Fishery
Other Species:	Roach, tench, perch and pike
Permits:	Boyer Leisure
Cost:	£30 per season; £20 juniors, OAPs and disabled
Control:	Boyer Leisure
Restrictions:	Unhooking mats compulsory
BK Rating:	Moderate
W/A:	NRA Thames Region

Claydon Lake

Location:	Middle Claydon, Winslow, near Leighton Buzzard
Type and Size:	Estate lake of about 3 acres
How to Find:	Take the A413 from Buckingham, and turn right to Middle Claydon just before the village of Winslow
Carp Stock:	Very heavily stocked with carp of 5-10lbs, with some doubles up to 20lbs. Mostly commons
Category:	Mixed Fishery
Other Species:	Roach, rudd, bream, pike and very large catfish and zander
Permits:	Season tickets for members only; Leighton Buzzard Angling Club, B Smalley, 3 Isis Walk, Leighton Buzzard, Beds. Tel: 0525 852227 or from Jim Brennan on the bank.
Cost:	£20 adult, £23 husband and wife
Control:	Club
BK Rating:	Easy
Restrictions:	No night fishing
W/A:	NRA Anglian Region
Comments:	This lake is on an estate with a house once lived in by Florence Nightingale. It is a shallow, very open water. Cars must be parked by the roadside and it is more than half a mile's walk across a field to the lake. The water is famous for its catfish of over 30lbs, but there are plenty of carp also. The Leighton Buzzard Club has a number of other carp waters on the same ticket. An excellent water to gain experience on

Common Pond

Location:	Common near Gerrards Cross
Type and Size:	One acre common land pond
Carp Stock:	Fairly well stocked with carp including some doubles up to about 20lbs
Category:	Mixed Fishery
Other Species:	Roach and tench
Permits:	Free fishing
Control:	Local council
BK Rating:	Easy
W/A:	NRA Thames Region

Furzton Lake

Location:	Chaffron Way, Furzton, Milton Keynes
Type and Size:	40 acre man-made lake
How to Find:	From junction 14 of the M1, take the A509 and turn right at the first roundabout. Follow this road (H5 Portway) for 6 miles to Watling Street roundabout, turn left and take the first right; then turn right at the second roundabout into Chaffron Way
Carp Stock:	Stocked in 1990 with about 1,400 carp, mirrors and commons, between 4lb and 14lb
Category:	Mixed Fishery
Other Species:	Tench, rudd and perch
Permits:	Day tickets from bailiff on bank
Control:	Milton Keynes AA - membership from local tackle shops or from the Secretary, 107 Baccara Grove, Bletchley, Milton Keynes.
Restrictions:	No fixed leads
BK Rating:	Easy
W/A:	NRA Anglian Region
Comments:	A new water, first opened in the 1990-91 season. Some areas out of bounds. Housing estate along one side

Gayhurst Lakes

Location:	Gayhurst Estate, near Newport Pagnell
Type and Size:	Two pretty stream-fed estate lakes of 2 acres and one acre, both on the same stream, which runs from the larger lake to the small one
Carp Stock:	The upper (larger) lake is very heavily stocked with carp to over 20lbs, although most are between 3lbs and 12lbs. The lower lake is said to contain some big carp but is so little fished that we have no records of catches
Category:	Carp Water
Other Species:	Bream, roach and perch. Some pike in lower lake
Permits:	Private syndicate water of Linear Fisheries, Linear House, 2 Northcroft, Shenley Lodge, Milton Keynes, Bucks MK5 7BE. Tel: 0908 607577 (24 hour Ansaphone).
Cost:	£60 per season, and a £10 entry fee for Gayhurst Lakes. Enquire from the Secretary for prices and details of other Linear waters, including the Linear Fisheries Club with membership open to all
Baits/Methods:	Standard carp fishing methods; sweetcorn, luncheon meat and boilies all doing well
Control:	Linear Fisheries
Restrictions:	Syndicate only - no day tickets. Membership in advance only. Alternate Saturday and Sunday rota to avoid weekend overcrowding. Small exclusive syndicate with limited membership, but vacancies at present
BK Rating:	Easy to Moderate
W/A:	NRA Anglian Region
Comments:	Only Linear's third season controlling these lakes. They are on a beautiful and peaceful private estate in the grounds of a large mansion, and are surrounded by trees and bushes. Three carp of over 20lbs were reported from the water in the 1990 to 91 season, with a good number of doubles. Mirrors and commons. Frequent vacancies

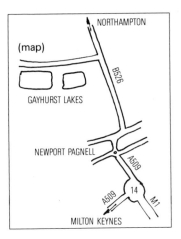

Haversham Lake

Location: The village of Haversham, near Milton Keynes

Type and Size: Big open gravel pit of more than 50 acres

How to Find: From Newport Pagnell take the Wolverton road and turn right down Little Linford Lane. Follow this past the other Linear waters to the T-junction, then turn left. In Haversham village, turn left down a rough track near the telephone booth

Carp Stock: Stocked by Linear with over 600 carp in 1986, and these fish are now being caught well into double figures, with the occasional 20 pounder

Category: Mixed Fishery

Other Species: Pike to 26lbs, tench to over 8lbs+, perch over 3lbs, and roach over 2lbs. There are also some shoals of very large bream

Permits: Linear Fisheries Club, open to all: Linear House, 2 Northcroft, Shenley Lodge, Milton Keynes, Bucks., MK5 7BE. Tel: 0908 607577.

Cost: £30 per season (dawn to dusk); £40 per season, to include night fishing. Day tickets £3 per rod per day, 24 hour tickets at £4 per rod. Reductions for juniors/disabled/OAP's. Tickets must be purchased before fishing - £1 excess is charged by bailiffs to anyone fishing without a ticket

Control: Linear Fisheries Club

Restrictions: Permits in advance only, or £1 excess charged by bailiffs on the bank

BK Rating: Moderate

W/A: NRA Anglian Region

Comments: This big, rich water is expected to produce some huge carp within the next few years, as they are growing very rapidly. Not heavily fished, and ideal for anyone who wants plenty of space. Price quoted above includes membership of Rocla Lake and Black Horse Lake and all other Linear Fisheries Club waters - details from Secretary as above. There is now sailing on this lake

Turn Grandad's old tackle into cash see page 287

Hyde Lane Reservoir

Location:	Hyde Lane, Buckingham
Type and Size:	Reservoir of about 40 acres
How to Find:	Near Buckingham
Carp Stock:	Not many carp, but some big fish to over 30 pounds
Category:	Mixed Fishery
Other Species:	A few catfish to over 25 pounds
Permits:	Season tickets from local tackle shops
Cost:	On application
Control:	Club
BK Rating:	Difficult
W/A:	NRA Anglian Region

Lodge Lake

Location:	Dansteed Way, Great Holm, Milton Keynes
Type and Size:	Eight acre man-made lake divided by a central island
How to Find:	Turn off the M1 at junction 14 and take the A509 to the first roundabout. Turn right into Portway and right again at the second roundabout into Brickhill Street. The left turn at the next roundabout will bring you into Dansteed Way and the lake will be seen on the left. Parking to the left of the lake in Bradwell Road.
Carp Stock:	Very well stocked with about 1,500 carp to 22lbs - mirrors, commons and leathers
Category:	Mixed Fishery
Other Species:	Golden koi, crucians, roach, perch, bream, rudd and tench
Permits:	Members only water of Milton Keynes AA (no day tickets). Membership open to all. Permits from local tackle shops or the Secretary, 107 Baccara Grove, Bletchley, Milton Keynes.
Control:	Club
BK Rating:	Easy
Baits/Methods:	Usual carp fishing methods, although no fixed leads are allowed.
W/A:	NRA Anglian Region
Comments:	Some areas are out of bounds and so cannot be fished

Newport Pagnell Gravel Pits

Location:	Newport Pagnell, off the Bedford Road
Type and Size:	Eight small pits
Carp Stock:	Most of the lakes contain carp, up to 20lbs in some of them
Category:	Mixed Fishery
Other Species:	Tench, pike, roach, perch and bream
Permits:	Newport Pagnell Fishing Association. Secretary: R D Dorrill, 7 Bury Street, Newport Pagnell. Tel: 0909 610639.
Cost:	About £12 per season
BK Rating:	Moderate
W/A:	Anglian

Parc Farm Carp Lakes, No 1

Location:	Linear Fisheries, Little Linford Lane, Newport Pagnell, Milton Keynes
Type and Size:	Five acre gravel pit
How to Find:	From the M1 Junction 14, turn on the A509 towards Newport Pagnell. At the first roundabout, turn left onto the A422 then right at the next roundabout. At the T-junction turn left and at the next mini-roundabout, turn right down Little Linford Lane. Cross the motorway and the humped-backed bridge over the river, pass the old sailing club entrance on your right, and Parc Farm Lakes car park is through a gate on your left. Do not take the left turn after this marked 'Parc Farm'
Carp Stock:	Heavily stocked with carp to 20lbs
Category:	Carp Water
Other Species:	Some trout
Permits:	Day tickets on bank or from Linear Fisheries, 2 Northcroft, Shenley Lodge, Milton Keynes, Bucks. Tel: 0908 607577
Control:	Linear Fisheries
Restrictions:	No bent hooks; no sacking of carp
Baits/Methods:	Carp are caught on all methods, including float fishing with sweetcorn
BK Rating:	Easy
W/A:	NRA Anglian Region
Comments:	A former trout fishery, opened for carp fishing in 1992. Soon expected to be the best day ticket carp water in the area. 14 other lakes and three miles of the River Great Ouse available from Linear Fisheries nearby, including waters containing carp to well over 30lbs. SAE for 48 page illustrated brochure

Parc Farm Lakes, No 2

Location:	Linear Fisheries, Little Linford Lane, Newport Pagnell, Milton Keynes
Type and Size:	7 acre gravel pit
Carp Stock:	The lake contains carp to doubles, but is now being very heavily stocked with small carp
Category:	Mixed Fishery
Other Species:	Roach, bream, trout and perch
Permits:	Day tickets on bank or from Linear Fisheries, 2 Northcroft, Shenley Lodge, Milton Keynes.Tel: 0908 607577
Control:	Linear Fisheries
Baits/Methods:	Match fishing methods ideal for big bags of carp
BK Rating:	Very Easy
W/A:	NRA Anglian Region
Comments:	This lake is at present an any method trout fishery, but it does contain some good carp and is being very heavily stocked with small carp, and will be opened soon mainly as a match fish water. Huge carp bags expected. Details from the Secretary, Linear Fisheries; can be booked for matches

Red House Lake

Location:	Linford Linear Fisheries, Little Linford Lane, Milton Keynes
Type and Size:	Gravel pit of 15 acres
How to Find:	From junction 14 of the M1, turn right on the A409 towards Newport Pagnell, left at the next roundabout, right at the next roundabout, and left at the T-junction. Go under the bridge, straight across the small roundabout, and the Linear Fisheries entrance is about 400 yards on the

	right. There is also access from Little Linford Lane
Carp Stock:	Heavily stocked with carp to double figures by Linear in 1986/88. A few originals caught to 21lbs.
Category:	Carp Water
Other Species:	Bream to 8lbs; tench to 6½lbs; pike to 20lbs; roach and perch
Permits:	Linear Fisheries Secretary: Len Gurd, Linear House, 2 Northcroft, Shenley Lodge, Milton Keynes, Bucks. Tel: 0908 607577. Seasonal (syndicate) only - frequent vacancies.
Cost:	About £65 per season
BK Rating:	Easy
Restrictions:	No sacking of carp, no day tickets.
Control:	Linear Fisheries
W/A:	NRA Anglian Region
Comments:	Attractive, pleasant reed-fringed lake with a long promontory. Double figure carp were being caught here in the early 1980's. Linear Fisheries has Elstow Pit, near Bedford, a top carp fishery with many doubles and twenties to 30lbs. Syndicate only, vacancies now - enquire from Secretary

Red House Lake,
Linear Fisheries

New and best selling carp books from Beekay Publishers. See page 14

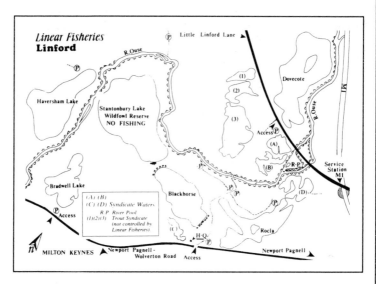

Rocla Lake

Location:	Linford Linear Fisheries, Little Linford Lane, Milton Keynes
Type and Size:	Old matured gravel pit of 35 acres
How to Find:	From junction 14 of the M1, turn right on the A409 towards Newport Pagnell, left at the first roundabout, right at the next roundabout and left at the T-junction. Go under the bridge, straight across the small roundabout and you will see Rocla on your right. The Linear Fisheries entrance and car parks are 400 yards on the right.
Carp Stock:	Stocked by Linear with very large numbers of carp to double figures; many doubles to 20lbs caught
Carp Stock:	Mixed Fishery
Other Species:	Bream to 8lbs; tench to 6½lbs; pike to 20lbs, roach and perch
Permits:	Linear Fisheries Secretary: Len Gurd, Linear House, 2 Northcroft, Shenley Lodge, Milton Keynes, Bucks. Tel: 0908 607577.
Cost:	£30 per season; £40 per 24 hour season ticket. Day tickets £3 per rod. Cost includes other Linear Fisheries waters.
BK Rating:	Easy
Restrictions:	No sacking of carp
Control:	Linear Fisheries
W/A:	NRA Anglian Region
Comments:	Another very attractive lake of irregular shape with trees and bushes. One large island which attracts the carp. Many bays and promontories. An angler had 21 carp in a day! This lake is featured in the 'Carp Fever' series of videos by Kevin Maddocks

Snowberry Lake

Location:	Bletchley, near Milton Keynes, just off the A5
Type and Size:	Attractive 3 acre lake
Carp Stock:	Well stocked with carp to upper twenties

Other Species:	Tench, zander, roach, bream and crucians
Permits:	Fourways Fisheries, Poplars Nursery, Harlington Road, Toddington, Dunstable LU5 6HE. Tel: 05255 5590.
Cost:	£175 per season
Restrictions:	No day tickets
BK Rating:	Moderate
W/A:	NRA Anglian Region
Comments:	A very pleasant water, once controlled by the late Richard Walker.

Teardrops

Location:	Loughton Lakes, Milton Keynes - behind the Milton Keynes Bowl
Type and Size:	Three lakes of about two acres each
Carp Stock:	Heavily stocked with small carp
Category:	Mixed Fishery
Other Species:	Roach, bream, perch, tench, chub and catfish
Permits:	£3 per day on bank
Control:	0908 649446
BK Rating:	Easy
W/A:	NRA Anglian Region

Tiddenfoot Pit

Location: On the Leighton Buzzard ring road, Mentmore Road
Type and Size: Sand pit of 10 acres
How to Find: Near the town of Leighton Buzzard
Carp Stock: A small number of carp to about 24lbs
Category: Few Carp
Other Species: Catfish, bream, pike, roach, perch
Permits: Leighton Buzzard Angling Club. Secretary: B Smalley, 3 Isis Walk, Leighton Buzzard, Beds. Tel: 0525 852227.
Cost: £20 per season. Joint husband and wife £23.
Control: Club
BK Rating: Moderate
W/A: NRA Anglian Region

Weston Tervell Reservoir

Location: Holton, Prestwood, near Great Missenden
Type and Size: 15 acre reservoir
Carp Stock: About 30 original fish up to 32lbs. Recently stocked with about 200 carp, sizes not known
Category: Mixed Fishery
Other Species: Usual coarse fish
Permits: Day time season tickets from Prestwood and District AC; enquire locally
Cost: £24 joining fee and £18 extra for night fishing
Restrictions: Lots... but our informant doesn't say what they are!
BK Rating: Difficult
W/A: NRA Thames Region
Comments: In or very near the reeds said to be the best area for carp

Wolverton Lakes

Location: Stratford Road, Wolverton, Milton Keynes
Type and Size: Two small man-made lakes of about one acre
Carp Stock: About 100 mirrors and commons to 6lbs
Category: Mixed Fishery
Other Species: Crucians, tench, roach, perch
Permits: Members only water of Milton Keynes Angling Association (no day tickets). Membership is open to all - permits from local tackle shops or from the Secretary, 107 Baccara Grove, Bletchley, Milton Keynes.
Control: Club
Restrictions: Members only
W/A: NRA Anglian Region
BK Rating: Easy
Comments: Small fish carp water, suitable for the non-carp specialist. Car park is at Wolverton Mill, opposite the footpath to the lakes.

CAMBRIDGESHIRE

WISBECH

PETERBOROUGH

WHITTLESEY

MARCH

ELY

HUNTINGDON

ST. IVES

ST. NEOTS

CAMBRIDGE

Barway Lake

Location:	Barway, near Ely
Type and Size:	5 acre lake
Carp Stock:	Well stocked with carp to 20lbs
Category:	Mixed Fishery
Other Species:	Tench, roach and crucians
Permits:	P S and J M Randall. Tel: 0353 720052
Cost:	Day tickets on application; 6am to dusk only
Control:	Private
BK Rating:	Not known
Restrictions:	No night fishing
W/A:	NRA Anglian Region

Brackhill Lake

Location: Earith between Huntingdon and Ely
Type and Size: 3 gravel pits
Carp Stock: Brackhill Lake said to contain 'a few' carp, has some to double figures. This complex is being developed as a carp fishery
Category: Few Carp
Other Species: Roach, perch, rudd, tench and bream
Permits: Enquire locally
Control: Private (ex A.R.C.)
BK Rating: Difficult
Restrictions: No night fishing
W/A: NRA Anglian Region

Burnside Lake

Location: Old Blue Circle Cement Works, Coldhams Lane, Cambridge
Type and Size: 10 acre chalk quarry
Carp Stock: About 200 carp, between 7lbs and 15lbs
Category: Mixed Fishery
Other Species: Roach, rudd, bream, perch, chub and pike
Permits: Season tickets only from Cherry Hinton AC. Secretary: Mr Hobson, 25 Ivory Close, Cherry Hinton, Cambridgeshire.
Cost: £11 per season
Control: Club
Restrictions: No day tickets
BK Rating: Moderate
W/A: NRA Anglian Region
Comments: The average depth of this quarry is about 25ft, with some areas 35ft deep. Most carp are caught in the margins or on floating or suspended baits because of the great depth.

Burwell Lode

Location: Cock-Up Bridge, Burwell, near Cambridge
Type and Size: Narrow drain-type river, a tributary of the River Cam
Carp Stock: Stocked in the winter of 1991 with about 400 carp to 15lbs, mostly very small and transferred from a local pit
Category: Mixed Fishery
Other Species: Tench, bream, rudd, roach and perch
Permits: Enquire in local tackle shops
Control: Cambridge FPAS
BK Rating: Not known
W/A: NRA Anglian Region
Comments: Let's hope your fishing here is not like the name of the bridge where the fish were put in!

Chawston Lake

Location: Chawston, near St. Neots
Type and Size: Gravel pit of about 8-10 acres
How to Find: One mile off A1 near St. Neots
Carp Stock: Quite well stocked with carp to 19-20lbs. Most are doubles of 10-14lbs

Category:	Mixed Fishery
Other Species:	General coarse fish
Permits:	Chawston AC - tackle shop in St. Neots
Cost:	On application
BK Rating:	Moderate
Control:	Club
W/A:	NRA Anglian Region
Comments:	Fish to around 20lbs.

Chesterford Fisheries

Location:	Great Chesterford, Saffron Walden
Type and Size:	3 lakes -7 acres, 2 of 3 acres. Mature gravel pits
How to Find:	Off M11, junction 9
Carp Stock:	Chesterford Lake (7 acres) - 100 carp to 30lbs plus; Borough Lake - 40 fish, doubles and twenties; Ickleton Lake - 100 plus doubles up to 18lbs, 3 thirties.
Category:	Mixed Fisheries
Other Species:	Big perch, roach, tench, pike
Permits:	Season tickets only from Paul Elsegood, 2 Wentfords Cottages, Clare Road, Poslingford, Sudbury, Suffolk. Tel: 0787 277468.
Cost:	£125
Control:	Private
Restrictions:	Fishing up to 10.30pm; and after 3am. No sacking
BK Rating:	Chesterford - Difficult for big fish. Borough - Difficult. Ickleton - Moderate.
W/A:	NRA Anglian Region
Comments:	Do not visit water until you have contacted the owner. Tickets in advance only. No day tickets. Guest tickets for members. Cooking hut. Toilets. Club-type image

Clearwaters Coarse Fishery

Location:	Near Earith, which is not far from St. Ives
Type and Size:	13 acre lake, matured gravel pit
Carp Stock:	Well stocked with carp to about 20lbs
Category:	Carp Water
Other Species:	Some other coarse fish, including tench
Permits:	Season tickets in advance only - for details telephone 0582 853307, between 6pm and 9pm.
Control:	Private
BK Rating:	Moderate
W/A:	NRA Anglian Region

Decoy Lake

Location:	Decoy Farm, Eastrea, Whittlesey, Peterborough
Type and Size:	Gravel pit of about 3½ acres
How to Find:	From Peterborough take the A605 to Whittlesey. Follow A605 towards March for 1½ miles, turn left opposite some white silos
Carp Stock:	11,000 small carp, up to 4lbs!
Category:	Mixed Fishery

Mark Churcher with a 27 pounder from Chesterford Fisheries

Borough Lake, Chesterford Fisheries; Paul Elsegood's excellent carp waters in Cambridgeshire

Other Species: Bream, tench, rudd, few roach
Permits: Club bookings and matches only; 10, 22 or 32 anglers only. From Peter Band on 0733 202230, or Tony Hudson on 0733 203428.
Cost: Approx £5 per peg for 6 hours fishing
BK Rating: Easy
Control: Private
Restrictions: Barbless hooks; keepnets supplied. No children. No night fishing.
W/A: Anglian
Comments: Spring fed water, specially stocked for match fishing. The 11,000 commons and mirrors were stocked at 7oz - 1lb, and some weigh 4lbs, after 6 months! No individual fishing - block bookings only. Enormous catches are routine. England International Ian Heaps, who regularly fishes the waters, says that he considers this the match fishing of the future, as heavily stocked carp match waters provide more sport for all. Something a bit different for our Guide — nearly 4,000 carp per acre!

Dickersons Pit

Location: Milton Pits, Milton Road, Cambridge
Type and Size: Large matured gravel pit
Carp Stock: Well stocked with carp to over 20lbs
Category: Mixed Fishery
Other Species: Pike, tench and rudd
Permits: Try Cooper Brothers Tackle Shop, Milton Road, Cambridge for permits and information
Cost: About £10 per person
Control: Histon AC
Restrictions: Most of this pit has recently been designated a 'Nature Reserve', and, as so often in these cases, has been closed to anglers, most of whom are true nature lovers! However, the small pit attached to the main one by a narrow stretch of water, remains open, and other pits on the site, including Todds Pit, which also contains carp, are still in the control of Histon AC - Secretary: R Cooper, 236 Histon Road, Cottenham, Cambridge (members only)

Earith Lakes

Location: Holme Fen Drove, Earith, near St. Ives
Type and Size: Originally an 18 acre matured gravel pit, now divided into two parts
Carp Stock: Larger lake (11 acres) - several hundred to 31lbs; smaller lake (7 acres) - heavily stocked with smaller carp to low twenties
Category: Carp Water (both lakes)
Other Species: Perch, rudd, roach, chub, tench and pike
Permits: From the owner, Ken McLennan, on site. Tel: 0487 740301.
Cost: Both lakes - syndicate at £120 per year
BK Rating: Moderate for both waters
Control: Private
Restrictions: No sacks. No tiger nuts or peanuts.
W/A: NRA Anglian Region
Comments: This is a very pleasant carp fishery, very well stocked with large numbers of good carp. There is also an 18 acre coarse fishery and a 36 acre trout lake on the site - details from the owner

Eaton Socon Lake

Location:	Eaton Socon, near St. Neots
Carp Stock:	Well stocked with carp to 20lbs
Category:	Mixed Fishery
Other Species:	Tench, rudd and bream
Permits:	Hitchin and District AC, L G Day, 14 Thatchers End, Hitchin, Herts or from local tackle shops
Cost:	Members only - season ticket at £17.50
Control:	Club
BK Rating:	Moderate
W/A:	NRA Anglian Region

Fen Drayton Complex

Location:	Fen Drayton, between Cambridge and Huntingdon
Type and Size:	Gravel pits - Drayton Fen quite large
How to Find:	Off the A604 Cambridge - Huntingdon road
Carp Stock:	Some large carp
Category:	Few Carp
Other Species:	General coarse fish including zander
Permits:	Head Bailiff: Neil Prior. Tel: 0954 303345 (evenings)
Cost:	On application
BK Rating:	Moderate
Control:	Private
Restrictions:	None
W/A:	NRA Anglian Region
Comments:	Also board sailing on this lake.

Fen Drayton Lake

Location:	Fen Drayton, near Fenstanton
Type and Size:	30 acre gravel pit
How to Find:	Fen Drayton between Huntingdon and Cambridge
Carp Stock:	Very few fish to 30lbs plus
Category:	Few Carp
Other Species:	Mixed coarse fish
Permits:	Enquire locally
BK Rating:	Very Difficult
Restrictions:	None
W/A:	NRA Anglian Region
Comments:	Sailing and windsurfing also take place on this pit

Fenland Fisheries

Location:	Earith, near Huntingdon
Type and Size:	Seven acre gravel pit
Carp Stock:	Well stocked with carp to 20lbs
Category:	Mixed Fishery
Other Species:	Koi, grass carp, roach, tench, perch and trout
Permits:	Day tickets, booked in advance from Fish Farm, Meadow Drive, Earith. Tel: 0487 841858
Cost:	£6
Restrictions:	No night fishing; no keepnets; barbless hooks only

BK Rating:	Not known
W/A:	NRA Anglian Region
Comments:	Limited number of anglers each day. Toilets and refreshments on site

Fourways Fishing Club

Location:	Baston, near Peterborough
Type and Size:	Lake of 5½ acres
Carp Stock:	Well stocked with carp to 26lbs
Category:	Mixed Fishery
Other Species:	Tench and roach
Permits:	£80 a season. Tel: 0406 380473/380557
Restrictions:	No day tickets; season tickets only
BK Rating:	Moderate
W/A:	NRA Anglian Region

Gerrards Carp Lake

Location:	Woodgate Lane, Maxey, Peterborough. Tel: 0945 780309
Type and Size:	10 acre pit
Carp Stock:	Well stocked with carp to 20lbs
Category:	Carp Water
Other Species:	Some coarse fish
Permits:	In advance only, telephone as above
Control:	Private
BK Rating:	Easy
W/A:	NRA Anglian Region

Hatton Park Pool

Location:	Longstanton, near Cambridge
Type and Size:	Gravel pit of 1½ acres
How to Find:	In the middle of a field on the east side of Station Road, 300 yards outside Longstanton
Carp Stock:	Stocked in 1982 with 15 carp to 10lbs that have since bred
Category:	Carp Water
Other Species:	Tench to 6lbs, plus rudd
Permits:	Free
BK Rating:	Moderate
W/A:	Anglian

Hinchingbrooke Country Park

Location:	Off the A1 near Huntingdon - the road to the lake is signposted
Type and Size:	Fifty acre lake
Carp Stock:	Well stocked with carp to 25lbs
Category:	Mixed Fishery
Other Species:	Roach, bream, perch, tench, pike, chub and eels
Permits:	Day tickets from Tim's Tackle, 88 High Street, Huntingdon
Cost:	£2 adults; £1 for juniors and OAP's
Control:	0480 450039
BK Rating:	Moderate
W/A:	NRA Anglian Region
Comments:	Food and drinks available; toilets

Lees Brook

Location:	Berry Lane, Godmanchester, near Huntingdon
Type and Size:	Small river, tributary of the Great Ouse
Carp Stock:	Some carp to about 10lbs
Category:	Few Carp
Other Species:	Chub, bream, roach, dace, perch and gudgeon
Permits:	In advance from Stanjay Fishing Tackle, Godmanchester. Tel: 0480 453303
Control:	Godmanchester AC
Restrictions:	More than half of the bank is private
BK Rating:	Difficult
W/A:	NRA Anglian Region

Little Paxton Fishery

Location:	Near St. Neots
Type and Size:	Gravel pits, 4 lakes, total about 30 acres
How to Find:	Take the A1 north from London. After the A45 turn off, take the left turn marked 'St. Neots - Little Paxton', B1041. Turn left at the signpost marked 'Paxton Quarry' and continue for 600 yards to car park
Carp Stock:	All lakes have some large carp to 20lbs. The car park lake has been stocked with carp to 20lbs
Category:	Mixed Fishery
Other Species:	Bream, tench, roach, rudd, perch, pike
Permits:	Day tickets from site office near car park. Must be obtained before fishing. At weekends ONLY anglers may fish from 8am before obtaining tickets and the bailiff will sell them later on the bank. Season tickets from Fishery Manager, Ian May, 8 Davis Close, Little Paxton. Tel: Huntingdon 212059.
Cost:	Day tickets: £2 (juniors/OAP/evenings £1). Season tickets: £25. Limited night fishing at £25 extra
BK Rating:	Moderate
Restrictions:	No night fishing. Open daily 7.30am until sunset. Season and advance day ticket holders may fish from sunrise till dark. No sacking.
Baits/Methods:	Normal modern carp methods and baits
Control:	Redland Angling Scheme
W/A:	NRA Anglian Region
Comments:	Commercial fishery. Season ticket holders may night fish for carp by arrangement with the fishery manager. Do not go to the works area. Park only in the car park

Long Reach

Location:	Off St. Ives by-pass
Type and Size:	20 acre gravel pit
How to Find:	Take A604 towards Cambridge, St. Ives turning (B1040); St. Ives by-pass, lake on right by third roundabout
Carp Stock:	Sparsely stocked to 35lbs plus
Category:	Few Carp
Other Species:	General coarse fish
Permits:	Enquire locally
BK Rating:	Difficult

Turn Grandad's old tackle into cash see page 287

Control: Private
Restrictions: None
W/A: NRA Anglian Region
Comments: Water ski-ing on this lake during the day. A good venue for the
                    pioneering type angler - full potential unknown

Milton Lake

Location: Near Cambridge
Type and Size: Large lake
Carp Stock: Stocked with carp to over 20lbs
Category: Mixed Fishery
Other Species: Most coarse fish
Permits: Try local tackle shops
Control: Club - possibly Cambridge AS
Cost: 65p per day
BK Rating: Difficult
W/A: NRA Anglian Region

Milton Pits

Location: Old School Lane, Milton, Cambridge
Type and Size: 4 acre gravel pit
How to Find: Take the A45 north to Cambridge to Milton village. Take the High Street,
                    turn into Coles Road and Old School Lane
Carp Stock: Well stocked with carp to 20lbs
Category: Mixed Fishery
Other Species: General coarse fish
Permits: Cooper Brothers Tackle Shop, Milton Road, Cambridge, in advance only
Cost: Approximately £10 per season, no day tickets
BK Rating: Moderate
Control: Histon Angling Club
Restrictions: None
W/A: NRA Anglian Region
Comments: Pleasant lake run by club

North House Lake

Location: The North House, Great North Road, Wyboston, near St. Neots
Type and Size: Gravel pit of 5 acres
How to Find: Can be seen from the A1 at Wyboston
Carp Stock: Quite well stocked — 40—60 fish to 23lbs. Average 14lbs
Category: Mixed Fishery
Other Species: Crucians, tench and rudd
Permits: Luton AC or Leslie's of Luton, 89 Park Street, Luton, Beds.
                    Tel: 0582 453542
Cost: Approximately £7.50 per season
BK Rating: Moderate
Control: Club
W/A: NRA Anglian Region
Comments: Pear-shaped open gravel pit. Luton Angling Club, D Bacon,
                    18 The Hedgerows, Parkside, Furzton, Milton Keynes, MK14 1BP.
                    No night fishing

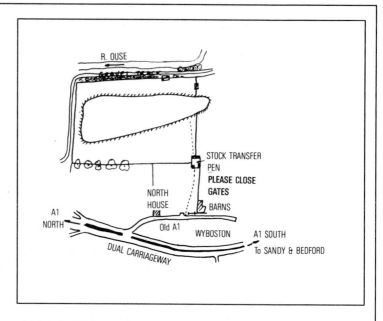

Offord Weirpool

Location:	Offord, near Huntingdon
Type and Size:	Very large millpool of the River Great Ouse
How to Find:	At Buckden turn off the A1 towards Offord. The pool can be seen in about two miles, with a car park on the right
Carp Stock:	Quite a number of doubles to nearly 30lbs
Category:	Mixed Fishery
Other Species:	Pike, chub, roach and bream
Permits:	Day tickets on bank
Cost:	£2 per day; OAP's and juniors 50p; season tickets £10 and £4
Control:	Offord and Buckden AC
Baits/Methods:	Legered luncheon meat and floaters work well
BK Rating:	Moderate
W/A:	NRA Anglian Region

Paxton Lake

Location:	Great Paxton, near St. Neots
Type and Size:	Medium sized lake
Carp Stock:	Well stocked with carp, said to go to 30lbs
Category:	Mixed Fishery
Other Species:	Tench, chub, bream and roach
Permits:	Day tickets on bank from bailiffs, or the Secretary, St. Neots and District, Watling, 43 Shakespeare Road, Eaton Socon, Cambs PE19 3HG.
Cost:	About £1 per day; £4 per week; £9.40 per season - includes fishing on the Great Ouse
Control:	Club
BK Rating:	Not known
W/A:	NRA Anglian Region

Pisces Caravan Park and Fishery   A

Location:	Bedford Bank, Welney, Wisbech, PE14 9TB. Tel: 035471 (Welney) 257
Type and Size:	Lakes of 4 acres and 2 acres
Carp Stock:	Larger lake well stocked with carp to about 15lbs. Smaller lake contains crucian carp
Category:	Mixed Fishery
Other Species:	Bream, roach, rudd, perch, pike; some tench in smaller lake
Permits:	No day tickets. Fishing is free, and is for residents only.
Control:	Pisces Caravan Park - private
BK Rating:	Not known
Restrictions:	Barbless hooks only. No keepnets. No groundbait. No boilies to be thrown in the lake
W/A:	NRA Anglian Region
Comments:	Catches listed includes pike to over 30lbs, bream to 11lbs 6ozs, tench to over 8lbs, perch to 2lbs, rudd to 3lbs 11ozs, roach to 2½lbs and an eel of 6½lbs.
	There are 16 letting caravans round the lake, and the rivers Bedford and Delph run alongside the Park - fishing free in the River Bedford, local tickets for the Delph. There is also a new trout lake on the site, with a small charge for the fishing. Rod licences and bait on site. Costs for caravans and bungalow from £100 to £205 per week according to time of year

Randalls Lake

Location:	Barway, south of Ely
Type and Size:	Small lake with two large islands
How to Find:	Take the A142 from Ely towards Soham. Go into Barway and take the right fork, when the lake is signposted
Carp Stock:	Well stocked with carp to doubles
Category:	Mixed Fishery
Other Species:	Crucians, rudd, roach, bream, tench, pike, chub, small zander and eels
Permits:	On bank at £3.50 per day
Restrictions:	No night fishing; fishing is 6am till dusk in summer, and 8am to dusk in winter
BK Rating:	Not known
W/A:	NRA Anglian Region
Comments:	Toilets and car park; river on one side

Silver Street Mill

Location:	Cambridge
Type and Size:	Large millpool on the River Cam
How to Find:	Silver Street or Queen's Road, Cambridge, close to the colleges
Carp Stock:	Some carp to doubles
Category:	Few Carp
Other Species:	Chub, roach and dace
Permits:	Free fishing
BK Rating:	Difficult
W/A:	NRA Anglian Region
Comments:	Very heavy boat traffic in summer; many punts

Soham By-Pass Lake

Location:	Soham, near Cambridge
Type and Size:	Small gravel pit
Carp Stock:	Well stocked with small carp, mostly commons, to doubles
Category:	Mixed Fishery
Other Species:	Crucians and rudd
Permits:	Enquire from tackle shops in Cambridge
BK Rating:	Not known, but very heavy catches of small carp are reported
W/A:	NRA Anglian Region

St. Ives Complex

Location:	Fen Drayton, near St. Ives
Type and Size:	Several gravel pits
How to Find:	Near St. Ives
Carp Stock:	Trior Lake contains some carp; St. Ives Lagoon - a few large carp; Anderson's Lake - good carp
Category:	Mixed Fisheries
Other Species:	General coarse fish
Permits:	Site Warden: Bernard Hunt. Tel: 0480 86444 (day); 0480 212815 (evenings).
Cost:	Day tickets on application
BK Rating:	Not known
Control:	Private
W/A:	NRA Anglian Region
Comments:	Lowry's also contains some carp. Little known about this fishery.

The Stew Pond

Location:	St. Neots
Type and Size:	Pit of about 1½ acres
How to Find:	The pit is in the Wyboston Complex just off the A1
Carp Stock:	Many carp up to 2lbs, with some bigger ones up to 18lbs
Category:	Carp Water
Other Species:	General coarse fish
Permits:	Day tickets from the Club House on the golf course next to the pit.
Cost:	Approximately £1 per day
Control:	Private
BK Rating:	Moderate
W/A:	NRA Anglian Region
Comments:	Night fishing allowed

Werrington Lake

Location:	Werrington, near Peterborough
Type and Size:	Medium sized pits
Carp Stock:	Very well stocked with carp to over 20lbs
Category:	Carp Water
Other Species:	Some tench, roach and catfish
Permits:	Seasonal - information and details on 0733 570266
Cost:	On application
Control:	Private
BK Rating:	Moderate
W/A:	NRA Anglian Region

Wimblington Mere

Location:	Wimblington, near Wisbech
Type and Size:	Small gravel pit
How to Find:	Just off the B1098 between Chatteris and Wisbech
Carp Stock:	Some carp, numbers and sizes unknown, but a schoolboy had a 21¼lb here in 1987, reported in Angling Times
Category:	Mixed Fishery
Other Species:	Crucians, rudd, roach, tench, bream
Permits:	Head Bailiff Keith Bradshaw. Tel: 0354 740350 (evenings)
Cost:	On application - about £12 per season.
BK Rating:	Moderate
Control:	Private
Restrictions:	No cereal groundbaits; no keepnets
W/A:	NRA Anglian Region
Comments:	On the same site as Browns Water, containing carp, and Honey Pond with some carp and tench. The 21¼ was caught on slow sinking flake

Woburn Close Lake   A

Location:	Hemingford Grey, St. Ives
Type and Size:	Gravel pit of 3 acres
Carp Stock:	Very heavily stocked with about 2,000 carp. Average size is about 8lbs and the best fish is about 17lbs
Category:	Carp Water
Permits:	Fishing can only be obtained by renting a holiday on the property. All information and bookings from: Jim Eggett, Woburn Close, Meadow Lane, Hemingford Grey, St. Ives, Cambridgeshire. Tel: 0480 62623
Cost:	On application
Control:	Private
Restrictions:	No night fishing
BK Rating:	Very Easy
W/A:	NRA Anglian Region

Woolpack Fishery

Location:	Godmanchester, on the main road north of Hilton, near St. Ives
Type and Size:	8 lakes
Carp Stock:	Quite well stocked with carp which range from 12lbs to 30lbs
Other Species:	Tench, roach, rudd, bream to 14lbs, pike to 30lbs, perch
Category:	Mixed Fishery
Permits:	At the time of going to press the control of this water was changing - visit lake for further details.
Cost:	£50 per season; £25 OAP's ; day tickets £3 in advance. £5 on bank
Control:	Stan Jay Fishing Tackle, 7 Old Court Hall, Godmanchester, Huntingdon. Tel: 0480 453303. SAE for details
Restrictions:	No peanuts to be used
BK Rating:	Moderate
W/A:	NRA Anglian Region

Turn Grandad's old tackle into cash see page 287

CHESHIRE

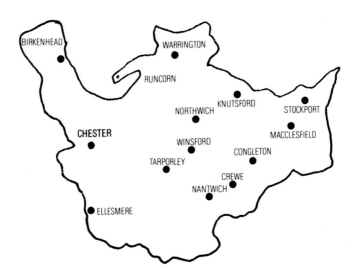

Ashenhurst Lakes

Location:	Blackely, Manchester
Type and Size:	Two lakes of about three-quarters of an acre each
Carp Stock:	Very heavily stocked with carp to about 16lbs, though most are singles
Category:	Carp Water
Other Species:	Roach and a few grass carp
Permits:	Club season tickets, very hard to obtain - try local tackle shops
Control:	Broughton Angling Club. G Guy, 27 Geralds Road, Salford M6 6DW, who may be able to help with membership
Baits/Methods:	Floaters and all other methods successful
BK Rating:	Very Easy
W/A:	NRA North West Region
Comments:	A very pleasant and attractive venue, which explains why it is so hard to obtain membership
Restrictions:	No night fishing; members only. Advertised for sale in 1990

Billinge Green

Location:	Off the A556, south of Northwich, near Davenham
Type and Size:	Small pool
Carp Stock:	Well stocked with carp to doubles
Category:	Mixed Fishery
Other Species:	Roach, bream, perch and tench
Permits:	Northwich AA, PO Box 18, Northwich CW9 5SE.
Control:	Club
BK Rating:	Moderate
Restrictions:	Members only
W/A:	NRA North West Region

Blakemere

Location:	Off the junction of the Shrewsbury/Whitchurch roads, about one mile from town centre of Ellesmere; park the car at the junction and walk 200 yards along canal towpath to lake
Type and Size:	Lake of about 7 acres
Carp Stock:	Carp to doubles
Category:	Mixed Fishery
Other Species:	Roach, bream, tench, perch and pike
Permits:	Ellesmere AC
Control:	Club
BK Rating:	Not known
W/A:	NRA North West Region

Bosley Reservoir

Location:	Bosley, near Macclesfield
Type and Size:	Huge reservoir of 90 acres
Carp Stock:	Carp were stocked in 1964. There are not many, but one thirty has been reported
Category:	Few Carp
Other Species:	General coarse fish
Permits:	Prince Albert AS, season tickets only. Secretary: C Clarke, 2 Avon Close, Upton, Macclesfield, Cheshire
Cost:	Around £35 entry fee and £35 per season
Control:	Club. Members only
BK Rating:	Very Difficult
W/A:	NRA North West Region

Bream Hole

Location:	Marsh Lane, Nantwich, off the A534 Wrexham road
Type and Size:	Wide opening on the Shropshire Union Canal. The lane crosses the canal and the 'hole' can be seen opposite the towpath side
Carp Stock:	Some carp to doubles
Category:	Probably Few Carp
Other Species:	Bream, hybrids, roach, eels, ruffe and gudgeon
Permits:	On bank at £3 per day, and £1.50 for juniors and OAP's
Restrictions:	None known, but there is quite a lot of boat traffic in the summer
BK Rating:	Difficult
W/A:	NRA North West Region

Brereton Pool

Location:	Off the A54 near Congleton
Type and Size:	Sand pit of 14 acres; a very attractive water
Carp Stock:	Some carp to over 20lbs
Category:	Mixed Fishery
Other Species:	Roach, bream and big pike
Permits:	£2 per day on the bank
Control:	Wheelock AS
Restrictions:	No night fishing unless you are a club member; over half the bank has no fishing. Leave the car park by 9.30pm, or your car will be locked in for the night!

BK Rating: Difficult
W/A: NRA North West Region
Comments: No close season; toilets and Ranger's hut on bank

Brereton Quarry

Location: Holmes Chapel, off the A54
Type and Size: Large quarry
Carp Stock: Some big carp
Category: Mixed Fishery
Other Species: Bream, pike and most other coarse fish
Permits: £2 per day on bank
Control: Wheelock AC; details from Dave's of Middlewich, 67 Wheelock Street, Middlewich CW10 9AB. Tel: 0606 835383
BK Rating: Difficult
W/A: NRA North West Region

Bridgewater Canal

Location: Broadheath Bridge to Preston Brook
Type and Size: Canal some miles in length
Carp Stock: Well stocked with carp to 17lbs
Category: Mixed Fishery
Other Species: General coarse fish
Permits: Warrington Anglers. Secretary: Mr J S Jackson, 23 Nora Street, Warrington
Control: Club
BK Rating: Moderate
W/A: North West
Comments: Carp have been growing well in this part of the canal and many are now caught in matches. There is some good carp fishing here as a change from lakes, and it should be noted that Warrington Anglers have several carp waters mentioned in this book, all on the same ticket

Brookside Carp Fishery

Location: Betley, south east of Crewe
Type and Size: Three acre pool, up to 15 feet in depth
How to Find: From Junction 16 of the M6, take the A500 towards Crewe. At the first roundabout go straight on towards Nantwich, and at the next roundabout turn left towards Keele, and you will find Betley in three miles. Opposite the Swan Inn, turn left, and you will see the fishery on the left in about half a mile
Carp Stock: Very well stocked with carp to 20lbs
Category: Carp Water
Other Species: Roach
Permits: On bank at £3.50 per rod
Control: Dave Barratt. Tel: 0270 820528/820271
Baits/Methods: Luncheon meat and sweetcorn; floaters do well in hot weather
Restrictions: Barbless hooks only; no boilies or nuts; no keepnets or sacks; micromesh landing nets only; no groundbaiting before fishing; no night fishing - 7.30am till dusk only

BK Rating:	Moderate
W/A:	NRA North West Region
Comments:	With all these bans, I sometimes wonder whether fishery owners want their fish caught! There is also a trout pool next to the coarse lake

Budworth Mere

Location:	Near Great Budworth, off the B5075, north of Northwich
Type and Size:	Large lake
Carp Stock:	Well stocked with carp to about 20lbs
Category:	Mixed Fishery
Other Species:	Tench, roach, rudd, bream, perch and pike
Permits:	Northwich AA, PO Box 18, Northwich ,CW9 5SE
Control:	Club. Try Scotts Tackle Tel: 0606 46543
Restrictions:	Members only
BK Rating:	Not known
W/A:	NRA North West Region

Burton Mere   A

Location:	Burton, off the A540 Chester to Hoylake road - in Burton, turn right into Puddington Lane, then take the first right to the lakes
Type and Size:	Two small man-made lakes
Category:	Mixed Fishery
Other Species:	Roach, rudd, perch, bream, crucians, tench, chub, catfish and trout
Permits:	Day tickets from the lodge on site. Tel: 051-253 0115.
Cost:	£4 per day; £2.50 per evening, from 5pm.
Control:	Private
Baits/Methods:	Float fishing works well, with standard baits
BK Rating:	Moderate
Restrictions:	No keepnets; no groundbaiting
W/A:	NRA Welsh Region
Comments:	The larger lake is day ticket, and the smaller one is a members only carp fishery. No close season on the day ticket water, as rainbow trout are stocked in March, but worm fishing only is allowed in the coarse fish close season

Canal Pit

Location:	Whatcroft, off the A530 south of Northwich
Type and Size:	Small pit
Carp Stock:	Some carp to doubles
Category:	Mixed Fishery
Other Species:	Usual coarse fish
Permits:	Northwich AA, PO Box 18, Northwich CW9 5SE; Scotts Tackle, Northwich. Tel: 0606 46543.
Control:	Club
Restrictions:	Members only
BK Rating:	Not known
W/A:	NRA North West Region

Capesthorne Hall Garden Pool

Location:	Capesthorne Estate, Siddington, near Macclesfield
Type and Size:	Estate lake of 7 acres
How to Find:	The estate is just off the A34, 3 miles from Macclesfield, and 6 miles from Knutsford and Wilmslow
Carp Stock:	The lake is well stocked with carp under 10lbs, and there are about 60 doubles, of which 6 are twenties - best 28lbs
Category:	Mixed Fishery
Other Species:	Tench, crucians, perch, roach, rudd, pike and gudgeon
Permits:	Season tickets form Stoke-on-Trent AS. Secretary: Mr Broadgate, 'Lynton', 5 Kingsfield Oval, Basford, Stoke-on-Trent ST4 6HN. Members only, some guest tickets. Tel: 0782 618833
Baits/Methods:	All methods and baits. Float fishing works well near lilies and bushes; surface fishing very successful in summer
Control:	Club. Bailiff: Mrs E Shapley. Tel: Wilmslow 520061
BK Rating:	Moderate
W/A:	NRA North West Region
Comments:	Stocked with mirror carp in 1958 and 1963. Good spawning and carp spawned in 1976 now up to 20lbs

Central Lake

Location:	Public park in Wallasey, near Birkenhead, on theWirral
Type and Size:	Four acre boating lake with an island
Carp Stock:	Well stocked with carp to doubles
Category:	Mixed Fishery
Other Species:	Crucians,roach, rudd and small tench
Permits:	In advance from local tackle shops
Cost:	£1 per day; £4 per year
Control:	Association of Wirral Angling Clubs
BK Rating:	Moderate
W/A:	NRA North West Region

Cheshire Fishing

Location:	Tattenhall, near Chester
Type and Size:	Three small lakes
How to Find:	From Chester take the A41 Whitchurch road. The Tattenhall turn is on the left in about 8 miles. At the T-junction in Tattenhall, turn left towards Burwardsley. In 1½ miles you will see a 'Cheshire Fishing' sign on the left
Carp Stock:	Lakes 1 and 2 well stocked with carp to 20lbs; Lake 3, the smallest contains many small carp
Category:	Mixed Fishery
Other Species:	Bream, tench, roach
Permits:	On site - match bookings in advance
Cost:	£6.50 per day per rod, dawn to dusk only; £4 for a 5 hour ticket, extra rods £1 each
Control:	Private. Tel: 0829 70041
Restrictions:	No night fishing; all fish over 1lb to be returned immediately; barbless hooks only

Baits/Methods:	Most baits and methods, though most carp are taken on boilies
BK Rating:	Moderate
Comments:	There are also two trout lakes on the same site.

Cicely Mill Pool

Location:	Knutsford
Type and Size:	Small mere of about 3 acres
Carp Stock:	Not many carp, but some to low doubles
Category:	Few Carp
Permits:	Warrington Anglers. Secretary: Mr Jackson, 23 Nora Street, Warrington
Control:	Club. Members only Tel: 0925 37525
BK Rating:	Difficult
W/A:	NRA North West Region

Crabmill Flash

Location:	Moston, near Sandbach
Type and Size:	Estate lake of about 10 acres
Carp Stock:	Plenty of doubles and about twenty 20's with the best fish over 30lbs
Category:	Carp Water
Permits:	Season tickets from Wheelock Angling Society, and local tackle shops
Control:	Club
BK Rating:	Moderate
W/A:	NRA North West Region
Comments:	Long, narrow canal-like lake, about ¼ mile long. Good twenties water

Crosemere

Location:	About 3 miles from Ellesmere on the main Shrewsbury road; parking down lane about half a mile past the lake
Type and Size:	Large Cheshire mere
Carp Stock:	Some carp to doubles
Category:	Few Carp
Other Species:	Roach, bream, perch, tench and pike
Permits:	Ellesmere AC
Control:	Club
BK Rating:	Very Difficult
W/A:	NRA North West Region
Comments:	As this area is an S.S.S.I., great care must be taken to observe rules and signs, and to keep to marked paths. No cutting of undergrowth etc

Dovemere, Sandmere and Woodlands

Location:	Allostock, near Knutsford
Type and Size:	3 lake complex, lakes dug to provide material for the motorway. Dovemere - 17 acres; Sandmere - 15 acres; Woodlands - 10 acres
How to Find:	Lakes are alongside the M6 at Allostock
Carp Stock:	Well stocked with mostly carp doubles

Category:	Carp Water
Other Species:	Mixed coarse fish
Permits:	Season tickets only from Prince Albert Angling Society. Secretary: C Clarke, 2 Avon Close, Macclesfield, Cheshire
Cost:	About £35 entry fee plus £35 annual subscription
Control:	Club
BK Rating:	Generally Easy, waters may vary
W/A:	NRA North West Region

Founders Pool

Location:	Near Warrington
Type and Size:	Small pond of 1 acre
Carp Stock:	Well stocked with carp to doubles
Category:	Mixed Fishery
Other Species:	Roach and perch
Permits:	Members only water of Lymm AC. Secretary: S Griffiths, 18 Manor Road, Lymm WA13 OAY. Tel: 092575 2765
Cost:	£23 per season, and a joining fee of £13
Restrictions:	No night fishing; members only.
BK Rating:	Easy
W/A:	NRA North West Region

Gale Green Farm Fishery

Location:	Gale Green Farm, off the A54 near Winsford
Type and Size:	Four acre lake
Carp Stock:	Well stocked with carp, mostly between 16lbs and 28lbs; commons and mirrors
Category:	Mixed Fishery
Other Species:	Pike, tench, roach, rudd, bream, chub, perch and eels
Permits:	Must be obtained from the farm by the car park before fishing
Cost:	£3.75 per day; £2.75 for summer evening tickets
Control:	Tel: 0606 552151
Restrictions:	Night fishing for club members only; difficult footpath to dense, wooded valley
BK Rating:	Moderate
W/A:	NRA North West Region

Godwins Pool

Location:	Near Congleton
Type and Size:	Small pool
Carp Stock:	Some carp to about 20lbs
Category:	Mixed Fishery
Other Species:	Tench and most other coarse fish
Permits:	Congleton Anglers' Society. Secretary: Mr N Bours, 8 Norfolk Road, Congleton. Tel: Congleton 277284
Cost:	Membership (to include other waters) costs £20 per season plus a £5 entry fee
Control:	Club
BK Rating:	Moderate
W/A:	NRA North West Region

Grey Mist Mere

Location:	Wooston, near Warrington
Type and Size:	Mere of about 10 acres
Carp Stock:	Very well stocked with carp. Plenty of doubles with a few low twenties, best fish 21lbs
Category:	Carp Water
Other Species:	General coarse fish
Permits:	Warrington Anglers, season tickets only. Secretary: Mr J S Jackson, 23 Nora Street, Warrington
Control:	Club
BK Rating:	Moderate
W/A:	NRA North West Region
Comments:	A well known carp water, very good for doubles

Grimesditch Pool

Location:	Stretton, near Warrington
Type and Size:	Small pool of 2 acres
How to Find:	Stretton is near junction 10 of the M56 motorway
Carp Stock:	Not many carp, sizes not known
Category:	Few Carp
Permits:	Lymm Angling Club. Secretary: S Griffiths, 18 Manor Way, Lymm WA13 OAY
Control:	Club
BK Rating:	Difficult
W/A:	NRA North West Region
Comments:	It should be noted here that Lymm Angling Club has several carp waters on the same ticket

Hack Green Lake

Location:	Hack Green, 3 miles from Nantwich
Type and Size:	Man-made lake of 2 acres
Carp Stock:	Well stocked with carp (in 1986) to doubles
Category:	Mixed Fishery
Other Species:	Tench, roach and bream
Permits:	See below
BK Rating:	Moderate
W/A:	NRA North West Region
Comments:	This water was advertised for sale, within a 4½ acre site, in March 1991 so you will need to enquire at local tackle shops to find out who controls it now. The agents were Wright-Manley. Tel: Tarporley (0829) 732151

King George V Pool

Location:	Altrincham
Type and Size:	Small, shallow lake of about 3 acres
How to Find:	Altrincham is near Sale on the SW outskirts of Manchester. Take the Manchester - Northwich road
Carp Stock:	Well stocked mainly with small carp, but there are fish to upper double figure size with the odd 20

Category:	Carp Water
Permits:	Day tickets from bailiff on bank
Control:	Trafford Metropolitan Council
BK Rating:	Easy
W/A:	NRA North West Region

Little Budworth

Location:	Little Budworth, near Tarporley
Type and Size:	5 acre lake
Carp Stock:	Some carp to doubles
Category:	Mixed Fishery
Other Species:	Tench, bream, roach and small perch
Permits:	Tarporley and District AC. Secretary: Mr M J Clays, 58 Churchill Drive, Tarporley CW6 OBZ; members only
Control:	Club
Restrictions:	Membership is restricted to those living within a 5 mile radius of Tarporley
BK Rating:	Not known
W/A:	NRA North West Region

Little Mill

Location:	Near Tarporley
Type and Size:	Mill pool of just over 3 acres
Carp Stock:	Carp to over 20lbs
Category:	Mixed Fishery
Other Species:	Tench, perch, bream, roach and a few crucians
Permits:	Tarporley and District AC. Secretary: Mr M J Clays, 58 Churchill Drive, Tarporley CW6 OBZ; members only
Control:	Club
Restrictions:	Membership is restricted to those living within a 5 miles radius of Tarporley
BK Rating:	Difficult
W/A:	NRA North West Region

Lymm Dam

Location:	Near the village of Lymm, near Warrington, Manchester
Type and Size:	15 acre lake
How to Find:	Go through Lymm onto the A56 and the lake will be seen on the right
Carp Stock:	There are not thought to be many carp but there are some very big ones. Largest known caught recently was 27lbs, but we know of a least one thirty caught a long time ago, and there are rumours of even bigger fish
Category:	Few Carp
Other Species:	Bream, roach, pike and a few catfish
Permits:	Day tickets from bailiffs on the bank.
Cost:	£1.50 per day
BK Rating:	Moderate
Baits/Methods:	Advanced carp fishing methods needed; high protein boilies
Control:	Lymm Angling Club, which has a number of other good carp waters. Secretary: S Griffiths, 18 Manor Way, Lymm WA13 OAY

W/A: NRA North West Region
Comments: This is known mainly as a match water, but there are some big fish of most species, and probably some very big carp, which are hard to find in this large water. Uncontrollable fish are occasionally hooked and lost - thought to be big catfish

Macclesfield Canal

Location: Kidsgrove and Congleton lengths especially good
Type and Size: Some miles of a narrow canal
Carp Stock: Plenty of carp to about 5lbs, with possibly some bigger fish present
Category: Mixed Fishery
Other Species: Bream, roach, tench and pike
Permits: Local angling clubs — try tackle shops in Congleton and Kidsgrove.
Control: Club
BK Rating: Easy
W/A: NRA North West Region
Comments: No close season

Marbury Mere

Location: Marbury
Type and Size: Mere of 30 acres
Carp Stock: Only a small number of carp, but some are upper 20's
Other Species: General coarse fish
Permits: Season tickets only. Prince Albert AS. Secretary: C Clarke, 2 Avon Close, Macclesfield, Cheshire
Cost: About £35 entry fee plus £35 per season
Control: Club
BK Rating: Very Difficult
W/A: NRA North West Region
Comments: All Prince Albert club waters are members only. This is one of the largest clubs in the country with a fine selection of waters

Mobberley Pool

Location: Small Lane, Mobberley, near Altrincham
Type and Size: Small pool of less than an acre
How to Find: Mobberley is near Knutsford on the B5085 road from Knutsford to Alderley Edge, south of Manchester
Carp Stock: Well stocked with small carp to lower double figure size
Category: Mixed Fishery
Permits: Altrincham AS. A Lea, 37 Crossgates Avenue, Sharston, Manchester.
Control: Club
BK Rating: Easy
W/A: NRA North West Region

Moreton Fishery

Location:	Just off the A34 Congleton to Kidsgrove road, at Astbury
Type and Size:	Newly dug, shallow, two acre lake
Carp Stock:	Heavily stocked with small carp, to about 10lbs
Category:	Mixed Fishery
Other Species:	Roach and rudd
Permits:	On site
Cost:	£3.50 per day; concessionary tickets; 50p for an extra rod
Control:	Tel: 0260 299496
Restrictions:	No boilies
BK Rating:	Easy
W/A:	NRA Severn Trent Region

Moreton Mere

Location:	Off the A553 at Moreton, Hoylake, Wirral
Type and Size:	Three acre lake, very recently dug
Carp Stock:	Well stocked with small carp of around 2lbs, with a few low doubles
Category:	Mixed Fishery
Other Species:	Roach, rudd, bream, perch and grass carp
Permits:	Day tickets on bank
Cost:	£2 per day; concessionary rates. Annual £10
Control:	Tel: 051 645 7211
Restrictions:	No night fishing; no keepnets
BK Rating:	Not known
W/A:	NRA North West Region

Moss and Mossbank Pools

Location:	Lymm, near Manchester
Type and Size:	Two small ponds
Carp Stock:	Well stocked with carp to about 10lbs
Category:	Carp Water
Other Species:	Crucians and grass carp (these are not really carp at all - Latin name: *Ctenopharyngodon Idella*!)
Permits:	Members only water of Lymm AA. Secretary: S Griffiths, 18 Manor Road, Lymm WA13 OAY. Tel: 092575 2763
Restrictions:	No day tickets; no night fishing
BK Rating:	Easy
W/A:	NRA North West Region

Ocean Pool

Location:	Winsford
Type and Size:	Medium sized lake
How to Find:	Winsford is south of Northwich on the A54 Chester to Congleton road
Carp Stock:	Small number of carp to mid-twenties
Category:	Few Carp
Other Species:	General coarse fish
Permits:	Winsford and District Angling Association, J Bailey, 22 Plover Road, Winsford

Control:	Club
BK Rating:	Easy
W/A:	NRA North West Region

Oulton Mill

Location:	Near Tarporley
Type and Size:	4 acre mill lake
Carp Stock:	Very well stocked with carp to 20lbs
Category:	Carp Water
Other Species:	A few tench and roach
Permits:	Tarporley and District AC - M J Clays, 58 Churchill Drive, Tarporley
Cost:	Season tickets at £60 per season, open to all
Control:	Club
BK Rating:	Moderate
W/A:	NRA North West Region
Comments:	Some waters in the NRA North West Region now have no close season

Petty Pool

Location:	Sandiway, off the A556 to the south west of Northwich
Type and Size:	Medium-sized lake
Carp Stock:	Some carp to doubles at least
Category:	Mixed Fishery
Other Species:	Usual coarse fish
Permits:	Northwich AA, PO Box 18, Northwich CW9 5SE; Scotts Tackle, Northwich. Tel: 0606 46543
Control:	Club
Restrictions:	Members only
BK Rating:	Not known
W/A:	NRA North West Region

Plex Flash

Location:	Oakwood Lane, Moston, Sandbach
Carp Stock:	Contains about 55 doubles to 18lbs 10ozs
Category:	Mixed Fishery
Other Species:	General coarse fish
Permits:	Wheelock Angling Club, and local tackle shops
Control:	Club
BK Rating:	Moderate
W/A:	NRA North West Region
Comments:	Little is known about this water. Further details from Club Secretary

Reddish Vale Mill Ponds

Location:	Reddish Vale Road, Stockport, off the B6167 Manchester to Stockport road
Type and Size:	Two small ponds
Carp Stock:	Both ponds quite well stocked with carp to over 20lbs
Category:	Mixed Fishery
Other Species:	Bream, tench, roach, perch and small pike

Permits:	On bank, or at the site Visitors Centre
Cost:	£2 per day; £3 for two rods; season tickets £15 and £6 for children under 15 and OAP's
Control:	Teme Valley Countryside Warden Service
Baits/Methods:	Boilies best for carp
Restrictions:	No night fishing (dawn till dusk only); floating crust is banned; livebaits banned; keepnets only allowed in matches
BK Rating:	Not known
W/A:	NRA North West Region

Redesmere

Location:	Capesthorne Estate, Siddington, Macclesfield
Type and Size:	Estate mere of 58 acres
How to Find:	The lake is just off the A34 Alderley Edge to Congleton road
Carp Stock:	There are reliably estimated to be about 150 doubles in the lake, of which 45 fish are over 20lbs. There are two thirties, a common of 33lbs 6ozs, and a mirror of 32lbs. Water was stocked with 150 fingerlings in 1958, and in 1963 a further 100 fish were stocked. Small number of carp including some doubles have been put in since
Category:	Mixed Fishery
Other Species:	Large bream, pike, tench, crucians, roach and perch
Permits:	Season tickets from Stoke-on-Trent Angling Society. Mr S Broadgate, 'Lynton', 5 Kingsfield Oval, Basford, Stoke-on-Trent ST4 6HN. Members only, some guest tickets allowed Tel: 0782 618833
Baits/Methods:	Normal carp fishing baits and methods
Control:	Club. Bailiff: Mrs E Shapley. Tel: Wilmslow 520061
BK Rating:	Difficult
W/A:	NRA North West Region
Comments:	This is one of the best big fish carp waters in the north west, but due to its large size it is not an easy water to succeed on. It has the potential to produce even bigger fish than at present. A 31 pounder was reported in 1990

Rhodes Lodges

Location:	Middleton, near Manchester
Type and Size:	Old mill pits - one of 5 acres and four smaller ones
Carp Stock:	Very well stocked with small carp, with some double figure mirrors and commons to about 15lbs
Category:	Carp Water
Other Species:	Some roach and perch
Permits:	Day tickets on site at £1.45; 70p for OAP's, juniors and the unemployed
Control:	Private. Tel: 061-654 8278
Restrictions:	No night fishing; no season tickets; no sacks
BK Rating:	Moderate
W/A:	NRA North West Region
Comments:	Heavily fished, crowded water open to all

New and best selling carp videos from Beekay Publishers. See page 19

River Weaver

Location:	Rises near Macclesfield and flows through Northwich to the Mersey
Type and Size:	Short river
How to Find:	Northwich area
Carp Stock:	100lb catches in a day reported, of carp to 5lbs and up to 9lbs
Category:	Mixed Fishery
Other Species:	General coarse fish
Permits:	On bank
Cost:	£1.50
BK Rating:	Easy when carp are located
Control:	Club
W/A:	NRA North West Region
Comments:	Fish caught on match tackle - waggler and double maggot. Best area is the Marina where the A54 crosses the river south of Winsford. Above Vale Royal locks also said to be good. For information try Northwich AA, R Hankey, PO Box 18, Northwich - tickets supplied

Roman Lakes

Location:	Near Marple
Type and Size:	Six acre lake, with islands and gravel bars
Carp Stock:	Well stocked with many low doubles, up to just over 20lbs
Category:	Carp Water
Other Species:	Roach and tench
Permits:	Day tickets from bailiff at the water
Cost:	About £4 per day
Control:	Private - B Sewart. Tel: 061 472 2039
Restrictions:	Barbless hooks only; no night fishing; no multiple baits; no fishing on one side
BK Rating:	Difficult
W/A:	NRA North West Region
Comments:	A hard fished carp water, which is now quite difficult because the fish are well educated

Sale Water Park

Location:	Rifle Road, Sale.
Type and Size:	Lake excavated to provide material to build the motorway, 55 acres
How to Find:	Come off the M63 at junction 8
Carp Stock:	Stocked with mirror carp in 1978, two years after the lake was completed. Numbers not known but there are now a reasonable head of carp mostly between 4 and 12lb, with some upper doubles and one or two lower twenties
Category:	Mixed Fishery
Other Species:	Catfish, grass carp, pike, eels, roach, perch, bream and tench
Permits:	About £1 per day from office on site, or £1.80 from bailiff on bank during the weekends; 20p extra on Bank Holidays and at weekends. Season tickets: Adults £10; Junior £4
Control:	Mersey Valley Joint Committee. Tel: 061 969 7063.
BK Rating:	Easy
Restrictions:	Fishing 8am till sunset only, unless special night permit obtained
Baits/Methods:	Legering with boilies best method
W/A:	North West

Comments: Water is 80 feet deep in places and the very deep areas would not be likely to produce carp. This water is only 4½ miles from Manchester City Centre

Shakerley Mere

Location: Allostock, near Northwich
Type and Size: Large mere of 17 acres
How to Find: Just off the M6 near Northwich
Carp Stock: Some carp to over 20lbs
Category: Mixed Fishery
Other Species: Tench, roach, perch, bream
Permits: Day tickets on bank
Cost: £3
Control: Club. Tel: 0260 277284
BK Rating: Insufficient information
W/A: NRA North West Region
Comments: Formerly Council controlled. Local tackle shops have details

Springwood Pool

Location: Mobberley, near Knutsford
Type and Size: Small pool
Carp Stock: Well stocked with carp to doubles
Category: Mixed Fishery
Other Species: Most common coarse fish
Permits: Congleton Anglers' Society. Secretary: Mr N Bours, 8 Norfolk Road, Congleton. Tel: Congleton 277284.
Cost: Membership costs £20 per season, with a £5 entry fee
Control: Club
BK Rating: Moderate
W/A: NRA North West Region

Statham Pool

Location: Lymm, near Warrington
Type and Size: Small pond
Carp Stock: Well stocked with carp to doubles
Category: Mixed Fishery
Other Species: Roach, bream, tench and perch
Permits: Day tickets from bailiff on bank — enquire local tackle shops for details.
Control: Club - name not known - possibly Lymm AA?
Restrictions: No night fishing
BK Rating: Moderate
W/A: NRA North West Region

Stock Pool

Location: Capesthorne Estate, Siddington, Macclesfield
Type and Size: Estate stock pond of ¼ acre
Carp Stock: This water is well stocked with small carp and is ideal for youngsters or beginners

Permits:	Day tickets can be booked in advance from the bailiff: Mr A Bradley. Tel: 861584.
BK Rating:	Easy

Taxmere

Location:	Near Sandbach
Type and Size:	Medium sized lake
Carp Stock:	Some carp, numbers and sizes not known
Category:	Mixed Fishery
Other Species:	Bream, roach, tench, perch and pike
Permits:	Day tickets from I F McDonald, 49 Welles Street, Sandbach
Control:	Club
BK Rating:	Moderate
W/A:	NRA Severn-Trent Region

Tetton Lake

Location:	Near Middlewich, off A533 near Elworth
Type and Size:	Three acre lake
Carp Stock:	Well stocked with carp to doubles and possibly larger
Category:	Mixed Fishery
Other Species:	Tench, bream and roach
Permits:	An Association of local angling clubs - try local tackle shops for details
Control:	An Association of Middlewich AS, Middlewich British Legion and Middlewich Big Lock AC. Permits also include river fishing and 8 miles of two local canals
BK Rating:	Moderate
W/A:	NRA North West Region

Thorneycroft Hall Lakes

Location:	Henbury, near Macclesfield
Type and Size:	2 lakes; Lower - 6 acres, Top - 12 acres
Carp Stock:	Lower Lake - well stocked with plenty of small carp to 20lbs. Top Lake - not many carp but some good ones to 19lbs
Category:	Lower - Carp Water. Top - Few Carp
Other Species:	Mixed coarse fish
Permits:	Prince Albert Angling Society, season tickets only. Secretary: C Clarke, 2 Avon Close, Macclesfield
Cost:	About £35 entry fee plus £35 per season
Control:	Club
BK Rating:	Lower - Easy to Moderate. Top - Difficult
W/A:	NRA North West Region

Town Park Lake

Location:	Housing estate on the outskirts of Runcorn; take the road to Castelfields and Norton Sports Centre - the lake is near the car park
Type and Size:	Man-made lake of about 3 acres with an island
Carp Stock:	Some carp to doubles
Category:	Mixed Fishery

Other Species:	Bream, pike, roach, perch, tench and gudgeon
Permits:	Day tickets on bank
Cost:	15 pence!
Control:	Council
BK Rating:	Moderate
W/A:	NRA North West Region

Village Pool

Location:	Whitley, near Warrington
Type and Size:	Village pond of about ½ acre
How to Find:	The pond is in the centre of the village of Whitley. Come off the M56 motorway at junction 10 and from Stretton take the A559 south of Whitley
Carp Stock:	Quite well stocked with carp, most of which are mid-doubles to about 21lbs
Category:	Mixed Fishery
Other Species:	Usual coarse fish
Permits:	Lymm Angling Club. Secretary: S Griffiths, 18 Manor Way, Lymm WA13 OAY
Control:	Club
BK Rating:	Moderate
Baits/Methods:	Normal carp fishing methods
W/A:	NRA North West Region

Walpool Lodge

Location:	Gawsworth, near Macclesfield
Type and Size:	Three acre shallow lake with island
How to Find:	Take the A536 south from Macclesfield, and in about 2 miles follow the signs to Gawsworth Hall. Pass the gates and the car park is about 100 yards from the pool
Carp Stock:	Well stocked with carp to upper doubles
Category:	Mixed Fishery
Other Species:	Crucians, tench, bream, rudd, roach, perch and gudgeon
Permits:	On bank
Cost:	£3 for one rod; £5 for two rods
Control:	John Birch. Tel: 0260 223442
Restrictions:	Beans are banned; night fishing by special arrangement only
Baits/Methods:	Legered boilies and luncheon meat. Surface fishing with floaters and crust
BK Rating:	Moderate
W/A:	NRA North West Region

Wetgate Pool

Location:	Near Lymm, west of Manchester
Type and Size:	Tiny pond
Carp Stock:	Well stocked with small carp - ideal for youngsters
Category:	Mixed Fishery
Other Species:	Rudd and tench
Permits:	Members only water of Lymm Angling Club. Secretary: S Griffiths, 18 Manor Road, Lymm. Tel: 092575 2763

Control:	Club
Restrictions:	No night fishing
BK Rating:	Easy
W/A:	NRA Severn-Trent Region

Whirley Pool

Location:	Henbury, near Macclesfield
Type and Size:	Small pit
Carp Stock:	Said to be quite well stocked with small carp to mid-double figure size
Category:	Mixed Fishery
Other Species:	Usual coarse fish
Permits:	Prince Albert Angling Society. Secretary: C Clarke, 2 Avon Close, Macclesfield
Cost:	About £35 entry fee plus £35 annual subscription. Season tickets only
Control:	Club
BK Rating:	Thought to be Moderate
W/A:	NRA North West Region
Comments:	It will be noticed that whilst the cost of joining Prince Albert Angling Society is high compared with many clubs, they have a number of very fine carp waters, all on the same ticket

Whitemere

Location:	About one mile from the town of Ellesmere, on the Shrewsbury road
Type and Size:	Large lake
Carp Stock:	Some carp to doubles
Category:	Mixed Fishery
Other Species:	Roach, bream, tench, perch and pike
Permits:	Ellesmere AC
Control:	Club
BK Rating:	Difficult
W/A:	NRA North West Region
Comments:	This mere is also used for sailing, and not all of the lake can be fished. It is also a Site of Special Scientific Interest (S.S.S.I.), and care must be taken only to use marked paths, and to observe all rules and notices.

Winterley Pool

Location:	Winterley Farm, Wheelock, near Sandbach
Type and Size:	Pleasant 8 acre lake, rather snaggy and surrounded by trees
Carp Stock:	Plenty of small carp to doubles, and a few 20's to about 25lbs
Category:	Mixed Fishery
Other Species:	Usual coarse fish
Permits:	Day tickets on bank
Cost:	£3 per rod; £5 for 24 hours
Control:	Private. Tel: 0270 582352
BK Rating:	Moderate
W/A:	NRA North West Region

Woodlands Lake

Location:	Allostock, near Knutsford, just off the M6
Type and Size:	10 acre lake, with two other lakes on site
Carp Stock:	Not many carp, but most are doubles to about 20lbs
Permits:	Prince Albert AS, J T Lovatt, 63 Beggerman's Lane, Knutsford or Queens Hotel, Waters Green, Macclesfield
Control:	Club - season tickets only
Restrictions:	No day tickets - check before night fishing.
BK Rating:	Fairly Hard
W/A:	NRA North West Region

THE
BEEKAY
GUIDE
TO
1500
BRITISH
& EUROPEAN
CARP
WATERS

Is YOUR Water listed? If so, are the details correct?

If you spot omissions, inaccuracies, or know of any changes, please let us know by filling in the Waters Questionnaire at the back of this guide and return it to us at:

FREEPOST
Beekay Publishers
Withy Pool
Henlow Camp
Bedfordshire
SG16 6EA

CLEVELAND

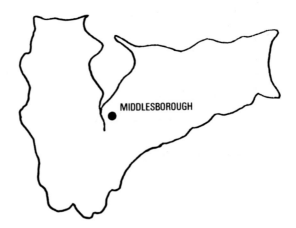

MIDDLESBOROUGH

Ascott Ponds

Location: Cleveland, North Yorkshire border
Type and Size: Three small lakes
Carp Stock: Well stocked with small carp
Category: Mixed Fishery
Other Species: Trout, tench, bream, dace, perch, gudgeon
Permits: D Speight, 10 Stainsby Gate, Thornaby, Cleveland. Members only
Control: Thornaby AA
BK Rating: Moderate
W/A: NRA Northumbrian Region
Comments: Floating baits produce good results. Club has many other good fisheries

Charlton Ponds

Location: Billingham, north east of Middlesbrough
Type and Size: Eight acre town-type lake, with half acre pond next door
How to Find: Take the A1185 north of Middlesbrough to Billingham and go over two roundabouts to Central Avenue. At the next roundabout turn left into Cowpen Lane, then right into Hereford Terrace. The ponds are on the left, with a car park close to the Community Centre
Carp Stock: Well stocked with carp between 4lbs and about 10lbs
Category: Mixed Fishery
Other Species: Tench, eels, roach and rudd. The small pond has crucians, roach, perch and tench only
Permits: Day tickets on bank
Cost: £1 for adults; 60p for juniors and OAP's. Season tickets £12 and £6
Control: Billingham Sportsman's AC
Restrictions: No night fishing; no keepnets; groundbait limited; no floating baits; one rod only (can we use hooks!?). No close season for larger lake
BK Rating: Not known
W/A: NRA Northumbrian Region

Hemlington Lake

Location: Hemlington, near Middlesbrough
Type and Size: Large lake, much used for match fishing
Carp Stock: Well stocked with small carp
Category: Mixed Fishery
Other Species: Crucians, bream and roach
Permits: On bank at £1.50 per day
Control: Middlesbrough Council/Middlesbrough AC. Tel: 0642 596546
BK Rating: Easy
W/A: NRA Northumbrian Region
Comments: No close season, best avoided at night! Try W P Adams Fishing Tackle, 42 Duke Street, Darlington. Tel: 0325 468069

Hutton Rudby Ponds

Location: Near Middlesbrough
Type and Size: Small ponds
Carp Stock: Some carp
Category: Mixed Fishery
Other Species: Roach, perch and bream
Permits: Members only water of Middlesbrough AC - membership open to all from Redcar Angling Centre, Cleveland Angling Centre, Thornaby, Adams Tackle, Darlington and Middlesbrough and the Tackle Box, Billingham
Cost: £12 per season, with a £6 joining fee, to include other waters; Juniors half price
Control: Club
Restrictions: No night fishing; members only
BK Rating: Not known
W/A: NRA Northumbrian Region

Locke Park

Location: Off the B1085 road from Middlesbrough at Redcar
Type and Size: Small public park lake, surrounded by houses
Carp Stock: Well stocked with carp to just over 10lbs
Category: Mixed Fishery
Other Species: Bream, roach and perch
Permits: Day tickets on the bank
Cost: £1; juniors - 55p. Permit needed for each rod. Season - £12
Control: Langborough Borough Council/Locke Park AC - Gordon Sanderson. Tel: 0642 477832
Restrictions: No night fishing; dawn till dusk only; no close season fishing
BK Rating: Not known
W/A: NRA Northumbrian Region

New Marske Reservoir

Location:	Near Middlesbrough
Type and Size:	10 acre reservoir
Carp Stock:	Well stocked with carp to over 20lbs
Category:	Mixed Fishery
Other Species:	Bream, roach, tench and perch
Permits:	Redcar Angling Centre, High Street, Middlesbrough
Cost:	£2 per day
Control:	Middlesbrough AC
Restrictions:	No night fishing
BK Rating:	Not known
W/A:	NRA Northumbrian Region
Comments:	No close season

Priory Cottage Lake

Location:	Guisborough, off the A171, opposite Butts Lane
Type and Size:	Two acre lake with islands
Carp Stock:	Well stocked with carp to 20lbs
Category:	Mixed Fishery
Other Species:	Bream, chub, roach, perch and rainbow trout
Permits:	From the cottage by the lake; weekend tickets must be booked in advance. Tel: 0287 638816
Cost:	£6.50 per day; £3.75 for juniors and OAP's
Restrictions:	No night fishing; barbless hooks
BK Rating:	Moderate
W/A:	NRA Northumbrian Region
Comments:	No close season; fishing is dawn till dusk

THE
BEEKAY
GUIDE
TO
1500
BRITISH
& EUROPEAN
CARP
WATERS

Is YOUR Water listed? If so, are the details correct?

If you spot omissions, inaccuracies, or know of any changes, please let us know by filling in the Waters Questionnaire at the back of this guide and return it to us at:

FREEPOST
Beekay Publishers
Withy Pool
Henlow Camp
Bedfordshire
SG16 6EA

CLWYD (Wales)

Llay Reservoir

Location:	Llay, near Wrexham
Type and Size:	Small reservoir
Carp Stock:	Well stocked with carp to doubles
Category:	Mixed Fishery
Other Species:	Tench, rudd, perch and pike
Permits:	Members only water of Llay AA. J Henshaw, 2 Queens Terrace, Mold Road, Cefn-y-Bedd, Wrexham, Wales; J Preston, 20 Mold Road Estate, Cworsyllt, Wrexham, Clwyd
Cost:	About £8.50 per year
Restrictions:	No cereal baits
BK Rating:	Moderate
W/A:	NRA Welsh Region

Padeswood Lake

Location:	Padeswood, off the A5118 between Buckley and Mold
Type and Size:	Two small lakes
Carp Stock:	Heavily stocked with carp to 20lbs
Category:	Carp Only
Permits:	Day tickets from Deeside Fishing Tackle. Tel: 0244 813674
Cost:	£3 per day for club members
Control:	Connah's Quay DAC. P Ryan, 5 New Brighton Road, Sychdyn, Mold
Restrictions:	You will need to join the club first
BK Rating:	Easy; multiple catches of doubles reported, including commons to over 15lbs
W/A:	NRA Welsh Region
Comments:	A new water opened in the summer of 1992; big catches on boilies

Ponky Pool

Location:	Johnstown, Wrexham
Type and Size:	1½ acre pond
Carp Stock:	Well stocked with carp to upper doubles
Category:	Mixed Fishery
Other Species:	Roach, tench and bream
Permits:	Day tickets at low cost from Morris Tackle, Wrexham. Tel: 0978 364450
Control:	Local club?
Restrictions:	No night fishing
BK Rating:	Moderate
W/A:	NRA Welsh Region
Comments:	There might be a 20 or two in this pond

Swan Lake

Location:	Near Connah's Quay, Deeside
Type and Size:	5 acre lake
Carp Stock:	Well stocked with carp to 20lbs
Category:	Mixed Fishery
Other Species:	Tench and roach
Permits:	Connahs Quay & Dist AC. P Ryan, 5 New Brighton Road, Sychdyn, Mold
Restrictions:	Members only - no day tickets; no night fishing
Control:	Club
BK Rating:	Moderate
W/A:	NRA Welsh Region
Comments:	Connahs Quay AC also has Wepre Park Lake in the area, which contains good carp; on the same ticket

Tan Llan

Location:	Pontybodkin, off the A5104 near Ffrith
Type and Size:	One and a half acre pool with islands
Carp Stock:	Well stocked with commons to about 8lbs
Category:	Mixed Fishery
Other Species:	Ghost carp, crucians, roach, bream, tench, orfe, rudd and perch
Permits:	On the bank at £2 for adults, £1 for juniors; advance booking weekends
Control:	Roger Roberts. Tel: 0352 770296
Restrictions:	No night fishing
BK Rating:	Moderate
W/A:	NRA Welsh Region

The Flash

Location:	Gresford, Llay, near Wrexham
Type and Size:	Small lake
Carp Stock:	Some carp, numbers and sizes not known
Category:	Mixed Fishery
Other Species:	Tench, pike and rudd
Permits:	Members only water of Llay AS - J Henshaw, 2 Queens Terrace, Mold Road, Cefn-y-Bedd, Wrexham
Cost:	About £6 per year
Control:	Club
W/A:	NRA Welsh Region

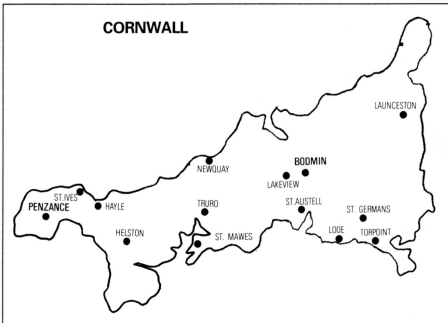

CORNWALL

Avallon Holiday Park   A

Location:	Near Newquay
Type and Size:	Small lake on dairy farm
Carp Stock:	Well stocked with carp to doubles
Category:	Mixed Fishery
Other Species:	Bream, tench and roach
Permits:	For information and permits phone 0502 501501
Control:	Private
BK Rating:	Not known
W/A:	NRA South West Region
Comments:	This is a small site on a farm, with self-catering Norwegian Pine Lodges to rent for holidays with fishing; open all year - no close season

Bilberry Pool

Location:	Bilberry, near Roche
Type and Size:	Old pit of about 5 acres
How to Find:	Roche is on the B3274 road between St. Austell and Newquay
Carp Stock:	Carp to mid doubles
Category:	Mixed Fishery
Other Species:	Rudd and tench
Permits:	Roche Angling Club. Membership available from D Burn, Angling Centre, 25 Penpol Terrace, Hayle. Tel: Hayle 754292
Control:	Club
BK Rating:	Moderate
W/A:	NRA South West Region
Comments:	Roche Angling Club have carp in some waters; details from the address given above. No close season

Bolingey Lake   A

Location:	Penwartha Road, Bolingey, Perranporth TR6 ODH
Type and Size:	Lake of 4 acres
How to Find:	From Perranporth take the road towards Cos Hill, and turn right at the crossroads towards Bolingey. Pass the Post Office on your right and the Bolingey Inn, and the entrance to the lake will be seen on your left
Carp Stock:	Well stocked with carp to about 22lbs. 100 doubles
Category:	Mixed Fishery
Other Species:	Tench, roach, rudd, perch and trout
Permits:	From the site lodge. Tel: Truro 572388.
Cost:	£4 per day for 2 rods
Restrictions:	No night fishing. No keepnets or sacks. April to October.
Control:	Private
BK Rating:	Very Easy
W/A:	NRA South West Region
Comments:	Tackle and comprehensive range of bait and snacks and drinks on site. No close season. Carp tackle hired on site. Accommodation at an anglers pub - The Airways, St. Mawgan. Tel: 0637 860595. (Voted one of Britain's top ten waters in Angling Times Yearbook!) Accommodation also at The Morgans Guesthouse, Perranporth. Tel: 0872 573904. B and B from £13. Atlantic View Hotel. Tel: 0872 573171

Bude Canal   A

Location:	From the sea at Bude
How to Find:	Town of Bude
Type and Size:	Shallow old canal about 2 miles long and 2ft to 8ft deep
Carp Stock:	Said to be fairly numerous, mostly to 10lbs. Commons to 20lbs caught in recent years by Gerry Savage of Lakeview Country Club, Lanivet, Bodmin
Category:	Mixed Fishery
Other Species:	Tench, roach, perch and big eels
Cost:	£1 day tickets, £5 for week from Tourist Info Centre, Bude. Hotels - The Globe, The Strand
Permits:	On the bank, or from tackle shops in Bude
Restrictions:	No fishing from 1st April to end of May
BK Rating:	Difficult
W/A:	South West
Baits/Methods:	Normal carp tactics and baits
Control:	Club. Bude Canal Angling Association. Day tickets, P Braund, Wesley House, Leven Terrace, Bude
Comments:	Clear weedy water, like many disused canals

Bussow

Location:	Near St. Ives
Type and Size:	Reservoir of 4 acres
How to Find:	Take the B3306 from St. Ives. Turn left onto the B3311 and then right. The entrance to the reservoir is then on the left.
Carp Stock:	Moderately stocked with carp to 16lbs
Category:	Mixed Fishery
Other Species:	Eels to 10lb, tench, bream, rudd and roach
Permits:	Ken's Tackle, 9 Beachfield Court, The Promenade, Penzance. Tel: (0736)

61969; Lanxon's Sports, 18 Causewayhead, Penzance Tel: (0736) 62736; The Shirehorse Inn, Towednack Road, Hessesveor, St. Ives. Tel: (0736) 796724; Newtown Angling Centre, Germoe. Tel: (0736) 763721.

Cost: Day £2.50. Concession rate for OAP's SDP/MOB, students and children under 16 £1.50: 24 hours £5: 7 day castabout (valid at all Peninsular Coarse Fisheries, except Jennetts and Crafthole), day £15, concession day £10: Day and night £30. No season permits

Control: Mr Dell Mills, Manager, Peninsular Coarse Fisheries, St Cleer Depot, Liskeard, Cornwall PL14 6EQ. Tel: (0579) 43929

W/A: NRA South West Region

BK Rating: Moderate

Restrictions: No keepnets for carp. Barbless hooks requested. Permits must be obtained before fishing

Comments: No closed season

Choone Farm

Location: Choone Farm, St. Buryan, Penzance. Tel: 0736 810220

Type and Size: Two small lakes

Carp Stock: Well stocked with carp to at least 10lbs

Category: Mixed Fishery

Other Species: Tench, rudd and perch

Permits: From Mr V B Care at the address above

Control: Private

Restrictions: No night fishing - open 7am to 8pm in summer

W/A: NRA South West Region

Comments: No close season

Chyraise Lodge Hotel   A

Location: Millpool, Goldsithney, Penzance TR20 9JD

Type and Size: Two large lakes ½ mile from hotel

How to Find: Just off the A394 between Helston and Marazion

Carp Stock: Some carp, numbers not known

Category: Mixed Fishery

Other Species: Tench, bream, roach

Permits: From hotel. Tel: 0736 763485

Cost: On application

BK Rating: Insufficient information

Control: Private

W/A: NRA South West Region

Comments: No close season. There are carp in some other waters in the Marazion area. Accommodation/holidays in hotel

College

Location: Near Falmouth

Type and Size: Reservoir of 38 acres

How to Find: Take the A38 from Falmouth to Penryn, then turn onto the B3291. A right turn will then take you into the car park

Carp Stock: The reservoir is well stocked with carp to 32lbs, with a good number in the 20-30lbs bracket. It was restocked in 1990 with 1850 carp to 15lbs and early 1991 with commons to 22lbs

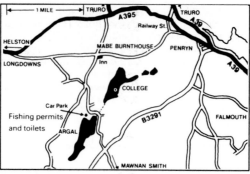

Category: Mixed Fishery
Other Species: Tench to 8½lbs, bream to 8lbs 6ozs, eels to 7lbs, roach, rudd and perch
Permits: Day permits from the self service unit at Argal car park: Ken's Tackle, 9 Beachfield Court, The Promenade, Penzance. Tel: (0736) 61969: Newtown Angling Centre, Germoe. Tel: (0736) 763721. Season permits from the Ranger, Bob Evans, Little Argal Farm, Budock, Penryn, Cornwall. Tel: (0326) 72544
Cost: Day £3. Concession rate for OAP's, SDP/MOB and students £2, children under 16 £1.50: 24 hour permits £6.00: 7 day castabout, (valid at all Peninsular Coarse Fisheries, except Jennetts and Crafthole), day £15, concession day £10: Day and night £30: Castabout season permits, (valid for College, Porth, Lower Tamar, Slade and Squabmoor), day £45, concession OAP's, SDP/MOB and students £30, children under 16 £15: Day and night £67.50
Control: Mr Dell Mills, Manager, Peninsular Coarse Fisheries, St Cleer Depot, Liskeard, Cornwall PL14 6EQ. Tel: (0579) 43929
W/A: NRA South West Region
BK Rating: Moderate
Restrictions: No cereal based groundbaits, except swimfeeders. No keepnets for carp. Barbless hooks requested. Permits must be obtained before fishing
Comments: Mature and picturesque water with NO CLOSED SEASON. Night fishing is now allowed. Long casting is necessary to reach deep water from some areas. Long stay carp anglers generally do well

Crafthole

Location: Village of Crafthole, near Torpoint
Type and Size: Disused reservoir of 2 acres
How to Find: Leave the A38, Plymouth to Liskeard road at Trerulefoot roundabout onto the A374, towards Torpoint. After Sheviock turn right to Crafthole. The pathway to the reservoir is almost opposite Crafthole Post Office
Carp Stock: Very heavily stocked with carp to 22lbs
Category: Carp Water
Other Species: Tench
Permits: Day permits only, (one hour before sunrise to one hour after sunset), from Post Office Store, Crafthole, St. Germans. Tel: (0503) 30225. Limited day permits
Cost: Day £3. Concession rate for OAP's, SDP/MOB and students £2, children under 16 £1.50. No season permits

Control:	Mr Dell Mills, Manager, Peninsular Coarse Fisheries, St Cleer Depot, Liskeard, Cornwall PL14 6EQ. Tel: (0579) 43929
W/A:	NRA South West Region
BK Rating:	Small carp: Very Easy. Larger carp: Easy
Restrictions:	Children under 16 must be accompanied by an adult. No cereal based groundbaits. No keepnets for carp. Barbless hooks requested. Permits must be obtained before fishing
Comments:	NO CLOSED SEASON. Very popular and attractive water, deep in a valley and surrounded by mature trees and hedgerows. Limited permits, so advance booking is sensible. Due to the rather long and steep climb from the water, this venue is not recommended for the elderly or infirm.

Dutson Water   A

Location:	Lower Dutson Farm, Launceston
Type and Size:	Old clay pit, about an acre
How to Find:	Take the A388 road from Launceston to Barnstaple. Lower Dutson Farm is about two miles from Launceston
Carp Stock:	Fairly well stocked with carp to about 15lbs
Category:	Mixed Fishery
Other Species:	Perch, rudd, tench, crucians
Permits:	From the farmer Mr E Broad at the farm. Tel: 0566 772607
Cost:	£3 per day in advance; £6 on bank
Control:	Private
Restrictions:	No groundbaiting
BK Rating:	Moderate
W/A:	NRA South West Region
Comments:	Some weed and depths to about 10ft. Float fishing or legering methods can be used and luncheon meat and bread will catch carp. Many small rudd. There are sometimes caravans at the water and there is also a cottage to rent

Forda Holiday Lodges   A

Location:	Kilkhampton, near Bude
Type and Size:	Small lake
How to Find:	Near Bude on the north coast
Carp Stock:	Some carp to double figures
Category:	Mixed Fishery
Other Species:	Bream, rudd, tench
Permits:	On site. Tel: 028 882 413
Cost:	On application
BK Rating:	Not known
Control:	Private
W/A:	NRA South West Region
Comments:	No close season. Scandinavian style self-catering lodges for 4/5 people by lake. Near Tamar Lake and Bude Canal. Sandy beaches 10 minutes. Other accommodation: Tamar Lake Farm, near Bude. Stable and barn cottages and caravan. Tel: 028 882 426 for details and brochures

Gwinear Pool

Location:	Near Newquay
Type and Size:	Small pool
Carp Stock:	Well stocked with carp to doubles
Category:	Mixed Fishery
Other Species:	Bream, tench, perch and roach
Permits:	Day tickets on site
Cost:	£3
Control:	Tel: 0637 880910
BK Rating:	Not known
W/A:	NRA South West Region
Comments:	No close season

Lakeview Country Club   A

Location:	Old Coach Road, Lanivet, Bodmin. Tel: 0208 831011
Type and Size:	Three lakes, dug in 1988; carp lake 2½ acres, stream-fed with island
How to Find:	Where the A391 St Austell road joins the A30 Bodmin by-pass, take the second exit at the roundabout, keeping in the outside lane, signposted 'Truro'. After 30 yards, turn right to Wheal Prosper, and in half a mile, turn left at the crossroads. Lakeview is in half a mile, on the right hand side
Carp Stock:	Long Island, the carp lake, is heavily stocked with many doubles and about 10 twenties, most of which are commons to 25lbs plus; the Cornish record common was caught here
Category:	Carp Water
Other Species:	A few big tench only
Permits:	Day tickets from the Lodge, or on bank from Gerry Savage or Frank Barry. Free to residents in 1991, but expected to be a charge for 1992
Cost:	£4.50 per day for two rods; juniors/OAP's £2.50 per day

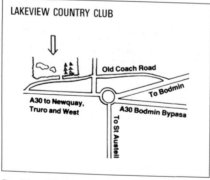

Control:	David and Barbara Daw, Lakeview Country Club
Restrictions:	Night fishing by arrangement with Gerry Savage, for residents only; no baiting with shelf-life boilies
Baits/Methods:	Standard methods work well, with boilies, sweetcorn and luncheon meat
BK Rating:	Moderate
W/A:	NRA South West Region

Gerry Savage, of Lakeview Country Club, Cornwall, with his 25¾lb Cornish record common, caught from Long Island Pool at the club

Comments: There are two other lakes at the Club - Moorland Lake, which is small, and contains some mirrors to about 8lbs, and the 3 acre Wood Pool, which has some small carp; both contain other species. Fishery Manager is Gerry Savage, one of the most successful carp anglers of all time, and former BBC radio angling programme presenter. For up to date information on the fishing, phone Gerry Savage at his Lodge and tackle shop on 0208 831079. Although a comparatively new water, this is rapidly becoming one of the best places in the country for top class carp fishing, with luxury accommodation.

There are over 60 A-Frame Lodges (very popular with the children), and fabulous detached bungalows, each set well away from anyone else, many with dishwashers, spa baths, and en-suite shower, and all self catering, with an outside barbecue. The Country Club, close to the carp lake, has a heated indoor swimming pool, sauna, solarium, fitness room, snooker room, and a first class restaurant. There is a shop and just about every conceivable facility for a luxury holiday for the family at reasonable prices - and all within sight of the big carp being caught! Outside there are tennis courts, pitch and putt golf course, facilities for other sports, and an 18 hole golf course, an hotel, and sports centre is planned for 1993.

This is one where we have been fortunate enough to stay, and we were very impressed with the fishing, the friendly but 'up-market' atmosphere of the country club, the pleasant surroundings and the beautiful detached bungalow, well away from others, and easily good enough for a permanent home. Lakeview is very strongly recommended, both for fishing and holidays; it is situated right in the centre of Cornwall, with easy access to both coasts, and is ideal for a day's fishing or for a long, luxurious family holiday

Langarth Pool

Location:	99 Polstain Road, Threemilestone, Truro. Tel: 0872 75638
Type and Size:	Two three-quarter acre ponds
Carp Stock:	Well stocked with carp to double figures
Category:	Mixed Fishery
Other Species:	Tench, roach, rudd, bream and perch
Permits:	From Des Hart at the address above
Cost:	£2.50 per day; £6 per week; season — £15; reduced prices for children and OAP's
Control:	Private
BK Rating:	Not known
W/A:	NRA South West Region
Comments:	No close season; open 24 hours a day. Swims for the disabled.

Mellonwatts Mill Fishery

Location:	Pensagillas Farm, Grampound, Truro - on the main road from Grampound to Mevagissey. Tel:087 253 232
Type and Size:	2¼ acre farm pond
Carp Stock:	Well stocked with carp to 20lbs
Category:	Mixed Fishery
Other Species:	Crucians, tench, roach and rudd
Permits:	From A W P Kent at the address above; self service permits in car park
Cost:	£3 per day; £6 per night; £35 per season. Reduced prices for children and OAP's
Control:	Private
BK Rating:	Not known
W/A:	NRA South West Region
Comments:	No close season. Camping, barbecues and picnic areas

Neets Valley Park

Location:	Near Bude
Type and Size:	Small lake
Carp Stock:	Well stocked with carp

Category: Mixed Fishery
Other Species: Tench and rudd
Permits: Full details and permits from Russell Baker, 02888 395
Cost: £3.50 per day - half price for juniors
Control: Private
BK Rating: Not known
W/A: NRA South West Region
Comments: This water was stocked in 1988, but had not been fished until 1991, so the potential is unknown. No close season

Old St. Erth

Location: St. Erth, near Penzance
Type and Size: 2½ acre lake
Carp Stock: Well stocked with carp to 20lbs plus
Category: Mixed Fishery
Other Species: Bream, roach, and some other coarse fish
Permits: Marazion Angling Club. W T Knott, Little Bosvenning, Newbridge, Penzance. Tel: 0736 65638; The Shop, Newtown. Tel: 0736 763721; Ken's Tackle, Penzance. Tel: 0736 61969
Cost: Day - £2.50; annual visitors - £10; annual - £25
Control: Club
Restrictions: Night fishing by arrangement only
BK Rating: Moderate
W/A: NRA South West Region
Comments: No close season. Permit includes several other waters

Porth   A

Location: Near St. Mawgan Airfield, Newquay
Type and Size: Reservoir of 40 acres
How to Find: From Bodmin, leave the A30 at Indian Queens and join the A39 towards Wadebridge. At St. Columb Major, turn left onto the A3059. Turn left at the water tower and the reservoir will be found on the left, after about three-quarters of a mile
Carp Stock: Moderately stocked with carp to 17lbs
Category: Mixed Fishery
Other Species: Tench to 10lbs, bream to 9lbs 2ozs, roach, perch and rudd
Permits: Day or day and night permits from the self service unit at the car park: Ken's Tackle, 9 Beachfield Court, The Promenade, Penzance. Tel: (0736) 61969: Newtown Angling Centre, Germoe. Tel: (0736) 763721. Season permits from Mrs P Ford, The Bungalow, Porth Reservoir. Tel: (0637) 879481
Cost: Day £3. Concession rate for OAP's, SDP/MOB and students £2, children under 16 £1.50: 24 hours £6: 7 day castabout, (valid at all Peninsular Coarse Fisheries, except Jennetts and Crafthole), day £15, concession day £10: Day and night £30: Castabout season permits, (valid for College, Porth, Lower Tamar, Slade and Squabmoor), day £45, concession OAP's, SDP/MOB and students £30, children under 16 £15: Day and night £65.50
Control: Mr Dell Mills, Manager, Peninsular Coarse Fisheries, St Cleer Depot, Liskeard, Cornwall PL14 6EQ. Tel: (0579) 43929.
W/A: NRA South West Region
BK Rating: Fairly Hard

Restrictions:	No cereal based groundbaits except swimfeeders. No keepnets for carp. Barbless hooks requested. Permits must be obtained before fishing
Comments:	NO CLOSED SEASON. Night fishing now allowed. Accommodation at White Lodge Hotel, Mawgan Porth Bay, Newquay. Tel: 0637 860512. Special holidays including fishing at reservoir, also fishing at Bolingey, Carnewas Farm, Frontier City, Lakeview, Meadowside Fam, Rosewater Lake - send for brochure

Retallack Water

Location:	Frontier City Wild West Theme Park, near Newquay
Type and Size:	4 acre lake
Carp Stock:	Well stocked with carp to double figures
Category:	Mixed Fishery
Other Species:	Very large perch, and some other species
Permits:	Day tickets on site
Control:	Private
BK Rating:	Moderate
W/A:	NRA South West Region
Comments:	No close season. There is a proposal at present to allow jet water ski-ing on this lake, which could ruin it for anglers

Rosewater Lake   A

Location:	Hendravossan Farm, Rose, Truro. Tel: 0872 573992/572261/573040
Type and Size:	1½ acre lake, with another soon to be built
Carp Stock:	Well stocked with carp, numbers and sizes not known
Category:	Mixed Fishery
Other Species:	Crucians, tench, roach, rudd, perch and chub
Permits:	From Mike or Andy Waters at the address above
Cost:	Day - £3; evening - £1.50; second rod - £1
Control:	Private
Restrictions:	Barbless hooks; no keepnets; no night fishing - open dawn till dusk only
BK Rating:	Not known
W/A:	NRA South West Region
Comments:	No close season. Bed and breakfast available at certain times of the year. Caravan Club

Sharkey's Pit

Location:	Strawberry Lane, Joppa, Hayle - one mile from Hayle Town Centre
Type and Size:	2½ acre lake
Carp Stock:	Some carp to double figures
Category:	Mixed Fishery
Other Species:	Tench, crucians, roach, rudd, gudgeon, golden orfe
Permits:	Self service at fishery
Cost:	On application from Dave and Jenny Burn at the above address
Control:	Private
Restrictions:	No night fishing
BK Rating:	Moderate
W/A:	NRA South West Region
Comments:	No close season - fishing dawn to dusk.

Shillamill Lakes   A

Location:	Lanreath, Looe off the B3359
Type and Size:	Four small dammed lakes
Carp Stock:	Heavily stocked with commons and mirrors to 10lb. Some doubles and a few 20's to 25lbs reported - record fish 33lbs 2oz
Category:	Mixed Fishery
Other Species:	Roach, rudd, tench, perch
Permits:	John Facey, Shillamill Lakes, Lanreath, Looe, Cornwall. Tel: 0503 20271 Day and week permits
Cost:	Day tickets £3.50 for one rod. Weekly £12
Baits/Methods:	Normal carp baits and methods
Control:	Private commercial fishery, day and season tickets
Restrictions:	Brolly camps must be booked in advance - night fishing by arrangement only
BK Rating:	Easy
W/A:	NRA South West Region
Comments:	Commercial fishery with caravans and accommodation in flats and cottages. No close season. Meals and bar snacks. Games room and TV in the Old Mill Country Club

St. Germans Lake

Location:	St. Germans, 1½ miles off the A38 between Saltash and Liskeard
Type and Size:	Two acre lake
Carp Stock:	Well stocked with carp to double figures
Category:	Mixed Fishery
Other Species:	Roach, rudd, perch, tench and bream
Permits:	Clives Bait and Tackle, Exeter Street, Plymouth.
Cost:	£2 per day
Control:	Plymouth and District Coarse Angling Club
BK Rating:	Moderate
W/A:	NRA South West Region
Comments:	No close season

St. Tinney Farm Holidays   A

Location:	Otterham, near Penzance PL32 9TA. Tel: 08406 274
Type and Size:	Small farm lakes
Carp Stock:	Well stocked with carp to doubles
Category:	Mixed Fishery
Other Species:	Tench, rudd, roach, bream, perch and trout
Permits:	From St. Tinney Farm
Control:	Private
BK Rating:	Not known
W/A:	NRA South West Region
Comments:	Comfortable chalets to rent for self-catering holidays with fishing. 70 acre farm off the A39 coastal road in north Cornwall. Free colour brochure. No close season

Tindeen Fishery

Location: Bostrase, Goldsithney, Penzance. Tel: 073676 3486
Type and Size: Three small pools of about one acre each
Carp Stock: Some carp, number and sizes not known
Category: Either Few Carp or Mixed Fishery
Other Species: Tench, rudd, roach and perch
Permits: From G J Laity at the above address
Cost: £2 per day; £1.50 for under 14's
Control: Private
Restrictions: Night fishing by arrangement only
BK Rating: Not known
W/A: NRA South West Region
Comments: No close season

Tredidon Barton Lake

Location: Near Launceston
Type and Size: Small farm pond
Carp Stock: Some carp, best reported 2334lbs
Category: Mixed Fishery
Other Species: Tench and some other coarse fish
Permits: G Jones. Tel: 056-686-288
Cost: About £2 per day
Control: Private
BK Rating: Moderate
W/A: NRA South West Region
Comments: No close season - open all the year round.

Trenestrall Lake

Location: Trenestrall Farm, Ruan High Lanes, near St. Mawes. Tel: 0872 501259
Type and Size: 2 acre lake on the King Harry Ferry road
Carp Stock: Well stocked with carp to at least 10lbs
Category: Mixed Fishery
Other Species: Tench and roach
Permits: From Mr Palmer at the above address
Cost: £1.50 per day
Control: Private
BK Rating: Not known
W/A: NRA South West Region
Comments: No close season

Trevella Caravan and Camping Park   A

Location: Crantock, Newquay. Tel: 0637 830308
Type and Size: Two man-made lakes of about 2 acres each
How to Find: Take the A30 to Indian Queens, turn right onto the A392, and follow the Newquay signs to Quintrell Downs roundabout. Take the Crantock road to the Trevemper Bridge roundabout, then turn left onto the A3075 Redruth road. In 200 yards you will see the signpost to Crantock
Carp Stock: Both lakes well stocked with carp including some twenties - best fish a mirror of 27¾lbs, caught in 1990

Category:	Mixed Fishery
Other Species:	Tench to 6lbs, bream, roach and rudd
Permits:	Free at reception to all residents
BK Rating:	Moderate
Control:	Trevella Caravan Park
Restrictions:	None listed
W/A:	NRA South West Region
Comments:	A very attractive site with many facilities, such as showers, launderette, childrens play area, heated swimming pool, restaurant, shop, games room etc. Lakes are on a Nature Reserve, with a new third lake nearby. Beautiful sandy beaches within half a mile. Featured in 'Coarse Fishing Today' (Angling Times) in February 1991, with a picture of Gerry Savage with a 23 pounder from the lake. Ideal for a family holiday with good fishing, and only an hour's drive from anywhere in Cornwall - 41 miles to Land's End. 4 to 8 berth caravans to rent from £115 per week to £429 per week, according to size of van and season. Sites to rent nightly for your own caravans, with no charge for tents, touring caravans, or motorhomes - electrical hook-up £1.75 per night. No close season

Wheal Grey Pool

Location:	Ashton, on the main Penzance-Helston road
Type and Size:	Old 4 acre pit, very deep
Carp Stock:	Well stocked with carp to nearly 30lbs
Category:	Mixed Fishery
Other Species:	Bream, roach, rudd and perch
Permits:	Marazion Angling Club. W T Knott, Little Bosvenning, Newbridge, Penzance. Tel: 0736 65638; The Shop, Newtown. Tel: 0736 763721; Ken's Tackle, Penzance. Tel: 0736 61969.
Cost:	Day - £2.50, £1.50 for juniors; annual visitor - £10; annual - £25
Control:	Club
Restrictions:	Night fishing by arrangement only
BK Rating:	Moderate
W/A:	NRA South West Region
Comments:	No close season. Permit includes several other waters

THE BEEKAY GUIDE TO 1500 BRITISH & EUROPEAN CARP WATERS

Is YOUR Water listed? If so, are the details correct?

If you spot omissions, inaccuracies, or know of any changes, please let us know by filling in the Waters Questionnaire at the back of this guide and return it to us at:

FREEPOST
Beekay Publishers
Withy Pool
Henlow Camp
Bedfordshire
SG16 6EA

White Acres   A

Location:	White Acres Holiday Park, White Cross, Newquay TR8 4LW. Tel: 0716 860220
Type and Size:	Five lakes, all of which contain carp
Carp Stock:	Carp to 25lbs in the specimen lake, and plenty of all sizes in the other lakes
Category:	Mixed Fishery
Other Species:	Tench, roach and ghost carp
Permits:	On site - details from the address above
Control:	Private
BK Rating:	Moderate; Easy for small carp in some of the lakes
W/A:	NRA South West Region
Comments:	Luxury caravans for rent close to the lakes. Sites for touring caravans and tents. Heated indoor swimming pool, sauna and gym. Club with nightly cabaret. A good place for a holiday combined with some very good fishing

Woodley Farm   A

Location:	Herodsfoot, Liskeard
How to Find:	Near Liskeard
Type and Size:	Six small farm lakes
Carp Stock:	Well stocked with carp to 24lbs
Category:	Mixed Fishery
Other Species:	Tench, roach, rudd
Permits:	A T Hawke, Woodley Farm, Herodsfoot, Liskeard. Tel: 0503 20221
Control:	Private
BK Rating:	Easy
W/A:	NRA South West Region
Comments:	Holiday fishery with a self catering country cottage. Picturesque surroundings. No close season. Send stamp for brochure

For information about
the Catfish
Conservation Group
write to:
The CCG Secretary
10 Heathfield Road
Basingstoke
Hampshire RG22 4PA
If you wish to join, send
£8 subscription for one
years membership
to include 'Whiskers'
colour magazine and two
copies of 'Silurus' newsletter.

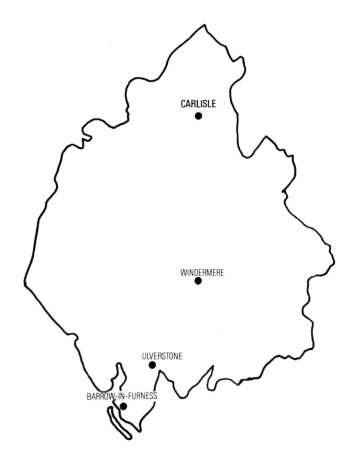

CUMBRIA

CARLISLE

WINDERMERE

ULVERSTONE

BARROW-IN-FURNESS

Bigland Hall Lake

Location:	Ulverstone, close to the canal
Type and Size:	Small lake
Carp Stock:	Some small carp to about 6lbs
Category:	Few Carp
Other Species:	Roach and tench
Permits:	Day tickets from local tackle shop
Control:	Local club, name not known
Restrictions:	No night fishing
BK Rating:	Difficult, due to hordes of other species
W/A:	NRA North West Region
Comments:	No close season

Brayton Pond

Location:	Brayton Hall Farm, Aspatria
Type and Size:	Large shallow lake of the farm type; 8 acres
How to Find:	Take the A596 from Carlisle, 15 miles west to Brayton
Carp Stock:	Very heavily stocked with genuine wild carp to about 8lbs. Fish up to 12lbs reported
Other Species:	Crucians
Permits:	Day tickets from the farm. Must be bought in advance
Control:	Private. Mr R H Ward, Home Farm, Brayton, Aspatria. Tel: Aspatria 20262
BK Rating:	Easy
Restrictions:	No night fishing
W/A:	NRA North West Region
Comments:	Heavily fished, especially at weekends. Many matches are held. Cafe

Cleabarrow Lake

Location:	Near the golf course at Windermere; take B5284 to Bowness
Type and Size:	Small lake
Carp Stock:	Well stocked with carp to 10lbs
Category:	Carp Water
Permits:	Day tickets from Smyths Record Shop, Ashe Street, Bowness-on-Windermere
Control:	Private
Restrictions:	No night fishing
BK Rating:	Moderate
W/A:	NRA North West Region

Holehird Tarn

Location:	Near Windermere, off the A592
Type and Size:	Three acre Lake District tarn
Carp Stock:	Quite well stocked with carp to 10lbs, and one or two low doubles
Category:	Mixed Fishery
Other Species:	Coarse fishing including perch; some trout
Permits:	Day tickets on site
Control:	Private
BK Rating:	Moderate
W/A:	NRA North West Region

Mockerkin Tarn

Location:	Mockerkin, near Loweswater
Type and Size:	Small tarn
How to Find:	Just off the A5086 Cockermouth road, west of Loweswater village
Carp Stock:	Well stocked with carp, sizes unknown
Category:	Carp Water
Other Species:	Not known
Permits:	Day and week tickets from The Gun Shop, Lorton Street, Cockermouth
Control:	Cockermouth Angling Association
Cost:	On application
BK Rating:	Insufficient information

W/A: NRA North West Region
Comments: This water has been stocked with carp by the club and we can find out little about it, but as there are so few carp in Cumbria...

Roanhead Fisheries

Location: Near Barrow-in-Furness
Type and Size: Six very deep pits of about 10 acres
Carp Stock: Quite a few carp to well over 20lbs
Category: Mixed Fishery
Other Species: Roach and rudd; big eels
Permits: Members only water of Furness AA, Hannay, 50 Crellin Street, Barrow
Cost: About £10 per year
Control: Club
BK Rating: Difficult
W/A: NRA North West Region

Ulverston Canal

Location: Ulverston, near Barrow-in-Furness, southern Lake District
Type and Size: Short, narrow canal
Carp Stock: Restocked water containing some carp, numbers and sizes not known
Category: Mixed Fishery
Other Species: Tench, roach and other coarse fish
Permits: Day and season tickets from the Canal Tavern Inn, Ulverston; Angling and Hiking Centre, 62 Forshaw Street, Barrow-in-Furness
Cost: About £2 per day, £15 per season
Control: Ulverston Angling Association. H B Whittam, 29 Lyndhurst Road, Ulverston
BK Rating: Difficult
W/A: NRA North West Region

DERBYSHIRE

BUXTON

ECKINGTON

CHESTERFIELD

MANSFIELD

BELPER

DERBY

BURTON

Aldamore Pool

Location:	Off the A50 at Sudbury, near Utoxetter
Type and Size:	Five acre estate lake
Carp Stock:	Very heavily stocked with many small carp
Category:	Carp Only
Permits:	Dove Valley AC; try local tackle shops
Cost:	£35 per season; joining fee £20
Restrictions:	One rod only
BK Rating:	Very Easy
W/A:	NRA Severn Trent Region

Belper Pond

Location:	Wyver Lane, Belper
Type and Size:	Three acre lake
Carp Stock:	Well stocked with carp to over 20lbs; plenty of doubles
Category:	Mixed Fishery
Other Species:	Pike and tench
Permits:	Season tickets from Belper and District AA; try local tackle shops
Cost:	£20 per season, with a £10 joining fee

Restrictions: No night fishing
BK Rating: Moderate
W/A: NRA Severn Trent Region

Chapel Wheel Dam

Location: Just outside Chesterfield
Type and Size: Old reservoir of about 10 acres
Carp Stock: Lake stocked long ago, but contains a few good carp
Category: Few Carp
Other Species: Mixed coarse fish
Permits: Enquire locally - no details obtainable
Control: Possibly small local angling club - name not known
Restrictions: No night fishing
BK Rating: Super-Difficult
W/A: NRA Severn-Trent Region

Codnor Park Reservoir

Location: Ambergate, near Belper
Type and Size: Small reservoir
Carp Stock: Some carp, sizes not known
Category: Mixed Fishery
Other Species: Roach, bream, tench and pike
Permits: From tackle shops and on bank
Cost: About £1 per day; £6 per season
Control: Club - Ripley and District AC. R Turner, 2a Argyll Road, Ripley
BK Rating: Not known
W/A: NRA Severn-Trent Region

Foxton Dam

Location: Eckington, just off the A616 between Sheffield and Bolsover
Type and Size: Small lake
Carp Stock: Probably only one or two to 20lbs — stocked many years ago
Category: Few Carp
Other Species: Roach, perch, tench and pike
Permits: Day ticket on bank
Control: Private - enquire locally
BK Rating: Super-Difficult
W/A: NRA Severn-Trent

Harwick Hall Lakes

Location: Between Mansfield and Chesterfield, close to the M1 at junction 29
Type and Size: Two estate lakes of 3 and 7 acres
Carp Stock: Very well stocked with small carp, and a few doubles and 20's to about 27lbs
Category: Mixed Fishery
Other Species: Roach, tench, perch and bream

Permits:	Day tickets from bailiff on bank at low cost. Season tickets also available at about £25
Control:	Private
Restrictions:	No night fishing
BK Rating:	Moderate
W/A:	Yorkshire
Comments:	This is a beautiful venue in the grounds of a National Trust property. Most of the bigger fish have come from the small lake. The water is shallow and weedy, but very attractive

Higham Farm

Location:	Higham Farm, near Alfreton
Type and Size:	4 farm lakes, about 3 acres each
How to Find:	Take the A61 road from Alfreton to Higham
Carp Stock:	Fairly well stocked with carp to 20lbs plus
Category:	Mixed Fishery
Other Species:	Tench, chub, roach and bream
Permits:	Higham Farm Hotel, Old Higham, Alfreton. Tel: Alfreton 833812.
Baits/Methods:	Normal carp methods and baits. Boilies are good
BK Rating:	Moderate
W/A:	NRA Severn-Trent Region
Comments:	Pleasant surroundings. Lakes contain little weed and are quite deep, up to 12ft in places

Locho Park

Location:	Spondon, near Derby - off Locho Road, Spondon
Type and Size:	15 acre estate lake
Carp Stock:	Some carp, number and sizes not known, as this water has only been fished for a short while, but carp have been reported to over 20lbs
Category:	Mixed Fishery
Other Species:	Tench and roach
Permits:	K Glynn. Tel: 0332 751938
Cost:	£50 per season, syndicate only
Restrictions:	No night fishing
BK Rating:	Very Difficult
W/A:	NRA Severn Trent Region

Mapperley Reservoir

Location:	Near Ilkeston
Type and Size:	Big reservoir
How to Find:	North west of Ilkeston off the A609
Carp Stock:	Some large carp
Category:	Few Carp
Other Species:	General coarse fish
Permits:	On site. Ranger post, Tel: 07737 5480
Cost:	On application
Control:	Derbyshire County Council
Restrictions:	Much of the lake cannot be fished
BK Rating:	Very Difficult

Ringwood Lake

Location:	In the town of Chesterfield
Type and Size:	Attractive, 4 acre town lake, very busy and open to the public
Carp Stock:	Heavily stocked with many doubles to over 15lbs
Category:	Carp Water
Permits:	Day tickets from bailiff on bank
Cost:	About £2 per day
Control:	Council
BK Rating:	Easy
W/A:	NRA Severn-Trent Region

Swarkestone Gravel Pits

Location:	Swarkestone
Type and Size:	67 acre gravel pit
How to Find:	South west of Derby on the A514
Carp Stock:	Few Carp to 26lbs
Other Species:	Roach, bream, tench, perch, pike
Permits:	Day tickets from the Rising Sun Public House, Willington
Cost:	£5 per week; £24 per season
Control:	Derby Angling Association, PO Box 167, Derby DE3 7UE. Enclose an SAE
BK Rating:	Easy to catch; hard to find
W/A:	NRA Severn-Trent Region

The Coppice Water

Location:	Heanor/Ilkeston
Type and Size:	5 acre lake
How to Find:	Near the American Adventure Theme Park, off the A6007 between Ilkeston and Heanor
Carp Stock:	Stocked with carp to 25lbs
Category:	Mixed Fishery
Other Species:	Tench, roach, perch, pike
Permits:	The Coppice Inn and Restaurant, Shipley Park, Shipley. Tel: 0773 712606
Cost:	Day tickets about £5; Season about £25.
Control:	Private
W/A:	NRA Severn-Trent Region

Trent and Mersey Canal

Location:	Egginton, on the A38 between Derby and Burton-on-Trent. Park by the road, walk over the bridge, and the canal is to your right towards the trees
Type and Size:	Attractive, narrow canal
Carp Stock:	Some carp to doubles
Category:	Few Carp
Other Species:	Roach, perch, gudgeon, and a few chub
Permits:	Season tickets from Derby AA - send an SAE to the Membership Secretary, Derby AA, PO Box 167, Derby DE3 7UE. Information from Mrs D Taft, Tel: 0332 766866
BK Rating:	Difficult
W/A:	NRA Severn-Trent Region

DEVON

ILFRACOMBE

● BARNSTAPLE
● INSTOW
● BIDEFORD

SWIMBRIDGE
● S. MOULTON

HOLSWORTHY ● ANGLERS PARADISE ● CREDITON ● TIVERTON

EXETER

● OKEHAMPTON

NEWTON ABBOT

PRINCETOWN

PLYMOUTH

KINGSBRIDGE

Abbrook Pond

Location:	Abbrook, near Kingsteighton, Newton Abbot
Type and Size:	Old matured pit of about 3 acres
Carp Stock:	Well stocked with carp to double figures; in the past this lake contain carp to over 30lbs, some probable 20's spotted recently
Category:	Mixed Fishery
Other Species:	Tench, roach and bream
Permits:	Exeter and District AA; Hon Sec, D Cornish, 9 Denmark Road, Exeter. Tel: 0392 56770; also from tackle shops in Exeter, such as Exeter Angling Centre, Smythen Street, Torquay and Newton Abbot
Cost:	Day visitors: £2; week - £6. Club membership £14 per season, open to all
Control:	Club
BK Rating:	Moderate
Comments:	There is a normal close season on this water. Could contain some very big carp, though those of the original stocking are almost certainly all dead

Alder Farm Quarry   A

Location:	On the left hand side of the A30 Okehampton-Launceston road, just before crossing into Cornwall
Type and Size:	Large, very old quarry, said by local people to be bottomless
Carp Stock:	Some carp, sizes not known, but probably to 10lbs or so
Category:	Mixed Fishery
Other Species:	Trout, roach, rudd, bream and tench
Permits:	Call at Alder Farm for day tickets and accommodation
Control:	Private
BK Rating:	Not known
W/A:	NRA South West Region
Comments:	There are self-catering chalets close to the lake, which can be rented from the farm. A very deep quarry

Allerton Ponds

Location:	Allerton, Loddiswell, near Kingsbridge. Tel: 550306
Type and Size:	Two small man-made ponds on private land — ½ acre and ¼ acre
Carp Stock:	About 30 carp in each pond, from 7lbs to 15lbs — best reported 24lb mirror
Category:	Carp Only
Permits:	From owner on bank
Cost:	£3 per day
Control:	Private
Restrictions:	Barbless hooks; no night fishing; no fixed leads. Minimum breaking strain - 6lbs. Two rods only. No dogs or radios
BK Rating:	Easy
W/A:	NRA South West Region

Zyg Gregorek, of Angler's Paradise, with 'Neptune', at 30¼lbs - the first ever 30 from his lakes, which he caught on New Year's Day, 1991

ANGLERS PARADISE
HOLIDAYS

Set in rural countryside with views of Dartmoor and close to the seaside. Twelve miles on the B3218 from Okehampton.

Twenty five luxurious villas and cottages (many with jacuzzis and four-poster beds) in a 128-acre estate with 9 lakes exclusively for residents.

Designer Fishing – different sizes and various species in separate lakes with rare water plants, carp, golden tench, orfe, koi, etc.

Lakes with walk-on islands, koi lake with dragon pull-raft.

Four carp lakes with fish to over 30lbs! African Safari bar, pets corner, ship climbing frame and unusual activities such as goat milking, wine making, mushroom picking and Woodland Sculpture Walk.

Leisure Facilities
Includes on site, table tennis, pool and video games. Clay pigeon shooting and donkey rides are available at extra cost, and of course fishing! With 9 lakes stocking carp, golden tench, koi, golden rudd and goldfish in lovely surroundings, the Angler will certainly feel on holiday.

**Contact: Zyg and Rose Gregorek
The Gables, Winsford, Halwill, Beaworthy, Devon EX21 5XT
Tel: 0409 221559**

Anglers Eldorado

Location:	Chilla Road, opposite the entrance to Anglers' Paradise, Halwill Junction, Beaworthy
Type and Size:	4 man-made lakes from one to 3 acres, with many more lakes soon to be opened on the same site
How to Find:	Take the old A30 from Okehampton, and at the top of the hill turn right on the B3218 to Halwill Junction (10 miles). At Halwill Junction, turn right by the new houses, pass the pub on your right, and the entrance to Eldorado is 400 yards on the left hand side
Carp Stock:	The two acre lake is very heavily stocked with high singles and some doubles; the 3 acre lake has many good doubles, including commons, and more good carp are being stocked regularly in both waters
Category:	Mixed Fishery (Carp Only lake now being made)
Other Species:	Big koi and other coarse fish, including golden carp, golden tench, golden rudd, and koi
Permits:	Day tickets from Zyg at Anglers Paradise, The Gables, Winford, Halwill Junction. Tel: 0409 221559 (down track opposite lakes); from the Newsagents in the village, from the bailiff's house in Chilla Road, close to the lakes; and from selected tackle dealers in the towns
Cost:	About £3.50 per rod per day
Control:	Private; Zyg Gregorek
Restrictions:	No night fishing; barbless hooks; fixed leads only if back-stops used; min. line b/s — 3lbs; no keepnets or carp sacks
BK Rating:	Easy for all lakes
W/A:	NRA South West Region
Comments:	No close season. A brand new day ticket water in a holiday area where there are very few fisheries of this kind. Pleasant, quiet fishing, which, we are sure will soon become as famous as Zyg's other fishery, Anglers' Paradise. Easy fishing for plenty of carp of all sizes, which will soon go to over 20lbs

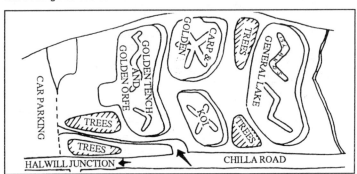

Anglers' Paradise Holidays   A

Location:	The Gables, Winsford, Halwill Junction, Beaworthy. Tel: 0409 221559
Type and Size:	Main lake: 4½ acres, stream fed with 5 islands and a boathouse; 4 other carp lakes close to each other, of about 1½ acres each
How to Find:	Call first at Zyg's house, The Gables. To get there take the B3218 Holsworthy road, turning right off the A30 a mile west of Okehampton. At Halwill Junction, turn right, pass the pub and take the right turn

signposted 'Winsford' in 400 yards, opposite the entrance to Zyg's day ticket water Anglers' Eldorado. Continue down the rough track until you reach Anglers' Paradise on your left

Carp Stock: Main Lake - very heavily stocked with carp to 30lbs, 20-30 twenties, and about 165 doubles, average size 16lbs; Spessy Lake - 18 carp, most of which are twenties! The first 30 was caught in January 1991 by the owner Zyg, and there have been several thirties caught since to about 32lbs. There are 5 thirties in this small lake and about 20 young fish of around 10lbs growing quickly for the future. Octopussy Lake — 40 doubles, many of which are over 15lbs. Beginners Lake - heavily stocked with small carp.

Category: All 4 lakes are Carp Only

Permits: Fishing only for those who book accommodation, except for occasional syndicate vacancies for the famous 'Five C's Carp Syndicate'. No day tickets

Control: Zyg and Rose Gregorek. Tel: 0409 221559

Baits/Methods: All normal carp fishing methods and rigs, and float fishing with sweetcorn often succeeds when boilies fail

Restrictions: Night fishing by arrangement only, barbless hooks; no bent hook rigs; minimum 8lb b/s line and size 10 hook

BK Rating: Main Lake - Moderate. Spessy - Difficult. Octopussy - Easy. Beginners - Very Easy

W/A: NRA South West Region

Comments: Beautiful 128 acre estate, with 5 other lakes full of koi, crucians, golden tench, golden rudd, golden and blue orfe, and even a tench-shaped lake! Plenty of easy float fishing for beginners and youngsters. Fish farm - quality fish for sale including golden tench and rudd, and blue orfe. Woodland sculpture walk.

A mid-double common from Anglers Paradise, Devon

Zyg and friends with some of the 20's and 30's from the Specimen Lake at Anglers' Paradise, Devon

Luxury up-market self catering accommodation, with 25 villas and cottages, some with whirlpool baths, ornate four posters, leather Chesterfields, and decorated with antique fishing rods and other valuable tackle. Anglers Paradise is justly rated as the best place in the country for an angling holiday, either for dedicated carp anglers, or for the family. There is clay pigeon shooting, a games room, a table tennis room, a tackle shop, and many attractions for the children, including donkey rides. The large, fabulously decorated African bar is the social centre of the complex, where you can drink Zyg's homemade wine and look at the many pictures of big carp caught in the lakes - some of which are soon expected to reach 40lbs, and all of which were 'grown on' from small fish by Zyg himself — no big imports here to create an instant fishery.

Anglers' Paradise has appeared on a number of TV programmes, and in 1990 was given the gold award by the English Tourist Board - a paradise indeed! PM stays there twice a year — and there is nowhere in the country where you can have a better angling holiday, with a

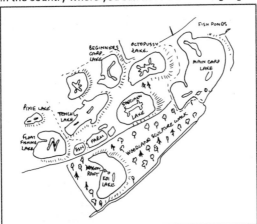

most pleasant and friendly atmosphere. Telephone Zyg for his first class colour brochure, and book well in advance, as those who holiday there once, usually keep going back. Zyg and Rose have three young daughters, Wanda, Anna, and Zenia, all of whom are very beautiful (they made me put that!), so Anglers' Paradise is understandably a family centre - but it's a serious carp fishery too: some of the leading carp anglers in the country have stayed and fished there, and more will do so now the fish are into the thirties - and the central location in Devon makes it ideal for all types of holidays

Arjays Fishing Retreat   A

Location:	Oldborough, Morchard Bishop, Crediton EX16 6SQ - off the A377
Type and Size:	Two spring-fed, interconnecting lakes of about two acres, in an old sandstone quarry
Carp Stock:	Some carp, sizes and numbers not quoted in brochure
Category:	Mixed Fishery
Other Species:	Tench, perch, rudd and eels
Permits:	Roy and Jenny Fancett, at the address above. Tel: 03637 437
Cost:	Day tickets at £3 per day; children £2
Restrictions:	No groundbait or boilies (the owners obviously don't know that boilies are about the best food for fish!); no fish over 1lb to be kept in keepnets
BK Rating:	Not known
W/A:	NRA South West Region
Comments:	This is a beautiful wildlife reserve with a stream, deer, badgers and foxes; much other wildlife and flowers. Three self-catering chalets; breakfast and evening meals at the house by arrangement. No pets. Prices £100 per week; fishing extra. Bed and breakfast in house from £12 per night. Lake has been stocked for 30 years, but was only recently opened for fishing. Car park and toilet facilities. Excellent location for holidays, between Dartmoor and Exmoor. Send for brochure

Berrynarbor Mill Pond   A

Location:	Mill Park Caravan and Camping Site, Berrynarbor, Combe Martin
Type and Size:	3 acre lake
How to Find:	The camping and caravan site is near the village of Berrynarbor in North Devon. Take the A399 from Combe Martin towards Ilfracombe, and turn south to the village
Carp Stock:	A reasonable number of mirrors to about 15lbs. One fish of 24lbs reported, but this could be the only 20
Category:	Mixed Fishery
Other Species:	Roach, perch and bream
Permits:	Mr Brain, Mill Park Caravan Site, Berrynarbor, Combe Martin. Tel: 027188 2647
Cost:	About £1 per day, day tickets
Control:	Private
BK Rating:	Moderate
W/A:	NRA South West Region
Comments:	No close season

Bulworthy Farm Cottage   A

Location: The Barton, Instow, Bideford, North Devon
Type and Size: Five small lakes
Carp Stock: Some carp to 20lbs
Category: Mixed Fishery
Other Species: Some coarse fishing (species not listed), rainbow trout to 4lbs
Permits: · From the address above (Mrs R May)
Control: Private
BK Rating: Not known
W/A: NRA South West Region
Comments: Cottage to rent at the lakes, with fishing for guests. Another lake with a rowing boat. Two other cottages about 7 miles away, but still with the same fishing rights. Cost weekly (sleeps 6-plus) from £167 to £362

Clifford Farm Holidays   A

Location: Woolsery, near Clovelly
Type and Size: Small farm pool
How to Find: Woolsery is a village near Clovelly on the North Devon coast
Carp Stock: Well stocked with carp of good size
Category: Carp Water
Other Species: Trout
Permits: On site
Cost: On application
BK Rating: Moderate
W/A: NRA South West Region
Comments: No close season. Luxury self catering cottages in beautiful countryside near coast. Brochure and information from: Tel: 02373 319. Also game and clay pigeon shooting

Cofton Park Farm   A

Location: Cofton Park Farm, Starcross, Dawlish
Type and Size: Small lake
How to Find: Between Starcross and Dawlish in South Devon
Carp Stock: Well stocked
Category: Mixed Fishery
Other Species: Tench, roach, skimmer bream
Permits: On site
Cost: On application
BK Rating: Moderate
Control: Private
W/A: NRA South West Region
Comments: Holiday caravans, tourers, camping. Heated swimming pool, shopping and all amenities. Free brochure and details from Mrs T Jeffery. Tel: 0626 890358. No close season

Coombe Water Fishery

Location: Near Kingsbridge, South Devon
Type and Size: One acre lake
How to Find: Enquire from owner

Carp Stock:	Well stocked with carp to 18lbs
Category:	Mixed Fishery
Other Species:	Bream and tench
Permits:	Jonathan Robinson. Tel: 0548 852038
Cost:	£3 per day
BK Rating:	Moderate
Control:	Private
W/A:	NRA South West Region
Comments:	This lake is in the beautiful South Hams area of Devon where there is little carp fishing. All details from the owner

Creedy Carp Lake

Location:	Off the A3072 Tiverton road; turn left one mile from Crediton, and then first right, and right again; the lake is opposite a farm
Type and Size:	18th century lake of about 5 acres
Carp Stock:	Heavily stocked with carp to over 20lbs, most of which are commons, though small mirrors have been stocked, and some have now reached 15lb
Category:	Mixed Fishery
Other Species:	Tench and eels
Permits:	Day tickets from machine on bank
Cost:	£4 for 5.30am to 11pm, and an evening ticket from 5pm to 11pm costs £2.50
Control:	Private Tel: 0363 772684
Restrictions:	No season tickets; no night fishing; no keepnets; 3 rods allowed
Baits/Methods:	Floaters, boilies, luncheon meat and sweetcorn
BK Rating:	Moderate, though an angler has taken more than 100lbs of carp in a day
W/A:	NRA South West Region

Darracott

Location:	Off the Bideford to Barnstaple road, near Torrington
Type and Size:	Reservoir of 2.6 acres
How to Find:	Turn off the A386 Okehampton to Bideford road opposite Torrington Church, and then turn right towards Huntshaw. The entrance to Darracott is past the factory on the right
Carp Stock:	Well stocked with carp to 14lbs
Category:	Mixed Fishery
Other Species:	Bream, perch, roach and rudd
Permits:	Sports, 9 High Street, The Square, Torrington: The Kingfisher, 22 Castle Street, Barnstaple. Tel: (0271) 44919: The Tackle Box, Kings Shopping Centre, Cooper Street, Bideford. Tel: (0237) 470043: Summerlands Tackle, 3 Golflinks Road, Westward Ho. Tel: (0237) 471291.
Cost:	Day £2.50. Concession rate for OAP's, SDP/MOB, students and children under 16 £1.50: 24 hours £5: 7 day castabout, (valid at all Peninsular Coarse Fisheries, except Jennetts and Crafthole), day £15, concession day £10: Day and night £30. No season permits
Control:	Mr Dell Mills, Manager, Peninsular Coarse Fisheries, St Cleer Depot, Liskeard, Cornwall PL14 6EQ. Tel: (0579) 43929
W/A:	NRA South West Region

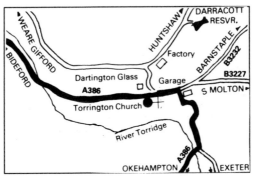

BK Rating: Moderate
Restrictions: No keepnets for carp. Barbless hooks requested. Permits must be obtained before fishing
Comments: NO CLOSED SEASON. Night fishing is now allowed

Dunsley Farm   A

Location: West Anstey, South Molton. Tel: 03984 246
Type and Size: Half acre farm pond
Carp Stock: Well stocked with small carp
Category: Mixed Fishery
Other Species: Tench, roach and rudd
Permits: On site
Control: Mrs M Robins, at the above address
BK Rating: Moderate
W/A: NRA South West Region
Comments: Self-catering cottage, overlooking a valley, and the woodland pond. Cost from £100 per week, to include fishing

East Devon Pond   A

Location: Near Honiton
Type and Size: Small farm pond - about half an acre
Carp Stock: Well stocked with carp to about 15lbs
Category: Carp Water
Other Species: Some coarse fish
Permits: Tel: 0404891 244 for information and details
Control: Private
BK Rating: Not known, as the water was not fished until 1991
W/A: NRA South West Region
Comments: Country bungalow to let for self catering holidays with fishing on own pond. Six acres of land - cottage sleeps six. Open during the winter for the week or weekend booking. No close season. Cost from £200 per week, to include fishing

Edison Pond

Location:	Kingsteignton, near Newton Abbot
Type and Size:	One acre clay pit with many snags and sunken trees
How to Find:	Take the B3193 north from Kingsteignton. About half a mile from the roundabout, and straight on, you will see the pond on the right, in some trees
Carp Stock:	Some carp, mainly commons, to about mid-doubles
Category:	Mixed Fishery
Other Species:	Roach, rudd and tench
Permits:	24 hour tickets from tackle shops in Newton Abbott, which must be obtained in advance
Control:	Newton Abbott FA
BK Rating:	Difficult
W/A:	NRA South West Region
Comments:	Heavy tackle needed - at least 15lb line - as most of the carp are taken in the heavy snags and lilies, often on floaters

Exeter Canal

Location:	Exeter
Type and Size:	6 mile canal from Basin to Turf
Carp Stock:	Some carp to doubles
Category:	Few Carp
Other Species:	Dace, roach, rudd, perch, tench, bream, pike and eels
Permits:	Exeter and District AA. Hon Sec D Cornish, 9 Denmark Road, Exeter. Tel: 0392 56770. Tickets from tackle shops in Exeter, such as Exeter Angling Centre, Smythen Street; Bennett's, Crediton; Drum Sports, Newton Abbot; Plainmoor Angling Centre, Torquay.
Cost:	Visitor's day ticket at £2; weekly - £6. Season £14. Reductions for juniors and OAP's
Control:	Club
Restrictions:	Limited access points - details from Agents and Secretary
BK Rating:	Very Difficult
W/A:	NRA South West Region
Comments:	No close season; said to have produced some lower twenties, but we have no proof of this

Fishponds House

Location:	Fishponds House, Dunkeswell, Honiton. Tel: 0823 680460
Type and Size:	3 acre lake
Carp Stock:	Carp to double figures
Category:	Mixed Fishery
Other Species:	Tench and rudd
Permits:	Mr and Mrs K Farmer at the address above
Cost:	Day tickets at £1.75
Control:	Private
Restrictions:	No night fishing - open 8am till sunset only
BK Rating:	Not known
W/A:	NRA South West Region
Comments:	No close season

Grand Western Canal

Location:	Tiverton Basin to Burlescombe
Type and Size:	Narrow, weedy disused canal
Carp Stock:	Said to be some carp to double figures
Category:	Few Carp?
Other Species:	Big pike and tench; perch, roach, rudd, bream and eels
Permits:	Local tackle shops, in Tiverton
Cost:	£17 per season (£12 associate member); £6 per week; £2.50 per day. Reduced prices for juniors and OAP's
Control:	Malcolm Trump, Canal Liaison Officer, 5 Middle Lane, Cullompton. Tel: 0844 34448 (home), or 0844 32059 (work)
Restrictions:	Dawn to dusk fishing only. Open from June 1st to last day in February
BK Rating:	Difficult
W/A:	South West

Hartsmoor Fisheries

Location:	One mile north of Tiverton on the A396
Type and Size:	Three small ponds, one of which is heavily stocked with carp to nearly 20lbs
Category:	Mixed Fishery
Other Species:	Tench, crucians and roach in carp pond
Permits:	Tel: 0823 680460
Restrictions:	None known
BK Rating:	Easy
W/A:	NRA South West Region
Comments:	No close season. The two other ponds are mainly match fisheries

Hogsbrook Lake

Location:	Greensdale Barton, Woodbury Salterton, Exeter
Type and Size:	Two lakes of 2½ acres and 1½ acres
Carp Stock:	Well stocked with carp to doubles
Category:	Mixed Fishery
Other Species:	Tench, roach and bream
Permits:	Miss M McDowell, FWS Carter and Sons Ltd, Greensdale Barton, Woodbury Salterton. Tel: 0395 32855 (day); 0395 68183 (evening)
Cost:	£2.50 per day; £1.25 evening after 6pm. Reduced prices for children under 8. Season ticket at £50 annually (no close season)
Control:	Private
BK Rating:	Not known
W/A:	NRA South West Region
Comments:	No close season; night fishing allowed. No fish under 1lb in keepnets (!); children under 14 must be accompanied by adults. Touring caravan and camping site

Hollies Trout Farm

Location:	Sheldon, near Honiton. Tel: 040484 428
Type and Size:	Half acre lake
Carp Stock:	Well stocked with carp to upper doubles
Category:	Mixed Fishery

Other Species:	Roach, bream, tench, dace and rudd
Permits:	From J Roles at the address above
Cost:	Day tickets at £3
Control:	Private
Restrictions:	No night fishing; open sunrise to sunset. No keepnets
BK Rating:	Not known
W/A:	NRA South West Region
Comments:	No close season

Indio Pond   A

Location:	Greywalls Lodge, Newton Road, Bovey Tracey, near Newton Abbot
Type and Size:	Estate lake of 2 acres - now for sale
How to Find:	Take the M5 to Exeter, then the A38 towards Plymouth. After 8 miles at the big roundabout turn right onto the road to Bovey Tracey; this is the Newton Road. After 1½ miles the entrance to Greywalls Lodge will be seen on the right, 200 yards after crossing the old railway bridge
Carp Stock:	Well stocked with carp to 27lbs
Category:	Mixed Fishery
Other Species:	Tench, trout, rudd, eels, perch
Permits:	Day tickets are limited, and are sold in advance only by the resident owner, Mr M Charlier, at the house on the property. Fishing is from 6am till dusk; night fishing is by arrangement with the owners. Fishing is available at a reduced price for those staying at the Lodge. There are plans for a unique free exclusive membership scheme - details from Mr Charlier
Cost:	On application
Restrictions:	No bolt rigs. Barbless hooks only. No keepnets
BK Rating:	Carp up to 10lbs - Easy; 10-15lbs - Moderate; 20lbs plus - Difficult (April till June). Carp to 20lbs - Moderate; over 20lbs - Difficult (June till October). Winter — Easy if you find the fish. (Categories provided by the proprietor in this instance)
Control:	Private
W/A:	South West
Baits/Methods:	Normal carp fishing baits and methods. Hard boilies needed to defeat the numerous tench
Comments:	First class accommodation is available at the Lodge which is only a few yards from the lake. Bed and breakfast and evening meal. Rooms have wash basins and tea-making facilities, and there is a guest lounge with colour TV. The house is a beautiful 100-year old stone built property in 10 acres of private grounds situated between Torquay and Dartmoor - ideal for a family fishing holiday. No close season. Brochure from Mr Charlier, Greywalls, Newton Road, Bovey Tracey, Devon TQ13 9DY. Tel: 0626 832508. Record fish a mirror of 27lbs 3ozs. The owner has planning permission for 12 holiday lodges, but wants to SELL this beautiful estate; if you're interested, try making an offer

Jennetts   A

Location:	Near Bideford, North Devon
Type and Size:	Reservoir of 8 acres
How to Find:	Signposted from the Torrington to Bideford road

Category:	Carp Water
Other Species:	Tench, roach and bream
Permits:	The Tackle Box, Kings Shopping Centre, Cooper Street, Bideford. Tel: (0237) 470043
Cost:	Day (6.30am to 10.00pm only) £3. Concession rate for OAP's, SDP/MOB and students £2. Children under 16 £1.50. No season permits
Control:	Mr Dell Mills, Manager, Peninsular Coarse Fisheries, St Cleer Depot, Liskeard, Cornwall PL14 6EQ. Tel: (0579) 43929
W/A:	NRA South West Region
BK Rating:	Moderate
Restrictions:	No night fishing. No cereal based groundbaits, except swimfeeders. No keepnets for carp. Barbless hooks requested. Permits must be obtained before fishing
Comments:	NO CLOSED SEASON. Attractive enclosed water. Accommodation at the Beaufort Hotel, Tors Park, Ilfracombe. Tel: 0271 865483

Little Comfort Farm   A

Location:	Little Comfort Farm, West Down, Braunton, North Devon. Tel: 0271 812414
Type and Size:	One acre farm pond
Carp Stock:	Well stocked with carp to double figures
Category:	Mixed Fishery
Other Species:	Rudd, bream and trout
Permits:	From Rolf Alvsaker at the address above
Cost:	£5 per day; £4 half day; £3 evening
Control:	Private
Restrictions:	No night fishing - daylight till dark only
BK Rating:	Moderate
W/A:	NRA South West Region
Comments:	No close season. Self-catering cottages available

Longlands Farm   A

Location:	Near Coombe Martin, Ilfracombe, North Devon EX34 OPD. Tel: 0271 883522
Type and Size:	Small farm pond
How to Find:	Off the A399 Ilfracombe—Lynmouth road; turn left by RAC box going south
Carp Stock:	Some carp, numbers and sizes not known
Category:	Mixed Fishery
Other Species:	General coarse fish
Permits:	Fishing free to residents, details from Mary Peacock at the address above
BK Rating:	Not known
W/A:	NRA South West Region
Comments:	Little is known, as the brochure only mentions a private fishing lake, but gives no details. Bed and breakfast, evening meal if required, on working farm near Exmoor and the sea. B and B £12.50 per person per night, £87 a week

Lower Tamar

Location: Between Holsworthy and Bideford, North Devon
Type and Size: Reservoir of 40 acres

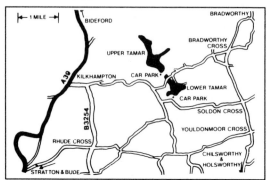

How to Find: Turn off the A39 Bideford to Bude road at Kirkhampton and proceed towards Bradworthy Cross. The water will be seen on the right. The car park is to the south of the lake
Carp Stock: Well stocked with carp to 28lbs. Restocked in early 1991 with commons to 26½lbs
Category: Mixed Fishery
Other Species: Tench, bream, roach and rudd
Permits: Day or day and night permits from the self service unit on the car park: The Tackle Box, Kings Shopping Centre, Cooper Street, Bideford. Tel: (0237) 470043: Summerlands Tackle, Golflinks Road, Westward Ho. Tel: (0237) 471291. Clive's Tackle and Bait, 182 Exeter Street, Plymouth. Tel: (0752) 228940. Season permits from the ranger at Upper Tamar Lake. Tel: (028882) 262
Control: Mr Dell Mills, Manager, Peninsular Coarse Fisheries, St Cleer Depot, Liskeard, Cornwall PL14 6EQ. Tel: (0579) 43929
W/A: NRA South West Region
BK Rating: Moderate
Restrictions: No cereal based groundbaits except swimfeeders. No keepnets for carp. Barbless hooks requested. Permits must be obtained before fishing
Comments: NO CLOSED SEASON. Night fishing is now allowed. Long casting is necessary to reach deep water in some areas. Long stay carp anglers generally do well

Melbury

Location: Parkham, near Bideford, North Devon
Type and Size: Reservoir of 12 acres
How to Find: From the Bradworthy to Bideford road, the fishery is 1 mile from Powlers Piece Garage
Carp Stock: Moderately stocked with carp to 22lbs. Restocked early 1991 with commons to over 20lbs - a 27 pounder was caught in 1990, hooked on a boilie
Category: Mixed Fishery

Other Species: Rudd, tench, bream and roach
Permits: The Tackle Box, Kings Shopping Centre, Cooper Street, Bideford.
Tel: (0237) 470043: Powlers Piece Garage, Powlers Piece, East Putford. Tel:
(02375) 282: Summerlands Tackle, Golflinks Road, Westward Ho.
Tel: (0237) 471291
Cost: Day £2.50. Concession rate for OAP's, SDP/MOB, students and children
under 16 £1.50: 24 hours £5: 7 day castabout, (valid at all Peninsular
Coarse Fisheries, except Jennetts and Crafthole), day £15, concession
day £10: Day and night £30. No season permits
Control: Mr Dell Mills, Peninsular Coarse Fisheries, St Cleer Depot, Liskead,
Cornwall PL14 6EQ. Tel: (0579) 43929
W/A: NRA South West Region
BK Rating: Moderate
Restrictions: Fishing is allowed from 6.30am to 10.00pm only. No cereal based
groundbaits, except swimfeeders. No keepnets for carp. Barbless hooks
requested. Permits must be obtained before fishing
Comments: No closed season

Milehead Fisheries

Location: Mill Hill, near Tavistock
How to Find: Take the A385 from Tavistock towards Launceston, and turn left towards
Mill Hill just outside the town. After about a mile you will see a turn on
the right which leads to the fishery
Type and Size: Small lake
Carp Stock: Well stocked with carp to doubles, including some ghost carp
Category: Mixed Fishery
Other Species: Tench and roach
Permits: At the fishery
Cost: £3.50 per day; £2.35 for the evening
Control: Andrew or Paul Evenden. Tel: 0822 610888
Restrictions: No keepnets; barbless hooks
BK Rating: Moderate
W/A: NRA South West Region
Comments: No close season

Millhayes Pond

Location: Kentisbeare, off the A373 between Honiton and Tiverton
Type and Size: Small pond
Carp Stock: Well stocked with small carp to about 5lbs
Category: Mixed Fishery
Other Species: Tench and rudd
Permits: Tel: 08846 412
Restrictions: Not known
BK Rating: Easy
W/A: NRA South West Region
Comments: No close season

Old Mill

Location: Near Dartmouth in South Devon
Type and Size: Reservoir of 4.7 acres

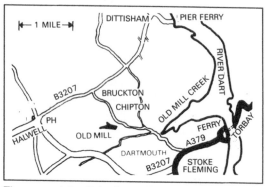

How to Find: The reservoir is off the B3207 Halwell to Dittisham road, near Old Mill Creek on the River Dart

Carp Stock: Well stocked with carp to 21lbs. Restocked early in 1991 with commons to 20½lbs

Category: Mixed Fishery

Other Species: Roach, bream and tench

Permits: The Sport 'n' Fish, 16 Fairfax Place, Dartmouth. Tel: (0803) 833509. No season permits

Cost: Day £2.50. Concession rate for OAP's SDP/MOB, students and children under 16 £1.50: 24 hours £5: 7 day castabout, (valid at all Peninsular Coarse Fisheries, except Jennetts and Crafthole), day £15, concession day £10: Day and night £30. No season permits

Control: Mr Dell Mills, Manager, Peninsular Coarse Fisheries, St Cleer Depot, Liskeard, Cornwall PL14 6EQ. Tel: (0579) 43929

W/A: NRA South West Region

BK Rating: Moderate

Restrictions: No cereal based groundbaits except swimfeeders. No keepnets for carp. Barbless hooks requested. Permits must be obtained before fishing.

Comments: NO CLOSED SEASON. Night fishing is now allowed. Very mature and attractive water

Pound Farm   A

Location: Butterley, near Tiverton
Type and Size: Tiny farm pond just big enough for four anglers
Carp Stock: Some carp to about 8lbs
Category: Mixed Fishery
Other Species: Tench and perch
Permits: Tel: 0884 (Tiverton) 855208 for information
BK Rating: Not known
W/A: NRA South West Region
Comments: Six berth caravan for hire at £100 to £130 weekly, fishing included

Pyewell Farm   A

Location:	Pyewell Farm, Holmacott, near Instow, North Devon. Tel: 0271 830357
Type and Size:	Two small farm ponds
Carp Stock:	Well stocked with carp to doubles
Category:	Mixed Fishery
Other Species:	Tench
Permits:	From Mrs Steer at the address above
Control:	Private
BK Rating:	Not known
W/A:	NRA South West Region
Comments:	Dinner, bed and breakfast in 16th century farmhouse with fishing from £16 per day, which includes food and overnight accommodation. Three miles from sandy beach and only 4 miles from the North Devon link road. No close season

Rackerhayes

Location:	Newton Abbot
Type and Size:	Island Pond is about 5 acres - old pit
How to Find:	Take the Exeter road from Newton Abbot, and the lakes are down a track opposite the Racecourse
Carp Stock:	Quite well stocked with small carp to 10lbs, small number of doubles including some twenties and one fish of about 30lbs
Category:	Mixed Fishery
Other Species:	General coarse fish
Permits:	For Rackerhayes you must live within a 25 mile radius of Newton Abbot. The Newton Abbot FA has other waters with carp in the area, for which day and season tickets ae issued. Detials and tickets from Percy Hodge (Sports), 104 Queen Street, Newton Abbot; Drum Sports, 48a Courtenay Street, Newton Abbot
Control:	Newton Abbot Fishing Association. Secretary: D Hooder, 22 Mount Pleasant Road, Newton Abbot, Totnes
BK Rating:	Rackerhayes - Difficult. Other water - Moderate to Easy
W/A:	NRA South West Region

Riverton Fishery

Location:	Off the A361 at Swimbridge. Tel: 0271 830009
Type and Size:	Two lakes of 4 acres and 3 acres
Carp Stock:	Well stocked with carp to at least 10lbs
Category:	Mixed Fishery
Other Species:	Tench, bream, roach, rudd and perch
Permits:	Martin or Brian Corke on the number above
Cost:	£2.50 per day; £1.75 for the evening; reduced price for juniors
Control:	Private
Restrictions:	No night fishing - open dawn till dusk only
BK Rating:	Not known
W/A:	NRA South West Region
Comments:	No close season

Salmonhutch Fishery A

Location:	Upton, near Crediton
Type and Size:	Three small spring fed lakes
Carp Stock:	Well stocked with commons and mirrors to doubles
Category:	Carp Water
Other Species:	Tench
Permits:	From the fishery. Tel: 03632 3570/2615
Control:	Private
BK Rating:	Moderate
W/A:	NRA South West Region
Comments:	Camping and caravan site; facilities for disabled anglers

Sampford Peverell Ponds

Location:	Just off the M5, where the A373 Tiverton road crosses the railway near the village of Sampford Peverell
Type and Size:	Two little pits of about half an acre and ¼ acre
Carp Stock:	Some good carp to upper doubles
Category:	Mixed Fishery
Other Species:	Tench, bream, pike and roach
Permits:	Members only water of Exeter and District AA (no day tickets). Permits from tackle shops in Exeter. Secretary: D Cornish, 9 Denmark Road, Exeter. Tel: 0392 567700. Includes a number of other good waters
Restrictions:	Normal close season
BK Rating:	Difficult
W/A:	NRA South West Region
Comments:	We have personal experience of this one. The pond on the Tiverton side of the railway line is known as The Clear Pond. This used to contain only a dozen or so carp, most of which were doubles to about 20lbs, which could be seen but were very hard to catch, (a friend had an 18 on a floating Osborne biscuit many years ago, believe it or not); we are not sure if these big fish still survive. The other pond, part of which was taken for road construction, was always so heavily weeded that it was almost impossible to get the fish out, even on very heavy line, though this may have changed now. PM once tried to go in for a hooked double, and sank in mud almost to chest level, managed to scramble out... and never did get the fish out!

Shobrooke Park

Location:	Off the A3072 between Crediton and Tiverton, on the Shobrooke Estate
Type and Size:	Attractive 20 acre estate lake
Carp Stock:	Quite well stocked with carp of over 20lbs
Category:	Mixed Fishery
Other Species:	Roach and tench
Permits:	Day tickets from Ladds Sports, High Street, Crediton
Cost:	£2 per day; £5 per week - half price for juniors, OAP's and the disabled
Control:	Shobrooke Park Estate, 27 South Street, Molton, North Devon EX36 4AA
Restrictions:	No night fishing; no fishing allowed on about half of the bank - the other side is private
BK Rating:	Moderate
W/A:	NRA South West Region

Simpson Valley Fishery

Location:	One and a half miles from Holsworthy on the A3072 Holsworthy to Hatherleigh road. Tel: 0409 253593
Type and Size:	4 small farm pools in valley
Carp Stock:	Carp Pool - heavily stocked with carp to upper doubles; other pools - some carp
Category:	Carp Pool - Carp Only; other pools - Mixed Fisheries
Other Species:	Tench, roach and rudd
Permits:	Day tickets from the farm - there is a sign on the main road
Cost:	Carp Pool - £3 per day; other pools - £2 per day; half price for children and pensioners on all pools
Control:	Private
BK Rating:	Easy
Restrictions:	Barbless hooks only; no boilies; no cereal groundbait
W/A:	NRA South West Region
Comments:	Two further ponds will probably be open by the time this book appears. Pleasant farm fishery with good fishing in the carp pool

Slade

Location:	Near Ilfracombe, North Devon
Type and Size:	Two reservoirs. Upper Slade 4 acres. Lower Slade 6 acres
How to Find:	From Ilfracombe, pick up the B3231, and the entrance to the reservoirs is on the left

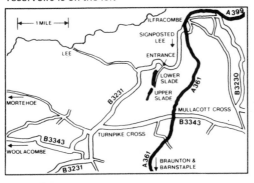

Carp Stock:	Well stocked with carp to 20lbs
Category:	Mixed Fisheries
Other Species:	Tench to 7lbs, roach to 3lbs 7ozs, bream and perch
Permits:	The Tackle Box, 2b Portland Street, Ilfracombe. Tel: (0271) 862570: The Kingfisher, 22 Castle Street, Barnstaple. Tel: (0271) 44919: Summerlands Tackle, 3 Golflinks Road, Westward Ho. Tel: (0237) 471291. Season and day permits from The Post Office, Slade. Tel: (0271) 862257
Cost:	Day £2.50. Concession rate for OAP's, SDP/MOB, students and children under 16 £1.50: 24 hours £5: 7 day castabout, (valid at all Peninsular Coarse Fisheries, except Jennetts and Crafthole),. day £15, concession £10: Day and night £30. Season permits day £37, concession OAP's SDP/MOB and students £20, children under 16 £12.50: Day and night £56
Control:	Mr Dell Mills, Manager, Peninsular Coarse Fisheries, St Cleer Depot, Liskeard, Cornwall PL14 6EQ. Tel: (0579) 43929

W/A: NRA South West Region
BK Rating: Moderate
Restrictions: No cereal based groundbait except swimfeeders. No keepnets for carp. Barbless hooks requested. Permits must be obtained before fishing
Comments: Attractive water with NO CLOSED SEASON. Night fishing is now allowed

South Farm Ponds   A

Location: Blackborough, Cullompton
Type and Size: Two small farm ponds
How to Find: South Farm, Blackborough, Cullompton, near Exeter EX15 2SE
Carp Stock: Well stocked with carp to 15lbs
Category: Mixed Fishery
Other Species: Tench and roach
Permits: From Colin and Sylvia Shortis, South Farm. Tel: 0823 681078
Cost: On application
BK Rating: Moderate
Control: Private
Restrictions: Not known
W/A: NRA Southern Region
Comments: No close season. Holidays in four holiday homes. Health spa, games room, swimming pool. Colour brochure on application

South Hay Farm   A

Location: South Hay Farm, Shebbear, Beaworthy. Tel: 040 928 614
Type and Size: Two acre lake
Carp Stock: Some carp to 10lbs
Category: Mixed Fishery
Other Species: Tench, rudd, orfe, chub and trout
Permits: Mr Nigel Brown or Miss Penelope Douglas, at the above address
Cost: £5 per day; £3 from 2pm
Control: Private
Restrictions: Open 7.30am till sunset, night fishing by arrangement. Barbless hooks
BK Rating: Not known
W/A: South West
Comments: No close season. Accommodation on site. Children's fishing pond. One mile salmon, sea trout and brown trout fishing on River Torridge

South Reed Fisheries Carp Lake

Location: Boasley Cross, Bratton Clovelly, near Okehampton EX20 4JJ
Tel: 083787 295
Type and Size: 3 acre man-made lake
How to Find: The fishery is signposted from the B3218 road between Okehampton and Halwill, about 4 miles from Okehampton, on the left hand side of the road
Carp Stock: 30 doubles, including several 20's
Category: Carp Only
Permits: In advance only - phone or call for bookings. Only 3 anglers per day from June till October
Cost: £10 per day

Control:	Private
Restrictions:	Barbless hooks, not smaller than size 8; nets to be knotless and not smaller than 30 inches; 8lb minimum line strength; no dogs
BK Rating:	Easy to Moderate
W/A:	NRA South West Region
Comments:	This lake has been specially stocked for specialist carp anglers - each fish is marked for identification purposes. Pleasant nature conservation area - other lakes on site (see separate entry). Quiet, peaceful site well away from main roads

South Reed Fisheries Coarse Lake

Location:	Boasley Cross, Bratton Clovelly, near Okehampton EX20 4JJ. Tel: 083787 295
Type and Size:	3½ acre man-made lake
How to Find:	Take the old A30 from Okehampton towards Launceston, and turn right onto the B3218 Holsworthy road at the top of Okehampton Hill. You will see a sign to the fishery on the left about 4 miles from Okehampton
Carp Stock:	Well stocked with carp to 23lbs
Category:	Mixed Fishery
Permits:	On bank
Cost:	£4 per day
Control:	Private
Baits/Methods:	All normal methods, including float fishing, with maggots, sweetcorn, luncheon meat and boilies
Restrictions:	Barbless hooks; no keepnets for carp; all fish to be returned; no dogs
BK Rating:	Easy
W/A:	NRA South West Region
Comments:	Tackle hire is available for £1 per day; angling tuition if required, by appointment only. Coarse fish, koi and ornamental fish for sale from fish farm on site, also water lilies and other aquatic plants. Some non-fishing ponds available for bird watching by special arrangement on this nature conservation area. Very quiet and peaceful site well away from main roads

South View Farm

Location:	Shillingford St George, south west of Exeter near Alphington
Type and Size:	Three small farm ponds with a total area of three acres
Carp Stock:	Top Pond well stocked with carp to over 20lbs; Middle Pond has carp to 17lbs
Category:	Mixed Fishery
Other Species:	Tench, golden tench, roach, rudd, gudgeon, bream and ghost carp
Permits:	Day tickets on bank
Cost:	£3.50 for adults; £2.50 for juniors, who must be accompanied by an adult. Evening tickets from 5pm at £2 and £1. Weekly permits at £17
Control:	Tel: 0392 832278
Restrictions:	No night fishing; no boilies or keepnets
BK Rating:	Moderate
W/A:	NRA South West Region

Squabmoor

Location:	Near Budleigh Salterton
Type and Size:	Reservoir of 4.3 acres
How to Find:	Turn off the A377 Exeter to Exmouth road at Clyst St. George into the B3179, and the reservoir is on the left, just before Knowle and Budleigh Salterton
Carp Stock:	Well stocked with carp to over 20lbs
Category:	Mixed Fishery
Other Species:	Roach to over 3lbs, tench to 5½lbs, bream and rudd
Permits:	The Tackle Shop, 20 The Strand, Exmouth; Exeter Angling Centre, Smythen Street, Exeter. Day and season permits from Knowle Post Office
Cost:	Day £2.50. Concession rate for OAP's, SDP/MOB, students and children under 16 £1.50: 24 hours £5: 7 day castabout, (valid at all Peninsular Coarse Fisheries, except Jennetts and Crafthole),. day £15, concession £10: Day and night £30. Season permits day £37, concession OAP's SDP/MOB and students £20, children under 16 £12.50: Day and night £56
Control:	Mr Dell Mills, Manager, Peninsular Coarse Fisheries, St Cleer Depot, Liskeard, Cornwall PL14 6EQ. Tel: (0579) 43929.
W/A:	NRA South West Region
BK Rating:	Moderate
Restrictions:	No cereal based groundbaits except swimfeeders. No keepnets for carp. Barbless hooks requested. Permits must be obtained before fishing
Comments:	Attractive water with NO CLOSED SEASON. Night fishing is now allowed

Star Barton Ponds

Location:	Cowley, near Exeter
Type and Size:	Two small farm ponds
Carp Stock:	Well stocked with carp to doubles
Category:	Carp Water
Other Species:	Tench
Permits:	Exeter and District AA. Secretary: D Cornish, 9 Denmark Road, Exeter. Tel: 0392 56770. Tickets from tackle shops such as Angling Centre, Smythen Street, Exeter; Bennets, Crediton; Drum Sport, Newton Abbot; Plainmoor Angling Centre, Torquay
Cost:	Day visitors - £2; weekly - £6; season - £14
Control:	Club
BK Rating:	Easy
W/A:	NRA South West Region
Comments:	No close season. Exeter and District AA is an excellent club with many other waters on the same ticket.

Stevenstone Lakes

Location:	St Giles in the Wood, near Great Torrington
Type and Size:	Three old estate lakes of three and a half acres, three-quarters, and one and a quarter acres, very attractive, in a steep valley
How to Find:	With difficulty! Take the B3227 Umberleigh road from Torrington and after two miles take a private road on the right, marked Stevenstone. After a mile the road becomes a track near some houses, and after this there is a turn in the track to the right, where you will see the entrance to the bungalow. The lakes can be seen from the house

Carp Stock:	All three lakes are well stocked with long commons, which are almost certainly genuine wildies, of which there are now very few in the country. These fish have been caught to just over 12lbs
Category:	Mixed Fishery
Other Species:	Tench, rudd and perch
Permits:	In advance only from the owner at the bungalow above the lakes
Cost:	£1.50 per rod
Control:	Private
Restrictions:	No night fishing; dawn to dusk only; no dogs
BK Rating:	Moderate
W/A:	NRA South West Region
Comments:	One of the few places left where king carp have not been stocked, and where you can catch genuine wild carp (most reported wildies are just long, thin commons); owner only requires genuine anglers; no families or picnickers

Stone Farm Quarry

Location:	Stone Farm, near Bridestow, just to the right hand side of the old A30, about 7 miles from Okehampton
Type and Size:	Large and remarkably deep quarry, with very steep sides at one end, but easy access and fishing from the farm end
Carp Stock:	Some carp, thought to go to about 10lbs
Category:	Mixed Fishery
Other Species:	Rudd, roach, tench and bream; possibly a few trout
Permits:	From Stone Farm
Control:	Private
BK Rating:	Difficult
W/A:	NRA South West Region
Comments:	PM has known this one for 50 years, although it probably only had a few trout in it from the nearby river then. Dangerous, almost vertical sides at the end away from the farm. Last time he put out an Arlesey Bomb from the 'easy' bank, it just kept going straight down, perhaps to 60 feet or more!

Stour Farm Fishery

Location:	Billingsmoor Farm, Butterleigh, Cullompton
Type and Size:	Small farm pond
How to Find:	Come off the motorway at junction 28, and take various lanes to the west. Butterleigh is south of Tiverton and west of Cullompton
Carp Stock:	The pond mentioned has been well stocked with carp to double figure size
Category:	Carp Water
Permits:	Day tickets from E Berry, Billingsmoor Farm, Butterleigh. Tel: 08845 248
Cost:	About £2 per day
Control:	Private
BK Rating:	Thought to be Fairly Easy
W/A:	NRA South West Region
Comments:	No close season. Two other ponds contain mixed coarse fish, on same ticket

Sunridge Nurseries   A

Location:	Worston, Yealmpton, off the A379 about eight miles west of Plymouth
Type and Size:	Very small pond of about half an acre
Carp Stock:	Well stocked with carp to 22lbs
Category:	Mixed Fishery
Other Species:	Roach and tench
Permits:	On site. Tel: 0752 880438
BK Rating:	Moderate
W/A:	NRA South West Region
Comments:	Fishing lodge to rent - an attractive converted barn with two bedrooms. Costs £150 to £295 weekly, including fishing

Swimbridge Pool

Location:	Swimbridge, near Barnstaple
Type and Size:	Small quarry
Carp Stock:	Quite well stocked with carp to doubles
Other Species:	Tench, bream, rudd and perch
Permits:	Barnstaple and District AA. Visitors tickets from local tackle shops, who give details of membership
Control:	Club
Restrictions:	Members only weekends and Bank Holidays; visitors' tickets weekdays only
BK Rating:	Moderate
W/A:	NRA South West Region

Tinney Waters   A

Location:	Pyworthy, Holsworthy EX22 6LF
Type and Size:	Three small lakes
How to Find:	From Holsworthy take Bodmin Street, and after about 3 miles, and past a white house, take the second turning marked 'Whitstone 4 miles'. After a mile, turn right, and then left in three-quarters of a mile
Carp Stock:	Well stocked with carp between 5lbs and 10lbs, with some much bigger mirrors and commons
Category:	Mixed Fishery
Other Species:	Rudd, tench and trout
Permits:	Jeff and Jane Mason at the address above. Tel: 0409 27362 (North Tamerton)
Restrictions:	Fishing probably only for those staying on site
BK Rating:	Easy
W/A:	NRA South West Region
Comments:	Two 6-berth static caravans to rent, or B and B in house - evening meals if required; full English breakfast at £2.95. Send for brochure. Caravan costs: from £95 per week to £195 a week; B and B: from £14.50 per person per night; fishing included in all prices. Weekend breaks

Trago Mills

Location:	On the Newton Abbot - Bovey Tracey road
Type and Size:	Small lake
Carp Stock:	Wells tocked with carp to double figures
Category:	Mixed Fishery
Other Species:	Rudd, roach, bream and tench
Permits:	The Warden on site; Geoff Mole. Tel: 0626 821111
Cost:	£3 per day; children and OAP's £2
Control:	Trago Mills
Restrictions:	Open March 1st to November 30th only, from 8.30am to 5pm
BK Rating:	Not known
W/A:	NRA South West Region
Comments:	Trago Mills is a large supermarket (see local papers for publicity)

Upham Farm

Location:	Upham Farm, Farringdon, Exeter
Type and Size:	6 small farm ponds
How to Find:	Farringdon is 6 miles east of Exter on the A3052 Exeter-Sidmouth road
Carp Stock:	Plenty of carp - many doubles to 24lbs
Category:	Carp Water
Other Species:	Tench
Permits:	J Willcocks, Upham Farm, Farringdon, Exeter. Tel: 0395 32247
Cost:	Day tickets £3
Control:	Private. J Willcocks 0395 32247
BK Rating:	Moderate
W/A:	NRA South West Region
Restrictions:	Night fishing must be booked in advance, no keepnets
Comments:	No close season. Parties of 20 or more must book in advance

Venn Pool

Location:	Near Barnstaple, North Devon
Type and Size:	Small and very deep quarry
Carp Stock:	Well stocked with carp to upper doubles
Category:	Mixed Fishery
Other Species:	Tench, bream, rudd, perch
Permits:	Barnstaple and District AA. Martin Turner, 67 Taw View, Freminton, Barnstaple. Visitors' tickets from local tackle shops
Control:	Club
Restrictions:	Visitors' tickets weekdays only; members only on weekends and Bank Holidays
BK Rating:	Moderate
W/A:	NRA South West Region

West Pitt Farm Pool   A

Location:	Uplowman, Tiverton, North Devon EX16 7DU
Type and Size:	Three farm ponds, the biggest 1¼ acres
How to Find:	Village near Tiverton, 2½ miles from the M5
Carp Stock:	Well stocked with carp to 21½lbs
Category:	Mixed Fishery
Other Species:	Tench, rudd, roach, koi

Permits:	From farm - Mrs G Brent. Tel: 0884 820296
Cost:	£3.50 per day - night by arrangement
BK Rating:	Fairly Hard
Control:	Private
Baits/Methods:	Normal carp methods
W/A:	NRA South West Region
Comments:	Farmhouse accommodation available. 21½lb mirror caught in 1987. Also self catering accommodation in cottages and lodge. Indoor heated swimming pool and sauna; tennis and games room. Groundbaiting limited. No close season

West View Pond

Location:	Ottery St. Mary, near Exeter
Type and Size:	5 acre lake
Carp Stock:	Plenty of small carp
Category:	Mixed Fishery
Other Species:	Rudd and roach
Permits:	Members only water of Exeter and District AA. Secretary: D Cornish, 9 Denmark Road, Exeter. Tel: 0392 56770; also from tackle shops in Exeter, Newton Abbot and Torquay
Cost:	£14 a year, open to all
Control:	Club
BK Rating:	Easy
W/A:	NRA South West Region
Comments:	Membership includes a number of other carp waters. Normal close season

THE
BEEKAY
GUIDE
TO
1500
BRITISH
& EUROPEAN
CARP
WATERS

Is YOUR Water listed? If so, are the details correct?

If you spot omissions, inaccuracies, or know of any changes, please let us know by filling in the Waters Questionnaire at the back of this guide and return it to us at:

FREEPOST
Beekay Publishers
Withy Pool
Henlow Camp
Bedfordshire
SG16 6EA

DORSET

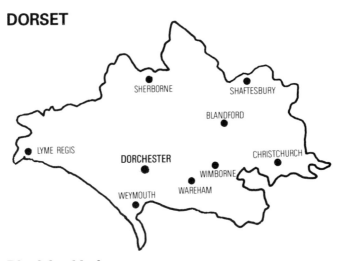

SHERBORNE
SHAFTESBURY
BLANDFORD
LYME REGIS
DORCHESTER
CHRISTCHURCH
WIMBORNE
WEYMOUTH
WAREHAM

Blashford Lakes

Location:	Off the A338 near Christchurch
Type and Size:	Two lakes, one large, and one small, which contain carp
Carp Stock:	Spinnaker Lake (large) - well stocked with carp, average low doubles. Roach Pit - few carp to 29lbs
Category:	Spinnaker - Carp Water; Roach Pit - Few Carp
Other Species:	Roach Pit - Roach, pike, tench, chub and bream
Permits:	Members only water of Christchurch AC; C Bungay, 8 Purewell, Christchurch or P Reading, 17 Mayford Road, Poole
Cost:	£54 per season, to include many other waters
Control:	Club
Restrictions:	No night fishing; some parts of the bank are out of bounds; locked gate open with club key for members only; no day tickets; fishing allowed to 11pm on Roach Pit
BK Rating:	Moderate
W/A:	NRA Wessex Region

Butterwick Farm   A

Location:	Butterwick Farm, Holnest, near Sherborne
Type and Size:	Half acre farm pond
How to Find:	Near Sherborne
Carp Stock:	Up to 6lbs, well stocked
Category:	Mixed Fishery
Other Species:	Tench, rudd, eels
Permits:	From Mrs Vickery. No day tickets
Cost:	Price on application
BK Rating:	Easy/Moderate
Control:	Private
Baits/Methods:	General angling baits and methods
W/A:	NRA Wessex Region
Comments:	This lake can only be fished by those who book mobile homes - no other permits available. Some accommodation in the farmhouse

Crow Pool

Location:	Ibsley Pools, near Christchurch, just off the A38
Type and Size:	Small, irregularly shaped pool alongside the Ibsley Trout Stream off the Avon
Carp Stock:	Well stocked with carp from 10-18lbs - about 20-30 doubles
Category:	Mixed Fishery
Other Species:	Chub, dace, perch, pike, roach, rudd and tench
Permits:	Members only water of Christchurch AC; C Bungay, 8 Purewell, Christchurch or P Reading, 17 Mayford Road, Poole, Dorset; details and some tickets from Ringwood Tackle, Ringwood. No day tickets
Cost:	£54 per season, to include many other waters
Control:	Club
Restrictions:	No night fishing; no cars before 9am; lakeside car park for disabled anglers only
BK Rating:	Moderate
W/A:	NRA Wessex Region

Dorset Springs Fishery

Location:	Sturminster Marshall, off the A350 west of Wimborne
Type and Size:	Three acre lake
Carp Stock:	Well stocked with carp from 7lbs to 25lbs
Category:	Mixed Fishery
Other Species:	Big pike, crucians, grass carp, tench, bream, roach and rudd
Permits:	Day tickets on site at £5 for one rod; £6 for two
Control:	Tel: 0258 857653
Restrictions:	No barbed or bent hooks. No hooks larger than size 4. No keepnets or carp sacks. No nuts. Night fishing by arrangement only
BK Rating:	Moderate
W/A:	NRA Wessex Region

Harrow Pond

Location:	Harrow Lodge, Holmesley, near Christchurch
Type and Size:	Small forest pool
Carp Stock:	A few carp to 22lbs
Category:	Few Carp
Other Species:	Pike, roach and tench
How to Find:	Take the Lyndhurst road from Christchurch (A35), and turn left just after the Cat and Fiddle pub, then turn first right up Harrow Hill. A white house - Beech House Lodge - is on the right, and the entrance to the pond is 100yds further on left
Permits:	Members only water of Christchurch AC; C Bungay, 8 Purewell, Christchurch or P Reading, 17 Mayford Road, Poole
Cost:	£54 per season, to include many other waters
Restrictions:	No night fishing; members only; locked gate with key; no litter; carp must not be retained in keepnets or sacks; no access in close season
BK Rating:	Difficult
W/A:	NRA Wessex Region

Hillview Farm Lake

Location:	Hillview Farm, Corfe Mullen
Type and Size:	Sheltered farm lake of 2 acres
Carp Stock:	Heavily stocked with carp from 4lbs to 20lbs
Category:	Carp Water
Other Species:	Crucians, tench and perch
Permits:	Day tickets from farmhouse. Tel: 0258 857238
Cost:	£4 per day; £2 half day
Control:	Private
Restrictions:	8am till dusk fishing only
BK Rating:	Easy
W/A:	NRA Wessex Region

Holtwood Ponds

Location:	Holtwood, Horton, near Wimborne
Type and Size:	Three small forest-type ponds
How to Find:	Take the B3078 from Wimborne towards Cranborne
Carp Stock:	All three ponds are well stocked with small carp, mostly 5-9lbs and possibly commons
Category:	Upper Pond - Carp Only; Middle Pond - Carp Water; Lower Pond - Mixed Fishery
Other Species:	Middle Pond - tench; Lower Pond - crucians, rudd and tench
Permits:	Members only water of Christchurch AC; C Bungay, 8 Purewell, Christchurch or P Reading, 17 Mayford Road, Poole
Cost:	£54 per season, to include many other waters
Restrictions:	Members only; barbless hooks only; no night fishing - open 6am to 11pm only; carp must not be put in sacks or keepnets; no picnics; no groundbait; entrance gate must be kept locked at all times; arrive and depart quietly
BK Rating:	Easy
W/A:	NRA Wessex Region

Hyde Lake

Location:	Hyde, near Wareham
Type and Size:	1½ acre lake
How to Find:	5 miles from Wareham, just off the Bovington to Wareham road
Carp Stock:	Stocked with mirrors and commons to 20lbs. Good head of carp
Category:	Mixed Fishery
Other Species:	Tench, roach, rudd and crucians
Permits:	Hyde AC. Secretary: Jim Bagley, Heather Lodge, Hyde, near Wareham. Tel: Bere Regis 471402 or Bindon Abbey 463127
Cost:	About £20 per season
BK Rating:	Moderate
Control:	Club/syndicate
Restrictions:	None
W/A:	NRA Wessex Region
Comments:	Night fishing allowed. 3 rods also allowed. Quiet countryside lake, very peaceful surroundings

Kingsbridge Lakes

Location:	Near Wareham, on a complex of trout waters
Type and Size:	Old pit of about 6 acres
Carp Stock:	Well stocked with carp to over 15lbs with quite a few doubles
Category:	Mixed Fishery
Other Species:	Roach and bream
Permits:	Members only water of Dumbourne and District AC. Season tickets only from local tackle shops
Control:	Club
BK Rating:	Easy
W/A:	NRA Wessex Region

Luckfield Lake

Location:	Broadmayne, near Dorchester
Type and Size:	Clay pit of about 1¼ acres
How to Find:	On the B352 Dorchester to Wareham road, about 3 miles from Dorchester
Carp Stock:	Good head of mirrors to about 18lbs. Two fish of 20lbs+. Recent stocking of commons to 9lbs
Category:	Carp Water
Other Species:	Tench and roach to over 2lbs
Permits:	Only from John Aplin Specialist Angling Supplies, 1 Athelstan Road, Dorchester. Tel: 0305 66500; in advance only
Cost:	£3.50 per day; £5 per night
BK Rating:	Moderate
Control:	Private
Baits/Methods:	Bottom baits at night; floaters during the day
W/A:	NRA Wessex Region
Comments:	A peaceful, attractive water in natural surroundings with overhanging trees

New Meadows Lake

Location:	Off the Christchurch to Lymington road (A337), turning right up New Road and Smugglers Copse Way, close to the bowling green
Type and Size:	3 acre lake
Carp Stock:	Well stocked with carp to 15lbs
Category:	Mixed Fishery
Other Species:	Roach, perch and bream
Permits:	Members only water of Christchurch AC; C Bungay, 8 Purewell, Christchurch or P Reading, 17 Mayford Road, Poole
Cost:	£54 per season, to include many other waters
Restrictions:	Members only; no night fishing
BK Rating:	Not known
W/A:	NRA Wessex Region

Turn Grandad's old tackle into cash see page 287

Osmington Mills Lake   A

Location:	Osmington Mills is by the sea, just off the A353 between Weymouth and Wareham. Turn off the main road at Osmington about 4 miles from Weymouth
Type and Size:	2 acre gravel pit
Carp Stock:	Many carp, average 10-13lbs, quite a few doubles to 19lbs and said to be two thirties
Category:	Mixed Fishery
Other Species:	Tench, roach, rudd, perch and crucians
Control:	Private. Tel: 0305 832311
Permits:	Tackle dealer L Rathbone, The Tackle Shop, West Bay, Bridport. Tel: 0308 23475. Also on bank and The Ranch House, Caravan Park, Osmington Mills
Cost:	£4 per day
Restrictions:	No night fishing; barbless hooks
BK Rating:	Easy
W/A:	NRA Wessex Region
Comments:	Busy in summer, fishes well in winter. Accommodation. Fishing for residents only

Pallington Lakes

Location:	Tincleton, near Dorchester
Type and Size:	Lake of about 7 acres
How to Find:	Off the B3390 at Waddock Cross, 7 miles east of Dorchester
Carp Stock:	Many small mirrors and commons. A few low doubles. Lake record is a common of 19lbs 4ozs
Category:	Mixed Fishery
Other Species:	Tench to over 7lbs; roach, chub, perch and bream
Permits:	On site to be purchased before fishing. Tel: 0305 848141
Cost:	£4.50 per day
BK Rating:	Moderate
Control:	Private
W/A:	NRA Wessex Region
Comments:	Fishing 8am to dusk only - open all year

Radipole Lake

Location:	In the town of Weymouth
Type and Size:	Very large lake close to the sea (70 acres plus)
How to Find:	Weymouth
Carp Stock:	Some commons to about 10lbs. Bigger fish rumoured but hard to find possibly up to 26lbs, but we are told this was 60 years ago! A 33lb mirror was caught in 1990
Category:	Few Carp
Other Species:	Eels, roach, dace and mullet
Permits:	Day tickets from tackle shops in Weymouth
Control:	Local council
BK Rating:	Difficult
W/A:	NRA Wessex Region
Comments:	Not seriously fished for carp, but might contain a few good fish. Boats, amusements, people, refreshments, etc especially at south end nearest town. No fishing in bird sanctuary

Revells Farm   A

Location:	Buckland Newton, near Dorchester
Type and Size:	5 small lakes - about an acre each
How to Find:	On the old Sherborne road about 8 miles from Dorchester
Carp Stock:	All varieties to 26lb in top pond. Small carp in other ponds; one lake doubles only
Category:	Mixed Fishery
Other Species:	Bream, tench, chub, perch, rudd and roach
Permits:	Obtainable from shop on site, or on bank. Tel: 03005 301
Cost:	£3 per day; £4.50 for 24 hours
BK Rating:	Easy
Control:	Private
W/A:	NRA Wessex Region
Comments:	A recently set up coarse fishery in pleasant surroundings. Accommodation available. Tackle for sale. No night fishing

River Stour

Location:	Different sections of the lower Stour
Type and Size:	Famous river where most fish grow very big
Carp Stock:	Not known, but big carp reported from time to time - a 16¾ was caught on luncheon meat in 1990, and the same angler had caught other Stour carp to 15lbs
Other Species:	Most of them, including big barbel and chub
Permits:	Local angling clubs - enquire in tackle shops for information and permits, especially in Christchurch
BK Rating:	Difficult, though once the carp are located, they can be quite easy to catch, as few have been taken before
W/A:	NRA Wessex Region

Throop Fisheries

Location:	2½ miles from Christchurch Station
Type and Size:	Dorset Stour and a mill pool
Carp Stock:	Well stocked with carp to 25lbs
Category:	Mixed Fishery
Other Species:	Pike to nearly 30lb, barbel to 13½lb, chub to over 7lbs, and roach to 3¾lb; some bream in mill pool
Permits:	Glen Sutcliffe, Manager, South Lodge, Holdenhurst Village, Bournemouth. Tel: 0202 35532
Cost:	Day tickets - £4; weekly tickets - £16; season - £54
Control:	Private
BK Rating:	Moderate
W/A:	NRA Southern Region
Comments:	Throop is a famous fishery, with 5½ miles of the River Stour and the mill pool. All species run to a very big size. Reduced rate for juniors and OAP's and special rates for clubs - booking essential

Wedgehill Ponds

Location:	Verwood, near Ringwood
Type and Size:	Three small forest ponds close to disused railway line - possibly old ballast pits
How to Find:	From Christchurch take the B3081 to Verwood, and turn left down Manor Road, then right into Church Hill and Margards Lane. Then turn left into Horton Way, and after going under the railway bridge turn right at the T-junction, and the ponds are at the end of the lane - 10mph speed limit
Carp Stock:	Well stocked with carp from 4-6lbs
Category:	Mixed Fishery
Other Species:	Goldfish, golden rudd, crucians and tench
Permits:	Members only water of Christchurch AC; C Bungay, 8 Purewell, Christchurch or P Reading, 17 Mayford Road, Poole
Cost:	£54 per season, to include many other waters
Restrictions:	Members only; barbless hooks; no carp to be put in sacks or keepnets; no night fishing - fishing is 6am to 11pm only; one rod only; gate must be locked at all times; quiet arrival and leaving essential
BK Rating:	Easy
W/A:	NRA Wessex Region

DURHAM

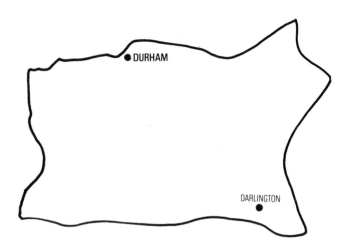

DURHAM

DARLINGTON

Brasside Pool

Location:	Newton Hall, Brasside, near Durham
Type and Size:	Five acre, weedy lake, with depths up to 10 feet, and gravel bars in one area
Carp Stock:	Well stocked with smallish carp, mostly 4 to 9lbs, a few low doubles, including some commons
Category:	Mixed Fishery
Other Species:	Roach, bream, tench and pike
Permits:	Members only water of Durham City AC - try local tackle shops
Cost:	About £35 per year
Control:	Durham City AC. Open to all - Secretary: G Hedley, 3 Hawthorn Crescent, Durham
Restrictions:	Members only
BK Rating:	Moderate
Comments:	There is no close season on this water, and it fishes well all the year

Fighting Cocks Reservoir

Location:	Middleton St. George, Darlington
Type and Size:	Two lakes, about 10 acres in all
Carp Stock:	Carp to about 15lbs; well stocked with fish from 5-8lbs
Category:	Mixed Fishery
Other Species:	Perch, roach, bream
Permits:	On bank at £2 per day, or from W P Adams Fishing Tackle, 42 Duke Street, Darlington. Tel: 0325 468069
Cost:	Day tickets £2. Annual permits £20 + 50p each visit
BK Rating:	Moderate
W/A:	NRA Northumbrian Region

Halneby Lake

Location:	Middleton Tyas, south west of Darlington
Type and Size:	5½ acre lake
Carp Stock:	Very well stocked with carp to 10lbs
Category:	Mixed Fishery
Other Species:	Bream, roach and tench
Permits:	W P Adams Fishing Tackle, 42 Duke Street, Darlington
Cost:	About £35 per season
Control:	Yarm AA - members only
BK Rating:	Easy
W/A:	NRA Yorkshire Region
Comments:	Carp growing well. Attractive water with good potential - recently taken over by Yarm AA

Kellow Law Pond

Location:	Deaf Hill, which we think is near Ferryhill, on the A167 between Darlington and Durham
Type and Size:	Small pond
Carp Stock:	Some commons
Category:	Mixed Fishery
Other Species:	Crucians, perch and rudd
Permits:	Mr Barry Hignett. Tel: 091 388 3557
Control:	Senior members of the Ferryhill and District AC
BK Rating:	Not known
W/A:	NRA Northumbrian Region

Middleton Water Park

Location:	Middleton St. George, Darlington
Type and Size:	Small park lake
Carp Stock:	Some carp, numbers and sizes not revealed by the Parish Clerk who replied to our questionnaire, but didn't divulge this information, nor the names of the other species which he said were present!
Category:	Mixed Fishery
Permits:	From the bailiff on site, or from the Parish Clerk, 8 Grendon Gardens, Middleton St. George, Darlington. Tel: 0325 332917
Cost:	£2 per rod per day (£1.50 for children). Annual permits also available
Control:	Council
BK Rating:	Not known
W/A:	NRA Northumbrian Region

Shotton Pond

Location:	Shotton Colliery, just off the A19 south of Peterlee, between Hartlepool and Sunderland
Type and Size:	Small pond
Carp Stock:	Some carp
Category:	Mixed Fishery
Other Species:	Crucians, rudd, roach, tench, perch and bream
Permits:	Limited day tickets from Mr L Evans, 100 Victoria Street, Shotton Colliery. Tel: 091 517 0296

Control: Shotton Colliery AC; Mr Ian Proudfoot, 19 Lincoln Walk, Great Lumley, Chester-le-Street. Tel: 091 398 2325 (after 6pm)
BK Rating: Not known
W/A: NRA Northumbrian Region

Turnside Pool

Location: Ferryhill, near Durham
Type and Size: Attractive one acre pool, very weedy and heavily fished
Carp Stock: There are only a small number of carp, but they go to over 20lbs
Category: Few Carp
Other Species: Roach, tench and perch
Permits: Try local tackle shops for club membership - no day tickets
Control: Ferryhill and District AC. Secretary: A Roxley, 60 Linden Road, West Cornforth, County Durham
Restrictions: Members only; one rod only; no multiple baits; no night fishing
BK Rating: Very Difficult
W/A: NRA Northumbrian Region

Wellfield Pond

Location: Wingate on the B1280 between Hartlepool and Shotton Colliery
Type and Size: Small pond
Carp Stock: Some carp
Category: Mixed Fishery
Other Species: Bream, tench, rudd, roach and perch
Permits: Alan Blackmore, 17 Station Road South, Murton, Seaham SR7 9RS. Tel: 091 526 7327
Control: Easington and District AC; some guest permits
BK Rating: Not known
W/A: NRA Northumbrian Region

West Farm Lake

Location: Off the A177 between Stockton and Sedgefield
Type and Size: Two acre lake, formerly a trout fishery
Carp Stock: Recently stocked with carp to 10lbs
Category: Mixed Fishery
Other Species: Tench, rudd and trout
Permits: On bank or at farmhouse
Cost: £3 per rod and £2 for OAP's and under twelves
Control: Tel: 0740 31045
Restrictions: Barbless hooks and no carp in nets. Night fishing by prior arrangement only
BK Rating: Not known
W/A: NRA North West Region

DYFED (Wales)

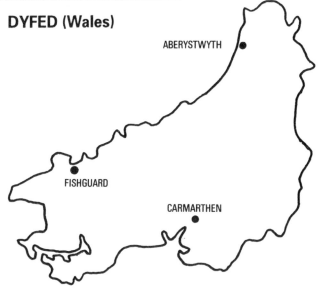

ABERYSTWYTH

FISHGUARD

CARMARTHEN

Glas-Llyn Fishery

Location:	Fynnon-Las-Isaf, Blaenwaun, Whitland, SA34 0JH
Type and Size:	Two acre lake
How to Find:	Glas-Llyn is one mile from the village of Blaenwaun, 8 miles north of Whitland, and 5 miles east of Crymch
Carp Stock:	Heavily stocked with carp to 20lbs
Category:	Carp Water
Other Species:	Tench to 8lbs
Permits:	On bank
Cost:	£5 per day - £3.50 juniors. £7 for 24 hours; £3.50 from 3pm
Control:	Private; Terry and Gwen Forbes. Tel: 0994 (Hebron) 419466
Restrictions:	Three rods only; no carp in keepnets; juniors must be accompanied by an adult. Barbless hooks preferred
BK Rating:	Not known
W/A:	NRA Welsh Region
Comments:	Toilet, fisherman's hut, and ample parking space. A former trout fishery, Glas-Llyn is set in a picturesque valley with much wild life. The lake is spring fed and is 30 feet deep in places. This is one of the very few carp fisheries in West Wales, and as it has been little fished it could produce some surprises

Two Acre Lake

Location:	Near Aberystwyth
Type and Size:	Two small lakes
Carp Stock:	Well stocked with carp to doubles
Category:	Mixed Fishery
Other Species:	Tench and roach
Permits:	Tel: 097 084 239 for information and permits
BK Rating:	Moderate
W/A:	NRA Welsh Region

EAST SUSSEX

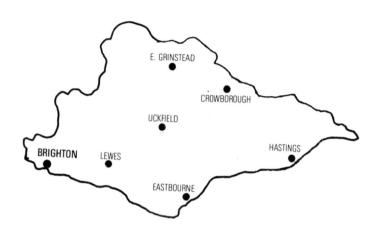

Belfrey Coarse Fishery

Location: Near Hailsham
Type and Size: Small, attractive lake
Carp Stock: Well stocked with carp to 26lbs
Category: Mixed Fishery
Other Species: Usual coarse fish
Permits: Day, night and evening tickets. Tel: 0323 841247/844238
BK Rating: Moderate
W/A: NRA Southern Region
Comments: Camping allowed

Buckshole Reservoir

Location: Hastings
Type and Size: 10 acre town reservoir
Carp Stock: Well stocked with carp to over 20lbs - a thirty was reported in 1991
Category: Mixed Fishery
Other Species: Roach, bream, tench and pike
Permits: Possibly Clive Vale AC - try local tackle shops
Control: Club
Restrictions: No night fishing; no day tickets
BK Rating: Moderate
W/A: NRA Southern Region

Buxted Park Fishery

Location:	Buxted, near Uckfield
Type and Size:	Attractive three and a half acre lake
Carp Stock:	Well stocked with carp to 10lbs
Category:	Mixed Fishery
Other Species:	Tench, roach, rudd, perch and chub
Permits:	Day tickets from Buxted Park Fishery, Buxted, near Uckfield, East Sussex. Tel: 0860 372625 (9am to 6pm) or 0825 812711 any time. Club bookings also available
BK Rating:	Not known
W/A:	NRA Southern Region

Clive Vale and Ecclesbourne Reservoirs

Location:	Hastings
Type and Size:	Small reservoirs
How to Find:	In Hastings
Carp Stock:	Well stocked with carp to 30lbs
Category:	Mixed Fishery
Other Species:	General coarse fish, including large pike
Permits:	Hastings Clive Vale Angling Club. J Greenhalf, 33 Hollington Park Road, St. Leonards-on-Sea, TN 0SE. Try local tackle shops
Cost:	About £2 per day. £11 per season
BK Rating:	Moderate
Control:	Club
Restrictions:	No juveniles
W/A:	NRA Southern Region
Comments:	Enquire locally for more information

Farthings Lake

Location:	Near Battle, Hastings
Type and Size:	Estate lake of 3 acres
How to Find:	Take the B2095 west from Battle towards Catsfield and Bexhill. After about 1½ miles you will see a track on the right marked 'Millers Farm'. The footpath to the lake is opposite this. The car park is a further 100 yards on the right
Carp Stock:	Some carp, sizes not known
Category:	Mixed Fishery
Other Species:	Tench, bream, roach and rudd
Permits:	Tickets must be obtained before fishing. Season tickets from 6 Warwick Road, Bexhill-on-Sea, East Sussex. Tel: 0424 224908
Restrictions:	No night fishing. Lake is open 8am till sunset. Season ticket holders may start at sunrise. No day tickets - syndicate only
BK Rating:	Moderate
Control:	Redland Angling Scheme
W/A:	NRA Southern Region
Comments:	Attractive lake in beautiful wooded valley. If you want to start before 9am you will need to hold a season ticket. Information on 0424 420358. New unique match lake opened in June 1992, built in channels

Furnace Pond

Location:	Near East Grinstead
Type and Size:	7 acre estate lake
How to Find:	Ordnance Survey Sheet No. 187; Ref. 348391
Carp Stock:	Carp to 18lbs, with some low 20's
Category:	Carp Water
Other Species:	Some coarse fish
Permits:	Wallington Specimen Group. No day tickets but season tickets at about £130. Contact: Mrs A Yexley, 25 Oakley Road, South Norwood, London SE25
Control:	Private
BK Rating:	Easy
W/A:	NRA Southern Region

Hastings Lake

Location:	In the town of Hastings
Type and Size:	10 acre lake
Carp Stock:	Heavily stocked with carp to 10lbs
Category:	Mixed Fishery
Other Species:	Tench and pike
Permits:	Local tackle shops, or the Secretary, Hastings, Bexhill and District FA, P K Jury, 5 Old Church Road, St. Leonards, East Sussex
Cost:	Day tickets at £1.25
Control:	Club; season tickets £12—£13 only for those living within 25 miles of Hastings
BK Rating:	Easy
W/A:	NRA Southern Region

Hurst Haven

Location:	Rickney Bridge, north west of Pevensey off the Hailsham road
Type and Size:	Narrow drain with sluice
Carp Stock:	Not many carp, but some doubles
Category:	Few Carp
Other Species:	Bream, roach, tench and pike to 25lbs
Permits:	Polegate Angling Centre, 101 Station Road, Polegate
Cost:	£2 per day
Control:	Hailsham AA. Tel: 0323 486379
Restrictions:	No livebaiting(!)
BK Rating:	Very Difficult
W/A:	NRA Southern Region

Iden Wood Fishery

Location:	Near Rye
Type and Size:	Three small ponds, the largest of which is about two acres
Carp Stock:	Well stocked with small carp to about 10lbs
Category:	Mixed Fishery
Other Species:	Perch and roach
Permits:	On bank for day tickets; 24 hour tickets must be booked in advance
Cost:	£4 per day; £6 for 24 hours

Control:	Tel: 079 721241
BK Rating:	Easy
W/A:	NRA Southern Region
Comments:	No night fishing unless booked in advance; no close season

Lynd Farm Pond

Location:	Near Haywards Heath
Type and Size:	Small pond
Carp Stock:	Well stocked with small carp to about 4lbs but growing
Category:	Mixed Fishery
Other Species:	Tench, roach and rudd
Permits:	Tel: 081-558 5718
Control:	Private
BK Rating:	Easy
W/A:	NRA Southern Region

Michelham Priory Moat

Location:	Michelham Priory, Upper Dicker, Hailsham, near Eastbourne (off the A22 Eastbourne-East Grinstead road)
Type and Size:	Possibly the largest moat in England, with several acres of water
Carp Stock:	Carp to 10lbs, probably commons and possibly wildies
Category:	Mixed Fishery
Other Species:	Tench, roach and bream
Permits:	Day tickets from the 14th century gatehouse
Cost:	£1.50 per day
Control:	Private
Restrictions:	Thought to be no night fishing; no dogs
BK Rating:	Not known
W/A:	NRA Southern Region
Comments:	One of the most beautiful buildings and grounds in the country - an Augustinian Priory which dates from the 13th century, but which became a farmhouse at the Dissolution of the Monasteries. There is an Elizabethan wing, and lovely gardens. There is a restaurant and halls for conferences and dinners, the specialities being home-made bread and cakes from their own bakery, using flour ground in the Priory Water Mill, fed from the moat, and local ale, apple juice and Sussex wines. Art exhibitions etc are held in the house, which is open from 25th March until 31st October from 11am to 5.30pm, and on Sundays in February, March and November. Information at the address above. Tel: 0323 440161 or 0323 844224

Piltdown Pond

Location:	Piltdown Common, near Newick, between Haywards Heath and Uckfield
Type and Size:	Small common land pond
How to Find:	Take the A272 from Maresfield towards Newick. Turn left at Piltdown Common. The pond is 100 yards further on the left
Carp Stock:	Some carp to 10lbs
Category:	Mixed Fishery
Other Species:	General coarse fish
Permits:	Free fishing

Cost: None
BK Rating: Difficult
W/A: NRA Southern Region
Comments: Very heavily weeded pond - but worth a try, as there's not much free fishing these days!

Pippingford Park Estate Lakes

Location: Pippingford Corner, Nutley, Near East Grinstead
Type and Size: 5 man-made lakes of ¾ acre to 5 acres
How to Find: Take the A22 from East Grinstead towards Eastbourne. Estate is one mile before Nutley and Pippingford Corner. Entrance on left. Pathfinder OS Map Ref. TQ43/53
Carp Stock: Army Lake (¾ acre) - 20 carp to 15lbs; Lake 1 (4 acres) - 40 carp to 18lbs (average 8lbs); Lake 2 - as for Lake 1; Lake 3 (5 acres) - many small commons to 15lbs; Lake 4 (¾ acre) - very few small fish
Category: Carp Waters
Other Species: Many good chub to 5lbs; bream, tench, orfe
Permits: Richard Morris, Home Farm, Pippingford Park, Nutley TN22 3NW. Tel: 081-571 2205 (estate office)
Cost: Senior - £100 per season. Junior - £30 per season
BK Rating: Army - Easy to Moderate. Others - Easy for small fish
Control: Pippingford Estate Co. Ltd.
Restrictions: No carp sacks or keepnets
W/A: NRA Southern Region
Comments: No day tickets. Half season tickets available. Camouflage clothing not advised as this is an army training area. A truly beautiful lake to fish, situated in Ashdown Forest in a peaceful wooded valley full of wild animals and rare plants. Weedy waters, excellent for stalking, 3 fish per day common, 7 to 8 a day possible. Army often on night manoeuvres - beware!

Searles Lake

Location: Near Nutley, off the A22 just south of Ashdown Forest (home of Winnie the Pooh)
Type and Size: 6 acre estate lake, much used for match fishing
Carp Stock: Carp to 20lbs
Category: Mixed Fishery
Other Species: Roach, rudd, tench, bream and pike to 35lbs
Permits: Tanyard Fisheries, Tanyard Lane, Furners Green, Danehill, Uckfield. Tel: 0825 791010 (9am to 7pm only)
Cost: £6 - one rod; £10 for 2 rods, in advance only
Control: Private, although a club fishes one bank
Restrictions: Barbless hooks; no keepnets; no night fishing - open 8am till 9pm; no pike fishing until October 1st; 40 anglers only per day
BK Rating: Not known
W/A: NRA Southern Region

Sparks Farm Fishery

Location:	Cuckfield, near Haywards Heath
Type and Size:	Farm pond with two islands
How to Find:	Take the B2115 road from Cuckfield, and turn at the farm shop about one and a half miles from the village
Carp Stock:	Well stocked with carp to doubles
Category:	Carp Water
Other Species:	Tench
Permits:	Day tickets from the farm shop, or on the bank
Cost:	£6 per day; £4.50 from 1pm; £3 from 5pm
Control:	Tel: 0444 441511
Restrictions:	No night fishing
BK Rating:	Easy
W/A:	NRA Southern Region

Sparks Farm Pond

Location:	Sparks Farm Shop, near Cuckfield
Type and Size:	Two small lakes of two acres
Carp Stock:	Heavily stocked with small carp to 2½lbs
Category:	Mixed Fishery
Other Species:	Roach, rudd, perch, bream and crucians
Permits:	Day tickets at Farm Shop. Tel: 0444 441511
Cost:	£5 per day
BK Rating:	Easy
W/A:	NRA Southern Region
Comments:	Easy day ticket water, used for small matches

Tanyard Fisheries

Location:	Tanyard Lane, off the A275 near Uckfield
Type and Size:	Two lakes of 1½ and one acre
Carp Stock:	Larger lake is a specialist carp water stocked with carp from 8lb to 20lb; smaller lake has carp to 15lbs
Category:	Larger lake - Carp Water; small lake - Mixed Fishery
Other Species:	Tench, roach, rudd, bream and perch
Permits:	Day tickets on site
Cost:	Carp Lake - £8 per day for two rods

Control: Tanyard Fisheries, Tanyard Lane, Furners Green, Danehill.
                 Tel: 0825 791010 (between 9am to 7pm only)
BK Rating: Not known
W/A: NRA Southern Region
Comments: No close season; any method trout fishing. Toilets and refreshment hut

Wilderness Lake

Location: Dormans Park, East Grinstead
Type and Size: Park lake, at the start of River Eden; main lake is 5 acres and a smaller
                 lake of an acre
Carp Stock: Heavily stocked with carp of 2-3lbs, with some bigger to 10lbs
Category: Mixed Fishery
Other Species: Roach, rudd and gudgeon
Permits: Isfield and District AS
Cost: £37.50 per year, plus an entrance fee
BK Rating: Easy
W/A: NRA Southern Region
Comments: Small water was only opened last year; good match waters

Wishing Tree Reservoir

Location: Near Hastings, off the B2092 towards Battle
Type and Size: Four acre reservoir
Carp Stock: Heavily stocked with carp to doubles
Category: Mixed Fishery
Other Species: Tench and a few roach and perch
Permits: Day tickets on the bank at £3
Control: Hastings and Bexhill DAA. Peter Maclean. Tel: 0424 715218
Restrictions: Night fishing for season ticket holders only
BK Rating: Very Easy
W/A: NRA Southern Region
Comments: Easy access for all, including the disabled. 10-15 carp possible in a day

Withyham Mill Carp Lake

Location: Near Crowborough
Type and Size: 6½ acre lake on private estate, 10 to 25 feet deep
Carp Stock: Well stocked with carp to 32lbs
Category: Mixed Fishery
Other Species: Tench, bream, roach and rudd
Permits: Cornell Fishery Developments, Charter House, 29a London Road,
                 Croydon CR0 2RB - syndicate only, to include other carp waters
Cost: About £30 per season
Control: Cornell Fishery Developments
BK Rating: Moderate
Restrictions: No night fishing at present - open from 5am to 7pm only
W/A: NRA Southern Region

Wyland Lakes   A

Location: Powdermill Lane, Catsfield, Battle
Type and Size: Six farm lakes
How to Find: Take the A2100 Hastings-Battle road and turn left on the B2095 just before Battle. Wyland Farm is on the left
Carp Stock: All the lakes contain some carp. One is designated as a specimen carp lake and the record fish for the water is said to be 28lbs. Three of the lakes produced 20's in 1991-92
Category: Carp Waters
Other Species: Rudd, tench, perch, bream and roach - all large
Permits: From Wyland Farm, Powdermill Lane, Battle. Tel: Ninfield (0424) 893394. Day tickets. Chalet tariffs include 24 hours a day fishing
Cost: Specimen Carp Lake - £6 per day (24 hours), other lakes about £5 per day
Control: Private - Colin Bourner, Wylands Lakes Angling Centre
Restrictions: No nuts or peas, barbless or semi-barbed hooks requested
BK Rating: Moderate
W/A: NRA Southern Region, available from farmhouse
Comments: This is a working farm, mainly sheep, where you can go for a holiday. There are chalets with various tariffs, for example £160 a week for two adults including fishing. One day costs £23, with £15 for each subsequent day. Touring caravans pay £3 per day (fishing extra). Tents are £2 per day; £10 per week, fishing extra. Bivvies allowed at lakeside at no extra charge - fishing rates only. Near Hastings, Eastbourne and Rye. Three 20's to 25lbs caught in October 1989. Please note prices are approximate

ESSEX

Ardleigh Reservoir

Location:	Near Colchester
How to Find:	On the road to Manningtree, about 4 miles out of Colchester
Type and Size:	440 acre reservoir
Carp Stock:	Few carp, but very large
Category:	Mixed Fishery
Other Species:	Most species to specimen sizes. Pike to 44¾lbs
Permits:	From the lodge at fishery entrance
BK Rating:	Super-Difficult
W/A:	NRA Anglian Region
Comments:	Location of carp very difficult. Depths to 60 feet. Upper 30's caught every year by the specialist - larger fish present

Arena Lake

Location: Near Thurrock - off the old A13 and not far from the M25/Dartford Tunnel
Type and Size: Open pit of about 10 acres; very weedy
Carp Stock: Well stocked with carp to mid-doubles, and a few 20's
Category: Carp Water
Permits: Day tickets on bank
BK Rating: Moderate
W/A: NRA Thames Region

Aveley Lakes

Location: Romford Road, Aveley, near Romford
Carp Stock: Well stocked with carp to over 20lbs
Category: Mixed Fishery
Other Species: Tench and rudd
Permits: Aveley Lakes, Romford Road, Aveley, near Romford... waiting list, season tickets only
Control: Private
BK Rating: Moderate
W/A: NRA Thames Region

Blunts Mere

Location: Alongside Cants, Hoe Mill, Hatfield Peverel, south of Witham
Type and Size: Gravel pit of three acres
Carp Stock: Not very many carp, to low 20's
Category: Few Carp
Other Species: Usual coarse fish
Permits: Chelmsford AA, 60 Delamere Road, Chelmsford
Restrictions: No night fishing
BK Rating: Easy
W/A: NRA Anglian Region
Comments: Could produce some good fish for anyone prepared to fish it hard

Bog Grove

Location: Near Totham, Malden area
Type and Size: Lake of about two acres
Carp Stock: Well stocked, mainly with fully-scaled mirrors to mid-twenties
Category: Mixed Fishery
Other Species: Usual coarse fish
Permits: Malden AC. Tel: Malden 854765
Control: Club
Restrictions: Night fishing on Mondays, Wednesdays and Fridays and only by special application
BK Rating: Easy
W/A: NRA Anglian Region
Comments: An excellent winter water

New and best selling carp videos from Beekay Publishers. See page 19

THE KENT GUIDE
TO TOP CARP GEAR

WIDE STOCK · GREAT DEALS · FRIENDLY ATMOSPHERE

3 Holborough Road
Snodland
Kent ME6 5NL
Telephone: 0634 243112

PHONE FOR A QUOTE, OR CALL IN
MAIL ORDER — OPEN 7 DAYS
'CARP CURRIES' BY ARRANGEMENT

Boreham

Location:	Wallace's Farm, Russell Green, Little Waltham, near Chelmsford
Type and Size:	Gravel pit of 1¼ acres
How to Find:	Take the A12 towards Chelmsford, then the B1137 towards Boreham. Keep to the right of the slip road and turn right at the traffic lights along 300 yards of dual carriageway under the main A12 to the roundabout. Take the Boreham exit and go through the village to the Cock Inn. Turn left over the A12 bridge and follow the road for about 1½ miles to the Anglia Building Supplies Yard on the left. Wallace's Farm is opposite this. Car park is opposite the RMC Plant area
Carp Stock:	About 40, mainly doubles
Category:	Mixed Fishery
Other Species:	Pike, bream, tench and roach
Permits:	This is a Leisure Sport Angling Special Venue. Limited tickets for the season from LSA, Thorpe Park, Staines Road, Chertsey, Surrey. Tel: Chertsey 64872
Cost:	£16 for the season, juniors/OAP/disabled £8
Restrictions:	No night fishing, dawn to dusk only
BK Rating:	Easy
Control:	Leisure Sport Angling
W/A:	NRA Anglian Region
Comments:	This is another of those waters which we have put in for those carp anglers who might want to fish a water where there is not much carp fishing, and few carp, but where they might just get a reasonable sized fish. Waters of this kind should not be regarded as carp waters; only as waters which are said to contain a few good carp

Boreham Mere

Location:	Wallace's Farm, Russell Green, Little Waltham, near Chelmsford
Type and Size:	Eight acre gravel pit alongside Boreham, the Leisure Sport water
Carp Stock:	Plenty of doubles, with 10-15 twenties
Category:	Mixed Fishery
Other Species:	Usual coarse fish
Permits:	Chelmsford AA, 60 Delamere Road, Chelmsford, Essex
Control:	Club
Restrictions:	Separate permit for night fishing
BK Rating:	Moderate
W/A:	NRA Anglian Region

Bournebridge Lakes

Location:	Bournebridge Lane, Stapleford Abbotts, Romford. Tel: 0708 688279
Type and Size:	Three small lakes
Carp Stock:	All well stocked with carp to about 12lbs
Category:	Mixed Fishery
Other Species:	Tench and rudd
Permits:	Day tickets in advance, from the above address — phone for details
Control:	Private
BK Rating:	Easy
W/A:	NRA Anglian Region
Comments:	Refreshments and toilets on site; good family water

Braxted Park Lake

Location:	Braxted Park, Braxted, near Witham
Type and Size:	11 acre estate lake
Carp Stock:	About 200 carp, of which most are over 10lbs, a number of 20's, including two commons, and at least one 30 pounder
Category:	Carp Water
Other Species:	Some coarse fish
Permits:	We think this water is now controlled by a syndicate; you might be able to get information from Mr M Clark, Braxted Park Estate Office, Braxted, near Witham. Cost is said to be £500 a season!
Control:	Private syndicate Tel: 0376 570401
Restrictions:	Syndicate membership only - no other permits
BK Rating:	Moderate
W/A:	NRA Anglian Region

Braxted Park Reservoir

Location:	Braxted Park, Braxted, near Witham
Type and Size:	7 acre estate reservoir
Carp Stock:	Stocked in 1987 with about 50 carp from 8-14lbs. As this has been a trout fishery several carp have been caught on the fly, the best weighing 24lbs
Category:	Mixed Fishery
Other Species:	Trout and possibly some other coarse fish apart from the carp
Permits:	Probably now controlled by a syndicate. For information try Mr M Clark, Braxted Park Estate Office, Braxted, near Witham

Control:	Private syndicate
Restrictions:	No permits - syndicate members only
BK Rating:	Moderate
W/A:	NRA Anglian Region

Bulphan Park

Location:	Off the A128 near Brentwood
Type and Size:	Tiny park lake
Carp Stock:	Well stocked with carp to 20lbs
Category:	Carp Water
Permits:	Day tickets on bank
BK Rating:	Fairly Easy
W/A:	NRA Thames Region

Cants Mere

Location:	Hoe Mill, near Hatfield Peverel, just south of Witham
Type and Size:	Gravel pit of about two and a half acres
Carp Stock:	Heavily stocked, mainly with commons, from 8 to 10lbs
Category:	Mixed Fishery
Other Species:	Usual coarse fish
Permits:	Chelmsford AA, 60 Delamere Road, Chelmsford, Essex
Control:	Club
Restrictions:	No night fishing
BK Rating:	Easy
W/A:	NRA Anglian Region

Central Park Lake

Location:	Chelmsford
Type and Size:	Good sized town park lake
Carp Stock:	Well stocked with carp - a 19 pounder was reported in 1990
Category:	Mixed Fishery
Other Species:	Tench, roach and rudd
Permits:	From tackle dealers in Essex
Cost:	Season £12.50 per rod; day tickets £1
Control:	RHP Angling Club - try tackle shops, or Chelmsford Borough Council for details
Restrictions:	No barbless hooks, boilies, particle baits or floating baits (sounds as if they don't want the carp caught, doesn't it?)
BK Rating:	Moderate
W/A:	NRA Anglian Region
Comments:	The draconian restrictions are apparently because the Council was under pressure by the Royal Society for the Prevention of Cruelty to Birds to close the lake to anglers (I hope no angler supports the RSPB in any way, as we have come across many 'anti-angling' instances by this organisation, which we understand often catches birds in fine nets in which they become trapped, so that they can examine and 'ring' them!)

Chigborough Lakes

Location:	Maldon, not far from Southend
Type and Size:	Several large, matured gravel pits with island and bars
Carp Stock:	Heavily stocked with carp to upper doubles
Category:	Mixed Fishery
Other Species:	Roach, bream, tench, perch and pike
Permits:	Day tickets from bailiffs on bank — season tickets also available at £85
Control:	Private Tel: 0621 852113
BK Rating:	Easy
W/A:	NRA Thames Region

Churchwood Fisheries

Location:	Doddington Place, Blackmore Road, Brentwood CM15 0HX
Type and Size:	Two estate lakes of 3 acres and 1 acre
Carp Stock:	Jenkinsons - carp between 12lbs and 24lbs. Bottom Lake (3 acres) - some small carp
Category:	Mixed Fisheries
Other Species:	Tench (Jenkinsons); tench, bream, roach, rudd and perch (Bottom)
Permits:	At the time of going to press control of this water was changing
Restrictions:	No animals; no carp sacks; no keepnets; barbless hooks recommended
BK Rating:	Moderate

W/A:	NRA Anglian Region
Comments:	Private nature reserve - over 400 species of wild flowers. 20 anglers per day only. Club bookings allowed. Tackle and bait to order when booking ticket - all bookings on 0277 200985

Claverhambury Lake

Location:	Claverhambury, Waltham Abbey
Type and Size:	Dammed estate lakes, a bit less than 2 acres each
How to Find:	Find Galley Hill Road, Waltham Abbey and follow this to Claverhambury Road
Carp Stock:	Well stocked with carp to double figure size
Category:	Carp Only
Permits:	P and B Hall, 44 Highbridge Street, Waltham Abbey. Tel: Waltham Cross 711932
Baits/Methods:	Normal carp methods with boilies and multiples as baits
Control:	Private, day ticket
BK Rating:	Moderate
W/A:	NRA Thames Region
Comments:	A pleasant little fishery, stream-fed with trees on one side. Depths from 2ft to just over 8ft

Cobblers Mead Lake

Location:	Herd Lane, Corringham
Type and Size:	5 acre gravel pit
How to Find:	In Corringham
Carp Stock:	Some big carp to 24lbs
Category:	Mixed Fishery
Other Species:	Bream, tench, roach and crucians
Permits:	M.G.H. Properties, Box 18, Canvey Island, Essex. Tel: 0268 683946
Restrictions:	Members only
BK Rating:	Moderate
Control:	Private
Comments:	Information and permits also from Basildon Angling Centre, Whitemore Way

Dedham Mill

Location:	Clovers Mill Ltd, Gunhill, Dedham, Colchester
Type and Size:	Mill Pool and River Stour
Carp Stock:	Well stocked with carp to at least double figure size
Category:	Mixed Fishery
Other Species:	Bream, pike and dace
Permits:	Day and season tickets from the mill, or from K D Radcliffe Fishing Tackle, High Street, Colchester
Cost:	£1 per day - £6 per season
Control:	Private
BK Rating:	Moderate
W/A:	NRA Anglian Region

Dunmow Lake

Location:	Near Dunmow in north Essex, just off the M11
Type and Size:	9 acre lake
Carp Stock:	Well stocked with carp to 20lbs plus
Category:	Carp Only
Permits:	Season (syndicate) only; for details tel: 0376 20662
Control:	Private
Restrictions:	No day tickets
BK Rating:	Moderate
W/A:	NRA Anglian Region

Epping Forest Ponds

Location:	Epping Forest
Type and Size:	Small ponds
How to Find:	Chingford, Loughton area off the A11
Carp Stock:	Most have small carp, but fish to over 30lbs have been taken
Category:	Mixed Fisheries
Other Species:	General coarse fish
Permits:	Many are free: Warren Pond; Perch Pond; Hollow Pond; Eagle Pond; Highams Park Lake; Connaught Water; Ornamental Water
Cost:	Day tickets about £1 per day on bank
BK Rating:	Moderate, some are Easy
Control:	Superintendent of Epping Forest, The Warren, Loughton
Restrictions:	On application
W/A:	NRA Thames Region
Comments:	Busy forest ponds, some of which contain more and bigger fish than might be expected - never despise 'public' waters

Gosfield Lake

Location:	Halstead
Type and Size:	Big 45 acre gravel pit
How to Find:	Gosfield, near Halstead, off the A1017 north of Braintree
Carp Stock:	Well stocked with carp over 20lbs, biggest common about 30
Category:	Mixed Fishery
Other Species:	Perch, roach, tench, pike
Permits:	C W Turp, Gosfield Lake, Church Road, Gosfield
Cost:	Season ticket - about £66. 12 hour - about £2.75 (1 rod); 24 hours - about £5.50
BK Rating:	Difficult
Control:	Private
Restrictions:	75% of the bank, fishing not allowed
W/A:	NRA Thames Region
Comments:	Details and permits from shop on site. Boats for hire

Grange

Location:	South Ockendon
Type and Size:	Gravel pit of about six acres
Carp Stock:	Quite well stocked with carp to about 35lbs
Category:	Mixed Fishery
Other Species:	Usual coarse fish
Permits:	Thurrock Angling Club - no day tickets. Fishing only by seasonal club membership
BK Rating:	Difficult
W/A:	NRA Anglian Region
Comments:	A famous water once fished by Fred Wilton

Grange Water

Location:	South Ockendon
Type and Size:	Gravel pit of about 20 acres
Carp Stock:	There are said to be only 20-40 carp, to well over 30lbs, including commons of this size
Category:	Few Carp
Other Species:	Usual coarse fish
Permits:	Day tickets from Thurrock Council - try the Council Offices
Control:	Thurrock Council
BK Rating:	Very Difficult
W/A:	NRA Anglian Region
Comments:	Lots of potential for the dedicated big fish angler, but there is much public use of the lake and surrounds

Hainault Park

Location:	Hainault, off the Romford-Chigwell road
Type and Size:	5 acre lake
Carp Stock:	Heavily stocked with small carp, doubles, several twenties and two 30's, the best about 35lbs
Category:	Mixed Fishery
Other Species:	Roach, perch and pike
Permits:	Day tickets on site. Night syndicate - enquire at lake
Restrictions:	No night fishing except for syndicate members
BK Rating:	Moderate
W/A:	NRA Thames Region
Comments:	A well known water, heavily fished - danger of cars being broken into

Hatfield Forest Lake

Location:	Near Bishops Stortford
Type and Size:	Large lake, plus a small lake
How to Find:	Information from the Lake Warden
Carp Stock:	Some carp in main lake, small lake contains carp to 30+
Category:	Mixed Fishery
Other Species:	Pike, tench, roach, rudd
Permits:	In advance only from: The Warden, The Shell House, Takeley, Bishops Stortford. Tel: 0279 870477
Cost:	Season tickets about £40; day tickets - £2
BK Rating:	Easy
Control:	National Trust
Restrictions:	No groundbait
W/A:	NRA Thames Region
Comments:	Little known - might be worth investigating

Holy Field Carp Fishery

Location:	Fishers Green Lane, Crooked Mile, Waltham Abbey. Tel: 0992 768012
Type and Size:	Large lake near London
Carp Stock:	Heavily stocked with carp, many doubles and several twenties to 23lb 14oz (a common)
Category:	Carp Water
Permits:	Don Spinks on the phone number above
Cost:	Season tickets at £115
Control:	Private
Restrictions:	Season tickets only
BK Rating:	Moderate
W/A:	NRA Thames Region
Comments:	Clubhouse, cafeteria, full licensed bar, toilets, showers and colour TV

Knights Pit

Location:	Nazeing, near Waltham Abbey
Type and Size:	6 acre lake
Carp Stock:	Very well stocked with carp to over 20lbs
Category:	Mixed Fishery
Other Species:	Tench and bream

Permits:	Lee Valley Regional Park Authority, Myddelton House, Bulls Cross, Enfield. Tel: 0992 717711
Cost:	Weekly permits, cost on application
Control:	Lee Valley RPA
BK Rating:	Moderate
W/A:	NRA Thames Region
Comments:	Known in the past as an excellent winter water, with some big commons present

Lake Meadows

Location:	Billericay
Carp Stock:	Well stocked with many carp up to low 20's
Category:	Carp Water
Permits:	Day tickets available on the bank
BK Rating:	Easy
W/A:	NRA Anglian Region

Layer Pits

Location:	Colchester
Carp Stock:	Very heavily stocked with many small carp, but plenty of doubles and 20's
Category:	Mixed Fishery
Control:	Colchester Angling Preservation Society. Secretary: D. Upsher, 36 Winsley Road, Colchester
Restrictions:	No night fishing
BK Rating:	Easy
W/A:	NRA Anglian Region
Comments:	A very easy water where you can catch many carp in a day. An ideal place for one to practice methods and tactics

Lyatts Lake

Location:	Just off main A120 between Dunmow and Braintree at Rayne in Essex
Type and Size:	Approx 10 acres - gravel pit, spring fed, very clear water
Carp Stock:	Recently stocked with 350 mirror, leather and common carp up to 20lbs. Most fish between 7lbs - 14lbs
Category:	Carp Water
Restrictions:	No night fishing, no sacking. See season ticket for all club rules
Control:	Privately owned. For season tickets, contact the owner, John Harvey, on (0376) 20662, numbers restricted
W/A:	NRA Anglian Region
Comments:	Attractive lake with excellent water quality, car parking available

Manningtree River Pools

Location: Off the A137 near Manningtree
Type and Size: Two large pools on the Suffolk Stour
Carp Stock: Well stocked with carp to doubles
Category: Mixed Fishery
Other Species: Bream, tench, roach, rudd and a few pike
Permits: Free
Control: Council
Restrictions: No night fishing; dawn to dusk only
BK Rating: Moderate
W/A: NRA Anglian Region

Marconi's Pit

Location: Close to Boreham
Type and Size: Three pits, of which Pit Two, of four acres is the main carp lake
Carp Stock: Well stocked with carp which include about 10 twenties and a common of about 30lbs
Category: Mixed Fishery
Other Species: Usual coarse fish
Permits: Edwards Tackle Shop, 16 Broomfield Road, Chelmsford
Cost: £20 per season
Control: Marconi AS
Restrictions: No day tickets; night fishing by special permit only, available from club
BK Rating: Moderate
W/A: NRA Anglian Region

Maybrand Fish Farm

Location: Stapleford Abbots, north of Romford
Type and Size: Three small lakes, quite deep in parts, two of which have islands
How to Find: Take the B175 from Romford. After Stapleford Abbots, turn left into Bournebridge Lane, and the lakes are on the left, past the houses
Carp Stock: All three lakes are well stocked with carp to doubles
Category: Mixed Fishery
Other Species: Roach, tench, chub, perch and eels
Permits: Day tickets on site
Cost: £6 for adults; £4 for juniors under 14, OAP's and the disabled
Control: Private. Tel: 04028 279
Restrictions: Barbless hooks; no boilies, bloodworm or groundbait
BK Rating: Moderate
W/A: NRA Thames Region

Newland Hall Carp Fishery

Location: Near Colchester
Type and Size: Lake of two acres
How to Find: The lake is on the A1060, 4 miles from Chelmsford
Carp Stock: Well stocked with carp to 25lbs
Category: Carp Water
Permits: Control changing at time of press
Cost: Day tickets at £12

BK Rating:	Fairly Easy
Control:	Private
W/A:	NRA Anglian Region
Comments:	Small spring-fed lake in pleasant surroundings

Old Heath Lake (Snake Pit)

Location:	Colchester
How to Find:	In the town of Old Heath, 5 miles from Colchester
Type and Size:	Sand pit of about 8 acres
Carp Stock:	Two fish! A 45lb common, and a 31lb common!
Category:	Mixed Fishery
Other Species:	Roach, rudd, bream, tench and pike
Permits:	Maulden AC. Available from local tackle shops
Cost:	Approx £20 a season
BK Rating:	Super-Difficult
W/A:	NRA Anglian Region
Comments:	A very difficult water producing only two or three carp each year including Britain's biggest ever common carp. About 30% of the lake has hawthorn bushes and trees in the water. There is a severe litter problem in and out of the water and the lake is slowly being filled in

Pipps Hill Fisheries   A

Location:	Basildon
Type and Size:	25 acre lake, with big hotel by the lake
How to Find:	Cranes Farm Road, Basildon
Carp Stock:	Some large carp, doubles and twenties
Category:	Mixed Fishery
Other Species:	General coarse fish
Permits:	Day tickets on bank
Cost:	£2 per rod for 12 hours; £3.50 per rod for 24 hours; weekend - £7.50 (two rods)
BK Rating:	Very Difficult
Restrictions:	No sacking
Control:	Pipps Hill Country Club, Cranes Farm Road, Basildon. Tel: Basildon 23456
W/A:	NRA Thames Region
Comments:	Formerly known as Aquatels. Carp caught to 25¾lbs in 1990

Priory Park Lakes

Location:	Priory Park, Southend
Type and Size:	Park lake
How to Find:	In Southend
Carp Stock:	Well stocked with carp to over 20lbs
Category:	Carp Water
Other Species:	Mixed coarse fish
Permits:	Day tickets on site
Cost:	On application
BK Rating:	Moderate

Control:	Council
W/A:	NRA Thames Region
Comments:	Busy park lake, heavily fished by carp anglers. Plenty of doubles

Rayne Lodge Farm

Location:	Rayne, near Braintree
Type and Size:	Two small lakes
Carp Stock:	Well stocked with carp to 20lbs
Category:	Mixed Fishery
Other Species:	Usual coarse fish
Permits:	From the farm. Tel: 0376 345719
Cost:	£5 per day; £6 for two rods
Restrictions:	Barbless hooks and no keepnets
BK Rating:	Moderate
W/A:	NRA Anglian Region

River Roding

Location:	Passingford Bridge, near Abridge
Type and Size:	30 miles long river, tributary of the Thames
Carp Stock:	Some carp in the Passingford Bridge area, sizes not known
Category:	Few Carp
Other Species:	Roach, chub, pike, bream and tench
Permits:	From bailiff on bank upstream of bridge
Control:	Woodford AS, north of bridge, members only, details from Secretary, 22 Evanrigg Terrace, Woodford Green, Essex (no day tickets). Barkingside and District AS has 1½ miles downstream of bridge, Secretary: D J French, 64 Khartoum Road, Ilford. Other information from Edko Sports, 136 North Street, Romford
BK Rating:	Difficult
W/A:	NRA Thames Region

Rochford Reservoir

Location:	Near Southend Airport; take the A127 then turn onto the B1013 towards Rochford. The reservoir is near the railway station
Type and Size:	Small reservoir
Carp Stock:	Some carp to 20lbs
Category:	Few Carp
Other Species:	Usual coarse fish
Permits:	Day tickets on bank at £1.50 for adults and 70p for juniors and OAP's
Restrictions:	Two rods only
BK Rating:	Moderate
W/A:	NRA Thames Region

Rockells Farm

Location:	Duddenhoe End, Saffron Walden
Type and Size:	34 acre lake, with fishing platforms
Carp Stock:	Heavily stocked with many small carp, and plenty of doubles to 18lbs
Category:	Mixed Fishery
Other Species:	Tench, roach and chub
Permits:	Day tickets on bank during the week; booking in advance only at weekends from the owner, E Westerhuis, at the above address. Tel: 0763 838053
Cost:	£4 per day
Control:	Private
Restrictions:	Weekend fishing must be booked in advance - no tickets on bank. Barbless or semi-barbed hooks only; no groundbait or boilies(!)
BK Rating:	Easy
W/A:	NRA Anglian Region
Comments:	Some good doubles, but 50-100lb 'bags' of fish using match tactics are common which is perhaps why they ban boilies... about the best food a carp could get!

Shoebury Park

Location:	Elm Road, Shoeburyness
Type and Size:	Small park lake of about 2 acres
Carp Stock:	Well stocked with small carp and several 20lb commons
Category:	Mixed Fishery
Other Species:	Tench and roach
Permits:	Day tickets on bank
BK Rating:	Moderate for small fish. Difficult for the big ones
W/A:	NRA Anglian Region

Silver End Pit

Location:	Silver End, near Witham
Type and Size:	Gravel pit of about two acres, with another of five acres nearby, called Silver End Back Lake
Carp Stock:	Well stocked with carp to low thirties; the 40 pounder is now dead. Back Lake has carp to over 20lbs
Category:	Mixed Fishery
Other Species:	Big eels, bream to over 10lbs, and pike to over 20lbs
Permits:	Permits from local tackle shops - no day tickets
Control:	Kelvedon Angling Club - fishing by seasonal membership only
BK Rating:	Moderate
W/A:	NRA Anglian Region

Slough House Lake

Location:	Bulphan, off the A21 between Basildon and Grays
Type and Size:	Four acre lake
Carp Stock:	Heavily stocked with carp to upper doubles
Category:	Mixed Fishery
Other Species:	Most coarse fish
Permits:	Basildon Angling Centre, 402 Whitmore Way. Basildon and County Angling

Cost:	Day tickets - £5 for one rod; £8 for two rods in advance, £2 extra on bank
Restrictions:	No night fishing - start at 7.30am; barbless hooks and no keepnets
BK Rating:	Easy
W/A:	NRA Anglian Region

Southminster Pits

Location:	Southminster, near Maldon
Type and Size:	Several very small pits
Carp Stock:	Well stocked with carp to doubles
Category:	Mixed Fishery
Other Species:	Pike, roach and bream
Permits:	Members only water of Billericay AC - membership from local tackle shops, open to all
BK Rating:	Easy
W/A:	NRA Anglian Region
Comments:	Billericay AC have other carp waters on the same ticket, including Straight Mill

South Weald

Location:	South Weald Park, near Brentwood
Type and Size:	Two estate lakes of 6 acres and 3 acres
Carp Stock:	Well stocked with carp, including a number of 20's
Category:	Carp Water
Permits:	Day tickets from Parks Office in car park. Tel: 0277 216297
Baits/Methods:	Advanced carp fishing baits and methods
Cost:	£35 per season
Control:	Essex County Council
BK Rating:	Difficult
W/A:	NRA Thames Region
Comments:	No night fishing. Top Lake day tickets at £2 per day. Bottom Lake season only - carp to 27lbs

Stanford-le-Hope

Location:	Wharfe Road, Stanford-le-Hope
Type and Size:	Two open gravel pits of 6 and 7 acres. Few carp, but fish to 18½lbs reported
How to Find:	Take the A13 from the Dartford Tunnel towards Southend. After 6½ miles take the A1014 Stanford-le-Hope/Crayton turn off. Follow the Stanford signs to Southend Road, fork left at the Burmah Garage, and take Wharfe Road under the railway bridge onto the unmade road and the entrance is on the left. Park cars in either car park but not on the causeway between the lakes
Carp Stock:	Not known; thought to be not many
Category:	Few Carp
Other Species:	Pike, perch, roach, bream, tench, rudd, eels, crucian carp, all of which grow to large sizes
Permits:	Season tickets only from Leisure Sport, Thorpe Park, Staines Road, Chertsey, Surrey. Tel: Chertsey 64872

Cost:	£22 per season. Juniors/OAP/disabled £11
Restrictions:	No restrictions - night fishing allowed
BK Rating:	Difficult as there are not many big carp, but quite easy for the smaller carp
Control:	Leisure Sport Angling
W/A:	NRA Anglian Region
Comments:	Like a number of gravel pit fisheries we have included this water because control (Leisure Sport) has reported carp from the water, but they are often few and far between on such waters, some of which may well not be worth serious carp fishing

Starlane

Location:	Wakering, near Southend
Type and Size:	Two small lakes, and a larger water
Carp Stock:	Small lakes - well stocked with carp to just under 20lbs; large lake - plenty of carp to 35lbs
Category:	Mixed Fishery
Other Species:	Pike, tench and roach
Permits:	Small lakes - day ticket on bank; larger lake - syndicate (enquire at small lakes)
BK Rating:	Moderate
W/A:	NRA Anglian Region

Swanscombe Farm Fishery

Location:	Lamberts Lane, off Tey Road, Earls Colne. Tel: 0787 223562
Type and Size:	Lake of about 3 acres
Carp Stock:	Well stocked with carp, best reported was 22lbs
Category:	Carp Water
Other Species:	Tench
Permits:	Day tickets on site
Cost:	£5 per day
Control:	Private
BK Rating:	Moderate
W/A:	NRA Anglian Region
Comments:	Reduced rates for OAP's and children. Lodge, toilets and tackle hire. Facilities for the disabled. There is also a 4½ acre trout lake stocked with rainbow and brown trout to 10lbs. The fishery is open all the year

The Chase

Location:	Dagenham
Type and Size:	Large gravel pit
How to Find:	Near Dagenham East Underground Station
Carp Stock:	Good carp
Category:	Mixed Fishery
Other Species:	Roach, bream, tench, pike, perch, crucians
Permits:	Day tickets from bailiff on bank
Cost:	On application
BK Rating:	Moderate
Control:	White Hart Anglers' Club

Restrictions: No night fishing
W/A: NRA Thames Region
Comments: Information from Edko Sports, 136 North Street, Romford

Thorndon Park

Location: Halway Lane, off the A127 near Brentwood
Type and Size: Park lake of 2-3 acres
Carp Stock: Only about twenty, from 20-25lbs
Category: Mixed Fishery
Other Species: Pike, tench, bream, roach
Permits: Day tickets on bank
Restrictions: No night fishing
BK Rating: Difficult
W/A: NRA Anglian Region

Totham Pit

Location: Just outside the village of Great Totham, near   Malden
Type and Size: Gravel pit of about six acres
Carp Stock: Quite well stocked with carp to low 20's
Category: Mixed Fishery
Other Species: Usual coarse fish
Permits: Malden AC. Tel: Malden 854765
Cost: About £27 per season
Control: Club
BK Rating: Easy
W/A: NRA Anglian Region

Tufnell's Mere

Location: Near Little Waltham
Type and Size: Gravel pit of about 12 acres
Carp Stock: Little known, but carp to 27lbs have been caught
Category: Mixed Fishery
Other Species: Usual coarse fish
Permits: Chelmsford AA, 60 Delamere Road, Chelmsford
Control: Club
Restrictions: No night fishing
BK Rating: Moderate
W/A: NRA Anglian Region
Comments: Lots of potential. Water table has been low for some time

Wanstead and Woodford Ponds

Location: Woodford and Snaresbrook areas
Type and Size: Small ponds
How to Find: Near Wanstead
Carp Stock: Some carp, sizes not known
Category: Eagle Pond, Hollow Pond, Whipps Cross Pond, Knighton Wood Pond -
Mixed Fisheries
Other Species: General coarse fish
Permits: None required

Cost:	Free
BK Rating:	Insufficient information
Control:	Public
W/A:	NRA Thames Region
Comments:	Some free fishing near London! Make sure that you have Water Authority Licences

Warren Pond

Location:	Near Chingford
Type and Size:	Medium sized gravel pit
Carp Stock:	Sizes and numbers not known, but some carp to double figures
Category:	Mixed Fishery
Other Species:	Bream and roach
Permits:	From bailiff on bank
Control:	Private, but we have not been able to find out much about this water, so we suggest you enquire about the location and other details from local tackle shops
BK Rating:	Not known
W/A:	NRA Thames Region

Weeley Bridge Holiday Park   A

Location:	Weeley, near Clacton
Type and Size:	Small lake on caravan park
Carp Stock:	Well stocked with carp to upper doubles
Category:	Mixed Fishery
Other Species:	Roach, tench and other coarse fish
Permits:	On site. Tel: 0255 830403 for details and brochure
Control:	Club
BK Rating:	Moderate
W/A:	NRA Anglian Region
Comments:	Caravans to rent on site for holidays with fishing

White House Carp Fisheries

Location:	Essex
Type and Size:	Pond of one and a quarter acres
Carp Stock:	Well stocked with doubles to about 24lbs
Category:	Carp Water
Other Species:	Tench to 9lbs
Permits:	Syndicate only
Cost:	£110 per season
Control:	Private. Tel: 0702 602610 for all information
Restrictions:	No day tickets; no seed baits
BK Rating:	Not known
W/A:	NRA Anglian Region

Willowside Carp Lake

Location:	Off the A112 between Waltham Abbey and Chingford
Type and Size:	One acre man-made lake
Carp Stock:	Well stocked with carp to about 15lbs
Category:	Mixed Fishery
Other Species:	Chub and golden tench
Permits:	Day tickets on bank
Cost:	£3 per day; £2 for the evening; £4 for a night
Control:	Tel: 081-529 1371
Restrictions:	No boilies or keepnets
BK Rating:	Easy
W/A:	NRA Thames Region

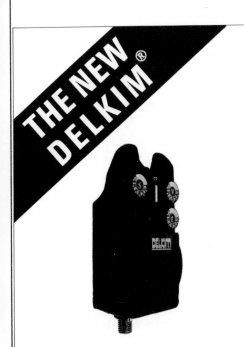

GLOUCESTERSHIRE

TEWKESBURY

MORETON

STOW

CHELTENHAM

GLOUCESTER

CANNOP

NORTHLEACH

STROUD

CIRENCESTER

LECHLADE

BADMINTON

S. CERNEY

Adlestrop Lake

Location: Near Adlestrop Station, Stow-on-the-Wold

How to Find: Take the A436 road from Stow-on-the-Wold towards Chipping Norton. After about 2 miles and immediately after a railway bridge, turn left towards Evenlode. The lake is on the right

Type and Size: Stream-fed dammed estate lake, long and narrow, 2½ acres

Carp Stock: Probably only 20—30 mirrors, mostly doubles to about 18lbs. Now restocked with smaller carp

Category: Few Carp

Other Species: Tench, roach

Permits: Moreton-in-Marsh Angling Club. Enquire locally

Control: Moreton-in-Marsh Angling Club

BK Rating: Difficult

W/A: NRA Severn-Trent Region

Comments: Weedy water, quite shallow, with a big bed of broad-leaved pondweed at the dam end. Most carp caught after dark, but can be stalked in weed at shallow end in daytime in warm weather. This is the only water we know of on which a sheep has been hooked and played! Whilst Roger Emmet was fishing there several sheep jumped into the water and swam across the lake. One of these swam through Roger's line before he could remove it and was hooked. He was unable to control the sheep, which swam across the lake, climbed the further bank and went through a barbed wire fence, breaking the line!

Apperley Pools

Location:	Apperley, near Tewkesbury
Type and Size:	Two pools, about 4 acres in all
How to Find:	Take the A38 Gloucester road from Tewkesbury, turn right at the sign for Apperley. Continue from village on Gabbs Lane to where road bears left. Pools are on your left
Carp Stock:	A few small carp to 3 or 4lbs
Category:	Few Carp
Other Species:	Bream, roach, chub, perch
Permits:	Birmingham Anglers Association (members only), 100 Icknield Port Road, Rotton Park, Birmingham B16 OAP. Tel: 021-451 9111 (9.30am to 1.30pm, and 7pm to 9pm)
Cost:	About £13 per year (includes all BAA waters)
BK Rating:	Difficult, as there are few carp
Control:	Birmingham AA
Restrictions:	No groundbait of any kind
W/A:	NRA Severn-Trent Region
Comments:	Not worth considering for serious carp fishing, unless you just want a day's fishing, with the chance of an occasional carp

Ashton Keynes Pool

Location:	Ashton Keynes, near Cirencester
Type and Size:	100 acre gravel pit
Carp Stock:	Well stocked with carp to doubles
Category:	Mixed Fishery
Other Species:	Bream, roach, rudd, perch and crucians
Permits:	£2 per day in advance, from the clubhouse on site or £4 on bank
Control:	South Cerney AC - Frank Wright. Tel: 0793 822137
Restrictions:	No carp in keepnets
BK Rating:	Moderate
W/A:	NRA Thames Region

Badminton Lake

Location:	On Duke of Beaufort's Badminton Estate, Badminton village
Type and Size:	Estate lake, 1½ acres
How to Find:	Turn off A46 Bath to Stroud road at traffic lights by Cross Hands Hotel. Right turn is signposted Badminton. In village, turn right and take left turn at end into the Badminton estate. Lake on right in front of house
Carp Stock:	Numerous small commons; a few mirrors to 19lbs recently introduced
Category:	Carp Water
Other Species:	Roach
Permits:	Badminton Estate Office, Badminton, Glos. Season only, limited
Cost:	About £25 per season
Baits/Methods:	Normal carp methods, some surface fishing. Usual baits
Control:	Season ticket, Badminton Estate
Restrictions:	No night fishing
W/A:	NRA Wessex Region
BK Rating:	Easy
Comments:	Muddy type water, very open with no cover and little weed

Bradley's Pit

Location: On the edge of the village of South Cerney, near Cirencester
Type and Size: Huge gravel pit of 115 acres
How to Find: Take the Cerney Wick road from South Cerney and Bradley's will be seen on the right just outside the village
Carp Stock: Few carp, but said to be some very big fish. Commons to about 15lbs and every year there are rumours of 30's and 40's being caught, none of which are authenticated. Authenticated 26¼lb common caught in July 1985. The lake almost certainly contains some thirties
Category: Few Carp
Other Species: Tench, pike, roach, bream, perch, chub
Permits: South Cerney Angling Club. Secretary: D Savage, 35 Alexandra Drive, Cirencester, Glos, and from tackle shops in Swindon and Cirencester
Cost: About £10 a season
Control: Club
BK Rating: Very Difficult
W/A: NRA Thames Region
Comments: South Cerney AC have a club house here and the club has most of the best fishing in this area, which contains thousands of acres of flooded gravel pits. Ignore the stories of huge carp caught from this lake and only believe what you see

Peter Mohan with a 20 caught from a Gloucestershire water on a KM Maestro Cream RM30 boilie in September 1990

Bredons Hardwick

Location:	Tewkesbury to Bredon road, about two miles from Tewkesbury
Type and Size:	10 acre gravel pit
Carp Stock:	Heavily stocked with small carp and doubles, and said to be fish to 30lbs
Category:	Mixed Fishery
Other Species:	Roach, bream tench, perch and rudd
Permits:	Tredworth Tackle, High Street, Gloucester. Tel: Gloucester 23009
Cost:	Season tickets only at £30 - syndicate
Restrictions:	No fishing allowed in the shallows(!)
BK Rating:	Fairly Hard
W/A:	NRA Severn-Trent Region
Comments:	Very clear, weedy water; fish location very important

Burley Fields Lake

Location:	Crippetts Lane, Leckhampton, Cheltenham. Tel: Cheltenham 862905
Type and Size:	2½ acre man-made, spring-fed lake
Carp Stock:	Heavily stocked with carp to 20lbs
Category:	Mixed Fishery
Other Species:	Perch, roach, bream, rudd and tench
Permits:	In advance only from the address above — open to all
Cost:	£5 per season, then £3 per day, or £5 per day for non-members
Restrictions:	No keepnets
BK Rating:	Easy
W/A:	NRA Severn-Trent Region
Comments:	Weed-free fishery with easily accessible pitches for disabled anglers

Cannop Ponds

Location:	Cannop Valley, Parkend, between Coleford and Lydney
Type and Size:	Two very beautiful forest lakes, in the Forest of Dean - 4½ and 5½ acres. Most of the carp are in the lower lake
Carp Stock:	Not a large number, and hard to locate, but they do go to over 20lbs, with some good commons
Category:	Few Carp
Other Species:	Bream, roach, tench and pike
Permits:	Bailiff on bank
Control:	Yorkley and District AC. Permits and details from Sport and Leisure, Market Place, Coleford; Robert Sports, 31 Market Street, Cinderford; Peter James Sports, 17 Newerne Street, Lydney. Tel: Dean 842515
BK Rating:	Very Difficult
W/A:	NRA Severn-Trent Region
Comments:	Ranges from 2 feet deep at the top end, where a stream comes in from the upper lake, to 18 feet at the big dam. There are said to be a few big carp in the upper lake

Chad Lakes

Location:	Near Stow-on-the-Wold, off the B4450 near Bledington
Type and Size:	2 acre lake
Carp Stock:	Well stocked with carp to about 14lbs
Category:	Mixed Fishery
Permits:	Day tickets. Information on 0608 74252

Cost: £2.50; £1.50 OAP's and children
Control: Private
Restrictions: Barbless hooks; no keepnets or groundbait; night fishing by arrangement
BK Rating: Moderate
W/A: NRA Thames Region
Comments: There is another lake on the site, a syndicate carp water; attractive Cotswold location, with toilet and car park

Claydon Park Fishery

Location: Off the A417 road between Lechlade and Fairford
Type and Size: Five acre matured gravel pit
Carp Stock: Well stocked with carp, sizes not known
Category: Mixed Fishery
Other Species: Tench, bream, pike, perch and roach
Permits: From the self-service hut on site
Cost: £3 per day; £1.50 for under 16's, OAP's and the disabled (two rods)
Control: Bernard Sparkes. Tel: 0367 52397 (day) or 0367 52689 (evenings)
Restrictions: No night fishing; sunrise to sunset only; no dyed baits; no dogs
BK Rating: Not known
W/A: NRA Thames Region

Cokes Pit

Location: On the road from South Cerney to Ashton Keynes
Type and Size: Gravel pit of about 12 acres
Carp Stock: Some carp to 18lbs; bigger fish have been seen and a fish of well over 30lbs was caught several years ago, although this fish is now dead
Category: Mixed Fishery
Other Species: Tench, roach, rudd, bream and pike
Permits: Ashton Keynes AC - tickets from local tackle shops in Cirencester and Swindon at £10 per season, to include other waters
Control: Club
BK Rating: Difficult
W/A: NRA Thames Region
Comments: This lake is little fished by carp anglers, though it is a good tench water. Since it is a Nature Reserve quite a large part of the bank cannot be fished. Very weedy with lots of shallow bars and islands

Cotswold Hoburne   A

Location: Cotswold Water Park, near Cirencester
Type and Size: Two quite large gravel pits
Carp Stock: Said to be some carp - numbers and sizes not known
Category: Few Carp?
Other Species: Roach, bream, tench, rudd and perch
Permits: Residents only - at reception
Control: Private
BK Rating: Difficult
W/A: NRA Thames Region

Comments: 70 acre site with timber built lodges to let. Swimming pool, licensed lakeside club, boating, shop etc - holiday camp type atmosphere. Open Easter to end of October. Bookings from Hoseasons Holidays, Sunway House, Lowestoft NR32 3LT. Tel: 0502 500 500. Dozens of other lakes in the area, a number of which hold carp to over 20lbs

Court Farm

Location: Court Farm, Lemington, near Moreton-in-Marsh
Type and Size: 2½ acre man-made lake
Carp Stock: About 150 fish to 16lbs, best to date is 20lbs, but the average is about 4lb
Category: Carp Water
Other Species: Rudd and roach
Permits: Bill Gadsby, Court Farm. Tel: 0608 50872
Cost: Day tickets at £5 per day
Control: Private
BK Rating: Moderate
W/A: NRA Severn-Trent Region
Comments: Night fishing is allowed, and another pond for carp is being constructed. There is also a one acre trout lake on the farm

Crooked Withies Lake

Location: Near Tewkesbury
Type and Size: 2½ acre lake
Carp Stock: Heavily stocked with carp only to about 14lbs
Category: Carp Only
Permits: Syndicate season tickets only from: The Fishery Controller, 15 Stafford Court, Riverside Close, Bedford MK42 9DE. Tel: 0234 212066. Some vacancies in April each year, and occasionally throughout the season
Cost: About £95 per season
Control: Private
BK Rating: Easy
Restrictions: No long stay fishing or camping (maximum 24 hours). Alternate Saturday and Sunday rota. No bivvies
W/A: NRA Severn-Trent Region
Comments: A very attractive lake with an island, and surrounded by mature flowering bushes and trees. Very quiet and peaceful. Plenty of mirrors and commons from 4 to 10lbs, and a good number of lower doubles. Small exclusive syndicate, with vacancies every year. Guest tickets for friends of members. Night fishing allowed, though the water fishes best in the daytime. Good winter water. Warning - private property; do not visit without permission. Season and day tickets available on other carp only waters, on application to the above address

Gardners Pool

Location: Village of Saul, 8 miles south of Gloucester
Type and Size: Mature gravel pit - 5 acres
How to Find: On the Gloucester-Bristol road (A38), turn right for Frampton-on-Severn just after roundabout. Cross Gloucester-Sharpness canal, water is on the right just before the village of Saul. Ordnance Survey Sheet 163
Carp Stock: Number not known, but not very heavily stocked. A number of doubles

and perhaps two or three 20's to about 21lbs. Bigger fish are mirrors - some commons to about 13lbs

Category:	Mixed Fishery
Other Species:	Roach, tench, many eels
Permits:	Gloucester United Anglers' Association, from tackle shops in Gloucester. Secretary: J Gibby, 70 Robert Raikes Avenue, Tuffley, Gloucester. Tel: 413972
Cost:	£10.50 per season, limited in number
Baits/Methods:	Normal, fairly advanced carp rigs and methods with boilies or some multiple baits
Control:	Club
W/A:	NRA Severn-Trent Region
BK Rating:	Difficult
Comments:	Shallow, weedy water. Very patchy - long spells with no takes

Peter Mohan with a typical Crooked Withies 10 pounder

Ham Pool

Location:	Near South Cerney, Cirencester
Type and Size:	Gravel pit of 11 acres
How to Find:	Ham Pool is the smaller water next to Bradley's on the edge of South Cerney village
Carp Stock:	Some carp, sizes and numbers unknown
Category:	Few Carp
Other Species:	General coarse fish
Permits:	South Cerney Angling Club. Membership Secretary: D Savage, 35 Alexandra Drive, Cirencester, Glos, and also from tackle shops in Swindon and Cirencester
Cost:	About £10 per season
Control:	Club
BK Rating:	Very Difficult
W/A:	NRA Thames Region

Highnam Court Lake

Location:	Just off the A40, three miles west of Gloucester on the Ross-on-Wye road
Type and Size:	Three acre attractive estate lake covered with lilies
Carp Stock:	Some carp to 20lbs
Category:	Few Carp
Other Species:	Tench, roach, bream and rudd
Permits:	Day tickets in advance from Tredworth Fishing Tackle, 78 High Street, Tredworth, Gloucester
Cost:	£4 per day; £5 on bank
Control:	Brian Ingram. Tel: 0452 23009
Restrictions:	No groundbaiting
BK Rating:	Very Difficult
W/A:	NRA Severn Trent Region

Huntley Carp Pools

Location:	Huntley, 10 miles north west of Gloucester, off the A40
Type and Size:	Two attractive stream-fed forest lakes of about four acres each, weedy and about 10 feet deep
Carp Stock:	Well stocked with carp to over 20lbs
Category:	Mixed Fishery
Other Species:	Roach, rudd, tench, eels and trout
Permits:	Seasonal membership only from J R Tipper, 20 Redpoll Way, Abbeydale, Gloucester LG4 7TH. Tel: 0452 422407
Cost:	On application
Control:	Private
BK Rating:	Moderate
W/A:	NRA Severn Trent Region
Comments:	Beautiful location in huge forest; former trout pools. Membership limited. No glass bottles because of possible fires. Well behaved anglers only. A fairly new water for carp requires genuine anglers; no families or picnickers

New and best selling carp videos from Beekay Publishers. See page 19

Lake 19

Location:	South Cerney, near Cirencester
Type and Size:	8 acre gravel pit
Carp Stock:	Well stocked with carp to 15½lbs, mostly commons from 8-10lbs, but growing well
Category:	Carp Water
Other Species:	Some other coarse fish
Permits:	Club membership of Isis Angling Club from local tackle shops in Cirencester and Swindon
Cost:	£15.50 per season
Control:	Isis Angling Club - P Gilbert, Havelock Street, Swindon, Wilts
BK Rating:	Easy
W/A:	NRA Thames Region

Lydney Boating Lake

Location:	On the edge of the town of Lydney, between Gloucester and Chepstow
Type and Size:	Town boating lake, 5 acres
How to Find:	Take the A40 from Gloucester towards Ross, then the A48 towards Chepstow. At Lydney, turn left opposite Woolworths, and then right again past the houses
Carp Stock:	Heavily stocked with commons to about 8lbs. Two or three mirrors to 19lbs
Category:	Mixed Fishery
Other Species:	Roach, tench, bream, rudd, eels, barbel
Permits:	Sports shop in Lydney High Street on left going towards Chepstow
Cost:	About £8 per season
Baits/Methods:	Fairly unsophisticated carp methods and baits. Float fishing
Control:	Lydney Angling Club. Secretary: M G Nash, 42 Templeway West, Lydney, Glos
BK Rating:	Easy
W/A:	NRA Severn-Trent Region
Comments:	Busy town water, walkers, children and boats which are restricted to one end only. Very large island. Fishes best at night

Manor Brook Lake

Location:	Lake 59, Friday Ham Lane, Ashton Keynes, Cirencester; off the A419 Swindon road
Type and Size:	40 acre gravel pit of irregular shape, with an island
Carp Stock:	Scheduled to be stocked with carp in late 1992
Category:	Mixed Fishery
Other Species:	Roach, perch, tench, pike and some big trout
Permits:	From the self service kiosk in the car park at £3 per day
Control:	Tel: 045382 2286
Restrictions:	No night fishing
BK Rating:	Depends on how many carp they put in!
W/A:	NRA Thames Region
Comments:	Boats can be hired for pike fishing; net divides the coarse fishery from a trout fishery

Mill Avon

Location:	Lower Lode Lane, off the Gloucester road in Tewkesbury
Type and Size:	Three-quarter of a mile stretch of river between the Severn and the Avon
Carp Stock:	Not many carp, but they have been caught to nearly 20lbs
Category:	Few Carp
Other Species:	Most coarse fish
Permits:	Tewkesbury Fishing Tackle. Tel: 0684 293234
Cost:	£10 per season; £5.50 for two weeks
Control:	Tewkesbury Popular AC
Restrictions:	No night fishing
BK Rating:	Very Difficult
W/A:	NRA Severn Trent Region

Norton Fruit Farm

Location:	Tewkesbury Road, Norton, Gloucester GL2 9LH. Tel: Gloucester 731203
Type and Size:	One acre irrigation reservoir
How to Find:	Norton Fruit Farm is on the A38 between Coombe Hill and Twigworth
Carp Stock:	Heavily stocked with 40 doubles to about 20lbs
Category:	Mixed Fishery
Other Species:	Roach, rudd, tench, bream and perch
Permits:	Mr Feakins, Norton Fruit Farm — day tickets
BK Rating:	Very Easy
W/A:	NRA Severn-Trent Region
Comments:	Open banks with room for about 20 anglers; night fishing allowed

River Severn

Location:	400 yard stretch of the River Severn at Wainlode, near Gloucester
Type and Size:	Wide lower Severn and about quarter of a mile of the River Chelt
How to Find:	Take the A38 from Gloucester towards Tewkesbury. Turn left at Norton, and follow signs to Wainlode and the river by the Red Lion pub
Carp Stock:	Only a few carp, but some to 20lbs
Category:	Few Carp
Other Species:	Roach, chub, bream, barbel and big pike
Permits:	Day tickets from Red Lion Inn
Cost:	£2 per day; £1 for juniors. Evening tickets £1
Control:	Red Lion Inn
Restrictions:	No night fishing
BK Rating:	Very Difficult
W/A:	NRA Severn Trent Region
Comments:	Ideal for family fishing. The Inn has a campsite for tents and caravans

Roughgrounds Farm Lake

Location:	Just north of Lechlade
Type and Size:	Gravel pit of about 3 acres
How to Find:	Take the A361 Lechlade to Burford road, and the entrance to the lake will be seen on the left hand side after about a mile, and just beyond the entrance to Horseshoe
Carp Stock:	Well stocked with carp including a number of doubles
Category:	Carp Water
Other Species:	Some small mixed coarse fish

Permits: Day tickets from the Paper Shop, Burford Road, Lechlade.
Tel: Lechlade 52323. Limited to 15 anglers per day
Cost: About £3 per day
Control: Private
BK Rating: Easy to Moderate
Restrictions: No keepnets
W/A: NRA Thames Region

Staunton Court

Location: A417 from Gloucester 8 miles. From M50 (junction 2) 3 miles A417
by church at Staunton
Type and Size: Lake ¾ acre and small deep lake
Carp Stock: Stocked well with mirrors, commons and crucians up to 20lbs
Category: Mixed Fishery
Other Species: Tench, rudd, roach and bream
Permits: On bank - £4 per day; or night
Control: Private
Restrictions: Night arrival before 10.30pm. Barbless hooks. No keepnets or weigh
sacks
BK Rating: Easy - Moderate
W/A: NRA Severn-Trent Region
Comments: Must dip nets on arrival in tanks provided

Stroudwater Canal

Location: Ryford to Bridgend, just to the west of Stroud off the A419
Type and Size: Narrow, shallow disused stretch of canal
Carp Stock: Some carp to doubles
Category: Few Carp
Other Species: Tench, roach, bream, perch and pike
Permits: Permits from local tackle shops at about £10 perseason
Control: Lobby's Tackle. Tel: 0453 791417
BK Rating: Difficult
W/A: NRA Severn Trent Region

Watersmeet   A

Location: Hartpury, near Gloucester. Tel: 0452 700358
Type and Size: Three mature pits of about 2 acres, half and a quarter of an acre
How to Find: Take the A40 Gloucester to Ross-on-Wye road and after about a
mile turn right on the A417 towards Ledbury. The ponds will be seen
on the left hand side just after the village of Hartpury and next to a
white-painted guest house called 'Watersmeet'
Carp Stock: Numbers not known, although there are enough to be worth fishing
for. Some commons to about 9lbs, and mirrors to around 15lbs. A few
larger fish have been reported
Category: Mixed Fishery
Other Species: Tench, roach, rudd, bream
Permits: From Mr and Mrs Ring at the guest house. Some day tickets are issued
and you can fish if you stay at the guest house, which is right on the
edge of the lake. There is a bar and you can have meals etc - quite a
pleasant spot for a fishing holiday, though quite busy in the summer.
Night fishing for residents only

Cost:	On application to Watersmeet, Hartpury, Gloucester
BK Rating:	Difficult
Control:	Private
Baits/Methods:	This is not an easy water and there are not great numbers of carp, so fairly advanced baits and methods would be needed
W/A:	NRA Severn-Trent Region
Comments:	Quite a pleasant place to stay and the fishing is very close to the accommodation. Most carp caught after dark. Front Pool - small carp only to 5lbs. Rear Pool - few carp, but two upper doubles. Main Pool - most fish up to 5lbs only; about 15 doubles to 18lbs. Very snaggy, line minimum 10lbs. Barbless hooks advised

Whelford Pools Specimen Lake

Location:	Whelford, near Lechlade
Type and Size:	Five acre lake
How to Find:	Take the A417 from Lechlade to Fairford; the Whelford road is a left turn after a few miles, with the lakes on the right
Carp Stock:	Very heavily stocked with more than 100 doubles to over 20lbs
Category:	Mixed Fishery
Other Species:	Pike over 20lbs, tench, roach and pike
Permits:	Day tickets from G Goddings. Tel: 0993 831533, or 0285 713649
Cost:	£2.50 for two rods; evening from 5pm - £1.50; 24 hours - £5
Restrictions:	No night fishing except by special arrangement; no keepnets; barbless hooks; unhooking mats must be used
BK Rating:	Moderate, but few carp under 10lbs
W/A:	NRA Thames Region

Whelford Pools Top Lake

Location:	Whelford, near Lechlade
Type and Size:	Two acre lake
How to Find:	Take A417 from Lechlade to Fairford. Take the Whelford left turn after a few miles. The lakes are on the right
Carp Stock:	Heavily stocked with carp of 6-8lbs, with some doubles
Category:	Mixed Fishery
Other Species:	Tench, roach and perch
Permits:	Day tickets from G Goddings. Tel: 0993 831533 or 0285 713649
Cost:	£2.50 for two rods; 5pm to 9pm - £1.50; 24 hours - £5
Control:	Private
Baits/Methods:	Usual carp bait floaters do well
Restrictions:	No night fishing except by special arrangement; no keepnets; barbless hooks; unhooking mats must be used
BK Rating:	Easy
W/A:	NRA Thames Region

GREATER LONDON

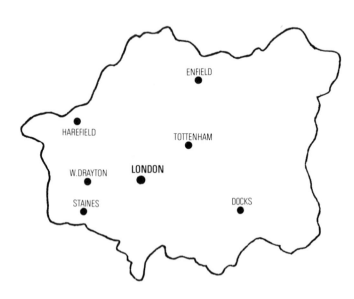

ENFIELD
●

HAREFIELD
●

TOTTENHAM
●

W.DRAYTON
●

LONDON
●

STAINES
●

DOCKS
●

Bedfont Lake

Location: Off the B137 between Ashford and Feltham
Type and Size: 9 acre lake
Carp Stock: Well stocked with carp to 20lbs; stocked 3 times recently with big fish
Category: Mixed Fishery
Other Species: Crucians, tench, perch, roach and pike
Permits: Boyer Leisure, Trout Road, West Drayton, Middx UB7 7SN. Adults £40 per season; juniors, OAP's, disabled £25. Open during close season for Any Method Trout Fishing £8 per day for 2 rods; £6 per day for 1 rod. Reductions for juniors, OAP's. Day tickets obtainable from Lakeside Garden Centre at entrance to lake
Control: Boyer Leisure
Restrictions: Unhooking mats compulsory
BK Rating: Moderate
W/A: NRA Thames Region
Comments: After Farlows, this is the best known of the Boyer lakes, and is a first class carp fishery. Night fishing on a day ticket is permitted

Clapham Common Pond

Location:	Clapham Common, SE London
Type and Size:	2 acre park lake
How to Find:	Clapham
Carp Stock:	Well stocked with carp to over 20lbs. Mirrors and commons
Category:	Mixed Fishery
Other Species:	General coarse fish
Permits:	Free fishing
Cost:	No cost
BK Rating:	Moderate
Control:	Council
W/A:	NRA Thames Region
Comments:	Crowded park lake. Anglers have reported up to 12 carp in a night's fishing, mostly of 8-10lbs, with the best at 20lbs

Colnbrook West

Location:	Between Langley and West Drayton
Type and Size:	5 acre lake
How to Find:	On the A4 off Lakeside Road
Carp Stock:	Well stocked with carp to over 20lbs
Category:	Mixed Fishery
Other Species:	Tench, perch, roach and pike
Permits:	Boyer Leisure, Trout Road, West Drayton, Middx UB7 7SN. Tel: 0895 824455
Cost:	£35 per season. Group permits available
Control:	Boyer Leisure
Restrictions:	Season tickets only
BK Rating:	Easy
W/A:	NRA Thames Region
Comments:	Regular catches of double figure carp reported in 1991

Coppermill Stream

Location:	Ferry Lane, Tottenham
Type and Size:	One mile of river
How to Find:	Near Tottenham Hale Underground Station, Ferry Lane
Carp Stock:	Some carp to about 16lbs
Category:	Mixed Fishery
Other Species:	Barbel, bream, roach, chub, dace, pike and grayling
Permits:	From machine. £1. 50p and 20p coins required. Day or season
Cost:	About £1.80 per day; £30 per season
Control:	Thames Water
Restrictions:	No night fishing. Fishing is from 7.30am to half an hour after sunset. No groundbaiting
BK Rating:	Moderate
W/A:	NRA Thames Region
Comments:	The only 'stream' in our Guide!

East Warwick

Location:	Ferry Lane, Tottenham N17 (opposite Ferry Boat Inn)
Type and Size:	Reservoir of 43 acres
How to Find:	Find the Ferry Boat Inn in Ferry Lane, Tottenham; Underground Station - Tottenham Hale
Carp Stock:	Some carp present, sizes not known
Category:	Few Carp
Other Species:	Tench, roach, bream, perch
Permits:	From machines at reservoir. £1, 50p and 20p coins needed
Cost:	£2.50 per day, £35 per season
Control:	Thames Water
Restrictions:	No night fishing; fishing 7.30am to half an hour after sunset. Closed Christmas Day
BK Rating:	Very Difficult
W/A:	NRA Thames Region
Comments:	Not a carp water, but it does contain a few. Suitable for ambulatory and some wheelchair anglers, although they may need help to net fish. Additional swims for anglers have been provided on steep banks

Farlows Lake

Location:	Ford Lane, off Iver Lane, Iver, Bucks SL0 9LL - can be seen from M25
Type and Size:	Large old gravel pit of 37 acres
Carp Stock:	Heavily stocked with carp to 35lb, four other 30's, about 200 twenties and many doubles
Carp Stock:	Carp Water
Other Species:	Bream, perch, roach, tench, pike and trout
Permits:	Boyer Leisure, Trout Road, West Drayton, Middx UB7 7SN
Cost:	Season tickets £60 adults; £35 OAP's, disabled, juniors
Control:	Boyer Leisure
Restrictions:	Unhooking mats compulsory
BK Rating:	Moderate, although Difficult for the big fish
W/A:	NRA Thames Region
Comments:	Farlows is the 'flagship' for Boyer Leisure, who have a number of well run waters with big fish and excellent facilities. The water is open all year round and during the coarse fish close season (March 14th to June 15th), any method trout fishing is allowed. Cost during this period is £6 for one rod and £8 per day for two rods, reductions for juniors and OAP's. Carp are caught on all methods and baits, from maggots to boilies.

On site at Farlows Lake is a cafeteria, open all day, 7 days a week. Hot meals, sandwiches and drinks supplied all the year round. There is also a bar. Toilets and a shower available for all users of the lake.

The Heron Point Bar is on the same site, and is open for normal pub hours, and is pleasantly situated on the water's edge. Drinks till midnight for sit-down meals at the cafeteria on Friday and Saturday nights. Low price drinks, pool table, juke box, fruit machine and darts - Farlows is one of the best big carp waters in the country. Tackle shop on site - Tel: 0895 444707.

For full details of all the Boyers Fisheries apply to the office for their excellent and well illustrated brochure and application form, which gives details and maps of all their waters

Hampstead Heath Pond

Location: Hampstead Heath
Type and Size: Small commons pond, very weedy and shallow
Carp Stock: A few carp to about 15lbs
Category: Few Carp
Other Species: Roach, rudd, bream and perch
Permits: None necessary - free fishing
BK Rating: Difficult
W/A: NRA Thames Region

'Big Carp' magazine editor, Rob Maylin with a Harefield Lake mirror of over 38 pounds caught in June 1991

Harefield Carp Lake

Location: Moorhall Road, Harefield, opposite the Horse and Barge pub and one mile from Denham station

Type and Size: 47 acre working gravel pit

Carp Stock: One of the best big fish carp waters in the country, with at least 19 thirties, and over 200 twenties

Category: Carp Water

Other Species: Large bream and large roach

Permits: Boyer Leisure, Trout Road, West Drayton, Middx UB7 7SN. Tel: 0895 444707

Cost: £225 per season - waiting list. Apply to Boyer Leisure to be put on waiting list

Control: Boyer Leisure

Restrictions: 100 places only on 2-weekly rotas. Unhooking mats compulsory. Carp sacks banned

BK Rating: Difficult

W/A: NRA Thames Region

Comments: Harefield is one of the best known and most famous carp waters in the country, and is fished by many of the leading carp anglers. Advanced methods and baits needed. Membership is available only if sponsored by existing member. Members are allowed to take guests, by arrangement in advance only from 1st October

Tim Hodges with a 34.6 from Harefield Lake

Heath Vale Pond

Location:	Hampstead Heath, London
Type and Size:	Small, weedy lake, one of several ponds containing carp on the Heath
Carp Stock:	Quite well stocked with carp to just over 20lbs
Category:	Mixed Fishery
Other Species:	Roach, rudd, bream and pike
Permits:	None necessary - free fishing. Rod licences essential
Restrictions:	No fishing on one bank
BK Rating:	Moderate
W/A:	NRA Thames Region
Comments:	Like most of the free London waters, this pond is heavily fished, and the carp are caught quite often

High Maynard

Location:	Blackhorse Lane, Walthamstow. Car park Ferry Lane, Tottenham, N17 (opposite Ferry Boat Inn)
Type and Size:	Reservoir of 38 acres
How to Find:	Blackhorse Lane, near Blackhorse Lane Underground Station or Tottenham Hale Underground Station (nearest)
Carp Stock:	Some carp to over 20lbs
Category:	Mixed Fishery
Other Species:	Mixed coarse fish, including tench and perch
Permits:	Day and season tickets available on site from ticket machine
Cost:	£2.50 per day; £35 season
Control:	Thames Water. Send for leaflet to Amenity and Recreation Officer, Thames Water, Nugent House, Vastern Road, Reading, Berks. Tel: 0734 593391. Thames Area Angling Guide also published at £1.95 from tackle dealers and bookshops
Restrictions:	No night fishing; fishing is from 7.30am to half an hour after sunset. No groundbait
Baits/Methods:	Boilies best at present
BK Rating:	Difficult
W/A:	NRA Thames Region
Comments:	It is said that this reservoir could produce a surprise in the form of a big carp; its potential is not really known

Hollow Pond

Location:	Whipps Cross Road (A114), north west of Wanstead, NE London
Type and Size:	Large, shallow and weedy forest/commons-type lake
Carp Stock:	Small number of carp to about 10lbs
Category:	Few Carp
Other Species:	Roach, bream, rudd, perch, pike and tench
Permits:	None necessary - free fishing. Rod licence essential
BK Rating:	Very Difficult
W/A:	NRA Thames Region

Kingfisher Lake (Pit 4)

Location:	Pass the entrance to Savay on your right, coming from Denham. Cross the canal bridge and the entrance is on the right, just before the houses. Very long rough track
Type and Size:	Mature gravel pit of 19 acres
How to Find:	With difficulty. The lake is down a very long track of about a mile between Savay Lake and Harefield. There is a locked gate at the beginning of the track so it is better not to visit until you have a permit
Carp Stock:	Most of the carp are doubles with a good number of twenties and one or two thirties. Probably not heavily stocked for its size. Carp occasionally escape upstream to next lake!
Category:	Carp Water
Other Species:	Tench, pike, roach, bream
Permits:	Formerly controlled by the Greater London Council, now Hillingdon Borough Council: M Francis, Civic Centre, Uxbridge UB8 1UW. Tel: Uxbridge 50111 ext 2352
Cost:	£50 season ticket
Control:	Council
Restrictions:	No night fishing. Rules against long stay fishing
BK Rating:	Difficult
Baits/Methods:	You will need the most advanced baits and methods at this water. Peanuts did well in the past but most now seem to use boilies
Comments:	A well-known carp water hard fished by leading carp specialists. Chance of some very good twenties, but you can go very long periods without a take. An attractive lake, L-shaped and surrounded by trees and bushes. Very tranquil and pleasant to fish

Korda Lake

Location:	Colne Valley, Harefield, near Savay Lake
Type and Size:	15 acre gravel pit
Carp Stock:	Well stocked with plenty of doubles and some twenties to nearly 30lbs
Category:	Mixed Fishery
Other Species:	Usual coarse fish
Permits:	Day tickets on bank
Cost:	£2.50 one rod; £5 for two rods (12 hours); £4 and £8 for a 24 hour session; season ticket (two rods) costs £50
Control:	Tel: 0895 824455
Restrictions:	Safe rigs and unhooking mats essential
BK Rating:	Difficult
W/A:	NRA Thames Region

Lea Valley Leisure Park   A

Location:	Enfield area
Type and Size:	A number of lakes and gravel pits
How to Find:	In the Lea Valley between Enfield and Ware
Carp Stock:	Some carp lakes - details from Fisheries Manager
Category:	Mixed Fisheries
Other Species:	General coarse fish
Permits:	Fisheries Manager, Lea Valley Park, PO Box 88, Enfield EN2 9HG. Tel: 0992 717711
Cost:	On application

BK Rating: Insufficient information
Control: Lea Valley Leisure Park
W/A: NRA Thames Region
Comments: Details of fishing holidays can also be obtained from the Fisheries Manager. Includes Northmet Pit, Cheshunt, with pike to 35lb

Lockwood Reservoir

Location: Forest Road, Walthamstow
Type and Size: Reservoir of 80 acres
How to Find: Lea Bridge Road, in Walthamstow. Underground Station - Blackhorse Road, 1 mile
Carp Stock: 300-500 carp to over 30lbs; average size about 18lbs
Category: Carp Water
Other Species: Bream, pike, chub, roach
Permits: Not easy to obtain membership - mainly for employees
Cost: £5 a season
Control: Private - EMWA Employees Sports Club
Restrictions: No night fishing - 7am till dusk only. No groundbaiting, no wading
BK Rating: Difficult
Comments: A huge London reservoir, sometimes with waves on it almost like the sea. Concrete bank. Very hard to find the fish. Leading carp angler Kevin Maddocks says that if this lake was drained he wouldn't be surprised to find a carp of over 40lbs

London Docks

Location: East End of London
Type and Size: Very large freshwater Docks; big areas of very deep water
Carp Stock: Said to be some very big carp, but they are hard to find because of the huge areas of these disused docks. One or two twenties have been reported caught
Category: Few Carp
Other Species: Most coarse fish
Permits: Try the Isle of Dogs AC, which is open to all; Jim's Tackle, Bethnal Green. Tel: 071-791 2961
Control: Club
BK Rating: Super-Difficult
W/A: NRA Thames Region

Low Maynard: Walthamstow Nos 2 and 3

Location: Forest Road, Tottenham N17
Type and Size: Reservoirs: Low Maynard - 25 acres; No 2 - 13 acres; No 3 - 12 acres
How to Find: Take the A10 from London and at Tottenham turn right along High Cross Road to Ferry Lane. Tottenham Hale tube station on left
Carp Stock: All well stocked with carp, with plenty of doubles. There was a 28 pounder from Low Maynard in 1985
Category: Mixed Fishery
Other Species: Tench, bream and roach
Permits: Day and season permits from machines at the reservoir
Cost: £2.50 per day; £35 per season. £1, 50p and 20p coins needed for machines

Control:	Thames Water
Restrictions:	No night fishing. Fishing is from 7.30am until half an hour after sunset. Closed Christmas Day
BK Rating:	Moderate
W/A:	NRA Thames Region
Comments:	Car park and toilets. Fishes quite well in winter

New Cut

Location:	Ferry Lane, Tottenham
Type and Size:	River Cut about ¾ mile long
How to Find:	Near Tottenham Hale Underground Station, Ferry Lane, Tottenham
Carp Stock:	Occasional carp only, but we hear some large carp have been sighted
Category:	Few Carp
Other Species:	Roach, chub, bream
Permits:	Day and season from machines. £1, 50p and 20p coins required
Cost:	£2.50 per day; £35 season
Control:	Thames Water
Restrictions:	No night fishing. Open from 7.30am to half an hour after sunset
BK Rating:	We cannot assess this, as we do not know of anyone who has taken carp from the water, so we should have to enter an estimated rating of Very Difficult
W/A:	NRA Thames Region
Comments:	Not suitable for disabled anglers

Norwood Lake

Location:	Norwood Hill, London SE25
Type and Size:	Town park lake of about three acres, with toilets on bank
How to Find:	Off the A215, near Selhurst Park. The entrance is just off Woodvale Avenue
Carp Stock:	Surprisingly well stocked with carp to doubles
Category:	Mixed Fishery
Other Species:	Roach, perch and bream
Permits:	On bank
Cost:	About £2 per day and £1.50 for juniors and OAP's. Season tickets - £27, £18 for juniors and £9 for OAP's
Control:	Parks and Recreation Dept, Borough of Croydon
Restrictions:	No night fishing. No fishing on either side of kiosk
BK Rating:	Difficult
W/A:	NRA Thames Region

One Island Pond

Location:	Mitcham Common, Greater London, off the A235 Croydon road; opposite Seven Island Pond
Type and Size:	Pond of three-quarters of an acre
Carp Stock:	Plenty of carp of 5-6lbs, some bigger fish to 16lbs
Category:	Mixed Fishery
Other Species:	Pike, roach, rudd, tench and perch
Permits:	None - free fishing

Control:	Local Council. Tel: 081-640 1171 (Parks Dept)
BK Rating:	Very Difficult for the big carp
Baits/Methods:	Boilies best for big fish; bread for the smaller carp
W/A:	NRA Thames Region

Orlitts Lakes

Location:	Alongside the River Colnbrook, Lakeside Road, off the M4 between Langley and West Drayton
Type and Size:	A pair of lakes, one 15 acres, one 4 acres
Carp Stock:	About 100 carp recently stocked - sizes not known, but thought to be small at present
Category:	Few Carp in large lake, number in Little Orlitts
Other Species:	Perch, bream, pike and large head of tench
Permits:	Boyer Leisure, Trout Road, West Drayton, Middx UX7 7SN. Tel: 0895 444707
Cost:	Season tickets at £30. Also available on group permit
Control:	Boyer Leisure
BK Rating:	Difficult in large; Moderate in small
W/A:	NRA Thames Region

Osterley Park

Location:	Osterley Park, near Twickenham
Type and Size:	Park lake of about 7 acres
Permits:	Season tickets - see notice on bank
Cost:	About £12
BK Rating:	Easy
W/A:	NRA Thames Region
Comments:	We could not find out much about this water, but it certainly contains carp

Potomac Pond

Location:	Gunnersbury Park, Brentford, West London
Type and Size:	Small pond
Carp Stock:	Well stocked with small commons to about 5lbs
Category:	Mixed Fishery
Other Species:	Roach, rudd and perch
Permits:	Day tickets from bailiff on bank
Control:	Council
Restrictions:	No night fishing
BK Rating:	Easy
W/A:	NRA Thames Region
Comments:	A good town water for beginners and float anglers

Regents Canal (Camley Street)

Location:	Off St Pancras Way, North London, near the Post Office building
Type and Size:	Narrow city canal
Carp Stock:	Some carp to doubles
Category:	Few Carp
Other Species:	Roach, perch, bream and a few rudd, tench and eels

Permits:	Day tickets on the bank at £1.50
Control:	Mac McEndoo. Tel: 081-904 4988; Raven AC
BK Rating:	Difficult
W/A:	NRA Thames Region

River Thames

Location:	Best areas for big carp are said to be at Twickenham, Canbury Gardens, Walton-on-Thames and Shepperton
Type and Size:	Wide river
Carp Stock:	Few fish, and hard to find, but carp to well over 20lbs have been caught
Other Species:	Nearly all of them!
Permits:	Most of the Thames in these areas is free fishing
W/A:	NRA Thames Region
Comments:	Carp to about 30lbs have been caught from the Thames, but there are not many of them, they are notoriously hard to find and to catch intentionally, although every now and then they are caught whilst fishing for other species

Savay Lake

Location:	Moorhall Road, Harefield, Denham. Ordnance Survey Map Sheet No. 160. Ref. 048 885
Type and Size:	Mature gravel pit of 60 acres
How to Find:	Take the A40 from London and at Denham turn right onto the A412 towards Watford. After half a mile go under the railway bridge and leaving Denham station on your right turn right into Moorfield Road towards Harefield. The Savay lake entrance is about half a mile on the right
Carp Stock:	Whilst this lake does not contain a huge number of carp there are plenty of very big fish, enough for it to be regarded as a specialist carp water although it is really a mixed fishery. There are many twenties and possibly more thirty pound carp than any other water in the country. Carp to 45lbs have been caught and this is almost certainly now the 'top' carp fishery in the country as far as very big carp are concerned
Category:	Carp Water/Mixed Fishery
Other Species:	Bream, tench, pike, roach and perch. The bream, tench and pike all grow very large
Permits:	Day tickets from Peverills Newsagents, 3 Moorhall Road, Harefield (out of fishery and half a mile to the right) or Balfours Newsagents, 12 Station Parade, Denham (near Denham station). Permits MUST be obtained before fishing. Season tickets from Fishery Manager, Peter Broxup, 309 Shirland Road, London W9. Tel: 071-969 6980 by written application only, enclosing an SAE or from Harefield Tackle Shop
Cost:	Day ticket £2 (juniors/OAP/evening fishing £1). Season tickets £25 (juniors/OAP £12.50)
Restrictions:	No night fishing. Fishery open daily 8am until sunset. Season ticket holders with a gate key may fish from 6am till 9pm. About half the lake is not open to the public and is fished by a club, but there are 100 swims on the open part. Unaccompanied juniors not allowed on the fishery unless they hold a season ticket
BK Rating:	Very Difficult

Baits/Methods: You will need all the latest rigs, methods and baits to stand much chance of catching any of the big carp from this famous water. Many are caught at ranges of 100 yards plus, although in some swims they are taken close in

Control: Redland Angling Scheme

W/A: NRA Thames Region

Comments: There is a night fishing syndicate on this huge water, but membership is expensive and very hard to obtain. Contact the Fishery Manager for details. Some of the leading carp anglers in the country fish here, and long-stay fishing is common and is often needed to catch the very big fish; you can go for weeks without a run. There are islands and sharp gravel bars, and most of the carp are caught from certain well-known areas. You do have some chance in the daytime but many big carp are caught at night. You will normally need the most sophisticated rigs and baits as the fish are wary and most have been caught a number of times. Not the sort of water to fish unless you are a very experienced carp angler, but you are always in with the chance of catching some of the biggest carp in the country - many of which, as you can see from this book are not in private and secret syndicate waters

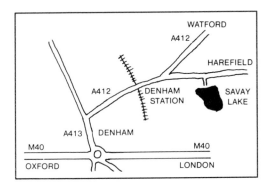

Seven Islands Pond

Location:	Mitcham Common, off the A236 Croydon road
Type and Size:	One acre pond
Carp Stock:	Quite well stocked with carp to 5-6lbs; a few bigger fish to 21lbs
Category:	Mixed Fishery
Other Species:	Roach, tench, perch, pike and rudd
Permits:	None - free fishing
Control:	Local Council. Tel: 081-640 1171 (Parks Dept)
BK Rating:	Very Difficult for the bigger carp
Baits/Methods:	Boilies best for the bigger fish
W/A:	NRA Thames Region

South Norwood Lake

Location:	Woodvale, South Norwood
Type and Size:	2 acre park lake, very shallow
Carp Stock:	The occasional carp is reported
Category:	Few Carp
Other Species:	Pike, roach, rudd, tench and perch
Permits:	Day tickets on bank at low cost
Restrictions:	No sacks; no night fishing
BK Rating:	Very Difficult
W/A:	NRA Thames Region

Stockley Road Lakes

Location:	Stockley Road, Hillingdon, Hayes
Type and Size:	Two old pits, of 3 acres and half an acre
How to Find:	Turn off the M4 at junction 4, go north through lights - 250 yards on right
Carp Stock:	Lightly stocked with carp to 20lbs; small pond - about 55 carp to upper doubles
Category:	Mixed Fishery
Other Species:	Tench, rudd, roach, perch and pike
Permits:	Boyer Leisure, Trout Road, West Drayton, Middx UB7 7SN. Tel: 0895 444707

Cost:	£35 per season. Permit for this water on application. Reductions for juniors, OAP's and the disabled
Control:	Boyer Leisure
Restrictions:	Entry gate must be locked at all times. Unhooking mats compulsory
BK Rating:	Moderate
W/A:	NRA Thames Region
Comments:	A former carp syndicate, and a very pleasant water

Stonebridge Lock

Location:	River Lea, Ferry Lane, Tottenham, near the Walthamstow Reservoirs
Type and Size:	Canal-like section of the River Lea
Carp Stock:	Some carp to nearly 20lbs
Category:	Few Carp
Other Species:	Chub, roach, bream, perch, gudgeon, dace, bleak and tench
Permits:	Day tickets £1 on bank
Control:	Club
BK Rating:	Difficult
W/A:	NRA Thames Region
Comments:	Near the Pipe Bridge is said to be a good area for carp

Swimming Lake

Location:	Parliament Hill, Hampstead Heath
Type and Size:	Small commons pond with concrete banks, much used by year round swimmers
Carp Stock:	A few carp to over 20lbs
Category:	Few Carp
Other Species:	Roach, rudd, perch and pike
Permits:	None necessary - free fishing
BK Rating:	Very Difficult
W/A:	NRA Thames Region

Thorney Pool

Location:	Thorney Road, West Drayton, just off junction 15 of the M25
Type and Size:	Small pool of about an acre
Carp Stock:	Match water, stocked with small carp
Category:	Mixed Fishery
Other Species:	Pike, tench, roach, crucian carp and bream
Permits:	Boyer Leisure, Trout Road, West Drayton, Middx UB7 7SN. Tel: 0895 444707
Cost:	£30 per season. Apply to Boyer's office if you want a permit to fish Thorney Pool only. Reduced prices for juniors, OAPs and the disabled
Control:	Boyer Leisure
Restrictions:	Unhooking mats compulsory
W/A:	NRA Thames Region

New and best selling carp videos from Beekay Publishers. See page 19

Vale of Heath Pond

Location: East Heath Road, Hampstead Common, off the A502
Type and Size: Attractive two acre common pond
Carp Stock: Well stocked with carp to over 20lbs
Category: Mixed Fishery
Other Species: Roach, perch, pike, eels, tench and bream
Permits: Free fishing, although you must have an NRA licence
Restrictions: None, for a change, although you cannot fish the area close to the houses and gardens - which is where the carp spend a lot of their time, of course!
BK Rating: Difficult - heavily fished free water
W/A: NRA Thames Region

Walthamstow No. 1

Location: Ferry Lane, Tottenham N17
Type and Size: Reservoir of 19 acres
How to Find: Near Tottenham Hale Underground Station, Ferry Lane, Tottenham
Carp Stock: Quite well stocked with carp, most of which are 6-12lbs. Record said to be 29lbs
Category: Carp Water
Other Species: Tench, roach and bream
Permits: Day and season from machines at the reservoir. £1, 50p and 20p coins needed
Cost: £2.50 per day; £35 season
Control: Thames Water
Restrictions: No night fishing. Fishing from 7.30am till half an hour after sunset
BK Rating: Moderate
W/A: NRA Thames Region
Comments: A platform has been built out into the lake suitable for wheelchair-bound anglers. Reservoir rim suitable for some ambulatory disabled

Wandsworth Common Pond

Location: Wandsworth Common, London SW18
Type and Size: Small, public 'commons' pond
Carp Stock: Some fish to about 15lbs, numbers unknown
Category: Few Carp
Other Species: Roach, rudd, bream and pike
Permits: Wandsworth Borough Council, Town Hall, Wandsworth
Control: Council
BK Rating: Difficult
W/A: NRA Thames Region

West Warwick

Location: Ferry Lane, Tottenham
Type and Size: Reservoir of 34 acres
How to Find: Car park near Tottenhale Hale Underground Station, Ferry Lane, Tottenham
Carp Stock: Well stocked with carp to mid-twenties. Average size 10½lbs. Growth rates of 4lbs a year recorded by Thames Water. More carp stocking in 1985

Category:	Carp Only
Permits:	From machines at reservoir. £1, 50p and 20p coins needed
Cost:	£2.50 per day; £35 season
Control:	Thames Water
Restrictions:	No night fishing. Fishing is from 7.30am to half an hour after sunset. No groundbait
BK Rating:	Moderate
W/A:	NRA Thames Region
Comments:	Suitable for ambulatory handicapped able to cover long distance. Toilets. On all Walthamstow reservoirs wardens will give help and advice on request

Wraysbury

Location:	Lake 1 - Douglas Lane, Wraysbury; Lake 2 - High Street, Wraysbury, near Staines
Type and Size:	Gravel pits; Lake 1 - 61½ acres, Lake 2 - 76½ acres
How to Find:	Take the A30 from Staines to the Staines by-pass. Take the B376 towards Wraysbury at the roundabout. Go through the village on Station Road, turn left onto Douglas Lane where there is a car park (Lake 1). For Lake 2: where the B276 turns left at Wraysbury village centre the entrance is on the right by the school
Carp Stock:	Not known, but probably few. However, some of these are thought by carp specialists to be very large and a 45 is reported from Lake 1. Carp are not listed in the Guide Book for Lake 2 but there are a few big ones to over 30lbs
Category:	Few Carp
Permits:	Season tickets only from Leisure Sport. Day tickets in advance from: Wraysbury Newsagents in Wraysbury High Street; Davies Angling, 47 Church Street, Staines, or from Leisure Sport
Cost:	£22 per season. Juniors/OAP/disabled £11
Restrictions:	Night fishing allowed. No fishing within casting distance of trout pens
Baits/Methods:	Sophisticated baits and methods possibly needed and probably long casting techniques
Control:	Leisure Sport Angling
BK Rating:	Super-Difficult
W/A:	NRA Thames Region
Comments:	Some of the top anglers in the country have tried these huge waters for the very big carp they are said to contain. Some of these anglers have reported losing big fish at extreme range, and it is thought there could be fish of up to 50lbs present, although we understand you could do a whole season of several thousand hours there and never contact a carp! Peter Springate caught a 47 pounder here in 1992

GREATER MANCHESTER

BOLTON

BLACKLEY

SALFORD

MANCHESTER

Ashton Canal

Location:	East side of Manchester
Type and Size:	Narrow city canal only about four feet deep
How to Find:	From Junction 26 of the M6, take the A5777 towards Orrell. Turn left at a pub called the Abbey Lake and park by the canal
Carp Stock:	Plenty of carp to about 5lbs
Category:	Mixed Fishery
Other Species:	Roach, bream, tench, perch and pike. Recently stocked with about 20,000 small fish for match fishing
Permits:	£1 per day from Gresty's tackle shops, or £1.50 on the bank
Control:	Gresty's AC
BK Rating:	Easy
W/A:	NRA North West Region

Bowker Lakes

Location:	Crumpsall, North Manchester, just off the A665
Type and Size:	Two small, attractive lakes
Carp Stock:	Well stocked with carp to upper doubles, and one possible 20
Category:	Mixed Fishery
Other Species:	Roach, tench and perch
Permits:	Season tickets - try local tackle shops, or enquire on bank
Control:	Bowker Vale Angling Club
Restrictions:	Members only; night fishing by syndicate
W/A:	NRA North West Region

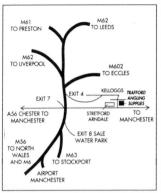

Chorlton Water Park

Location: Maitland Avenue, Chorlton, Manchester 21
Type and Size: Water park lake of 19 acres
How to Find: Come off the M63 motorway at junction 9 and find Maitland Avenue. Water is 5 miles from Manchester centre and five miles from Stockport
Carp Stock: Quite well stocked from 1977 onwards with carp to upper doubles, the majority of which are commons
Category: Mixed Fishery
Other Species: Usual coarse fish
Permits: About £1 per day from office on site or £1.80 from bailiffs on the bank, 20p extra on Bank Holidays and weekends. Juniors about 40p and 80p. Season tickets: adults £10; juniors £4
Control: Mersey Valley Joint Committee. Water Parks Manager Tel: 061-881 5639
BK Rating: Moderate
Restrictions: Fishing 8am till sunset only, unless special night permit obtained
Baits/Methods: Normal carp fishing tactics and baits
W/A: NRA North West Region
Comments: Lake is up to 18 feet deep in parts

Clifton Marina

Location: Clifton House Road, Salford, off the A666 Bolton road
Type and Size: 16 acre gravel pit
Carp Stock: Quite well stocked with carp to about 25lbs
Category: Mixed Fishery
Other Species: Tench, bream, roach and pike
Permits: On the bank at £1.25 per day for adults; 50p for juniors, OAP's and the disabled
Control: Tel: 061-792 2684
Restrictions: No night fishing
BK Rating: Moderate
W/A: NRA North West Region

Debdale Lakes

Location: Gorton, near Manchester
Type and Size: Three reservoirs of about 6 acres each
Carp Stock: Some carp to over 20lbs
Category: Few Carp
Other Species: General coarse fish, including some pike
Permits: Day tickets on bank. Season tickets from Manchester City Council
Control: Council
Restrictions: No night fishing
BK Rating: Very Difficult
W/A: NRA North West Region
Comments: Uninteresting, like most reservoirs, but could produce a very big fish

Heaton Park Lake

Location: Bury Old Road, Manchester
Type and Size: 8 acre park lake with islands, and used by boats
Carp Stock: Well stocked with small carp, but some doubles
Category: Mixed Fishery

Other Species:	General coarse fish
Permits:	On bank at £1.60 per day
Control:	Council - Ron Telford. Tel: 061-773 1085
BK Rating:	Easy
W/A:	NRA North West Region
Comments:	Typical park lake, but quite pleasant and easy fishing

Huddersfield Canal

Location:	Uppermill, east of Oldham on the A669
Type and Size:	Narrow canal with little boat traffic
Carp Stock:	Well stocked with carp from 8lb to 12lbs
Category:	Mixed Fishery
Other Species:	Roach, perch and a few chub
Permits:	On the bank, or from Brownhill Visitors Centre, Uppermill
Cost:	£1.50 per day
Control:	Pete Pearce. Tel: 0457 834327
Restrictions:	No night fishing
BK Rating:	Moderate
W/A:	NRA North West Region

Lankys Mill Pond

Location:	Blackley, north Manchester
Type and Size:	Very clear, weedy pond of about 1½ acres
Carp Stock:	Just half a dozen or so, but possibly a couple of 20's
Category:	Few Carp
Other Species:	Roach and bream
Permits:	None necessary - free fishing
BK Rating:	Very Difficult
W/A:	NRA North West Region
Comments:	No close season; little more than a rubbish dump, but a few good fish. Usual town water problems

Melches

Location:	Farnworth, near Bolton
Type and Size:	Tiny, half acre pond
Carp Stock:	Over 100 carp, with plenty of doubles to 22½lbs
Category:	Carp Water
Permits:	Season tickets only from Greater Manchester Transport Angling Club and Farnworth Cricket and Angling Club
Control:	Club
BK Rating:	Easy
W/A:	NRA North West Region

Myrtle Road Reservoirs

Location: Myrtle Road, Middleton, off the A669 Oldham road
Type and Size: Two small reservoirs
Carp Stock: Quite well stocked with carp to over 20lbs
Category: Mixed Fishery
Other Species: Tench, bream, roach and perch
Permits: Day tickets on bank at £1.50
Control: Tel: 061-643 8134
Restrictions: One rod only; no night fishing
BK Rating: Moderate
W/A: NRA North West Region

Platt Fields

Location: Fallowfield, on the edge of Manchester
Type and Size: Small, shallow lake of about three acres
Carp Stock: Quite well stocked with plenty of doubles up to about 15lbs
Category: Mixed Fishery
Other Species: Roach, tench and perch
Permits: Day tickets on bank. Day and season tickets from Manchester City Council
Control: Council
Restrictions: No night fishing
BK Rating: Moderate
W/A: NRA North West Region
Comments: Used for boating, and often very busy; good fishing throughout the season

River Irwell

Location: Salford area of Manchester
Type and Size: Small river
Carp Stock: Stocked with small carp in 1990 by the Mayor of Salford
Category: Mixed Fishery
Other Species: Roach, bream and perch
Permits: Jubilee Disabled Angling Club
Control: Salford City Council
Restrictions: No night fishing
BK Rating: Not known
W/A: NRA North West Region
Comments: 30 wooden platforms installed with ideal facilities for the disabled

Swan Lodge

Location: Between Bury and Radcliffe, off the A56 north west of Manchester
Type and Size: Small shallow lake
Carp Stock: Some carp, mostly very small
Category: Few Carp
Other Species: Roach, tench and bream
Permits: Day tickets on the bank or from Elton Tackle, Radcliffe. Tel: 061724 5425
Cost: £1.50; £1 for juniors, OAP's and the disabled
Restrictions: No night fishing
BK Rating: Moderate
W/A: NRA North West Region

GWENT (Wales)

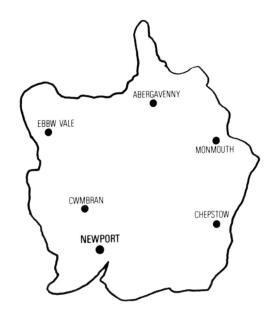

ABERGAVENNY

EBBW VALE

MONMOUTH

CWMBRAN

CHEPSTOW

NEWPORT

Blue Lake

Location:	Waun-y-Pound Industrial Estate, Ebbw Vale
Type and Size:	4 acre reservoir
How to Find:	Find the Waun-y-Pound Industrial Estate in Ebbw Vale, which is on the road from Newport
Carp Stock:	Quite well stocked with smallish carp, average 4-5lbs. There are some bigger fish, with some 20's reported
Category:	Mixed Fishery
Other Species:	Perch, roach, chub, tench and gudgeon
Permits:	Season tickets only by club membership. Ebbw Vale Welfare Angling Club Membership (no day tickets) from: 52 Bethcar Street, Ebbw Vale. Tel: 301392; or E Bynon Tackle Shop, King Street, Brynmawr; R Satterley, 8 Pen-y-Lan, Ebbw Vale. Tel: 308457
Cost:	About £7 per season
Control:	Club
BK Rating:	Moderate
Baits/Methods:	Modern carp fishing baits and methods needed
W/A:	NRA Welsh Region
Comments:	This lake goes down to a depth of 35 feet in places and has concrete and shale banks and no features

Boat Pond, Beaufort

Location:	Highlands Road, Beaufort Hill, Ebbw Vale
Type and Size:	Reservoir of 3½ acres
How to Find:	Address as above. Beaufort is north of Ebbw Vale just off the A465, 8 miles east of Abergavenny
Carp Stock:	Well stocked with mirrors and commons to a good size
Category:	Mixed Fishery
Other Species:	Dace, roach, perch, crucians
Permits:	Season tickets only by membership of Ebbw Vale Welfare Angling Club. Membership from 52 Bethcar Street, Ebbw Vale. Tel: 301392; or Pen-y-Lan, Ebbw Vale. Tel: 308547
Cost:	About £7 per season
Control:	Club
BK Rating:	Difficult
Baits/Methods:	Standard carp fishing baits and methods
W/A:	NRA Welsh Region
Comments:	Fish location is easy in this very clear and very heavily weeded water, but the fish are not easy to tempt

Cwmbran Boating Lake

Location:	Cwmbran, between Malpas and Pontypool
Type and Size:	Man-made boating lake of 1½ acres
How to Find:	The lake is near the Police HQ, just off the A4042, at Cwmbran between Malpas and Pontypool
Carp Stock:	Quite well stocked with commons and mirrors to 18lbs
Category:	Mixed Fishery
Other Species:	Tench, bream, roach, perch
Permits:	Day tickets available on the bank, but best to phone the day before to book a ticket. Torfaen Borough Council. Tel: Cwmbran 67642
Cost:	About £1 per day
BK Rating:	Easy
Baits/Methods:	Standard carp fishing methods with boilies and floaters
W/A:	NRA Welsh Region, Wye Division
Comments:	'Public' water, boats etc

Cwmcelyn Club Water

Location:	Blaina, near Ebbw Vale
Type and Size:	Man-made lake of 1½ acres
How to Find:	Take the A467 from Abertillery north, through Blaina and at the second roundabout take the third exit. Turn left at the next junction
Carp Stock:	Well stocked with commons and mirrors to 17lbs
Category:	Mixed Fishery
Other Species:	Crucian carp, tench, trout, chub, roach, dace, perch, gudgeon and goldfish
Permits:	Day tickets from Granville Derrick. Tel: Blaina 291110; or Des Hillman, 99 Roundhouse Close, Nantyglo. Tel: Nantyglo 311977
Cost:	On application
Control:	Club
BK Rating:	Easy
W/A:	NRA Welsh Region

Lliswerry Pond

Location:	Three miles north of Newport
Type and Size:	Narrow, canal-like lake, very weedy and on housing estate - about 2 acres
Carp Stock:	Well stocked with doubles to about 20lbs
Category:	Mixed Fishery
Other Species:	Tench, roach, bream and rudd
Permits:	Day tickets on bank
Cost:	£3 per day
Control:	Newport AA, L Clarke, Tel: 0633 267047 - night fishing for members only, not on day ticket
BK Rating:	Moderate
W/A:	NRA Welsh Region

Machine Pond

Location:	Warwick Road, Brynmawr, between Abergavenny and Merthyr Tydfil
Carp Stock:	Well stocked with commons and mirrors to about 12lbs, average size about 7lbs
Category:	Mixed Fishery
Other Species:	Pike, perch, roach, chub, tench and gudgeon
Permits:	Season ticket only by club membership. No day tickets. Ebbw Vale Welfare Club Angling Club. Club membership from Petsville, 52 Bethcar Street, Ebbw Vale. Tel: Ebbw Vale 301292; E Bynon Tackle Shop, King Street, Brynmawr; Ray Satterley, 8 Pen-Y-Lan, Ebbw Vale. Tel: Ebbw Vale 308547
Cost:	About £7 per season
Control:	Club
BK Rating:	Easy
Baits/Methods:	Traditional baits and methods, and also boilies and multiple baits
W/A:	NRA Welsh Region

Monmouthshire and Brecon Canal

Location:	The canal runs between Newport and Brecon, about 40 miles
Type and Size:	Narrow, shallow canal
Carp Stock:	Some carp to 20lbs, mostly in concentrated areas, and hard to locate
Category:	Few Carp, except in some areas which would qualify as Mixed Fishery
Other Species:	Most coarse fish
Permits:	Newport AA, L Clarke, Tel: 0633 267047
Control:	Club
BK Rating:	Very Difficult
W/A:	NRA Welsh Region
Comments:	A 16 pounder was caught on floating crust in 1990

Morgans Pool

Location:	Close to the M5, junction 26 to Cymbran
Type and Size:	Lake of about 4 acres
Carp Stock:	Well stocked with small carp to lower doubles
Category:	Carp Water
Permits:	Day tickets on bank

Cost: £2.50 per day
Control: Newport AA. Secretary: P Climo, 2 Darwin Drive, Newport. Club membership open to all at about £20; night fishing for members only
BK Rating: Easy
W/A: NRA Welsh Region

Woodstock Pool

Location: Cymbran, near Newport
Type and Size: 2½ acre lake with island
Carp Stock: Quite well stocked with carp, mostly doubles, to about 20lbs
Category: Mixed Fishery
Other Species: Roach and tench
Permits: Day tickets on bank
Cost: £2.50 per day
Control: Newport AA. Secretary: P Climo, 2 Darwin Drive, Newport. Membership open to all at about £20 per season; night fishing for members only
BK Rating: Moderate
W/A: NRA Welsh Region

GWYNEDD (Wales)

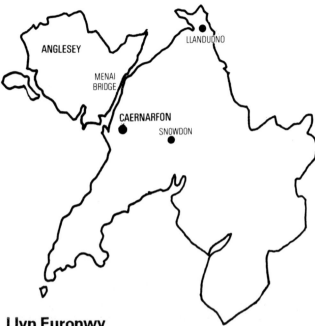

Llyn Euronwy

Location:	Rhosneigr, Anglesey
Type and Size:	1½ acre farm pond
How to Find:	Ty-Len Farm, Rhosneigr
Carp Stock:	Some carp - sizes not known
Category:	Mixed Fishery
Other Species:	Tench, rudd, roach
Permits:	Mr Summerfield, Ty-Len Farm, Rhosneigr. Tel: 0407 810331
Cost:	Approx £2 per day
BK Rating:	Insufficient information
Control:	Private
W/A:	NRA Welsh Region

Llyn-y-Gors Lakes   A

Location:	Llyn-y-Gors, Llandegfan, Menai Bridge, Anglesey, Gwynedd, Wales LL59 5PN
Type and Size:	Two man-made lakes; carp lake - 3½ acres; other lake - 2¾ acres
How to Find:	Follow the A5 towards Holyhead. Cross the Britannia Bridge to Anglesey and take the left hand spur (A5025) to Amlwych. Follow signs to Llandegfan. Turn left at church to Llyn-y-Gors
Carp Stock:	300 fish to 24lbs, average 10-15lbs in carp lake
Category:	Carp Only
Permits:	On site. Tel: 0248 713410 (Roger Thompson)
Cost:	£6 per day; £8 per night, bookable in advance. Prices approximate
BK Rating:	Easy

Restrictions:	No particle baits. Unhooking mats must be used
Control:	Private - the owner is an experienced carp angler
W/A:	NRA Welsh Region
Comments:	No close season. Attractive lakes. Regularly stocked. Other lake - mixed coarse fish - 50lb bags of ghost carp common. Four holiday cottages to let; send for brochure. 38 twenties reported from carp lake in summer 1991. This is a place we can both strongly recommend, as we have stayed there. There couldn't be anywhere pleasanter for a relaxed holiday of any kind, with the bonus of big carp only 75 yards from your cottage door, and a fabulous view of the Snowdon mountain range from your window...

A typical twenty pound common from Lyn-y-Gors

Ty-Hen Farm

Location:	Anglesey
Type and Size:	One and a half acre spring-fed farm pond
Carp Stock:	Heavily stocked with carp to doubles
Category:	Mixed Fishery
Other Species:	Tench
Permits:	Tel: 0407 810331
Cost:	£6 per day
BK Rating:	Not known
W/A:	NRA Welsh Region

HAMPSHIRE

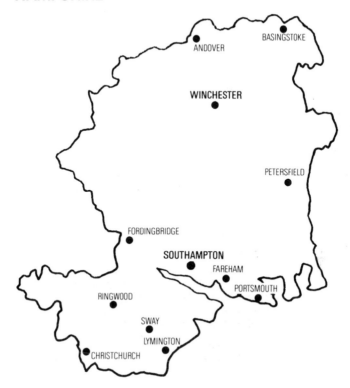

Avon Tyrell   A

Location: Bransgore, near Christchurch
Type and Size: Two attractive lakes of 5 acres and one acre, close to each other
Carp Stock: Well stocked with carp to at least doubles
Category: Mixed Fishery
Other Species: Tench and roach
Permits: Group bookings only, minimum 6 persons; fishing free with full board
                     and accommodation from Guest Services Co-ordinator, Avon Tyrell
                     Residential Centre, Bransgore BH23 8EE. Tel: 0425 72347
Cost: £41 each per weekend, and £85 per week
Control: Private
BK Rating: Moderate
Restrictions: No day tickets
W/A: NRA Wessex Region
Comments: This Centre used to belong to the National Association of Youth Clubs,
                     and when PM was working for some years for the Avon and Bristol
                     Federation of Boys' Clubs, he was instrumental in having the lakes
                     partially drained, the little fish taken out, and the water stocked with
                     carp. This was at least 10 years ago, and he has heard nothing of the
                     place since, so there should be some good fish in there. The many

acres of grounds are very beautiful, and the huge mansion is one of the finest in the country. There is a bar, pool table, heated swimming pool, tennis courts and mountain bikes; and, I am sure, still the lovely walks in the grounds close to the famous Severals Fishery on the Hampshire Avon

Baffins Pond

Location:	Portsmouth
Type and Size:	Five acre lake
How to Find:	Details from Portsmouth and District Angling Society
Carp Stock:	Well stocked with carp to double figures
Category:	Carp Water
Other Species:	Bream, rudd and tench
Permits:	Portsmouth and District AS: Mr R Snook, 86 Carnarvon Road, Copnor, Portsmouth PO2 7NL. Tel: Portsmouth 662986
Cost:	Club membership costs £45 including entrance fee, with reductions for OAP's and youngsters. The club is a member of the Hants and Sussex Anglers Alliance
Control:	Club
BK Rating:	Moderate
W/A:	NRA Southern Region
Comments:	Some of the waters mentioned as controlled by the Portsmouth club may be controlled by other clubs belonging to the Hants and Sussex Anglers Alliance; Crawley AS; Michelmarsh and Timsbury Angling Club; Salisbury and District AS; Eastleigh and District AS; Goring Fire Services AC; Shiplake and Binfield AC; Farnham AS; Guildford AS; Pulborough AC..... Members have exchange ticket facilities with the clubs mentioned above. All details, including information on waters from Mr Snook

Basingstoke Canal

Location:	Aldershot - Basingstoke
Type and Size:	Narrow restored canal, about 15 miles long
How to Find:	Try Claycart Bridge, off the A323 between Aldershot and Fleet
Carp Stock:	Plenty of carp especially at Claycart, with fish to 20lbs
Category:	Mixed Fishery
Other Species:	General coarse fish
Permits:	Day and monthly tickets from local tackle shops and on the bank
Cost:	Day tickets in advance about £1; on bank £1.50
Control:	Basingstoke Canal Anglers Association
BK Rating:	Moderate
W/A:	NRA Thames Region
Comments:	Claycart area produced 14 doubles to two carp anglers on the first day of the 1988 season. This canal could produce some very big fish in the future

Broadlands Lake

Location:	Ower, between Romsey and Totton, Southampton
Type and Size:	Large lake formed in 1977 by the construction of the M27 motorway
Carp Stock:	Well stocked with carp to about 30lbs

Category:	Mixed Fishery
Other Species:	The lake is noted for its pike to over 30lbs, best 39¼, and perch, roach, tench, bream and rudd
Permits:	Day and season tickets from Fishery Manager, Mark Simmonds. Tel: Southampton 733167 or 869881
Cost:	About £3 per day, £40 per season
BK Rating:	Moderate
Baits/Methods:	Carp can be caught on luncheon meat and sweetcorn, but better methods are the use of boilies on bolt or hair rigs
Control:	Private
W/A:	NRA Wessex Region
Comments:	A new lake which has produced huge pike and may well contain some big carp in the future. All information from the Fishery Manager. 35 pounder stocked in 1988 and caught twice already

Broadleafe Lake

Location:	Broadleafe Estate, Lymington
Type and Size:	15 acre, very attractive estate lake, and heavily weeded
Carp Stock:	Well stocked with carp to over 20lbs; many of the smaller fish are commons
Category:	Mixed Fishery
Other Species:	Rudd and pike
Permits:	Syndicate only - M Barry, 19 Saxon Way, Alder Holt, Hants
Control:	Private
BK Rating:	Moderate
W/A:	NRA Southern Region
Comments:	A beautiful place, with lovely gardens. Water is shallow, and not far from the sea

Brockhurst Moat

Location:	Between Fareham and Gosport
Type and Size:	Large moat
Carp Stock:	Well stocked with carp, sizes not known
Category:	Mixed Fishery
Other Species:	Tench, bream, perch, roach and pike
Permits:	Portsmouth and District AS. Mr R Snook, 86 Carnarvon Road, Copnor, Portsmouth PO2 7NL. Tel: Portsmouth 662986, including all information about water location etc
Control:	Club
BK Rating:	Moderate
W/A:	NRA Southern Region

Brownwich Pond

Location:	Titchfield, near Portsmouth
Type and Size:	4 acre lake
How to Find:	Enquire from Portsmouth and District AS
Carp Stock:	A specimen carp fishery, well stocked with large carp
Category:	Carp Only
Permits:	Portsmouth and District AS. Mr R Snook, 86 Carnarvon Road, Copnor, Portsmouth PO2 7NL. Tel: Portsmouth 662986

Control:	Club
BK Rating:	Moderate
W/A:	NRA Southern Region

Cadmans Pool

Location:	In the New Forest at Stoney Cross, just off the end of the M27
Type and Size:	Small forest pool
How to Find:	Leave the M27 at Junction 1, and take the B3078 north. Turn left towards Stoney Cross, the right. Lake is on the right, with car park
Carp Stock:	Well stocked with carp to 10lbs
Category:	Mixed Fishery
Other Species:	Roach, rudd and small bream
Permits:	Day tickets from local tackle shops, campsites and the Forestry Commission at Queen House, Lyndhurst (hope you have better luck at the Forestry Commission H/Q than we did; we wrote to ask them for details of all their waters, but they didn't reply!)
Cost:	£3.20 per day (two rods), half price for juniors; £7.20 per week; £16.20 per month; £51.50 per season. Details on 0703 283771 ext 283 (I expect they do answer the phone)
Restrictions:	No night fishing; barbless hooks
BK Rating:	Easy; good for youngsters
W/A:	NRA Wessex Region

Carrow Row Farm Lakes

Location:	Segensworth Road, near Titchfield
How to Find:	Take the A27 from the M27 at Junction 9, then turn left to Segensworth Road. The ponds are on the left
Type and Size:	Three small shallow ponds
Carp Stock:	Well stocked with carp to upper doubles
Category:	Mixed Fishery
Other Species:	Rudd and tench
Permits:	Day tickets on bank
Cost:	£4.50 per day; £3.50 half day; £2.50 evenings
Control:	Ian Hammond. Tel: 0329 45102
Restrictions:	No night fishing
BK Rating:	Easy
W/A:	NRA Southern Region

Charlton Pits

Location:	Charlton, near Andover
Type and Size:	Matured gravel pit of about 10 acres
Carp Stock:	Well stocked with carp to 20lbs, including some good commons
Category:	Mixed Fishery
Other Species:	Perch, roach, rudd, tench and dace
Permits:	Andover AC, day tickets from local tackle shops or from the Secretary, R L Adcock, Flat 2, Bridge House, 154 Junction Road, Andover
Cost:	Day tickets - £2.50; season - £18
Control:	Club
BK Rating:	Difficult
W/A:	NRA Southern Region

Comments: Back in the seventies, this was a well known (and rather secret) big carp water, but later the lake was partially drained, and most of the big fish netted and sold. The pits are flooded by the River Anton, and are said now to contain grayling as well as other species

Fishers Pond   A

Location: Colden Common, near Winchester
Type and Size: 10 acre estate lake, part of an ancient fish pond
How to Find: Take the A33 from Winchester and the fishery will be found just to the south of Colden Common where the B3051 joins the main road
Carp Stock: Well stocked with carp to 20lbs - many doubles
Category: Mixed Fishery
Other Species: Tench, roach and bream
Permits: From Mr Paton, Fishers Pond Secretary. Tel: Southampton 694412. Mr Paton lives at the fishery and details of costs and permits can be otained from him at the house
Baits/Methods: The carp are caught by specialist carp methods and boilies. Floating crust may work at times
BK Rating: Moderate
W/A: NRA Southern Region
Comments: This attractive lake was connected with the local monastery and carp are still reared here. It would almost qualify under our 'Carp Water' category as there are plenty of good carp present. Wildflowers and much bird life. Self-catering accommodation - cottage and houseboat with free fishing and boating

Frimley

Location: Frimley High Street, Frimley, Farnborough
Type and Size: 10 gravel pits, most of which are small, but one is 11 acres and one about 6 acres
How to Find: Find the A325 and go through Farnborough to Farnborough Green roundabout. Continue on the A325, and cross the railway bridge, to park in Frimley High Street car park. No car parking elsewhere - access to lakes by foot only
Carp Stock: Not known; Leisure Sport say 'carp to 25lbs plus'
Category: Few Carp
Other Species: Bream, tench, roach, perch, pike, crucian carp
Permits: Season tickets only from Leisure Sport, Thorpe Park, Staines Road, Chertsey, Surrey. Tel: Chertsey 64872
Cost: £21 per season. Juniors/OAP/disabled £10.50
Restrictions: No night fishing. Access not available to some parts of area which are a Nature Reserve - details from Leisure Sport Guide Book
BK Rating: Difficult
W/A: NRA Thames Region
Comments: We have only included this and some other venues of this kind because the Leisure Sport Guide Book reports large carp. They are possibly very few as these waters are not recognised carp waters

Golden Springs Lakes

Location:	Near Christchurch
Type and Size:	12 small pools
Carp Stock:	Most of the pools contain carp to about 10lbs
Category:	Mixed Fishery
Other Species:	Tench, roach and trout
Permits:	Christchurch AC - tickets from local tackle shops or C Bungay, 8 Purewell, Christchurch
Control:	Club
Restrictions:	No night fishing - 6am to 30 minutes after sunset only - do not go onto the banks of the River Frome
BK Rating:	Moderate
W/A:	NRA Wessex Region

Hatchett Pond and Cadmans Pool

Location:	Near Cadnam, New Forest
Type and Size:	Medium sized forest pools
How to Find:	Enquire from Forestry Commission
Carp Stock:	Some carp
Other Species:	General coarse fish
Permits:	Forestry Commission, Queens House, Lyndhurst, on site and local tackle shops
Carp Stock:	Season about £38, weekly about £3.50; day about £2.30
BK Rating:	Difficult
Control:	Forestry Commission
Comments:	Licences not required for New Forest ponds

Hightown Lake

Location:	Near Ringwood
Type and Size:	20 acre gravel pit
Carp Stock:	Quite well stocked with carp to 20lbs
Category:	Mixed Fishery
Other Species:	Tench, roach and eels
Permits:	Members only water of Ringwood and District AA. Secretary: R Smith, 1 Avon Castle Drive, Matchams Lane, Ringwood
Restrictions:	No day tickets; no night fishing except for members
BK Rating:	Moderate
W/A:	NRA Wessex Region

Hilsea Moat, Eastern

Location:	Hilsea, Portsmouth
Type and Size:	Large moat of about 4 acres
Carp Stock:	Well stocked with carp to a good size
Category:	Mixed Fishery
Other Species:	Tench, crucians, roach and rudd
Permits:	Portsmouth and District AS. Mr R Snook, 86 Carnarvon Road, Copnor, Portsmouth PO2 7NL. Tel: Portsmouth 662986
Cost:	About £45 for new members, which includes many other local ponds and many miles of river fishing on the Rivers Arun, Rother, River Stour in Dorset, and the Chichester Canal

Control:	Club
BK Rating:	Not known
W/A:	NRA Southern Region
Comments:	Like the other Portsmouth AS waters mentioned in this book, details can be obtained from the Secretary

Hilsea Moat, Western

Location:	Hilsea, Portsmouth
Type and Size:	Smaller part of the moat, about one acre in size, and separate from the Eastern part mentioned above
Carp Stock:	Plenty of carp, sizes not known
Other Species:	Tench, crucians, rudd and roach
Permits:	Portsmouth and District AS, Mr R Snook, 86 Carnarvon Road, Copnor, Portsmouth PO2 7NL. Tel: Portsmouth 662986
Cost:	About £45 per year for new members, to include many other club waters
Control:	Club
BK Rating:	Moderate
W/A:	NRA Southern Region

H.M.S. Dryad Lake

Location:	Portsmouth
Type and Size:	4 acre lake
Carp Stock:	Well stocked, mostly small carp
Category:	Mixed Fishery
Other Species:	Mixed coarse fish
Permits:	Controlled by the Royal Navy
Carp Stock:	On application
BK Rating:	Easy
Control:	Royal Navy
W/A:	NRA Southern Region
Comments:	You could try the Admiralty, but more seriously, local tackle shops would be able to tell you how to go about getting permission - a Naval uniform might help!

Hollybush Lane Lakes

Location:	Farnborough
Type and Size:	3 lakes totalling 20 acres. Mature gravel pits
How to Find:	From London take the M3 motorway and leave at junction 4. Take the A325 towards Farnborough for 3 miles and at the Queens Hotel roundabout turn left onto the A3011. The fishery entrance is one mile along this road opposite the Fir Tree public house. Car park is 300 yards down the lane on the left
Carp Stock:	Middle lake mainly carp with several 20's. Others contain some carp. Main lake suffered a fish kill in 1991
Category:	Mixed Fishery
Other Species:	Bream, tench, roach, perch, pike
Permits:	Day tickets £3 (juniors/OAP/ £1.50) from J and A Newsagents, 201 Lynchford Road, or Raison Bros Tackle Shop, Farnborough. Tel: 0252 543470. Tickets must be obtained before fishing. Season tickets: £30 adults, £15 juniors

227

Restrictions:	No night fishing. No sacking
Baits/Methods:	Normal carp rigs and baits
Control:	Redland Angling Scheme
BK Rating:	Moderate
W/A:	NRA Thames Region
Comments:	Commercial fishery, Redland. Carp to 20lbs reported. Number 44 bus from Aldershot to Woking passes fishery entrance. Ash Vale railway station 10 minutes from fishery. We are reliably informed that the lake itself is just in Surrey!

Home Farm

Location:	Home Farm, Rotherwick, near Hook, Basingstoke
Type and Size:	One acre farm pond
Carp Stock:	Well stocked with carp to about 15lbs
Category:	Mixed Fishery
Other Species:	Rudd, roach and tench
Permits:	Day tickets booked in advance at £6 per day
Control:	Tel: 0256 760281
BK Rating:	Difficult
W/A:	NRA Southern Region

Huckelsbrook Lake

Location:	Off the A338, Christchurch to Fordingbridge road, near Huckelsbrook Garage. Lake entrance on the left hand side going north, past Ibsley and over Huckelsbrook Stream
Type and Size:	Unfished 12 acre matured gravel pit, with large island
Carp Stock:	Sizes not known, as the water has not been fished until recently, but thought to be only about 30 fish
Category:	Mixed Fishery
Other Species:	Roach, rudd, perch and tench
Permits:	Members only water of Christchurch AC. C Bungay, 8 Purewell, Christchurch or P Reading, 17 Mayford Road, Poole
Cost:	£54 per season, to include many other waters
Restrictions:	Barbless hooks; members only; no guest tickets; carp must not be put into sacks; some areas out of bounds, as this is an S.S.S.I. Car parking inside and outside gate only; no carp in nets; open for night fishing
BK Rating:	Not known
W/A:	NRA Wessex Region

Kingfisher Lake (a)

Location:	Teswood Lane, near Southampton
Type and Size:	Gravel pit of 3 acres
How to Find:	From Southampton take the Bournemouth road (A35) and at the roundabout take the Totton road (A36). At the Salmon Leap pub, take a track on the right to Kingfisher Lake. Ordnance Survey Sheet No 196. Grid Reference 358146
Carp Stock:	Well stocked with carp doubles; a 31 has been reported which was probably genuine, but spawn bound. Many commons of 6-12lbs. We are reliably informed that the best 'normal' fish is a common of 14lbs 6ozs
Category:	Mixed Fishery

Other Species: Tench, roach, perch, pike and chub
Permits: Day tickets from Mr Hoskins, 40 Aldermoor Aven, Aldermoor, Southampton. Tel: Southampton 780105, who will also give information on costs etc
BK Rating: Moderate
Control: Private
W/A: NRA Southern Region

Kingfisher Lake (b)
Location: Near Ringwood
Type and Size: Matured gravel pit of 40 acres
Carp Stock: Very well stocked with good carp, many of which are 20's, up to just over 30lbs. Some big commons to 28lbs
Category: Carp Water
Permits: Privately owned by limited company, now a syndicate water
BK Rating: Moderate
Control: Private Tel: 0703 293376
W/A: NRA Wessex Region
Comments: Water is hard fished by good carp anglers, although numbers are limited. Caravans, cafe and other facilities

Lake Farm
Location: Near Fordingbridge - to the west, off the road which joins the A354
Type and Size: Small farm pond
Carp Stock: Hundreds of small carp, with some to 18lbs
Category: Carp Water
Other Species: Some good tench
Permits: Members only water of Ringwood and District AC. Mr K Grozier, 15 Greenfinch Walk, Hightown, Ringwood BH24 3RJ
Cost: £40 per year, to include many other waters
Control: Club
Restrictions: Members only
BK Rating: Very Easy for the little fish
W/A: NRA Wessex Region

Longbridge Lake
Location: Broadlands Estate, Romsey
Type and Size: Two estate lakes, one narrow and canal-like, the other larger with an island
Carp Stock: Well stocked with commons and mirrors to doubles
Category: Mixed Fishery
Other Species: Crucians, ghost carp, perch, roach, rudd, tench, bream, chub, grass carp and eels
Permits: Day tickets from Poingdestres Angling Centre, Shirley; Home Stores Tackle, Swaythling; Sports Centre in Chandlers Ford; and at the lake
Cost: £5 for two rods from 7am to 9pm until October; from October fishing finishes at 6pm. 24 hour tickets at £9.50
Control: Mark Simmonds. Tel: 0703 733167/869881

Restrictions:	No boilies; no keepnets
BK Rating:	Moderate
W/A:	NRA Southern Region
Comments:	No close season; any method trout fishing

Mopley Farm Fishery   A

Location:	Mopley Farm, Mopley Road, Blackfield, Southampton. Tel: 0703 891617
Type and Size:	Three acre farm lake
How to Find:	At Blackfield, 15 miles from Southampton on the edge of the New Forest
Carp Stock:	Well stocked with carp to double figures
Category:	Mixed Fishery
Other Species:	Trout, grayling and some other fish
Permits:	From Brian at farm - phone first
Cost:	From about £4 per day
Control:	Private
BK Rating:	Moderate
W/A:	NRA Southern Region
Comments:	Accommodation nearby. Any method trout fishery with some good carp

Northfield Lakes

Location:	Just north of Ringwood, off the A31 - take the Fordingbridge road, and the lakes are on the left
Type and Size:	Three small pits
Carp Stock:	Well stocked with carp to 27lbs
Category:	Mixed Fishery
Other Species:	Big tench, bream and roach; pike and big eels
Control:	Ringwood and District AC
Permits:	A members only fishery of Ringwood AC; Mr K Grozier, 15 Greenfinch Walk, Hightown, Ringwood BH24 3RJ
Cost:	£40 per season, to include many other waters
Control:	Club
Restrictions:	Members only
BK Rating:	Moderate
W/A:	NRA Wessex Region

Petersfield Heath Lake

Location:	On the edge of town of Petersfield
Type and Size:	8 acre park lake
How to Find:	Just off the A3 at Petersfield
Carp Stock:	Good carp to 27lbs
Category:	Mixed Fishery
Other Species:	General coarse fish
Permits:	Day tickets from local tackle shop. Enquiries to Petersfield AC. Tel: 0730 66793
Cost:	About £2 per day
BK Rating:	Moderate
Control:	Club

Restrictions:	Not known
W/A:	NRA Southern Region
Comments:	Petersfield AC has a large number of other lakes, some of which contain carp

Queens Road Pond

Location:	The Inn on the Sea, Queen's Road, Lee-on-Solent
Type and Size:	Small pond in the grounds of the pub - 10 swims only
Carp Stock:	Quite well stocked with carp to doubles
Category:	Mixed Fishery
Other Species:	Tench, rudd and roach
Permits:	Day tickets from South Coast Tackle, 7 Marine Parade West, Lee-on-Solent
Cost:	£2 and £1 for juniors (who must be accompanied by an adult) OAP's and the disabled
Control:	Mike Sweeney. Tel: 0705 550209
Restrictions:	Fishing from the Queen's Road bank only
BK Rating:	Moderate
W/A:	NRA Southern Region
Comments:	This pond is very close to the sea - as well as to the pub!

Rotherwick Lakes

Location:	Hook, near Basingstoke; off the A30 towards Fleet
Type and Size:	Tiny farm ponds
Carp Stock:	Carp to doubles
Category:	Mixed Fishery
Other Species:	General coarse fish and trout
Permits:	Tel: 0256 763700
Cost:	About £4 per day, on bank
BK Rating:	Fairly Easy
Control:	Private
W/A:	NRA Thames Region
Comments:	Our correspondents are not impressed with this place; they say carp are small and the fishing is poor

Sinah Warren Lake

Location:	Hayling Island, near Havant and Portsmouth, and adjoining the Golf Course
Type and Size:	Huge 35 acre lake
Carp Stock:	Said to be well stocked with carp to well over 20lbs, with possibly some 30's
Category:	Mixed Fishery
Other Species:	Tench, perch, bream and roach
Permits:	Portsmouth and District AS. Mr R Snook, 86 Carnarvon Road, Copnor, Portsmouth PO2 7NL. Tel: Portsmouth 662986
Cost:	Club membership costs about £45 for new members, but includes many other lakes and ponds, and river and canal fishing
Control:	Club
BK Rating:	Difficult
W/A:	NRA Southern Region

Somerly Lakes

Location:	Near Ringwood
Type and Size:	Gravel pit of about 17 acres
Carp Stock:	Well stocked with carp to upper 20's, best 27lbs
Category:	Carp Water
Permits:	Must be obtained in advance from Ringwood Tackle. Tel: 0452 475155
Cost:	£5 per day
Control:	Ringwood AC - John Level. Tel: 0425 477827
BK Rating:	Fairly Hard
W/A:	NRA Southern Region
Comments:	A well-known water, very popular and hard fished. Night fishing by prior arrangement only

St Patrick's Lane Carp Lakes

Location:	Near Frensham, which is just in Surrey
Type and Size:	Small lakes
Carp Stock:	Heavily stocked with carp to 8lbs
Category:	Mixed Fishery
Other Species:	Usual coarse fish
Permits:	Try local tackle shops
Restrictions:	Much used for match fishing
BK Rating:	Very Easy
W/A:	NRA Southern Region

Sway Lakes

Location:	Barrow Lane, Sway, near Brockenhurst
Type and Size:	Two lakes, about an acre and 1½ acres
How to Find:	From Brockenhurst take the Sway road and turn left into Barrow Lane
Carp Stock:	Smaller lake has some carp. Larger lake contains carp to 27lbs - 6 twenties and about 10 doubles, average size 6—8lbs
Category:	Larger lake - Carp Water
Other Species:	General coarse fish
Permits:	From owner on bank
Cost:	About £2.50 per day, £3 per night
Control:	Private
BK Rating:	Moderate
W/A:	NRA Wessex Region
Comments:	For information - Mr T Clarke. Tel: 0590 682010

Topacre Lake

Location:	Alresford, near Winchester
Type and Size:	Very small estate pond
Carp Stock:	Small number of carp to about 30lbs
Category:	Carp Water
Permits:	Syndicate only; details from K Cayzer, Keepers Cottage, New England Estate, Alresford. Tel: 096273 2837
Control:	Private
BK Rating:	Difficult

Turcroft Farm

Location:	Four miles east of Ringwood - turn off the A31 at Picket Post and take the Burley road, then first left into Forest Road
Type and Size:	Small farm lake
Carp Stock:	Well stocked with mirrors, commons and ghost carp, sizes not known
Category:	Mixed Fishery
Other Species:	Roach, rudd, tench and crucians; also stocked rainbow and brown trout
Permits:	Day tickets from Turcroft Farm. Tel: 04253 3743
Cost:	£5.50 for one rod for any method trout fishing during the close season; £5 from June 16th. £1 for an extra rod
Restrictions:	Barbless hooks only. No night fishing. No boilies or keepnets
BK Rating:	Moderate
W/A:	NRA Southern Region
Comments:	No close season. Attractive lake with islands and picnic tables

Waggoner's Wells

Location:	Near Hindhead (which is Surrey, but lakes are in Hampshire)
Type and Size:	3 lakes, one of which is a trout lake
How to Find:	Hindhead area
Carp Stock:	Some carp in the two coarse fishing lakes
Category:	Mixed Fisheries
Other Species:	Perch, tench, roach
Permits:	On site - The Ranger, Summerden North, Waggoner's Wells, Grayshott, Hindhead, Surrey. Tel: Liphook 723722
Cost:	About £10 - season; £1.50 - day; 50p extra for a second rod
BK Rating:	Insufficient information
Control:	National Trust
Restrictions:	Not known
W/A:	NRA Southern Region
Comments:	National Trust property, so likely to be busy

Willow Park Lakes

Location:	Willow Park, near Aldershot
Type and Size:	Large but attractive gravel pit; shallow with gravel bars
Carp Stock:	Heavily stocked with over 500 carp, about 150 doubles and at least 10 twenties to about 28lbs
Category:	Mixed Fishery
Other Species:	Roach, tench, rudd, bream, perch and pike
Permits:	In advance only; day tickets from John Raison on 0252 543470
Control:	Private
Restrictions:	No boilies until after November; unhooking mats must be used
BK Rating:	Moderate
W/A:	NRA Thames Region
Comments:	A well known and pleasant water often featured in the angling press. Fishes well all the year, and is run by a fishing tackle shop owner. Also used for windsurfing, unfortunately

HEREFORD & WORCESTER

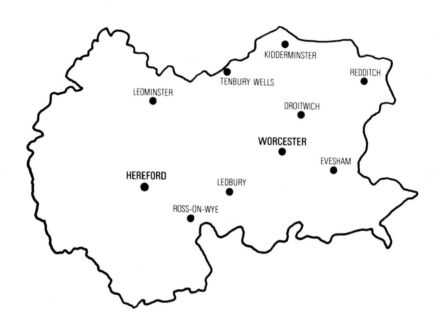

KIDDERMINSTER

REDDITCH

TENBURY WELLS

LEOMINSTER

DROITWICH

WORCESTER

EVESHAM

HEREFORD

LEDBURY

ROSS-ON-WYE

Abbots Salford Park

Location:	Abbots Salford, Evesham
Type and Size:	Small pool
How to Find:	Off the A439 near Evesham
Carp Stock:	Not known
Category:	Unknown
Other Species:	Tench
Permits:	On site
Cost:	On application. Tel: 0386 870244
BK Rating:	Insufficient information
Control:	Private
W/A:	NRA Severn-Trent Region
Comments:	A country park on the banks of the River Avon, which advertises 'a carp and tench pool'. Self-service shop, licensed club, bowling green and 'all pursuits enjoyed by country lovers'

A.C.R. Fisheries, Evesbatch

Location:	Evesbatch, near Worcester
Type and Size:	Two small pools
How to Find:	Take the A4103 from Worcester to Evesbatch - 11 miles
Carp Stock:	Heavily stocked with carp to 20lbs; especially the big lake
Category:	Big lake - Carp Water, small lake - Mixed Fishery
Other Species:	General coarse fish
Permits:	Day tickets in advance only, from Alans Fishing Tackle, St Johns, Worcester
Cost:	On application
Control:	Private
BK Rating:	Easy
W/A:	NRA Severn-Trent Region
Comments:	Popular, heavily stocked lakes

Arrow Fisheries

Location:	Leominster
Type and Size:	Extraordinary man-made 'lakes' in the form of narrow, parallel, canal-like stretches of water constructed for match fishing purposes
Carp Stock:	Heavily stocked with small carp; the owner says he will take out any which reach 3lbs!
Category:	Unique, I should think; a Mixed Fishery
Other Species:	Roach, bream, chub, perch, gudgeon and hybrids
Permits:	Geoff Daw. Tel: 056 884 540
BK Rating:	No idea - should be Easy
W/A:	NRA Welsh Region (we think)
Comments:	There is a licensed bar and club-house; every angler is said to have a level platform, with a gap between islands opposite. The fishery is still being developed - perhaps the bar might at present be the most interesting part!

Arrow Valley Lake

Location:	Batten Drive, off Holloway Drive, Redditch
Type and Size:	Large excavated lake
Carp Stock:	Well stocked with carp to 25lbs
Category:	Mixed Fishery
Other Species:	Roach, rudd, perch, bream and tench, many very large
Permits:	Day tickets from the Warden's hut by the side of the lake. Tel: Redditch 68337
Cost:	About £2 per day; reductions for juniors and OAP's
Control:	Redditch Borough Council, Amenities Dept, Town Hall, Redditch B98 8HA
BK Rating:	Moderate
W/A:	NRA Severn-Trent Region
Comments:	Said to be one of the best waters in the area, with bream to 11lbs, and roach to 3lbs. Next to the lake is Redditch Angling Centre, with all the tackle, baits and information you need

Ashperton Moat

Location:	Ashperton Village, on A417 between Leominster and Gloucester
Type and Size:	Small pool, the remains of a castle moat
How to Find:	Go to Ashperton Village Church, the pool is at the bottom of the path leading through the graveyard!
Carp Stock:	Some small carp to 5-6lbs
Category:	Mixed Fishery
Other Species:	Bream, tench and roach
Permits:	Day tickets in advance only, from the Ledbury Tackle Centre
Cost:	On application
Control:	Ledbury Angling Association
BK Rating:	Easy
W/A:	NRA Severn Trent Region
Comments:	A small, long and narrow lake in pleasant surroundings

Bankes Pool

Location:	Great Witley, near Stourport
Type and Size:	Small pool
How to Find:	On the A451, 5 miles south-west of Stourport
Carp Stock:	Well stocked with carp to doubles
Category:	Mixed Fishery
Other Species:	General coarse fish
Permits:	Day tickets from the farm near the pool
Cost:	On application
BK Rating:	Easy
Control:	Private
W/A:	NRA Severn-Trent Region
Comments:	Very small, overstocked water. Enquire from the farm or local tackle shops

Betula Water

Location:	South Herefordshire
Type and Size:	Small private fishery
Carp Stock:	Well stocked with commons and mirrors to double figure size, with a couple of 20's caught
Category:	Carp Only
Other Species:	None except for a few golden orfe
Permits:	Occasional vacancies for the season only (no day tickets) from Roger Emmet, 10 Digby Drive, Mitton, Tewkesbury, Glos. Tel: Tewkesbury 292533
Cost:	On application
Control:	Syndicate
BK Rating:	Fairly Easy to Moderate
W/A:	NRA Severn-Trent Region
Comments:	Private property - do not visit without permission for any reason

Bewdley Pool   A

Location:	Bewdley, near Kidderminster
Type and Size:	Small pools
How to Find:	In Severn Valley near Bewdley

Carp Stock: Well stocked with carp
Category: Mixed Fishery
Other Species: General coarse fish
Permits: Severn Valley Guest House, Westbourne Street. Tel: 0299 402192
Cost: On application
BK Rating: Moderate
Control: Private
Restrictions: Not known
W/A: NRA Severn-Trent Region
Comments: Accommodation available in guest house. Licences, tackle and bait. Licensed bar. Also famous for its barbel fishing in the River Severn

Birmingham-Worcester Canal

Location: Best area is said to be Hanbury Wharf, Shernal Green, near Droitwich
Type and Size: Narrow canal
How to Find: Hanbury and the canal are a few miles west of Droitwich
Carp Stock: Said to be plenty of carp to 20lbs
Category: Mixed Fishery
Other Species: Usual coarse fish
Permits: Birmingham Anglers Association (members only), 100 Icknield Port Road, Rotton Park, Birmingham B16 OAP. Tel: 021-454 9111, 9.30am to 1.30pm and 7pm to 9pm, weekdays
Cost: About £13 a season, which includes all other BAA waters
BK Rating: Insufficient information, but good carp are notoriously hard to find on canals
Control: BAA
Restrictions: No groundbait of any kind
W/A: NRA Severn-Trent

Bransford Golf Course Pool

Location: Bransford, near Worcester
Type and Size: Small open pool
How to Find: In the village of Bransford, outside Worcester on the A4103
Carp Stock: Well stocked with small carp
Category: Mixed Fishery
Other Species: General coarse fish
Permits: From the main building on the golf course
Cost: On application
Control: Bransford Golf Club
BK Rating: Easy
W/A: NRA Severn Trent Region
Comments: A new, recently constructed fishery on the edge of the golf course. Both the pool and golf course are very well signposted

Church Pool

Location: Opposite the church in the village of Clehonger, near Hereford
Type and Size: Farm pool of approximately one acre
How to Find: Take the A465 from Hereford to Abergavenney. After two miles turn right past Belmont Abbey and then right again after one mile (signed

Clehonger). Park on verge, without obstructing access to the church. The pool is opposite the church

Carp Stock: Well stocked with small carp. Possibly a few doubles present
Category: Carp Water
Other Species: Two or three terrapins, very fond of maggots!!
Permits: Perkins of Hereford, Commercial Road, Hereford. Permits must be obtained before commencing fishing
Cost: £2 per day
Baits/Methods: Any bait and method will score here
Control: Private, day ticket
Restrictions: No keepnets, barbed hooks, groundbait, unsupervised children or litter
W/A: NRA Welsh Region
BK Rating: Very Easy
Comments: A small water, set in a field by a quiet village. Picturesque surroundings. Source of the terrapins - unknown

Court Farm

Location: Bottom of farm track, Court Farm, Tillington, near Hereford
Type and Size: Irrigation reservoir, approx 1½ acres
How to Find: Head north from Hereford on A4110. Turn left at the Three Elms public house and follow signs for Tillington. In Tillington, turn right and follow signs for Court Farm
Carp Stock: Stocked with small mirrors and commons to 8lb
Category: Carp Only
Permits: On site from farmhouse
Cost: £1.50 per day
Baits/Methods: Standard baits and methods work well here
Control: Day ticket water Tel: 0432 760271
W/A: NRA Welsh Region
BK Rating: Easy

Docklow Pools   A

Location: West End Farm, Docklow, Leominster
Type and Size: 5 estate lakes, 2-3 acres each
How to Find: From Leominster take the A44 Worcester road. Docklow is about 3 miles from Leominster
Carp Stock: All the lakes are well stocked with carp although one is mainly a trout pool. Two of the lakes contain carp to 34½lbs, although most of the fish are mirrors of under 10lbs
Category: Carp Water
Permits: Day tickets from Mrs J Bozward, West End Farm
Cost: £3 per day
BK Rating: Easy for the smaller carp; Difficult for the bigger fish
Restrictions: No groundbait; no peanuts; no hemp; barbless hooks
Baits/Methods: Normal carp methods; maggots, luncheon meat and boilies
Control: Private
W/A: NRA Welsh Region (Wye Division)
Comments: 305lbs of carp was once caught in a day on one of these pools. Most carp are small. Accommodation in the farmhouse (bed and breakfast).

There are also 6 attractive self-catering cottages of high standard, some very near the lakes. Brochure from Mrs Bozward at West End Farm. Tel: 056-882256. Ideal for the family or fishing holiday. No close season; excellent fishing in the spring

Eastnor Castle

Location:	Eastnor, near Ledbury
Type and Size:	Estate lake about 5 acres
How to Find:	Take the A449 towards Malvern and then about half a mile outside the town fork right on the A438 towards Tewkesbury. You will pass entrance to the water on the right about 3 miles further on
Carp Stock:	Quite well stocked with mirrors and commons to about 15lbs
Category:	Mixed Fishery
Other Species:	Roach, rudd, bream, tench
Permits:	From bailiffs on bank, about £3 per day
Control:	Private
BK Rating:	Moderate
W/A:	NRA Severn-Trent Region
Comments:	A beautiful lake surrounded by trees. A big area is thickly covered by lilies which make much of this area almost impossible to fish. Most of the carp are caught from the dam end or near the lilies

Eric's Pool

Location:	Shatterford, Kidderminster
Type and Size:	Small lake
Carp Stock:	Sparsely stocked with carp to about 16lbs
Category:	Few Carp
Other Species:	Roach, bream and pike
Permits:	Day tickets at the lake
Control:	Private
BK Rating:	Difficult
W/A:	NRA Severn Trent Region

Evesbatch Top Pool

Location:	Evesbatch, near Worcester
Type and Size:	Small, dammed pool
How to Find:	Continue up the track past ACR Fisheries and the pool is at the top of the hill
Carp Stock:	Quite well stocked with carp to mid doubles
Category:	Mixed Fishery
Other Species:	General coarse fish
Permits:	Day tickets, in advance only from the Ledbury Tackle Centre
Cost:	On application
Control:	Ledbury Angling Association
BK Rating:	Moderate
W/A:	NRA Severn Trent Region
Comments:	A very picturesque pool, quite well match fished during the summer

Golden Valley

Location:	Golden Valley Common, near Castlemorton, Ledbury
Type and Size:	Dammed estate-type lake, stream fed, but on very open common land
How to Find:	From Tewkesbury take the A438 Ledbury road and turn right on the B4208 after about 6 miles. After about a mile, a lane leads onto the common on the left, and the lake will be seen on the right
Carp Stock:	Numbers not known but quite well stocked with commons to about 6lbs
Category:	Mixed Fishery
Other Species:	Crucians, roach, perch and bream
Permits:	This used to be a free fishery but recently someone, presumably the local Council, has been charging 50p a day from bailiffs on the bank
BK Rating:	Moderate
W/A:	NRA Severn-Trent Region
Comments:	A high and open water with some quite good fun fishing for small commons. Most fish caught at night

Haye Farm Fishery

Location:	Bewdley, near Snuff Mill
Type and Size:	Small farm pond
Carp Stock:	Well stocked with carp to 15lbs
Category:	Carp Water
Other Species:	Few coarse fish
Permits:	Day tickets on bank
Cost:	Low
Control:	Private
BK Rating:	Moderate
W/A:	NRA Severn-Trent Region
Comments:	Man-made pond on farm. In same lane as Snuff Mill Pool

Herriots Pool

Location:	Near Droitwich
Carp Stock:	Said to contain large carp. Nothing else known
Permits:	Talbot Hotel, High Street, Droitwich
Control:	Droitwich and District AS. Secretary, Talbot Hotel, Droitwich
Cost:	On application. Day tickets open to all
BK Rating:	Fairly Hard
W/A:	NRA Severn-Trent Region
Comments:	We can find out little about this water, except that it is there! Further details from the Talbot Hotel

Lodge Park Lake

Location:	Redditch
Type and Size:	Small estate lake
How to Find:	In the town of Redditch
Carp Stock:	Very heavily stocked with small carp
Category:	Carp Water
Other Species:	Few
Permits:	R Mayall, 19 Chaddesley Close, Lodge Park, Redditch. Apply in writing only - with an SAE

Cost:	On application
Control:	Private
BK Rating:	Very Easy
W/A:	NRA Severn-Trent Region
Comments:	Many thousands of little carp

Moorlands Farm

Location:	Hartlebury, near Kidderminster, off the A449
Type and Size:	Eight small pools, two of which are for youngsters
How to Find:	From Kidderminster take the A449 Worcester road, turn left where the dual carriageway starts, and turn left again on a farm track signposted to the fishery
Carp Stock:	Meadow Pool and Bank Pool contain carp to doubles
Category:	Mixed Fishery
Other Species:	Crucians, bream, tench, chub, rudd, dace and goldfish
Permits:	Day tickets from the snack bar on the site. Tel: 0299 250427
Cost:	£3 per day; £2 after 2pm
Restrictions:	Fishing is from constructed platforms, and cars can be driven to swims; keepnets banned; barbless hooks recommended
BK Rating:	Moderate
W/A:	NRA Severn-Trent Region
Comments:	Toilets; swims for the disabled

Moors Pool

Location:	Hartlebury, Kidderminster
Type and Size:	Small pool
Carp Stock:	Heavily stocked with small carp, much used for match fishing; said to contain carp to about 10lbs
Category:	Mixed Fishery
Other Species:	Roach, bream and perch
Permits:	Try local tackle shops
Control:	Club
Restrictions:	No night fishing
BK Rating:	Easy
W/A:	NRA Severn-Trent Region

Pixley Pool

Location:	Just off A4172 Leominster to Gloucester road
Type and Size:	Irrigation reservoir of approx two acres
How to Find:	Go south east on A4172. Cross junction with A438 Hereford to Ledbury road. The pool is 500 yards past on the right at the top of an embankment
Carp Stock:	Heavily stocked with carp up to mid doubles
Category:	Carp Only
Permits:	£3.50 per day, available from bailiffs on the bank
Baits/Methods:	Boilies tend to work for the better fish. Floaters go very well in summer
Control:	Private, day ticket; Brian Powell. Tel: 0531 85455
Restrictions:	Night fishing by prior arrangement only - not for the heavy sleepers

W/A: NRA Severn-Trent Region
BK Rating: Moderate
Comments: Some matches take place here. There are other waters run by Brian Powell

Red Bank Farm Lake

Location: Ledbury, near Hereford
Type and Size: Man-made carp fishery of approximately one acre
How to Find: Take the road from Ledbury to Little Marcle, go past the Preserves factory and the fishery is on the right
Carp Stock: Well stocked with carp to 20lbs
Category: Carp Water
Permits: From Bailiffs on the bank, about £3.50 per day
Control: Private. Contact Mr B Powell. Tel: 0531 85455
BK Rating: Moderate
W/A: NRA Severn Trent Region
Comments: This is a man-made fishery, approximately 5 years old. Another similar lake containing smaller carp plus tench, roach and rudd is on the same property

Red Beck Lake

Location:	Near Evesham
Type and Size:	4 acre lake
Carp Stock:	300+ of 2lbs to 10lbs, mostly mirrors. Thousands up to 2lbs, best 15¼lbs
Category:	Carp Only
Other Species:	None
Permits:	Season tickets only, limited membership, from Fishery Controller, 15 Stafford Court, Riverside Close, Bedford MK42 9DE. Tel: 0234 212066
Cost:	About £45 per season
Baits/Methods:	All known methods including legering with all baits, surface fishing, float fishing with maggots and sweetcorn
Control:	Season ticket only; private
Restrictions:	No long-stay fishing or camping. No hair rigs; no pulses (beans and peas) as bait; barbless hooks. No bivvies
BK Rating:	Very Easy
W/A:	NRA Severn-Trent
Comments:	Possibly the easiest water we know. Catches of 40 carp a day quite common. Ideal for beginners and non-carp specialists. Private estate water - do not visit for any reason without permission. Frequent vacancies throughout the season. Guest day tickets for members' friends. Other carp waters available. Warning: private property - do not visit without permission

Ann Pillinger, from Bedford, with a nice carp from Red Beck Lake - one of 17 carp she caught in 8 hours on freelined floating crust

River Severn

Location:	Holt Fleet, between Ombersley and Tenbury Wells - turn right off the A443, where there is an island and a lock
Type and Size:	Attractive, medium-sized river, deep above the weir, and shallow below
Carp Stock:	Some carp to 17lbs
Category:	Few Carp
Other Species:	Barbel, chub, roach, pike, bream and perch
Permits:	Day tickets from lock keeper
Cost:	£3 per day - £35 per season (no day tickets on Sundays - season ticket holders only)
Restrictions:	No night fishing - 5am to 10pm only; fishing on main river side only
BK Rating:	Difficult
W/A:	NRA Severn-Trent Region

River Wye

Location:	Upstream of A49 road bridge in Hereford
Type and Size:	Slow reach of large, normally rapid running river
How to Find:	Go to A49 road bridge and look down
Carp Stock:	Few commons, possibly up to 20lbs
Category:	Mixed Fishery
Other Species:	Chub, roach, perch, bream, tench, barbel, pike, gudgeon, salmon, trout, dace, bleak, eels, grayling, shad during May, and the occasional sturgeon has been seen!
Permits:	Hattons of Hereford, St Owens Street, or Perkins of Hereford, Commercial Road
Cost:	£2 daily
Baits/Methods:	Most baits and methods will work here, but unless cast to specific fish, bait could be taken by the hordes of other fish present
Control:	Club - day ticket
Restrictions:	No night fishing
W/A:	NRA Welsh Region
BK Rating:	Difficult
Comments:	Location is *the* key to avoid problems with other fish. The water is heavily matched fished during summer

Rotherwas Long Pool

Location:	Industrial Estate, south east of Hereford
Type and Size:	Small, rectangular pool of about one and a third acres
How to Find:	Take B4399 from Hereford. Turn left signed Rotherwas Chapel. The pool is on the left
Carp Stock:	Very heavily stocked with small carp up to 5lbs
Category:	Carp Only
Permits:	On bank
Cost:	£2.50 daily
Baits/Methods:	Anything works on this easy water
Control:	Private, day tickets
Restrictions:	No keepnets
W/A:	NRA Welsh Region
BK Rating:	Very Easy
Comments:	This water is unusual in that many of the fish are fully scaled mirrors

Royal Oak Pool

Location: Village of Portway, five miles north of Hereford on A4110
Type and Size: Farm pond of approx one acre
How to Find: Leave Hereford on A4110. Royal Oak public house is on the left in village of Portway. The pool is behind the public house
Carp Stock: Well stocked with commons and mirrors up to low doubles
Category: Carp Water
Other Species: Roach
Permits: Royal Oak public house
Baits/Methods: Any standard baits and methods
Control: Private, day ticket
W/A: NRA Welsh Region
BK Rating: Easy
Comments: Some match fishing takes place. Ideally positioned for those days when it gets too hot and dry to fish!

Snuff Mill

Location: Bewdley
Type and Size: Small old pool
How to Find: Near the River Severn at Bewdley
Carp Stock: Carp to 15lbs
Category: Mixed Fishery
Other Species: Tench, roach, bream
Permits: S Lewis Tackle, Severnside South, Bewdley
Cost: On application
Control: Private Tel: 0299 403358
BK Rating: Moderate

Stanklin Pool

Location: Just to the south of Kidderminster
Type and Size: 6 acre lake, shallow and heavily reeded, with very boggy surrounds and smelly, silty mud
Carp Stock: Very heavily stocked with small carp to about 8lbs, many of which are commons
Category: Carp Water
Other Species: Some tench, roach and eels
Permits: Phoenix AC - small local club with limited membership - enquire locally or in tackle shops
Baits/Methods: Very good floating crust water
BK Rating: Very Easy
W/A: NRA Severn-Trent Region

Two Five Nine

Location: On the left hand side of the B4077 Stow-on-the-Wold to Tewkesbury road, about 2 miles before you reach the A435 at Teddington Cross Hands
Type and Size: Pit of about two acres, with some caravans near it
Carp Stock: Quite well stocked with carp to about 15lbs
Category: Mixed Fishery

Other Species:	Usual coarse fish
Permits:	Enquire from the owner whose house is alongside the road (Brooklands Farm)
BK Rating:	Moderate
W/A:	NRA Severn Trent Region

Twyford Farm Lake

Location:	Twyford County Centre, one mile north of Evesham on the A435
Type and Size:	Small specially dug pond of about two acres, with island
Carp Stock:	⋅ⁿ⋅ ιty of small carp and a few bigger fish to 20lbs
Category:	M ⋅ ¯ishery
Other Species:	Roach, chub, perch, crucians, bream, tench and gudgeon
Permits:	On bank at £3 per day
Control:	May Vince. Tel: 0386 446108
Restrictions:	Fishing is 7am till dusk only; no keepnets
BK Rating:	Moderate
W/A:	NRA Severn Trent Region

Uckinghall Pool

Location:	Ripple, Uckinghall, between Worcester and Tewkesbury
Type and Size:	Small pit alongside River Severn
How to Find:	South from Worcester on A38 towards Tewkesbury, and then to Uckinghall
Carp Stock:	Fairly well stocked with carp to about 10lbs
Category:	Mixed Fishery
Other Species:	Pike, roach, perch, a few rudd
Permits:	Birmingham Anglers Association (members only), 100 Icknield Park Road, Rotton Park, Birmingham B16 OAP. Tel: 021-454 9111, 9.30am to 1.30pm, and 7pm to 9pm, Monday to Friday
Cost:	About £13 a season, which includes all other BAA waters
BK Rating:	Not known
Control:	BAA
Restrictions:	No groundbait of any kind
W/A:	NRA Severn-Trent Region

Upton Warren Lake

Location:	Between the M5, junction 5, and Droitwich, about a mile from the town
Type and Size:	Lake of nearly 20 acres
Carp Stock:	Quite well stocked with carp to 20lbs
Category:	Mixed Fishery
Other Species:	Bream, roach, rudd, perch, dace and eels
Permits:	Day tickets from the office on the site
Cost:	£1.50 per day; £1 for the unemployed, under 21's and OAP's
Control:	Council
Restrictions:	No night fishing - 8am till dusk only; 8am till 5pm on Tuesdays
BK Rating:	Moderate
W/A:	NRA Severn-Trent Region
Comments:	Stands for disabled anglers; some match pegs often booked; no fishing on one bank, which is a Nature Reserve; sailing takes place on this lake, as well as many matches

Wellfield Pool

Location: Highley, Kidderminster
Type and Size: Small pool
Carp Stock: Some carp, mostly small
Category: Mixed Fishery
Other Species: Tench, bream, roach
Permits: Day tickets on bank
Cost: On application
BK Rating: Insufficient information
Control: Private
W/A: NRA Severn-Trent Region
Comments: Try local tackle shops for information

Wilden Pool

Location: Wilden, Stourport-on-Severn
Type and Size: Medium-sized pool
How to Find: Near the River Stour at Wilden, just south of Kidderminster
Carp Stock: Heavily stocked with small carp to 3lbs. A few doubles
Category: Carp Water
Other Species: Some coarse fish
Permits: Day tickets on the bank. Night fishing extra
Cost: On application
BK Rating: Easy
Control: Private - Ron Russell
W/A: NRA Severn-Trent Region
Comments: Standard float fishing methods and baits, as well as legering, will catch these small carp, especially near the island. Try local tackle shops for information

HERTFORDSHIRE

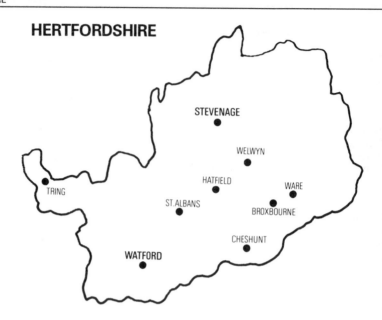

STEVENAGE

WELWYN

HATFIELD

WARE

TRING

ST.ALBANS

BROXBOURNE

CHESHUNT

WATFORD

Aldenham Country Park Reservoir

Location:	Aldenham, near Elstree
Type and Size:	65 acre reservoir
Carp Stock:	Some carp, numbers and sizes not known
Category:	Mixed Fishery
Other Species:	Tench, roach, pike and bream
Permits:	From bailiff on site
Cost:	£3 per rod: £1.50 juniors
Control:	Herts County Council; tickets and information from Park Manager, Park Office, Dagger Lane, Elstree. Tel: 081-953 0932
Restrictions:	No night fishing; no boilies
BK Rating:	Not known
W/A:	Thames
Comments:	Fishing is also alllowed from punts which can be hired at about £5 per day. Evening tickets £1.50

Bowyers Water

Location:	Cheshunt, on the outskirts of North London
Type and Size:	27 acre gravel pit
Carp Stock:	Well stocked with carp to over 30 lbs
Category:	Carp Water
Permits:	Season tickets only from Lee Valley Regional Park Authority, Craig Baldwin, Myddelton House, Bulls Cross, Enfield. Tel: 0992 717711
Cost:	On application
Control:	Lee Valley RPA
BK Rating:	Difficult
Comments:	There was an authenticated carp from this water of 32lbs 3ozs in 1986

Broxbourne

Location:	Meadgate Lane, Broxbourne, Hoddesdon
Type and Size:	Gravel pits. Lake 1 - 24 acres; lake 2 - 30 acres, lake 3 - 68 acres; lake 4 - 3½ acres
How to Find:	Take the A121 to Waltham Abbey, then the B194 1½ miles to Lower Nazeing. Take Pecks Hill Road for 3/4 mile. Turn left into Meadgate Road, keep left at Tile Works, and you can then see the lakes. Car parking at Meadgate Lane only
Carp Stock:	Not known but carp to 28.14 reported; Brackens (No 4) well stocked
Category:	Mixed Fishery
Other Species:	Pike, tench, chub, bream, roach, crucian carp, perch, eels
Permits:	Season tickets only from Leisure Sport, Thorpe Park, Chertsey, Surrey. Tel: Chertsey 64872
Cost:	£22 per season. Juniors/OAP/Disabled £11
BK Rating:	Very Difficult
Control:	Leisure Sports
W/A:	NRA Thames Region
Comments:	The large lakes are also used for sailing. Brackens has heavy weed growth and is hard fished

Crown Fishery

Location:	Off Station Road, Broxbourne, near Wormley off the A10
Type and Size:	Stretch of the River Lea, with much boat traffic in summer
Carp Stock:	Not very many, but some go to over 20lbs
Category:	Few Carp
Other Species:	Chub, roach, perch, tench, bream and pike
Permits:	Day tickets on bank at £1.50 and 80p for juniors and OAP's
Control:	Private. Tel: 0992 463656
Restrictions:	No night fishing
BK Rating:	Very Difficult
W/A:	NRA Thames Region

Fairlands Park

Location:	In Stevenage
Type and Size:	Park lake of about 16 acres, 25 ft deep in places
How to Find:	Enquire at Stevenage
Carp Stock:	Fairly heavily stocked with carp to 20lbs+. Plenty of doubles
Category:	Carp Water
Other Species:	Roach, rudd, bream, tench, pike
Permits:	Day tickets from bailiff on the bank
Cost:	£2.50
Control:	Council
Restrictions:	One bank only can be fished; no night fishing
BK Rating:	Easy
W/A:	NRA Thames Region
Comments:	Sailing boats and canoes

Frogmore Lake

Location: Near St. Albans

Type and Size: Small lake

Carp Stock: Said to contain some carp to a good size, but numbers and sizes not known

Category: Mixed Fishery

Other Species: Usual coarse fish

Permits: Members only water of the London Anglers Association, Forest Road Hall, Hervey Park Road, Walthamstow, London E17 6LJ. Tel: 081-520 7477

Cost: About £20 per season, to include many other waters, including rivers and canal fishing

Control: LAA

BK Rating: Not known

Restrictions: No night fishing

W/A: NRA Thames Region

Grand Union Canal (a)

Location: Watford to Milton Keynes (Herts/Beds/Bucks)

Type and Size: Canal of several miles in length

Carp Stock: Well stocked in certain area along this stretch with many carp up to 30lbs - a fish of 30lbs was reported from the Kings Langley area in 1990

Category: Mixed Fishery

Other Species: General coarse fish

Permits: Day tickets from various clubs in the area - you will need to enquire locally

Control: Mainly clubs

BK Rating: Easy to difficult depending on area

W/A: NRA Thames/Anglian Region depending on area

Grand Union Canal (b)

Location: Marsworth Basin, Tring

How to Find: Take the A489 road from Tring to Marsworth

Carp Stock: Heavily stocked with commons and mirrors mainly to 5lbs, with occasional bigger fish

Category: Mixed Fishery

Other Species: Perch, roach, bream and catfish

Permits: Permits are obtainable on the bank

Baits/Methods: Float fishing and legering with maggots, bread or sweetcorn. Specialist carp tactics not needed

Control: Tring Angling Club. Secretary: B Boucher. Tel: Chesham 782713

BK Rating: Easy

W/A: NRA Thames Region

Comments: Good water for fun fishing and as a change from lakes

Hatfield Broadwater

Location: Essendon, near Hatfield, on River Lea
Type and Size: 7 acre lake
Carp Stock: Carp to over 20lbs
Category: Mixed Fishery
Other Species: Bream, roach and tench
Permits: Members only water of Hatfield and District AS, E F Denchfield, 44 Stockbreach Road, Hatfield, Herts
Control: Club
Restrictions: No day tickets, club members only
BK Rating: Moderate
W/A: NRA Thames Region

Henlow Grange

Location: Between the villages of Henlow and Arlesey, both of which are in Bedfordshire!
Type and Size: Gravel pits of 9, 5 and 3 acres
Carp Stock: Large lake fairly well stocked with carp to 44lbs (although this was a spawnbound fish which is thought to be dead). In 1991 a 31½lb common and a mirror of over 30lbs were caught. Other two lakes well stocked with carp to low twenties
Category: Mixed Fishery
Permits: Letchworth Angling Club - season tickets from local tackle shops, in Letchworth and Hitchin
Cost: About £25 per season - no day tickets
BK Rating: Large lake - Difficult; other lakes - Moderate
W/A: NRA Anglian Region
Comments: Good club waters, with a few very large fish

Holwell Hyde Lake

Location: Cole Green near Welwyn Garden City
Type and Size: 2 acre lake
How to Find: Find Hatfield and take the A405 to the left, turn onto the A414 Hertford road. After 3 miles turn left onto the B195 and continue for 1½ miles. Turn left into Holwell Hyde Lane. The lake is half a mile down the lane on the left
Carp Stock: Well stocked with carp which are thought to be small, but some upper doubles and two 20's
Category: Mixed Fishery
Other Species: Tench, roach and rudd
Permits: Day tickets from bailiffs on the bank or in advance from Fishery Manager, V Bamford Esq., Holwell Hyde Cottage, Holwell Hyde Lane, Welwyn Garden City. Season tickets about £15 (£10 for Juniors/OAP's/ evening fishing from Fishery Manager
Cost: Day tickets about £2.50 (£1.25 Juniors/OAP's). Season tickets £25
Restrictions: No night fishing. Sunrise to sunset for season ticket and advance day ticket holders. Those without tickets must not be on the fishery before 8.30am. No unaccompanied juniors unless they hold season tickets. No sacking. One rod only till October
Control: Redland Angling Scheme

BK Rating: Easy
W/A: NRA Thames Region
Comments: Little is known about this water which has been little fished previously.
                Do not park anywhere other than in the car park. Bus No. 324 from
                Welwyn Garden City to Hertford passes the end of Holwell Hyde Lane.
                Car parking close to water

Hook Lake

Location: Northaw, near Potters Bar
Type and Size: 1½ acre pool
How to Find: Enquire from Fourways Fisheries
Carp Stock: Well stocked with carp to 20 lbs, mostly doubles
Category: Mixed Fishery
Other Species: Tench, catfish, zander, pike
Permits: Fourways Fisheries, Poplars Nursery, Harlington Road, Toddington,
                Dunstable, Beds. Tel: 0525 55584
Cost: About £80
BK Rating: Not known
Control: Fourways Fisheries
W/A: NRA Thames Region
Comments: Details supplied on receipt of an SAE

Kings Weir Fishery

Location: Lea Navigation, near Wormley
Type and Size: River, weir pool, and one bank of a local lake
How to Find: From the A10 turn towards Turnford (!) and follow the A1170 to
                Wormley. At Wormley turn right into Wharfe Road, cross the railway,
                and park in the car park by the river
Carp Stock: Some carp to about mid-doubles
Category: Few Carp
Other Species: Barbel to well over 10lbs, chub, bream, perch, pike, dace and eels
Permits: Day tickets, booked in advance only from B Newton. Tel: 0992 468394
Cost: £5 per day for river and weir pool; £1 per day on lake
Control: Private
BK Rating: Difficult
W/A: NRA Thames Region
Comments: A very attractive and unusual fishery close to London

Marsworth Reservoir

Location: Marsworth, near Tring
Type and Size: 40 acre reservoir
How to Find: Take the A41 from Tring, and turn right on the B489. You will see the
                car park on the right
Carp Stock: Some carp to over 20lbs, with a chance of a 30
Category: Mixed Fishery
Other Species: Big tench and bream; roach, perch, rudd, pike and catfish
Permits: Day tickets on bank
Cost: £3 per day; OAP's and those under 14, £2 per day
Control: Bernard Double. Tel: 044282 2379

Restrictions: No keepnets or baits; night fishing for syndicate members only
BK Rating: Very Difficult
W/A: NRA Thames Region

North Met Pit

Location: Cheshunt, Herts. in the Lea Valley, North London
Type and Size: Gravel pit of 58 acres
Carp Stock: Well stocked with carp to mid-thirties; stocked with 2000lbs of carp between 14 and 18 lbs in 1990, with 2,500 more pounds to come
Category: Carp Water
Other Species: Big pike and tench
Permits: Lee Valley Regional Park Authority, Craig Baldwin, Myddleton House, Bulls Cross, Enfield. Tel: 0992 717711
Cost: Season only, on application
Control: Lee Valley R.P.A.
BK Rating: Fairly Hard
W/A: NRA Thames Region
Comments: Heavy stocking with big fish should make these lakes excellent carp waters in the near future

Redlands Crown Fishery

Location: Broxbourne
Type and Size: 3 lakes totalling about 40 acres
How to Find: Take the A10 from London and turn off at Hoddesdon. At the roundabout after 400 yards take first exit sign marked 'Dobbs Weir Industrial Estate'. Pass the Fish and Eels public house and after another 600 yards enter the fishery through gates on the left near Richard White Sluices
Carp Stock: Not many carp but some are large
Category: Few Carp
Other Species: Tench, bream, roach, perch, pike
Permits: No day tickets. Season tickets only from Fishery Manager. Peter Brill, Carthagena Lock, Broxbourne, Herts. Tel: Hoddesdon 463656
Cost: About £12 a season. Juniors/OAP £6
BK Rating: Difficult, as there are few carp
Control: Redland Angling Scheme
W/A: NRA Thames Region

River Gade

Location: Cassiobury Park, off the A412, just after Watford Town Hall
Type and Size: Small river with weirs and sluices
Carp Stock: Some carp to nearly 10lbs
Category: Few Carp
Other Species: Chub, perch, roach, dace, rudd, pike and gudgeon
Permits: Free
Control: Council
BK Rating: Difficult
W/A: NRA Thames Region

Springwell Lake

Location:	Rickmansworth, near Watford
Type and Size:	Medium sized matured gravel pit
Carp Stock:	Well stocked with carp to 20lbs
Category:	Mixed Fishery
Other Species:	Tench, roach and perch
Permits:	Members only water of London Anglers Association, Forest Road Hall, Hervey Park Road, Walthamstow, London E17. Tel: 081-520 7477
Cost:	About £20 per season, to include a number of other waters - 100 miles of fishing in rivers, canals, lakes and reservoirs
Control:	LAA
Restrictions:	No night fishing
BK Rating:	Not known
W/A:	NRA Thames Region

Stanborough Lake

Location:	Welwyn Garden City
Type and Size:	Gravel pit of about 20 acres
How to Find:	Edge of A1M near Welwyn Garden City
Carp Stock:	Very heavily stocked with many doubles to 20lbs. Few twenties to 27lbs
Category:	Carp Water
Other Species:	Roach, rudd, tench, bream and catfish
Permits:	Day tickets and club membership available on bank. £3.50 at weekends; £2.50 on weekdays
Control:	Welwyn Garden City AC
BK Rating:	Very Easy
Restrictions:	One rod only - you won't need more on this easy water. Two rods after 1st November - no groundbaiting and no boilies; no night fishing
W/A:	NRA Thames Region
Comments:	Sailing boats and many people

Stanstead Abbots

Location:	High Street, Stanstead Abbot, Ware, Herts
Type and Size:	Two gravel pits of 3 acres and 7½ acres
How to Find:	From London take the A10 Cambridge road and then the A414 to Stanstead Abbots. Park cars in the public car park in the High Street and walk down the path at the rear of the car park to the lakes
Carp Stock:	Stocked with 1,500 carp in 1983, sizes not known, and also a few bigger carp to 31lbs, were stocked in 1984. Mixed fishery although if enough of these carp survived there should be enough to take this into our Carp Water category in the future. Many 20's and 30's caught. Fish up to 42lbs in the bigger lake
Category:	Mixed Fishery
Other Species:	Tench, bream, roach and chub
Permits:	Season tickets from LSA, Thorpe Park, Staines Road, Chertsey, Surrey. Tel: Chertsey 64872
Cost:	£33 per season; Juniors/OAP/Disabled £11.50. Limited tickets on a first come, first served basis
Restrictions:	Usual LSA rules but night fishing is allowed
BK Rating:	Difficult to Very Difficult

Control:	Leisure Sport Angling
W/A:	NRA Thames Region
Comments:	The big lake is so difficult that a correspondent tells us that all the anglers look like zombies and won't talk to you - yet Rob Maylin had a 35 in half an hour!

Startops, Tring Reservoirs

Location:	Near Tring
Type and Size:	Reservoir of 30 acres
Carp Stock:	Not many carp, but there are some 20's and possibly much bigger fish present
Category:	Few Carp
Other Species:	Bream, tench, roach, perch, pike, catfish
Permits:	Day tickets from bailiff on the bank
Restrictions:	No night fishing, but there is a night syndicate
Control:	Private
BK Rating:	Very Difficult
W/A:	NRA Thames Region
Comments:	Night syndicate, members only

Weston's Lake

Location:	Just outside the village of Weston, near Stevenage
Type and Size:	Lake of about three acres
Carp Stock:	Lightly stocked with carp to upper doubles
Category:	Mixed Fishery
Other Species:	Crucians, tench, rudd and bream
Permits:	Weston AC; details from local tackle shops
Restrictions:	Members only; no night fishing
BK Rating:	Difficult
W/A:	NRA Anglian Region
Comments:	An attractive lake, used mainly for matches

Wormleybury

Location:	Wormley, near Broxbourne, Church Lane
Type and Size:	Estate lake of 5 acres
Carp Stock:	Not many carp, mostly very large with about 15 20's including two commons of over 25lbs, some upper 20's. Lake record is 36lbs, but this fish has since died. Possibly one other low 30 in the lake
Category:	Mixed Fishery
Other Species:	Tench, roach, rudd, bream, perch, pike
Permits:	From the owner, Graham Barnes, Wormleybury House, Church Lane, Broxbourne, Herts. At the time of going to press he had stopped all fishing due to bad behaviour of anglers
Cost:	About £80 a season; 1 rod and 2 rod tickets
Cost:	Private
Baits/Methods:	The most up-to-date advanced carp tactics/methods required for this water
BK Rating:	Very Difficult
W/A:	NRA Thames Region
Comments:	A beautiful crescent shaped estate water in the grounds of a big house. Lots of reeds, lilies etc. Apply in writing to the owners as fishing might never be allowed on this water again

HUMBERSIDE

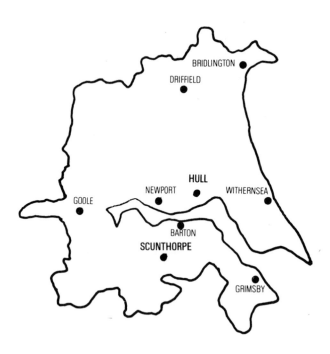

Bakers Pond

Location:	Thimble Hall Lane, Newport, near Hull (white bungalow)
Type and Size:	2½ acre lake
How to Find:	Newport Village is at the end of the M62
Carp Stock:	Well stocked with carp to 26lbs+
Category:	Carp Water
Other Species:	Crucians, tench and bream
Permits:	On site - Tel: Bill Baker on 0430 440350 (7am to 10.30pm)
Cost:	£1 per day
BK Rating:	Moderate
Control:	Private
W/A:	NRA Yorkshire Region
Restrictions:	No tic beans, no keepnets
Comments:	Owner lives on the site. Big catches reported. 10-20 feet deep - snag and weed free except for central island supported by telegraph poles

Barton Broads   A

Location:	Barton-on-Humber, South Humberside
Type and Size:	11 acre clay pit
How to Find:	Off the A15 just before the Humber Bridge
Carp Stock:	Heavily stocked with 3,000 carp to 21.7lbs. Many doubles
Category:	Mixed Fishery
Other Species:	Catfish, tench, bream roach, rudd
Permits:	On site or telephone 0652 32237
Cost:	About £1.50 per day; £2.50 for 24 hours; syndicate £100
BK Rating:	Moderate to Difficult
Restrictions:	No hemp
Control:	Private
W/A:	NRA Anglian Region
Comments:	The site includes a cafe, a tackle and bait shop, and caravans for holidays - contact the resident owners for details

Big Hole Pit

Location:	Rawcliffe, just west of Goole off the M62
Type and Size:	5 acre brick pit, with bars, bays and weed
Carp Stock:	Well stocked with small carp to about 10lbs
Category:	Mixed Fishery
Other Species:	Roach, rudd, tench and bream
Permits:	Members only water of Goole and Dist., AA. Secretary, L Roger, 29 Westfield Square, Goole N. Humberside DN15 6QR
Cost:	About £12 per season
Restrictions:	No day tickets; no night fishing; no carp sacks or weighing slings!
BK Rating:	Easy
W/A:	NRA Yorkshire Region

Burstwick Ski Pond

Location:	Burstwick, Hedon, Hull
Type and Size:	Large lake
How to Find:	From Hull take the A1033 to Hedon, then the B1362 to Burstwick. Go through the village towards Keyingham, and the lake is down an old railway track
Carp Stock:	Quite well stocked with carp to 20lbs
Category:	Mixed Fishery
Other Species:	Bream, tench, roach, rudd, perch and trout
Permits:	Day tickets from clubhouse on site
Cost:	Tel: 0964 622674 for costs and information
Control:	Private
BK Rating:	Thought to be quite hard
W/A:	NRA Yorkshire Region
Comments:	There is water skiing on this lake. Night fishing is permitted

Burton Constable Lakes

Location:	Burton Constable Hall, Sproatley, near Hull
Type and Size:	Several estate lakes, of about 25 acres in all
Carp Stock:	Quite well stocked with carp to double figures

Category:	Mixed Fishery
Other Species:	Roach, bream, perch, tench and pike
Permits:	The Warden, Old Lodge, Sproatley, Nr. Hull
Cost:	Season - £23; month - £11; week - £5.50
Control:	Private
Restrictions:	Open for fishing from lst March to 31st October only
BK Rating:	Moderate
W/A:	NRA Yorkshire Region
Comments:	Very good fishing on an attractive private estate

Emmotland Carp Syndicate

Location:	Emmotland, North Frodingham, near Driffield
Type and Size:	Small lake, formerly Pond One of Langholme Hill Fisheries
Carp Stock:	Well stocked with carp to over 20lbs
Category:	Carp Water
Other Species:	Some coarse fish
Permits:	Syndicate only, from Brian Skoyles, 1 Thornwich Avenue, Willerby, near Hull HU10 6LS (waiting list)
Cost:	On application
Control:	Brian Skoyles, but some information from Mrs M Whitmore, Fishery owner. Tel: 0262 488226
BK Rating:	Moderate
W/A:	NRA Yorkshire Region

Fishponds Farm Fishery

Location:	Bridlington
Type and Size:	Three small farm ponds
How to Find:	From Bridlington town centre, follow Woldgate, which becomes a narrow country lane, and the lakes are on the right
Carp Stock:	Well stocked with mirrors and commons, sizes not known
Category:	Mixed Fishery
Other Species:	Crucians, bream, tench, roach, rudd, perch, brook trout, brown and rainbow trout
Permits:	Day tickets at the office. For details, telephone the owner, Mr J Nadin, on 0262 605873
BK Rating:	Insufficient information
Control:	Private
W/A:	NRA Yorkshire Region
Restrictions:	Barbless hooks only. No keepnets. No one under 18 unless accompanied by an adult angler
Comments:	This is said to be the most attractive water in Yorkshire, surrounded by woodland and very peaceful

Fish Trades Pond

Location:	Newport, between Hull and Goole, on B1239
Type and Size:	Small pond of 1 acre
How to Find:	Just off the A64 at Newport Village
Carp Stock:	Well stocked with carp to upper doubles
Category:	Carp Water
Other Species:	Tench, bream, roach, perch, pike, trout

Permits: Day tickets
Cost: Low
Restrictions: No night fishing; no keepnets
BK Rating: Moderate
Control: Not known - enquire from local tackle shops
W/A: NRA Yorkshire Region
Comments: Popular day ticket water. Try Hull and District AA, J Holdenbury, 1 Grebe Road, Thimblehall Lane, Newport, N. Humberside HU15 2PJ for information. This club has some excellent carp fisheries in Humberside. No close season

Halsham Pond

Location: Behind the New Stag public house on the B1362 at Halsham, near Withernsea
Type and Size: Small pond
Carp Stock: Quite well stocked with carp to double figures
Category: Mixed Fishery
Other Species: Bream, tench and rudd and perch
Permits: From Mr Allison, New Stag Inn, Halsham, N. Humberside. Tel: 094 70487
Cost: Low cost day tickets
Control: Private
BK Rating: Moderate
Restrictions: No night fishing - 7.30am till dusk only. Barbless hooks
W/A: NRA Yorkshire Region
Comments: Park in the pub car park! Some areas suitable for disabled anglers

Hoe Hill Fishery

Location: Pasture Road North, off the A1077 near Barton-on-Humber
Type and Size: Three acre shallow lake
Carp Stock: Quite well stocked with carp to mid-doubles
Category: Mixed Fishery
Other Species: Tench, roach, rudd, perch, chub and bream
Permits: On the bank or from the house on the property
Cost: £2 per day; £3 for night fishing, by special arrangement
Control: John Smith. Tel: 0652 635119
Restrictions: No boilies
BK Rating: Moderate
W/A: NRA Anglian Region

Holme Lake Fishery

Location: Holme Lane, Messingham, near Scunthorpe. Three miles from junction 4 off the M18
Type and Size: 20 acre sand pit
Carp Stock: Stocked in 1988 with 5,500 carp from 4oz to 8lbs and one 27 pounder
Category: Mixed Fishery
Other Species: Roach, bream, rudd and perch
Permits: Day tickets from Alan Barton. Tel: 0724 850197
Cost: £3 per day

Control: Private
BK Rating: Moderate
W/A: NRA Yorkshire Region

Kingfisher Lodge   A

Location: Hibaldstow, off the B1206 south east of Scunthorpe
Type and Size: Man-made lake of about five acres, with a large island
Carp Stock: Heavily stocked with doubles
Category: Mixed Fishery
Other Species: Tench, chub, bream, perch and rudd
Permits: On the bank at £2 per day
Control: Nigel Coulson. Tel: 0652 654652
Restrictions: No night fishing; no groundbaiting
BK Rating: Moderate
W/A: NRA Anglian Region
Comments: No close season. Six caravans for hire. Toilets and camping areas. Cars can be driven to swims

Langholme Hill Fishery

Location: Emmotland, North Frodingham
Type and Size: Four smallish lakes
How to Find: Take the B1249 from Driffield to North Frodingham, and after the village turn right to Emmotland. The lakes are on the left at the end of this road
Carp Stock: Well stocked carp to over 20lbs
Category: Mixed Fishery
Other Species: Big bream and tench, roach, perch, pike, trout
Permits: On bank, at £3 per rod
Control: Private. M Whitfield. Tel: 0262 488226
Restrictions: No night fishing. No keepnets
W/A: NRA Yorkshire Region
Comments: Open for 11 months of the year. Fishing dawn till dusk

Lindholme Lake

Location: Off the A164 and the M180 south of Thorne
Type and Size: Three small lakes, one a carp fishery
Carp Stock: Heavily stocked with carp to 5lbs
Category: Carp Water
Other Species: Big tench, roach, perch, bream and a few trout
Permits: Day tickets on site
Cost: £3.50 or £2 for an evening session
Control: Brian Lindley, Tel: 0427 872015; Head Bailiff, Tel: 0427 872906
Restrictions: No night fishing
BK Rating: Easy
W/A: NRA Yorkshire Region

Motorway Pond

Location:	Near Hull
Type and Size:	Lake of 18½ acres
How to Find:	On the edge of Hull
Carp Stock:	About 100 big carp to 29lbs 14oz and some smaller carp
Category:	Mixed Fishery
Other Species:	Double figure bream and good tench
Permits:	Hull and District AC - local tackle shops
Cost:	On application
BK Rating:	Moderate
Control:	Club. Kevin Cliffod, Sandholme Grange, Newport, North Humberside HU15 2QG. Tel: 0430 440624
W/A:	NRA Yorkshire Region
Comments:	Enquire for details from local tackle shops, and Hull AC

Rushyvars Lakes

Location:	Near Preston, off the A1033 Hull road to Hedon
Type and Size:	Medium-sized lake
Carp Stock:	Well stocked with carp, sizes not known
Category:	Mixed Fishery
Other Species:	Tench, bream, rudd and roach
Permits:	On site, low cost
BK Rating:	Moderate
Restrictions:	No night fishing - dawn to dusk only. Barbless hooks. No groundbait
Control:	Private
W/A:	NRA Yorkshire Region
Comments:	Toilet facilities, and level banks for disabled anglers. There is also a small trout lake on the site. Tel: 0482 898970 for full details of this fishery

The Billabong Caravan Park   A

Location:	Hempholme Bridge, Brandesburton, near Driffield YO25 8NB. Tel: 0964 543631
Type and Size:	11 acre pit
How to Find:	Off the A165
Carp Stock:	Well stocked with carp to 15lbs
Category:	Carp Water
Other Species:	Pike, perch, roach, bream and trout
Permits:	From owner on site - free at present for those staying on site, but day ticket charge being considered
BK Rating:	Not known
W/A:	NRA Yorkshire Region
Comments:	There is water skiing and other water sports on the lake, with most fishing during the mornings, evening and after dark

The Nest

Location:	Wintringham, near Scunthorpe, S.Humberside
Type and Size:	One acre man-made pond
How to Find:	Just off the A1077 between Scunthorpe and Barton-upon-Humber
Carp Stock:	Well stocked, mostly 6-8 lbs; a few doubles to 11lbs

Category:	Mixed Fishery
Other Species:	Crucians, grass carp, tench, rudd, roach, perch
Permits:	On bank. Tel: Wintringham 732465
Cost:	About £2 per day (6am to 8pm)
BK Rating:	Easy
Control:	Private
Baits/Methods:	Sweetcorn, maggots, luncheon meat, cheese paste
W/A:	NRA Yorkshire Region
Restrictions:	No night fishing
Comments:	Well coloured water with slippery banks when wet. Booking may be necessary in advance as only 20 anglers are allowed to fish the water. Also fished by 'small fish' anglers

Tilery Lake

Location:	Broomfleet Tile Factory, near Hull
Type and Size:	Clay pit of 20 acres
Carp Stock:	Thought to contain about 70 carp, all of which are said to be doubles averaging 18lbs in weight. Plenty of 20's to 32lbs
Category:	Carp Water/Mixed Fishery
Other Species:	Pike, bream, roach
Permits:	Hull and District Angling Association, Hull. Secretary: J Holdenby, 1 Grebe Road, Thimblehall Lane, Newport HU15 2PJ
Cost:	Club membership about £10 a year, with an additional £40 for night fishing (waiting list)
BK Rating:	Difficult
Control:	Club; Kevin Clifford, Sandholme Grange, Newport, North Humberside. Tel: 0430 440624
W/A:	NRA Yorkshire Region
Comments:	Night fishing for those living locally only. Carp said to be growing fast. Open and featureless water, 4-17ft deep

Westfield Lakes   A

Location:	Westfields Hotel, Barton-on-Humber, off the A15 near the south side of the Humber Bridge
Type and Size:	Two small lakes in grounds of hotel
Carp Stock:	Well stocked with carp to over 20lbs
Category:	Mixed Fishery
Other Species:	Tench, roach, rudd, bream and pike
Permits:	From Westfields Hotel
Cost:	£2 per rod, or £3.50 per rod on the bank
Control:	Tel: 0652 32313
Restrictions:	No night fishing; no live baiting
BK Rating:	Moderate
W/A:	NRA Anglian Region
Comments:	No close season

Winter's Pool

Location: East Halton, in S. Humberside between Grimsby and Barton-under-Humber

Type and Size: Two acre clay pit with clear banks

How to Find: Take the A180 from Grimsby, then turn onto A1173, then follow signs for East Halton

Carp Stock: Quite well stocked with carp to upper doubles, with possibly a low 20 or two

Category: Mixed Fishery

Other Species: Roach and bream

Permits: Day tickets. Tel: 0469 40238

Control: Private

BK Rating: Moderate

W/A: NRA Yorkshire Region

Comments: No close season

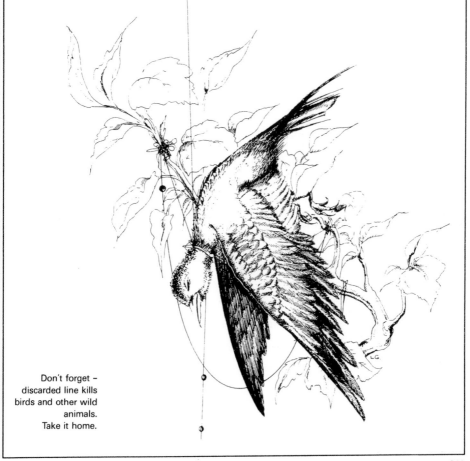

Don't forget –
discarded line kills
birds and other wild
animals.
Take it home.

IRELAND

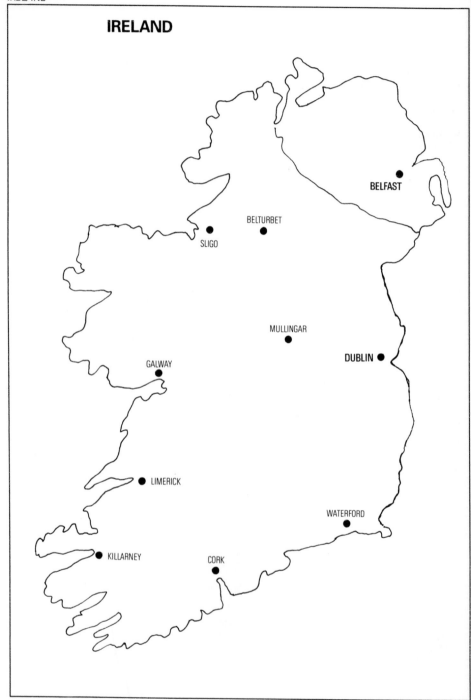

BELFAST

BELTURBET

SLIGO

MULLINGAR

DUBLIN

GALWAY

LIMERICK

WATERFORD

KILLARNEY

CORK

Ballinafid Lake

Location: North of Mullingar, off the N4 Mullingar-Longford road
Type and Size: Small lake
Carp Stock: Quite well stocked with carp to about 15lbs
Category: Mixed Fishery
Other Species: Bream and tench
Permits: Irish State Rod Licence, cost about £10
BK Rating: Moderate
Comments: No close season. Best fishing opposite main road. Soft banks, reeds and a platform

Bun Lough

Location: Car park on the N3 Belturbet-Cavan road, and across two fields
Type and Size: 21 acre Irish lough, very weedy, with a soft bottom
Carp Stock: Stocked with small carp about 5 years ago, present number and sizes not known
Category: Mixed Fishery
Permits: Irish State Rod Licence required, cost about £10
BK Rating: Difficult - you're likely to catch lots of tench and bream!
Comments: No close season. If you do catch any carp, please report them to the Irish Fisheries Board, Mobhi Boreen, Glasnevin, Dublin 5 or local Fisheries Board offices, the address of which can be had locally. Make sure you cause no problems crossing the farmer's fields to get to the lake

Cork Lough

Location: Off the Western Road in Cork City
Type and Size: 10 acre town lake near houses, very shallow and a wildfowl sanctuary
Category: Mixed Fishery
Other Species: Tench, rudd, perch and big eels
Permits: Irish State Licence, cost about £10
Baits/Methods: Sweetcorn works well, and so do most normal carp baits and methods
BK Rating: Moderate
Comments: No close season; public water, very busy, and heavily fished, as it holds the Irish carp record of 25¾lbs, caught on sweetcorn and 3lb line. This is Ireland's best carp water. Do not leave line or tackle to damage birds

Doolin Pond

Location: Off the R400 road from Mullingar, near Gaybrook Cross
Type and Size: Small muddy, weedy lake
Carp Stock: This water was set up as an experimental carp fishery, and carp are now caught to about 10lbs
Category: Carp Water
Permits: Irish State Rod Licence, costing about £10
Baits/Methods: Standard specialist carp methods needed
BK Rating: Difficult
Comments: No close season. Easy access

Galmoylestown Lake

Location:	North of Mullingar - turn left off the R394 Mullingar-Castlepollard road
Type and Size:	Small lake, weedy and only about 4 feet deep
Carp Stock:	Stocked with small carp by the Central Fisheries Board some years ago. These fish are now being caught up to about 10lbs
Category:	Carp Water
Other Species:	Some trout at this former trout fishery
Permits:	State Rod Licence required, the cost which is about £10
Baits/Methods:	The water is heavily fished and the carp now need sophisticated baits and methods to be caught
BK Rating:	Moderate
Comments:	One of Ireland's few carp waters, this pleasant little lake has good access for disabled anglers. You should not require any permits except the Irish State Licence. No close season. An angler had 46 carp to 8lbs in one session in 1992

Paddy McNamara Lake

Location:	Near O'Briens Bridge, at the junction of the R463 Limerick-Killaloe road, and the R466 O'Brien's Bridge-Broadford road, south west of Killaloe
Type and Size:	10 acre weedy lake, about 10 feet deep
Carp Stock:	Stocked with carp to about 8lb by the late Paddy Mac, a well known and distinguished developer of fishing in the area
Category:	Mixed Fishery
Other Species:	Rudd, perch and tench
Permits:	Irish State Rod Licence required, cost about £10
BK Rating:	Moderate
Comments:	No close season

Westmeath Farm   A

Location:	Co. Westmeath, near Lakes Ennel and Owel
Type and Size:	Large lake
Carp Stock:	Some carp to doubles
Category:	Mixed Fishery
Other Species:	Trout, bream and tench
Permits:	Tel: 010 353 44 55292
Control:	Private
BK Rating:	Not known
Comments:	Bed and breakfast, evening meal and packed lunch from £18, on working farm. Carp fishing nearby. No close season

Turn Grandad's old tackle into cash see page 287

ISLE OF WIGHT

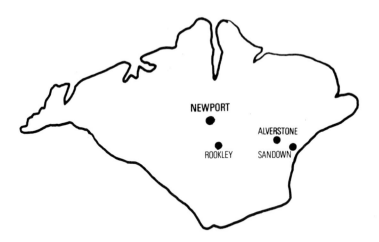

Gunville Pond

Location: Gunville Pool, Carisbrooke, near Newport
Type and Size: Lake of 3 acres
Carp Stock: Well stocked with carp to 11lbs
Category: Mixed Fishery
Other Species: Perch, tench, rudd, pike and roach
Permits: Tickets from tackle shops in most towns, such as G C Young, 74 Regent Street, Shanklin. W Bates, 5 Springhill, Ventnor. (Members only)
Cost: About £9 per season, £4 per week, £1.50 per day
Control: Isle of Wight Freshwater Angling Association. M Steed, 6 Priors Walk, Newport PO30 5RN. Tel: 0983 521267
Restrictions: Members only
BK Rating: Easy
W/A: NRA Southern Region

River Yar (a)

Location: Alverstone
Type and Size: Small, shallow river, only about 25ft wide
Carp Stock: Some carp to 6lbs
Category: Few Carp
Other Species: Dace, roach, perch, gudgeon and eels
Permits: Day tickets from Scotties Tackle Shop, Lugley Street, Newport or Doug Stephens, Bait and Tackle, Union Street, Newport
Control: Isle of Wight Freshwater AA. Mr Mick Steed, 6 Priors Walk, Newport PO30 5RN. Tel: 0983 521267
BK Rating: Difficult
W/A: NRA Southern Region

River Yar (b)

Location:	Just south of the main road (A3055) between Sandown and Brading, behind the 'Anglers Inn' public house
Type and Size:	Small river, only about 40ft wide
Carp Stock:	Some carp to double figures
Category:	Few Carp
Other Species:	Dace, roach, perch, gudgeon, tench, rudd, bream and eels
Permits:	Day tickets from Scotties Tackle Shop, Lugley Street, Newport or Doug Stephens, Union Street, Newport
Control:	Isle of Wight Freshwater AA, Mr Mick Steed, 6 Priors Walk, Newport PO30 5RN. Tel 0983 521267
BK Rating:	Difficult
W/A:	NRA Southern Region

Rookley Country Park   A

Location:	Rookley, near Godshill
Type and Size:	Small lake in 20 acres of parkland
Carp Stock:	Some carp
Category:	Mixed Fishery
Other Species:	Roach and perch
Permits:	On site. Tel: 0983 70606
Cost:	On application
Control:	Private
BK Rating:	Unknown
W/A:	NRA Southern Region
Comments:	Luxury caravans, licensed bar, restaurant, games room, pitch and putt course, children's adventure playground, darts, pool and video games, take-away food. Prices from £80 - £200 per caravan including fishing. Rose Award caravan park 1991. Hoseasons for booking

Somerton Reservoir

Location:	On the A3020 Newport to West Cowes road, about 3 miles from Newport
Type and Size:	Small reservoir
Carp Stock:	Well stocked with carp from 2lbs to 5lbs, best about 10lbs
Category:	Mixed Fishery
Other Species:	Roach, rudd and perch
Permits:	Day tickets from bailiff on bank
Cost:	£3; Juniors £.50
Control:	Isle of Wight Freshwater AA, Secretary Mr M J Steed, 6 Priors Walk, Newport PO30 5RN. Tel: 0983 521267
Baits/Methods:	Luncheon meat very good for the carp
BK Rating:	Easy
W/A:	NRA Southern Region

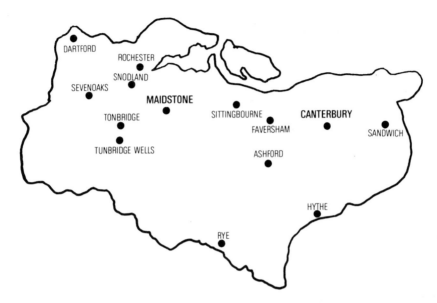

KENT

Alders Lakes

Location:	Near Snodland, close to Reeds Lakes
Type and Size:	Three gravel pits with island etc, the biggest of which is about 6 acres
Carp Stock:	All three lakes are well stocked with carp. The biggest lake has a number of 20's to about 29lbs; the Trout Lake contains many low doubles, and the Castle Lake contains small commons
Category:	Mixed Fisheries
Other Species:	Roach, bream, pike, perch and big eels
Permits:	Alders AC, a private club which is hard to get into - try local tackle shops for information - season tickets only
Control:	Club
BK Rating:	Big Lake - Moderate; others - Easy
W/A:	NRA Southern Region

Allhallows Leisure Park　　　A

Location:	Allhallows-on-Sea, ME3 9BR
Type and Size:	Small lake
Carp Stock:	Well stocked with carp, sizes not known
Category:	Mixed Fishery
Other Species:	Usual coarse fish
Permits:	All information from the address above, or Tel: 0800 521178
BK Rating:	Not known
W/A:	NRA Southern Region
Comments:	Caravans for sale; usual entertainment and sports etc

Ashby Farm Lakes   A

Location:	Appledore, Ashford
Type and Size:	2 reservoirs of 2 acres each
How to Find:	Near Ashford
Carp Stock:	Carp to 18lbs
Category:	Mixed Fishery
Other Species:	General coarse fish
Permits:	On site - residents only. Tel: 023-383-378
Cost:	Approx £2.75 per day; group week ticket also available
BK Rating:	Moderate
Control:	Private
Restrictions:	Not known
W/A:	NRA Southern Region
Comments:	Holiday centre; self catering accommodation in Scandinavian style chalets at waters edge. £110 to £245 according to season. Fishing extra. No fishing unless resident. Beautiful woodland setting

Ashford Pit

Location:	Near the town of Ashford
Type and Size:	Small pit
Carp Stock:	Well stocked with carp to double figures
Category:	Mixed Fishery
Other Species:	Big tench and rudd
Permits:	Ashford Working Mens Club, members only - no day tickets. For details enquire from local tackle shops, such as M and H Angling, 1 Thirlstane Terrace, Hythe
Control:	Club
BK Rating:	Not known
W/A:	NRA Southern Region

Barden Park Lake

Location:	Barden Park, Brook Street, Tonbridge
Type and Size:	10 acre lake
Carp Stock:	Not heavily stocked for the size of water, but one or two big fish to over 30lbs. Many small commons
Category:	Mixed Fishery
Other Species:	Roach, bream, tench, pike, perch and eels
Permits:	Enquire locally, or from local tackle shops
Restrictions:	Members only; no night fishing
BK Rating:	Fairly Hard
W/A:	NRA Southern Region

Biddenden Lake

Location:	Bettenham Manor, Biddenham, near Tenterden
Type and Size:	Two acre estate lake
How to Find:	Take the Sissinghurst road from Tenterden, and in one mile, opposite a pub, turn right for another two miles
Carp Stock:	Mirrors and commons to 23lbs; numbers not known
Category:	Mixed Fishery
Other Species:	Roach, bream and perch

Permits:	Day tickets at £5 in advance only from the address above
Control:	Private - J Hampshire
BK Rating:	Moderate
W/A:	NRA Southern Region
Comments:	Very old lake with established stock of fish. Limited to only two anglers per day

Blue Lake

Location:	Near Northfleet
Type and Size:	Old chalk pit of 20—30 acres
How to Find:	The pit is just off the A2 road at Northfleet
Carp Stock:	Quite well stocked with doubles and 20's to 30lbs
Category:	Carp Water
Other Species:	Tench, bream and eels
Permits:	No day tickets, club membership only
Control:	Thameside Working Mens Club
BK Rating:	Difficult
W/A:	NRA Thames Region
Comments:	This pit is 60-70 feet deep in places; surface fishing works well at times. Enquire locally for membership

Brooklands

Location:	Dartford
Type and Size:	Gravel pit of 16-20 acres
How to Find:	Just off the A2 at the traffic lights where you turn towards Dartford
Carp Stock:	Huge stock, many doubles and twenties, and two thirties. Said to contain more doubles and 20's for its size than any other water in England
Category:	Carp Water
Other Species:	Bream, tench, roach, pike, rudd
Permits:	Day tickets from bailiffs on bank at £3
Control:	Club. Dartford and District APS. Hon. Secretary: D E Reeve, 29 Berkeley Crescent, Dartford, Kent. Membership very hard to obtain; mainly for locals. Tel: 0322 228532
Restrictions:	No night fishing; no peanuts
BK Rating:	Moderate
W/A:	NRA Thames Region
Comments:	A very well-known carp water, where some of the leading carp anglers have fished and where some of the early bait experiments with high protein baits took place. Undoubtedly one of the most heavily fished waters in the country. Here they actually queue for swims and people have been known to wait several days and nights behind someone who is fishing in order to get their place when they leave! Some of the best pitches are permanently fished, day and night for the whole season.

We have heard it said that before the start of the season carp anglers camp on the bank for a week before the season to obtain the best places

Bysingwood

Location:	Bysingwood Road, Faversham
Type and Size:	Mature gravel pit of about 10 acres
How to Find:	Take Bysingwood Road from Faversham and the lake is on the left about 2 miles from the town centre
Carp Stock:	Very heavily overstocked with doubles. Occasional 20's to 23lbs
Category:	Carp Water
Other Species:	Tench, bream and eels
Permits:	Faversham Angling Club. Hon Secretary: A O Baldock, 5 Kennedy Close, Faversham. Tel: 533240. It is very hard to get into the club and you will almost certainly have to live in the Faversham area; worth a try for others
Cost:	Approx £15 per season
Control:	Club
BK Rating:	Very Easy
W/A:	NRA Southern Region
Comments:	This is most certainly one of the best known doubles carp water in the country. 10-12 doubles a day is possible and we have heard that an angler once had 25 doubles in one day. For this reason it is very hard to get into, but we have included it because it is on the same club ticket as the School Pool and you may be able to obtain membership if you live locally. For others it is unlikely, but you can apply and hope for the best. A number of well known carp anglers have fished this water

Chiddingstone Castle Lake

Location:	Chiddingstone Castle, near Tonbridge
Type and Size:	Estate lake of 3 acres
How to Find:	Take the B2027 road from Tonbridge to Edenbridge
Carp Stock:	Well stocked with commons to 10lbs. A few lower doubles
Category:	Mixed Fishery
Other Species:	Roach, perch, bream, gudgeon, rudd
Permits:	From the bailiff on the bank. Details from the Secretary, Chiddingstone Castle, Edenbridge. Tel: Edenbridge 870347
Cost:	Approx £5 per day
Baits/Methods:	Normal carp fishing methods and baits. Bread will still catch the carp
Control:	Private - day ticket book in advance if possible
Restrictions:	No night fishing
BK Rating:	Easy
W/A:	NRA Southern Region
Comments:	Peaceful situation with tree-lined banks, weed and lilies. Grounds of ancient castle

Chilham Castle Carp Syndicate

Location:	Chilham Castle grounds, Chilham
Type and Size:	5 acre estate lake
How to Find:	7 miles south west of Canterbury on the A252
Carp Stock:	Very heavily stocked with thin commons to about 8lbs
Category:	Carp Water
Other Species:	Some coarse fish
Permits:	Albert Brown, Heronsview Fisheries, Drovers End, Pudding Lane, Ash CT3 2EJ. Tel: 0304 812651 or 0843 296031

Cost:	On application
Control:	Private
BK Rating:	Easy
Restrictions:	On application; no day tickets
W/A:	NRA Southern Region
Comments:	In the beautiful grounds of one of the finest English castles, in one of the prettiest villages in the country. Big catches in fine surroundings

Chilham Mill

Location:	Chilham Mill, near Canterbury
Type and Size:	Lake of 25 acres
Carp Stock:	Well stocked with mirrors and commons to over 20lbs, with a possible 30
Category:	Mixed Fishery
Other Species:	Big pike, double figure bream and roach
Permits:	Mid Kent Water, Odsal House, Harbledown, Canterbury, Kent CT2 8ND
Cost:	About £100 a season
Control:	Mid Kent Water
BK Rating:	Not known, but probably Difficult
W/A:	NRA Southern Region
Comments:	Former day ticket lake now taken over by Mid Kent Water. Bird watching, and livebait is banned

Chipstead Lakes

Location:	Near Sevenoaks
Type and Size:	Lake of 20 acres plus
Carp Stock:	Well stocked with carp to over 30lbs
Category:	Mixed Fishery
Other Species:	Tench, bream, roach and rudd
Permits:	Mr S Banks, 58 Chevening Road, Chipstead, Sevenoaks
Cost:	Seasonal only at £35, with £15 joining fee
Control:	Holmesdale AC
BK Rating:	Moderate
W/A:	NRA Southern Region

Cotton Farm

Location:	Near Dartford, just to the east end of the Dartford Tunnel, and almost within sight of the toll booths and the River Thames
Type and Size:	Open pit of nearly 10 acres - once twice this size, but partly filled in
Carp Stock:	Well stocked with low doubles, and a number of 20's to about 30lbs
Category:	Carp Water
Other Species:	Roach, bream and pike
Control:	Private; membership and permits from The Tackle Box, Sutton-at-Hone
BK Rating:	Fairly Hard
W/A:	NRA Southern Region
Comments:	Quite a well known water, and fished by some of the top carp anglers. Fishes well in winter, with a good chance of a winter twenty

Danson Park

Location:	Between Welling and Bexleyheath
Type and Size:	Large shallow park lake
How to Find:	Just off the A2 at Blackfen
Carp Stock:	Quite heavily stocked with carp to doubles
Category:	Carp Water
Other Species:	Roach, tench, perch, crucians and gudgeon
Permits:	Day tickets on bank at £3
Control:	Council - GLC. Tel: 081-304 5386
Restrictions:	No night fishing
BK Rating:	Moderate
W/A:	NRA Thames Region

Darenth

Location:	Parsonage Lane, Darenth, near Dartford
Type and Size:	4 gravel pits: Big Lake - 13 acres; Long Lake - 4 acres; Tree Lake - 3 acres; Tip Lake - 9 acres
How to Find:	Take the A2 to the traffic lights at Dartford. Turn right onto the A225, after 2 miles turn left at Parsonage Lane (signposted Darenth). Continue for half a mile and the main entrance is on right just after 2 river bridges
Carp Stock:	Big Lake - well stocked with doubles and twenties to over 30 pounds. Long Lake - some doubles and 20's to about 29 pounds. Tree Lake - a few doubles and one or two twenties. Tip Lake - a few twenties and more than a dozen thirties to about 40 pounds
Category:	All four lakes are Carp Waters
Other Species:	Bream, tench, pike, perch, roach, rudd, chub
Permits:	Leisure Sport Special Venue. Thorpe Water Park, Staines Road, Chertsey, Surrey. Tel: Chertsey 64872. Season tickets only
Cost:	Approx £33 per season. Juniors/OAP/disabled - £21
Control:	Leisure Sport Angling
Restrictions:	See Leisure Sport Guide Book for very strict rules
BK Rating:	Big Lake - Moderate; Long Lake - Fairly Hard; Tree Lake - Difficult; Tip Lake - Fairly Hard
W/A:	NRA Thames Region
Comments:	One of the best known big carp waters in the country. Heavily fished by experienced and successful carp anglers. Modern rigs and sophisticated baits needed

Eridge Green Lake

Location:	Just off the A26 at Eridge, south west of Tunbridge Wells
Type and Size:	3 acre estate lake
Carp Stock:	Well stocked with carp to doubles
Category:	Mixed Fishery
Other Species:	Usual coarse fish
Permits:	County Leisure AA, 65 Pelham Road South, Gravesend DA11 8QS. Tel: 0474 332399
Cost:	£25 per season to include other carp waters
Control:	CLAA
BK Rating:	Not known
Comments:	CLAA has a number of carp lakes, and its members can also fish all the CALPAC waters, some of which contain good carp

TRILENE

	MAXIMA	TRILENE XL	TRILENE XT	BIG GAME
STATED B/S	2lb	2lb	2lb	not available
MEASURED B/S	3¾lb	3¾lb	5¼lb	n/a
MEASURED DIA.	.0055"	.0045"	.006"	n/a
STATED B/S	6lb	6lb	6lb	not available
MEASURED B/S	8lb	8½lb	9¼lb	n/a
MEASURED DIA.	.009"	.0075"	.0085"	n/a
STATED B/S	10lb	10lb	10lb	10lb
MEASURED B/S	10¾lb	13¼lb	17lb	13lb
MEASURED DIA.	.011"	.0105"	.0125"	.0105"
STATED B/S	12lb	not available	not available	12lb
MEASURED B/S	13½lb	n/a	n/a	17¼lb
MEASURED DIA.	.012"	n/a	n/a	.013"
STATED B/S	15lb	not available	14lb	15lb
MEASURED B/S	16¼lb	n/a	22¼lb	21¾lb
MEASURED DIA.	.015"	n/a	.014"	.0145"

Independent tests conducted at NASA conference 4th April 1992

more than just another line

WHAT THE EXPERTS SAY

Its abrasion-resistant qualities are really quite remarkable for a mono line, I use it with total confidence — **JIM GIBBINSON**

When it comes to fishing amongst weed or any form of snags, there is no line I know in comparable breaking strains to compare with Terry Eustace Big Game Line — **ROD HUTCHINSON**

Too good to be true, the most impressive line I've ever seen — **LEE JACKSON**

Incredible abrasion resistance yet still very soft, available in 12lb but to be honest it casts as smoothly as many 8lb lines — **SHAUN HARRISON**

It's a fact . . . the best lines are not made in Europe any more — **CHRIS BALL**

BIG GAME

The ultimate line for the big fish angler. Superb line lay, casting performance, high shock and abrasion resistance, incredibly strong for diameter and almost invisible in water. Do you really need any other line? Used by many of Britain's leading carp and pike anglers.

CLEAR - £15.99
Ref
295 - 10lb x 1500 yards
295 - 12lb x 1175 yards
296 - 15lb x 900 yards
297 - 20lb x 700 yards
298 - 25lb x 595 yards
299 - 30lb x 440 yards

200 - 40lb x 370 yards
201 - 50lb x 275 yards
GREEN - £15.99
Ref
260 - 10lb x 1500 yards
261 - 12lb x 1175 yards
262 - 15lb x 900 yards
263 - 20lb x 700 yards

TRILENE XT

Trilene XT (Extra Tough) will stand a tremendous amount of knocking about. Its superior abrasion resistance is due to an extra tough layer of protection that resists nicks, cuts and scrapes. For all those anglers who want Big Game performance in lower strains this is the answer.

CLEAR - 110 yards
Ref
300 - 2lb - £4.85
301 - 4lb - £4.85
302 - 6lb - £4.85
303 - 8lb - £4.85
304 - 10lb - £5.95

CLEAR - 330 yards
301 - 4lb - £12.75
311 - 6lb - £12.75
312 - 8lb - £12.75
313 - 10lb - £14.95
314 - 14lb - £14.95
315 - 20lb - £18.95
316 - 25lb - £18.95
317 - 30lb - £18.95

TRILENE XL

Trilene XL (Extra Limp) has a unique nylon alloy formulation which gives incredible strength whilst its extra limpness and low memory provide exceptional handling, casting characteristics and outstanding knot strength. A brilliant floating line for the angler who wants supreme control.

GREEN - 110 yards
Ref
320 - 2lb - £4.85
321 - 4lb - £4.85
322 - 6lb - £4.85
323 - 8lb - £4.85
324 - 10lb - £5.95

GREEN - 330 yards
Ref
331 - 4lb - £12.75
332 - 6lb - £12.75
333 - 8lb - £12.75
334 - 10lb - £14.95

WHITE/FLUORESCENT BLUE now available

YOU HAVE THE LATEST TECHNOLOGY TRILENE ONLY IF THE BOX CARRIES A GOLD LABEL STICKER

Terry Eustace

Gold Label Tackle

FLUO-BOBBINS

High Visibility bobbins, with our favourite colours being Yellow and Green, which show up extremely well in daylight and are also, as with the Blue, extremely visible after dark with an isotope fitted. The red is not good in darkness. Unlike some coloured bobbins, which have to be released by hand before you strike, these drop smoothly off the tangle free stainless loops. As with the Pendulators shown below, two weights are supplied and these can be interchanged with the Pendulator weights.

Yellow Fluo-Bobbin Ref 285 - £7.95
Red Fluo-Bobbin Ref 358 - £7.95
Green Fluo-Bobbin Ref 287 - £7.95
Blue Fluo-Bobbin Ref 288 - £7.95

SUPER CLIPS

These ball end line clips with rubber tension adjuster, have an extended shank 33mm long and have many different applications

Ref 299 - £1.95 per pair

THE PENDULATOR

In a range of high visibility Yellow, Green, Blue and Red bodies, these indicators are available with standard nine inch, or long fifteen inch arms. The clear arm is attached to a hinge and clip which fits securely onto standard buzzer bars or banksticks. The body is detachable from the arm, and isotopes, when inserted, are retained when the arm is fitted back into the body.

Two weights are supplied with the indicator, and these fit precisely both the indicator body, and themselves, allowing the indicator to be used either with or without weights attached. The two weights supplied total 2oz. Extra weights are also available. The clips used in this indicator have the same ends as the Super-Clip, and can be tensioned to give minimal pressure against line release, or to support several ounces. The hinge which fits the buzzer bar remains stable, even on the long arm indicator when it drops in "free fall" with a six ounce load. Weights can be simply added or removed, with the Pendulator in place.

Yellow Pendulator Ref 293 - £10.75
Red Pendulator Ref 294 - £10.75
Green Pendulator Ref 295 - £10.75
Blue Pendulator Ref 296 - £10.75
Long Arm Yellow Pendulator Ref 289 - £10.95
Long Arm Red Pendulator Ref 359 - £10.95
Long Arm Green Pendulator Ref 291 - £10.95
Long Arm Blue Pendulator Ref 292 - £10.95

Spare Standard Arm Only Ref 297 - £2.75
Spare Long Arm Only Ref 298 - £2.95
Extra Bobbin/Pendulator Weights Ref 357 - £1.95 per pair

Standard *(top)* Long Arm *(below)*

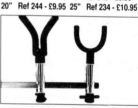

ROD/LEAD STRAPS

...how how extremely useful these are, but I still ...nnot believe the amount we have sold. After ...ding the rod, go once around both joints with the ...ap, then drop the lead along the material, then ...ntinue around, until the velcro holds securely. The ...er strap holds the butt- end together. One of the ...st useful items we have ever sold.

...f 174 - £3.45 per pair

BUZZ BOMBS

...til the introduction of the Buzz Bomb, you couldn't ...* an aerodynamic lead which lifted clear of weeds, ...'s and snags on the retrieve. The problem with ...ed bombs, was that they either spun and twisted ...the retrieve, and often cast so badly, that where ...y were going to land was pure guesswork. Not ...y does the Buzz Bomb cast well but, the positioning ...he fins seems to make them even more stable in ...ss winds than a standard bomb. Swivels used are ...rkley 100lb. Three leads per pack.

...z Buzz Bombs Ref 204 - £1.99
...₂oz Buzz Bombs Ref 205 - £2.25
...z Buzz Bombs Ref 206 - £2.45

'THE' RIG

...ll the most successful anti-tangle rig that I have ...ed, and the many thousands sold last year confirm ...efficiency. One point well worth considering is ...t last season, many dealers informed me of ...glers complaining about all brands of line breaking ...anly "for no reason at all". When asked if they ...ed anti-tangle rigs, the answer was invariably yes, ...t not "The" Rig. When you use a helicopter type ...you should hold the main line in one hand, take ...hook and do what the fish does — pull! You will ...e that if you don't use tubing, the swivel, even ...me of those designed for this type of rig, pulls ...ross the bottom bead at right angles, with a ...illotine effect. With "The" Rig, the tubing and the ...ft rubber buffer-stop, cushions this effect.

...f 172 - £1.95 per packet of three

Terry Eustace
Gold Label Tackle

FLOATER FLOATS

I was using these floats ten years before I had the first models produced for sale a couple of years ago, and there simply isn't anything available anywhere near as good. It is not possible to see the top of floats which sit virtually level with the surface, if you have cast to any distance.

With The Floater Floats, as soon as the hookbait is taken, the float will tilt and sink at the same time.

To set up, simply put the float on the line (no stops above the float) pop on a black or brown carp bead and then tie on a swivel. Tie a length of nylon to the swivel and allow three to six feet between the swivel and the hook. The Small Floater will cast forty yards with 8lb line and the Standard Floater out of sight.

Floater Float Small Ref 071 - £2.95
Floater Float Standard Ref 072 - £3.25

CARP BEADS

Shatterproof beads with smooth bores to eliminate problems of line wear. The 5mm dia. and 6mm dia. sizes have bores which allow the bead to sit over the swivel knot to avoid damage in this area when casting or playing fish. The 4mm size is suitable to use above the swivel or bomb swivel and also, being small and light, is ideal in floating line situations.

4mm Olive colour Ref 073 - £1.55
5mm Black colour Ref 074 - £1.65
6mm Brown colour Ref 075 - £1.75

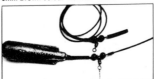

SUPER RIG SHRINK

Available in two sizes. Ideal for firmly positioning hairs, joining different diameter rig or silicone tubes, and a number of other uses. Super Rig Shrink 1 has a bore of approx 1mm, Shrink 2 approx 2mm. Super-Shrink contracts drastically, merely with the application of hot water.

Super Rig Shrink 1 (1mm Bore) Ref 353 - 95p
Super Rig Shrink 2 (2mm Bore) Ref 354 - 99p

BLACK ALLOY NET SPREADER

To replace that broken plastic one or why not replace it before it breaks, and costs you a Whacker?

Ref 038 - £8.95

THE CV SAFETY RIG

This brilliant new rotary rig alleviates the problem of fish being tethered to a lead weight. If your main line breaks, you can be sure that the fish will be able to swim free of the rig. An absolute must for all conservation-minded anglers.

Ref. 398
£3.85 per packet

Fordwich Lake

Location:	In the Stour valley near Fordwich
Type and Size:	Large gravel pit of 33 acres, with a very irregular bottom
How to Find:	Take the A28 from Canterbury to Sturry, and turn right. Follow the road past the George and Dragon Hotel, the Fordwich Arms on the left, and go down past the church on 'The Drove' a private road to the parking area
Carp Stock:	Very well stocked with carp to over 20lbs
Category:	Mixed Fishery
Other Species:	Tench and pike
Permits:	Members only water of Canterbury and District AC - Riversdale, 14 Mill Road, Sturry, Canterbury CT2 OAF. Tel: Canterbury 710830
Cost:	£31 per season, with a £15.50 entry fee, which includes many other waters
Control:	Club
BK Rating:	Moderate
W/A:	NRA Southern Region
Comments:	A well known big fish carp water in very attractive surroundings, well looked after by Canterbury club

Great Hollanden Farm Reservoir

Location:	Near Sevenoaks, off the A25
Type and Size:	Small farm irrigation reservoir, with only a few swims, very clear water
Carp Stock:	Some small carp
Category:	Mixed Fishery
Other Species:	Tench, roach, perch, rudd and a few trout
Permits:	The County Leisure Angling Association, 65 Pelham Road South, Gravesend DA11 8QS. Tel: 0474 332399 - seasonal membership only
Cost:	About £25; under 16's and additional family members £15 each
Control:	CLAA
BK Rating:	Not known
W/A:	NRA Southern Region
Comments:	The CLAA is a new club, with a magazine, competitions, social functions, and some other waters. Members can also fish the CALPAC waters

Horton Kirby

Location:	Horton Kirby, near Dartford
Type and Size:	3 gravel pits; total area 10—14 acres
How to Find:	Five minute walk from Farningham Road railway station
Carp Stock:	Well stocked with many doubles and twenties to about 28lbs, and lots of small carp also
Category:	Carp Water
Other Species:	Tench, bream and pike
Permits:	Day tickets from bailiff on banks
Control:	Club; Dartford and District Angling and Preservation Society. Hon Secretary: D E Reeve, 29 Berkeley Crescent, Dartford, Kent. Membership very hard to obtain
Restrictions:	No night fishing
BK Rating:	Easy
Comments:	A well known water, very heavily fished by day ticket anglers

Johnsons Pit

Location:	Larkfield, near Maidstone
Type and Size:	Two gravel pits covering about 20 acres in all
How to Find:	Just off the M25 at New Hythe junction, Larkfield
Carp Stock:	Doubles and 20's to about 30lbs
Category:	Mixed Fishery
Other Species:	Very big tench, pike, roach, bream
Permits:	Day ticket from the bailiff on the bank
Control:	Private
BK Rating:	Fairly Hard
Comments:	This water is said to be not very heavily fished and night fishing is allowed

Kentish Stour

Location:	From Fordwich to Plucks Gutter and Grove Ferry, on the River Stour, a tributary of the Medway
Type and Size:	Small river
Carp Stock:	Some carp to 14lbs
Category:	Probably Few Carp
Other Species:	Famous for its big roach, and also trout, bream, rudd, tench, pike, gudgeon, dace, chub, eels and even some sea trout
Permits:	Members only water of Canterbury and District AC, Riversdale, 14 Mill Road, Canterbury CT2 OAF (C Jardine, Hon Sec). Tel: Canterbury 710830
Cost:	Membership, which includes other waters, costs £31 per year, with an entrance fee of £15.50
Control:	Club
Restrictions:	Upstream of Fordwich church is fly fishing only
BK Rating:	Difficult
W/A:	NRA Southern Region
Comments:	3¼lb roach caught in 1985

Kingfisher Lakes

Location:	Various lakes at Paddesworth and Hoo, near Rochester
Type and Size:	Several small lakes, and a big chalk pit of about 30 acres known as Pollard Lake. At Hoo, three small gravel pits
Carp Stock:	The three lakes at Paddesworth are all well stocked with carp up to upper 20's in size. The Hoo lakes are quite well stocked with fish to upper doubles
Category:	Mixed Fisheries
Other Species:	Roach, bream, perch and pike
Permits:	Kingfisher Angling and Preservation Society. Mrs A Thomas, 23 Everest Drive, Hoo, Rochester ME5 9AN
Control:	Club; members only, no day tickets, and membership not easy to obtain
BK Rating:	Moderate
W/A:	NRA Southern Region
Comments:	The club has a number of other waters, several of which are quite easy fishing. One or two of the lakes may produce a thirty

Longford Lake

Location:	Just north of the A25 near Sevenoaks
Type and Size:	12 acre lake, 10 to 35 feet deep
Carp Stock:	Well stocked with carp; plenty of doubles and six 20's reported in 1990
Category:	Mixed Fishery
Other Species:	Tench, bream, roach, rudd, perch and pike
Permits:	Holmesdale AS, 4 Shoreham Lane, Riverhead, Sevenoaks, Kent
Cost:	About £45 per year plus £15 entry fee
Restrictions:	No night fishing at weekends; no fishing on competition weekends; members only
BK Rating:	Moderate
W/A:	NRA Southern Region

Maidstone Lakes   A

Location:	Near Maidstone
Type and Size:	Local lakes
How to Find:	Near Maidstone town centre
Carp Stock:	Well stocked with good carp
Category:	Mixed Fisheries
Other Species:	General coarse fish
Permits:	Tel: 0622 676586
Cost:	On application
BK Rating:	Moderate
Control:	Private
W/A:	NRA Southern Region
Comments:	Fishing weekends and holidays offered in private hotel. Accommodation and all meals, bar, TV lounge. Fishing in nearby lakes and the River Medway (carp to 20lbs+)

Nicholls Pit

Location:	Hythe
Type and Size:	Large pit
How to Find:	By the Army ranges on the coast road to Hythe
Carp Stock:	Quite well stocked with doubles and twenties
Category:	Mixed Fishery
Other Species:	Tench, bream and roach
Permits:	Day tickets from bailiffs on the bank
Control:	Private
BK Rating:	Fairly Hard
W/A:	NRA Southern Region

Orpington and District

Location:	Near Sidcup
Type and Size:	Two fair-sized lakes
How to Find:	On the A20 at Klingers roundabout
Carp Stock:	Quite well stocked with some doubles and some 20's
Category:	Mixed Fishery
Other Species:	Tench, bream, pike and roach
Permits:	Day tickets from local tackle shop at St. Mary's Cray

Control: Club - Orpington and District
BK Rating: Fairly Hard
W/A: NRA Thames Region

Pett Pools

Location: Between Winchelsea and Hastings
Type and Size: Small pools
How to Find: Winchelsea - 2 miles; Rye - 4 miles; off the Winchelsea-Hastings road
Carp Stock: Some carp
Category: Mixed Fishery
Other Species: General coarse fishing
Permits: M Piddington, Market Stores, Pett
Cost: Approx £2.50 per day; season tickets
BK Rating: Moderate
Restrictions: None
W/A: NRA Southern Region
Comments: Local clubs have other waters containing carp on Romney Marsh; try Cinque Ports AS - R MacGregor, 31 Burmarsh Road, Hythe, Kent. Bob MacGregor is a well known local carp angler

Pittlands Lakes

Location: Pittlands Farm, Churn Lane, Horsmonden TN12 8HL
Type and Size: Small lakes
Carp Stock: Well stocked with carp to over 20lbs
Category: Mixed Fishery
Other Species: Roach, rudd, tench and bream
Permits: Send an SAE for details to the address above or Tel: 089272 3838/3142/3143
Cost: On application
Control: Private
BK Rating: Not known
W/A: NRA Southern Region

Plucks Gutter

Location: River Stour near Sarre, between Canterbury and Ramsgate
Type and Size: Fast flowing river
How to Find: Take the A28 from Canterbury, then the right hand Ramsgate turn, and the next right turn to Preston. This road crosses the river at Plucks Gutter
Carp Stock: Some carp to 20lbs
Category: Few Carp
Other Species: Pike, bream, roach, dace, chub and the occasional sea trout
Permits: On bank at £3 per day
Control: Canterbury DAA, Riversdale, 14 Mill Road, Sturry, Canterbury
BK Rating: Super-Difficult
W/A: NRA Southern Region

Radnor Park Pool

Location:	Radnor Park, in Folkestone
Type and Size:	Shallow town park lake of about three acres, with island, heavily fished
How to Find:	In Cheriton Road; pass the Folkestone football ground, and take the third left turn. The lake is on the right
Carp Stock:	Well stocked with commons to mid-doubles
Category:	Mixed Fishery
Other Species:	Crucians, tench, roach, perch, rudd and bream
Permits:	On bank
Cost:	£1.50
Control:	Shepway and District AC - Paul Foot. Tel: 0503 58778
Restrictions:	Fishing is 6am to 10pm only; no night fishing; no floaters; no fishing in the reeds
BK Rating:	Easy
W/A:	NRA Southern Region

Reeds Lake

Location:	Near Snodland, just on the London side of the M20 at junction 4
Type and Size:	Three attractive estate-type lakes
Carp Stock:	Well stocked with carp to about 20lbs, many of which are lower doubles
Category:	Carp Water
Permits:	N Martin, 13 Masefield Road, Larkfield, Maidstone - in advance only
Control:	Private
BK Rating:	Moderate
W/A:	NRA Southern Region

Royal Military Canal   A

Location:	Hythe and Ashford areas
Type and Size:	Short, shallow canal
How to Find:	Off the A2070 south of Ashford
Carp Stock:	Some very good carp up to 35lbs
Category:	Mixed Fishery
Other Species:	General coarse fishing
Permits:	Day tickets on the bank for some stretches; also from J B Walker Ltd, 84 Slade Street, Hythe. Tel: 0303 66228; and Ashford and District A and PS, C Hyder, 37 Northumberland Avenue, Kennington, Ashford
Cost:	Approx £1.50; season £10
Control:	Club
Restrictions:	None
W/A:	NRA Southern Region
Comments:	A very hard water, with some big fish if you can find them. Tickets also available from some local pubs. Ashford APS also has a lake with some big carp - enquire from Secretary. Accommodation at the Railway Hotel, Appledore. Tel: 023-383-253 for brochure. B'B from £25 per night for a double room

Scarlett's Lake

Location:	Near East Grinstead
Type and Size:	3 acre lake, stream fed
How to Find:	East Grinstead area, access from the A264 near church at Hammerwood
Carp Stock:	Many carp, to 23lbs
Category:	Mixed Fishery
Other Species:	Crucians, grass carp, tench, rudd, roach and perch
Permits:	On bank, or J Jackson, Furnace Lane, Cowden, Edenbridge, Kent. Tel: 0342 850414 (6.30 to 9.30pm)
Cost:	Day - £3.50, season - £42 (from 8am on bank). Reduced prices for OAP's, the disabled, students and unemployed
BK Rating:	Fairly Hard
Control:	Private
Restrictions:	No preserved boilies. No groundbait till July 16th. Season ticket holders may night fish
W/A:	NRA Southern Region
Comments:	Picturesque lake suitable for well controlled families. Easy access for wheelchairs. 20p per ticket donated to conservation or wildlife charities. Bus passes end of road - alight Hammerwood; Tunbridge Wells - East Grinstead

School Pool

Location:	In the town of Faversham
Type and Size:	Old gravel pit of about 18 acres, many gravel bars
How to Find:	Just off the M2 at the Faversham junction; in the town
Carp Stock:	Fairly well stocked with quite a number of twenties, and at least two thirties. These include a common of around 33lb and 'She', a famous mirror of about 35lbs
Category:	Carp Water
Other Species:	Bream, tench, pike
Permits:	Day tickets from the Club Secretary in advance only - Faversham and District AC membership
Control:	Faversham and District AC, 5 Kennedy Close, Faversham. Tel: Faversham 533240
Restrictions:	No night fishing
BK Rating:	Difficult
W/A:	NRA Southern Region
Comments:	Another water very well known to carp anglers. Twenties including some upper 20's have been caught here, for as long as we can remember, and the water is famous for a couple of good thirties including 'She', already mentioned which has been caught by a large number of carp anglers including some of the best known names in the country. The lake is surrounded by a school, houses, a road and a factory!

Sittingbourne Lakes

Location:	Murston, near Sittingbourne
Type and Size:	3 large gravel pits
How to Find:	Murston is 1½ miles north of Sittingbourne
Carp Stock:	Plenty of good carp to over 20lbs
Category:	Mixed Fishery
Other Species:	General coarse fishing

Permits:	No day tickets; information from Hon Sec, Sittingbourne AC, C Brown, 5 Sunnybanks, Murston, Sittingbourne, Kent
Cost:	On application
BK Rating:	Difficult
Restrictions:	Ask the club secretary
W/A:	NRA Southern Region
Comments:	Try also Deans Tackle Shop, East Street, Sittingbourne, Kent

Station Pool (Rookery Lake)

Location:	Near Bromley
Type and Size:	Small lake of about 1¾ acres
How to Find:	Enquire from owners
Carp Stock:	Well stocked with carp to 25lbs
Category:	Mixed Fishery
Other Species:	Tench, bream, roach and pike
Permits:	Fourways Fisheries, Poplars Nursery, Harlington Road, Toddington, Dunstable. Tel: 0525 55584
Control:	Fourways Fisheries
W/A:	NRA Thames Region
Comments:	Season tickets only, about £65

Stonar Lake

Location:	Near Sandwich
Type and Size:	Small lake
Carp Stock:	Well stocked with carp to 20lbs; plenty of doubles
Category:	Mixed Fishery
Other Species:	Roach, bream and perch
Permits:	Try local tackle shops - possibly an angling club in Sandwich?
Control:	Club?
BK Rating:	Easy
W/A:	NRA Southern Region

Sundridge Lakes

Location:	Sundridge, near Sevenoaks
Type and Size:	Gravel pits of about 5 and 15 acres
Carp Stock:	Carp to over 20lbs
Category:	Carp Water
Permits:	Holmesdale AS, 4 Shoreham Lane, Riverhead, Sevenoaks, Kent
Cost:	Approx £45 per year, plus £15 entry fee
Control:	Members only
BK Rating:	Moderate
W/A:	NRA Southern Region
Comments:	There are rumours that the water contains some very big carp

Sutton

Location:	Sutton-at-Hone, near Dartford
Type and Size:	Gravel pit of about 10 acres
How to Find:	On the Horley road from Farningham

Carp Stock: Heavily stocked with many doubles and plenty of 20's to 28lbs
Category: Carp Water
Other Species: Tench, pike, roach and bream
Permits: Dartford and District Angling Society. D E Reeve, 29 Berkeley Crescent, Dartford, Kent. Very long waiting list, membership difficult to obtain. No day tickets, club members only
Restrictions: No sacks
BK Rating: Easy
Comments: This club is mainly for people living in the Dartford area; it is difficult to obtain membership. We thought we would include it as it is a good water and you may obtain membership if you live locally

Vauxhall Lakes

Location:	Canterbury Nature Reserve, off Broad Oak Road, on the edge of the city
Type and Size:	Very large old gravel pits
Carp Stock:	Stocked with carp in 1973, which are now being caught to mid-twenties; plenty of doubles
Category:	Mixed Fishery
Other Species:	Roach, perch, bream, rudd, tench, eels and pike
Permits:	Members only water of Canterbury and District AC, Riversdale, 14 Mill Road, Sturry, Canterbury. Tel: 710830
Cost:	£31 per season with an entry fee of £15.50
Control:	Club
BK Rating:	Moderate
W/A:	NRA Southern Region
Comments:	A pleasant Nature Reserve on the edge of the city, with a Field Centre. No fishing from jetties or bridges. Rich waters with big fish of most species. Some restrictions on fishing hours, indicated on notice boards. Available to local members only. The Canterbury AA is an excellent club with a permanent headquarters with offices open from 9am to 4pm on weekdays

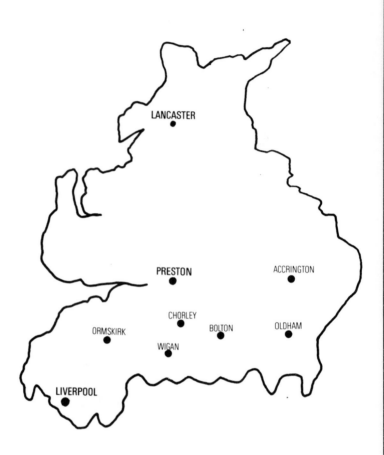

LANCASHIRE

LANCASTER

PRESTON   ACCRINGTON

CHORLEY
ORMSKIRK   BOLTON   OLDHAM
WIGAN

LIVERPOOL

Abbey Lane Lake

Location:	Burscough, near Ormskirk
Type and Size:	Three acre lake
How to Find:	Take the A59 north from Ormskirk. The lake is on the right just after the B5242
Carp Stock:	Fairly well stocked with carp to low doubles
Category:	Mixed Fishery
Other Species:	Tench, roach, bream, perch and thousands of small rudd
Permits:	Local tackle shops at £1.50 per day, and £1 for juniors
Control:	Maghull and Lydiate AC. J Johnson. Tel: 051-526 4083
Restrictions:	No night fishing
BK Rating:	Moderate
W/A:	NRA North West Region

Barrow Lodge

Location: Just off the A59 Preston road at Clitheroe
Type and Size: 10 acre lake
Carp Stock: Well stocked with small carp to about 6lbs
Category: Mixed Fishery
Other Species: Crucians, tench, perch and bream
Permits: In advance from Ken Varey, 4 Newmarket Street, Clitheroe.
Tel: 0200 23267
Cost: Day tickets £2; season tickets £10. All permits half price for under 16's and OAP's. Free to the registered disabled
BK Rating: Moderate
W/A: NRA North West Region
Comments: This lake is often busy with boats during daytime

Baubles Pools

Location: Near Pilling, Fylde - enquire locally
Type and Size: Three small pools, with the best fish in the middle one
Carp Stock: Mainly small carp to doubles
Category: Carp Waters
Permits: Day tickets on bank
Control: Private
BK Rating: Very Easy
W/A: NRA North West Region
Comments: Many waters in this area now have no close season

Brian Hey Reservoir

Location: Scout Road, near Brian Hey tearooms, off the A58 five miles north west of Bolton
Type and Size: Two and a half acre mill reservoir
Carp Stock: Quite well stocked with carp to doubles, average about 7lbs
Category: Mixed Fishery
Other Species: Bream, roach, tench, crucians and a few perch
Permits: On the bank at £1.50 for adults and 75p for juniors, OAP's and the disabled
Control: Twenty Sixth Lancashire Home Guard AS (sounds like Dad's Army!) (Tel: 0257 253650, Password DA 1939)
Restrictions: No night fishing
BK Rating: Moderate
W/A: NRA North West Region

Brinsall Lodges

Location: Brinsall, Chorley
Type and Size: Small pond of about 1½ acres
Carp Stock: Quite well stocked with carp to about 10lbs
Category: Mixed Fishery
Other Species: Roach, tench and bream
Permits: Day tickets from local tackle shops
Control: Private
BK Rating: Difficult
W/A: NRA North West Region
Comments: No close season in some places in this area - check first

Cargate Farm Pool

Location:	Near Oldham
Type and Size:	Small farm pool, much used for match fishing
Carp Stock:	Well stocked with small commons and mirrors
Category:	Mixed Fishery
Other Species:	Roach, tench, crucians and perch
Permits:	Day tickets in advance only
Cost:	£3
Control:	Oldham and District AA. Secretary: B Boff, 369 Shaw Road, Oldham OL1 3JZ. Tel: 061-620 0883 - season tickets available
Restrictions:	No night fishing - sunrise to sunset only
BK Rating:	Easy
W/A:	NRA North West Region

Clevely Bridge

Location:	Garstang - on the A6 between Preston and Lancaster
Type and Size:	Small, pleasant fishery
Carp Stock:	Well stocked with carp to about 14lbs
Category:	Mixed Fishery
Other Species:	Usual coarse fish
Permits:	In advance only
Control:	Private
BK Rating:	Moderate
W/A:	NRA North West Region

Coronation Lodge

Location:	Near Oldham
Type and Size:	Tiny pond, with room for 9 anglers only; very weedy
Carp Stock:	Quite well stocked with carp to doubles
Category:	Mixed Fishery
Other Species:	Tench, roach, rudd, perch and crucians
Permits:	Members only water of Oldham and District AA. Secretary: B Boff, 369 Shaw Road, Oldham. Tel: 061-620 0883 - memberships available
Cost:	About £12 per season
Restrictions:	No night fishing
BK Rating:	Moderate
W/A:	NRA North West Region

Doffcocker Reservoir

Location:	Manchester Road, Bolton
Type and Size:	Small reservoir
Carp Stock:	About 100, and stocked recently with 6—10lb fish. Quite a few doubles
Category:	Mixed Fishery
Other Species:	Usual coarse fish
Permits:	Bolton and District AC - members only. Secretary: T McKee, 1 Lever Edge Lane, Great Lever, Bolton, Greater Manchester
Control:	Club
BK Rating:	Easy
W/A:	NRA North West Region

Elton Reservoir

Location:	Elton, off the A58 Bury to Bolton road
Type and Size:	Small reservoir, 40 feet deep off the dam
How to Find:	Turn off the A58 opposite the Washington Hotel towards Eaton Sailing Club. Cross the bridge to Nightingale Hospital, and the reservoir is at the side of the hospital
Carp Stock:	Some carp to about 20lbs
Category:	Few Carp
Other Species:	Pike, bream, roach, perch and tench
Permits:	On bank at £2.20 per day
Control:	Try T Taylor. Tel: 061764 2858 for information
BK Rating:	Very Difficult
W/A:	NRA North West Region
Comments:	There is a sailing club on this lake

Farington Lodge Pools

Location:	Farington, between Leyland and Preston and between the A59 and the A582, five miles south of Preston
Type and Size:	Two small mill lakes
Carp Stock:	Well stocked with carp to about 10lbs
Category:	Carp Water
Permits:	Day tickets from bailiff on bank
Control:	Private
Restrictions:	No night fishing except by special arrangement
BK Rating:	Easy
W/A:	NRA North West Region
Comments:	Some of the waters in this area have no close season

Greenbank Park Lake

Location:	Greenbank Drive, off the A5058 road in Liverpool
Type and Size:	Small attractive park lake
Carp Stock:	Well stocked with carp to about 10lbs
Category:	Mixed Fishery
Other Species:	Tench, roach, perch and a few bream
Permits:	Free, like all Liverpool park lakes
Control:	Council
BK Rating:	Moderate
W/A:	NRA North West Region
Comments:	No close season

Heapey Lodges

Location:	Chorley, near Manchester
Type and Size:	4 reservoirs, totalling about 30 acres, and up to 30 feet deep
How to Find:	Off the M61 north west of Manchester
Carp Stock:	Fairly well stocked
Category:	Mixed Fisheries
Other Species:	General coarse fish and trout
Permits:	Wigan AA. W Gralton, 66 Balcarres Road, Asphull, Wigan. Day tickets on the bank
Cost:	Approx £12 season ticket

BK Rating: Insufficient information
Control: Club
Restrictions: Not known
W/A: NRA North West Region
Comments: Only Lodge No. 1 worth fishing for carp - contains many doubles and a few 20's. Floater fishing best. No close season

Hoddlesdon Reservoir

Location: Darwen, off the A666 north of Bolton
Type and Size: 20 acre reservoir
Carp Stock: Not many to lower doubles
Category: Few Carp
Other Species: Roach, bream, pike, some trout
Permits: Darwen AA - F W Kendall, 45 Holden Fold, Darwen; and from County Sports, Duckworth Street, Darwen
Cost: About £10 per season — no day tickets; in advance only
Restrictions: No night fishing
BK Rating: Very Difficult
W/A: NRA North West Region
Comments: No close season

Hollingworth Lake

Location: Hollingworth Lake Country Park, two miles from Junction 21 on the M62 near Rochdale
Type and Size: Reservoir of more than 100 acres
Carp Stock: Some carp to doubles
Category: Few Carp
Other Species: Big pike, roach, bream, rudd and a few tench and trout
Permits: On bank at £1.45 per day for adults and 80p for OAP's and juniors
Control: Warden. Tel: 0706 373421
BK Rating: Difficult
W/A: NRA North West Region
Comments: Drained and restocked by the Council in 1986. Public access

Leeds-Liverpool Canal

Location: Jacksons Bridge, 12 miles from Liverpool
Type and Size: Small canal with little boat traffic
How to Find: Take the M58 or M57 from Liverpool, then the B5147 north past Lydiate towards Halsall. After the church, turn right to Jacksons Bridge
Carp Stock: Recently stocked with carp, numbers and sizes not known
Category: Mixed Fishery
Other Species: Bream, tench, roach and perch
Permits: Day tickets and annual tickets on bank, or from local tackle shops
Cost: £1.75 per day; £8 per year for juniors, OAP's and the disabled
Control: Jack Johnson. Tel: 051-526 4083 (Liverpool and District AA)
BK Rating: Difficult, until the carp grow and become established
W/A: NRA North West Region
Comments: No close season

Mere Brow Lakes

Location:	Near Tarleton, just off the A565 between Southport and Preston
Type and Size:	Two lakes, total 20 acres
Carp Stock:	Some carp to about 20lbs, exact number and sizes not known
Category:	Mixed Fishery
Other Species:	Roach and bream
Permits:	Day tickets from office on site
Cost:	About £2 per rod
Restrictions:	No night fishing
BK Rating:	Moderate
W/A:	NRA North West Region

New Water

Location:	Leigh, near Wigan
How to Find:	Take the A579 from Wigan and turn right towards Leigh on the A578. Turn right into Smiths Lane and the lake will soon be seen on the left
Type and Size:	Five acre lake
Carp Stock:	Heavily stocked with carp to mid-doubles and several thousand little ones
Category:	Mixed Fishery
Other Species:	Roach, perch, tench, crucians, bream and pike
Permits:	Day tickets on bank at £1
Control:	Tom Kelly. Tel: 0942 676291 (Leigh and District AA)
Restrictions:	No night fishing; no boilies, bloodworm or joker; no keepnets
BK Rating:	Easy
W/A:	NRA North West Region
Comments:	No close season

Ogdens Reservoir

Location:	Ogden Lane, Wickenhall, Oldham, off the A640
Type and Size:	Two little ponds of less than an acre each
Carp Stock:	Some small carp, and a few doubles
Other Species:	Roach and bream
Permits:	Day tickets on bank at £1.50 - £1 in advance from 6 Water Works Road
Control:	Council
Restrictions:	No night fishing; no groundbaiting
BK Rating:	Fairly Hard
W/A:	NRA North West Region

Oldham Reservoirs

Location:	Oldham
Type and Size:	Two large reservoirs
How to Find:	Near Oldham
Carp Stock:	Some carp in Upper Strinesdale and Ogden Reservoirs
Category:	Few Carp
Other Species:	General coarse fish
Permits:	Oldham United AC. A Dyson, 7 Raven Avenue, Chadderton, Oldham
Cost:	Approx 50p per day; £5 per season
BK Rating:	Not known, probably Difficult

Control: Club
W/A: NRA North West Region
Comments: Tackle etc from Grundy's, 292 Manchester Street, Werneth, Oldham

Ormsgill Lower Reservoir

Location: Near Barrow-in-Furness
Type and Size: Large reservoir
Carp Stock: Some carp, numbers and sizes not known
Category: Mixed Fishery
Other Species: Trout and tench
Permits: Hannay's, 50 Crellin Street, Barrow-in-Furness
Control: Furness Fishing Association
BK Rating: Difficult
W/A: NRA North West Region

Orrell Water Park

Location: West of Wigan, off junction 26 of the M6; Lodge Road, off the B5206
Type and Size: Long, narrow lake, stream-fed
Carp Stock: Quite well stocked with carp of around 8lbs, to lower doubles
Category: Mixed Fishery
Other Species: Bream, tench, roach, perch and gudgeon
Permits: Day tickets on bank
Cost: £3.20; £1.60 for OAP's and the unemployed during the week; £1.05
                    for juniors
Control: Tel: 0695 625338
Restrictions: No night fishing; open from 6am; no groundbait
BK Rating: Easy
W/A: NRA North West Region
Comments: There is another lake on site, which is not day ticket but is used for
                    matches. Car park and toilets

Pennington Flash

Location: Leigh, near Oldham
Type and Size: Small lake
How to Find: Near Leigh, west of Manchester off the A580
Carp Stock: Some good carp
Category: Mixed Fishery
Other Species: General coarse fishing
Permits: Pennington Flash AA. G Unsworth, 142 Chestnut Drive, Leigh
Cost: Day ticket - approx 50p; season £2.50
BK Rating: Moderate
Control: Club
W/A: NRA North West Region

Pilsworth Fishery

Location: Pilsworth, Heywood
Type and Size: 7 lakes
How to Find: Take the M66 towards Bury from Manchester, and come off at junction 3

Carp Stock:	Well stocked including plenty of doubles
Category:	Mixed Fishery
Other Species:	Mostly coarse fish
Permits:	Day tickets from the bank
Control:	Private Tel: 0706 30619
BK Rating:	Moderate
Baits/Methods:	Normal carp fishing baits and methods
W/A:	NRA North West Region
Comments:	This water is controlled by famous match fishermen Kevin and Benny Ashurst

Platts Lane Lakes

Location:	Burscough, near Ormskirk
Type and Size:	Five acre lake, very deep in parts
How to Find:	Platts Lane, off the A59, just past Dean's Newsagents
Carp Stock:	Some carp to about 10lbs
Category:	Mixed Fishery
Other Species:	Tench, roach, rudd, bream and crucians
Permits:	Day tickets at Dean's Newsagents; tickets limited
Cost:	£1.25; 60p for juniors
Control:	Burscough AC
BK Rating:	Moderate
W/A:	NRA North West Region

Redwell Carp Fishery

Location:	7 miles north east of Lancaster - there are signs to the fishery on the B6254 Carnforth-Kirkby Lonsdale road; near Arkholme and Carnforth
Type and Size:	Three acre lake in attractive surroundings
Carp Stock:	Well stocked with small carp, and some doubles to about 15lbs
Category:	Carp Water
Permits:	In advance from the house on the way in
Cost:	£4 per day
Control:	Private. Duncan Cummings. Tel: 05242 21979
BK Rating:	Easy to Moderate
W/A:	NRA North West Region
Comments:	Fishing is 7am to dusk only

River Calder

Location:	Wigan area
Type and Size:	Small river
Carp Stock:	Quite well stocked with small carp, and a few doubles
Category:	Mixed Fishery
Other Species:	Most coarse fish and some trout
Permits:	From local tackle shops
Control:	Wigan AA. Secretary: W Gratton, 66 Balcarres Road, Aspull, Wigan
BK Rating:	Moderate
W/A:	NRA North West Region
Comments:	Possibly no close season in some areas

River Crossens

Location:	Just east of Southport on the A565 Preston road
Type and Size:	Narrow, shallow stretch of drain-type river
Carp Stock:	Some carp to doubles
Category:	Few Carp
Other Species:	Bream, tench, roach, perch, pike, rudd and eels
Permits:	Chorley Anglers, Chorley; Ted Carter, Preston and F Foster, Tarleton
Cost:	Day tickets at £2 for adults and £1 for juniors and OAP's
Control:	Southport DAA
Restrictions:	No bloodworm!
BK Rating:	Difficult
W/A:	NRA North West Region

Sabden Reservoir

Location:	Whalley, near Accrington
Type and Size:	Small reservoir
How to Find:	Enquire from Secretary
Carp Stock:	Some carp
Category:	Few Carp
Other Species:	Small trout
Permits:	Accrington and District FC. A Balderstone, 42 Townley Avenue, Huncoat, Accrington. Tel: 0254 33517
Cost:	Approx £4 per day
BK Rating:	Moderate
Control:	Club
W/A:	NRA North West Region

Smiths

Location:	Manchester Road, Bolton
Carp Stock:	Quite well stocked with good doubles and 20's to 23lbs (common) and 24lbs (mirror)
Category:	Mixed Fishery
Permits:	Bolton and District Angling Club - members only. Secretary: T McKee, 1 Lever Edge Lane, Great Lever, Bolton, Greater Manchester
Control:	Club
BK Rating:	Moderate
W/A:	NRA North West Region

Swantley Lake

Location:	Off the B6254, about 8 miles north east of Lancaster
Type and Size:	2½ acre lake, specially dug as a fishery a few years ago
Carp Stock:	Well stocked with commons and mirrors to mid-doubles
Category:	Mixed Fishery
Other Species:	Roach, rudd and bream
Permits:	Day and season tickets - for information and permits telephone Morecambe 422146
Control:	Lonsdale Angling Club - details from local tackle shops
BK Rating:	Easy
W/A:	NRA North West Region

Twin Lakes

Location:	Croston, near Chorley
How to Find:	Take the B5249 from Chorley, then turn right at Croston onto the A581 and left just after the railway bridge. You will see the lake on the left
Type and Size:	Small clay pit
Carp Stock:	Recently stocked with very small carp
Category:	Mixed Fishery
Permits:	On site at £3 per day
Control:	Graham Cooper. Tel: 0722 601093
Restrictions:	No keepnets, bloodworm or joker
W/A:	NRA North West Region
Comments:	Stocked mainly with small fish. Bar and hot meals from the site lodge

Worthington Lake

Location:	Worthington, a suburb of Wigan
Type and Size:	Two acre pond
Carp Stock:	Well stocked with carp to about 15lbs
Category:	Mixed Fishery
Permits:	Day tickets from local tackle shops
Control:	Wigan and District AA. Secretary: W Gratton, 66 Balcarres Road, Aspull, Wigan - includes other carp waters
Restrictions:	No night fishing
BK Rating:	Moderate
W/A:	North West

Wrightington Lake

Location:	Off the A5209 at Wrighton Hospital, between Ormskirk and the M6
Type and Size:	10 acre estate type lake
Carp Stock:	Quite a number of carp to upper doubles
Category:	Mixed Fishery
Permits:	From local tackle shops - day and season tickets
Control:	Wigan and District AA. W Gratton, 66 Balcarres Road, Aspull, Wigan
Restrictions:	No night fishing
BK Rating:	Difficult
W/A:	NRA North West Region

Wyreside Fisheries

Location:	Hampton Lane, Dolphinholme, Lancaster
Type and Size:	Five man-made lakes, with more than 20 acres of water
Carp Stock:	All 5 lakes contain carp, many of which are small, though there are some doubles to about 20lbs
Category:	Mixed Fishery
Permits:	Day tickets on the bank
Cost:	£5 per day for two rods; £3 for one
Control:	Larry Fitzgerald. Tel: 0524 792093
BK Rating:	Easy
W/A:	NRA North West Region
Comments:	A pleasant and attractive complex to fish, with the chance of some big fish within a few years. Close season February 17th to April 10th

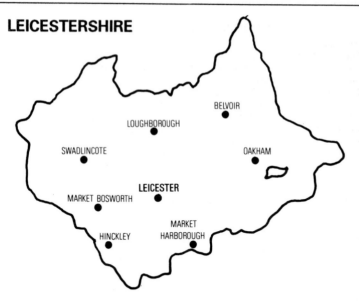

LEICESTERSHIRE

BELVOIR

LOUGHBOROUGH

SWADLINCOTE

OAKHAM

LEICESTER

MARKET BOSWORTH

MARKET HARBOROUGH

HINCKLEY

Barlestone Lake

Location:	Village of Barlestone, near Market Bosworth
Type and Size:	1½ acre farm pond
How to Find:	To centre of village, then right towards Nailstone; lake is on right behind Baxters Farm
Carp Stock:	110-130 carp to 16lb. Few doubles
Category:	Mixed Fishery
BK Rating:	Easy
Permits:	Day tickets on the bank
Cost:	£3 per day. £1.50 per half day
Restrictions:	No night fishing
W/A:	NRA Severn-Trent Region
Comments:	Plenty of carp, most 6-9lb. Margin fishing (keeping well away from the bank) and surface fishing most successful

Beadles Pit

Location:	Off Broome Lane, East Goscote, north of Leicester. Down long track next to railway line
Type and Size:	29 acre gravel pit
Carp Stock:	150 carp to 23lb. Average 8—14lbs
Category:	Mixed Fishery
Other Species:	Tench to 7lb. Pike to 25lb. Roach, bream, perch
Permits:	Day tickets on bank - £2.50
Control:	Private
Restrictions:	No restrictions
BK Rating:	Moderate
W/A:	NRA Severn-Trent Region
Comments:	Large open gravel pit with few features; fish are not at all hard to catch - once located

Belvoir Lakes
Location: Belvoir Castle, between Melton Mowbray and Grantham
Type and Size: Chain of small estate lakes
Carp Stock: Well stocked with carp to a good size
Category: Carp Waters
Other Species: Some coarse fish
Permits: Season tickets only from the Estate Office at Belvoir Castle
Control: Private
BK Rating: Easy
W/A: NRA Severn-Trent Region

Birstall Carp Pool
Location: In centre of Country Park, near Birstall
Type and Size: 2½ acre pool
Carp Stock: Heavily stocked with fish to upper doubles
Category: Carp Water
Other Species: Usual coarse fish
Permits: Season tickets £25 from Alan Smith, Broome AS. Membership open to all. Occasionally a waiting list for tickets
Control: Club
BK Rating: Easy - good winter water
W/A: NRA Severn-Trent Region
Comments: Small pool with good head of carp, ideal for someone starting carp fishing

Bosworth Water Trust   A
Location: Half a mile west of Market Bosworth on the B585. Tel: 0455 291876
Type and Size: 20 acres of lake
Carp Stock: Some carp to doubles
Category: Mixed Fishery
Other Species: Usual coarse fish
Permits: Nigel and Jo Riley, at the site office before fishing
Cost: £1.50 per day - free to campers and members
Control: Private
BK Rating: Not known
W/A: NRA Anglian Region
Comments: There is camping, and facilities for caravans near the lake, with toilets, showers and a snack bar. From the publicity, this 'leisure and water park' is more for sailing and board-sailing than for angling, but there are certainly some carp, so it might be worth a try

Charnwood Lake
Location: In Loughborough, two miles from the centre of the town
Type and Size: Lake of about eight acres and very deep
How to Find: Close to the A6 Loughborough-Leicester road. Go via Beeches Road, then turn right into Tuckers Road, and the lake is at the end, with a car park
Carp Stock: Well stocked with small carp, and a few to about 20lbs
Category: Mixed Fishery

Other Species:	Roach, bream, chub, perch, pike and tench
Permits:	Day tickets in advance only from local tackle shops
Cost:	£1.40 per day; juniors - 70p; season - £18, juniors and unemployed - £9
Control:	J Stephens. Tel: 0509 267330
Restrictions:	No night fishing
BK Rating:	Difficult for the big carp; Moderate for the smaller ones
W/A:	NRA Severn Trent Region
Comments:	Some special swims for the disabled

Grand Union Canal

Location:	Near Market Harborough
Type and Size:	About 5 miles of canal
Carp Stock:	Quite well stocked with carp up to 10lbs, some bigger fish
Category:	Mixed Fishery
Other Species:	Tench, bream, roach
Permits:	Market Harborough Anglers. Seasonal membership; day tickets from bailiffs on the bank, or in advance from Sports Shop, 7 St Mary Road Market Harborough. Secretary: R Haycock, 16 Maurice Road, Market Harborough
Cost:	Approx £3 per season; 50p per day
Control:	Club
BK Rating:	Moderate
W/A:	NRA Severn-Trent Region

Groby

Location:	Off A50 at Groby - visible from the A50
Type and Size:	Small lake in centre of pick your own farm. Watering pond (for strawberries) of 1 acre
Carp Stock:	Heavily stocked with carp to 20lb - 25+ doubles, most fish 2-8lb
Category:	Carp Water
Other Species:	Tench to 6lb, crucian carp
Permits:	Day tickets on bank - £4. Juniors £3
Control:	Private Tel: 0533 874190
Restrictions:	No boilies, nuts, groundbaits, hemp. No line under 6lb. No hooks smaller than 14 - must be barbless. Night fishing by arrangement
BK Rating:	Moderate
W/A:	NRA Severn-Trent Region
Comments:	Surface fishing at start of season gives the best chance of one of the bigger fish. During the season, mass baiting with casters, tares or any other allowed tiny bait gives the best results

Halstead House Farm

Location:	Halstead, off the B6047 Melton Mowbray road
Type and Size:	Small farm lake
Carp Stock:	Quite well stocked with carp to about 7lbs
Category:	Mixed Fishery
Other Species:	Roach, dace, gudgeon and a few tench
Permits:	On the bank or from the shop
Cost:	£3.50 per day; £2 for OAP's, juniors and the disabled

Control:	Tel: 053754 239
Restrictions:	No night fishing. No keepnets, barbed hooks or groundbait
BK Rating:	Moderate
W/A:	NRA Severn Trent Region

Hartshorne Dams Carp Fishery

Location:	Hartshorne, off the A514 near Swadlincote and Burton-upon-Trent
Type and Size:	3 acre lake
Carp Stock:	Well stocked with carp to upper doubles, and possibly larger
Category:	Carp Water
Permits:	AMR Country Clothing, Ashby de la Zouche; Melbourne Tackle and Gun, Melbourne; The Rodney Inn, Hartshorne (opening hours only); The Farmhouse, Manor Farm, Hartshorne. No tickets on bank - tickets must be purchased before fishing at £2.50 per day
Control:	Private. Tel: 0283 215769
BK Rating:	Moderate
W/A:	NRA Severn-Trent Region
Comments:	There is also a 2½ acre general coarse lake on the site, and a £40 a season night syndicate on the carp lake

Hermitage Leisure Centre

Location:	Hermitage, near Coalville. Signposted for Leisure Centre
Type and Size:	Old gravel pits of 10 acres
Carp Stock:	Reasonable head of carp to 19lb. 40% are doubles
Category:	General coarse fish
Permits:	Day tickets: £1 on bank - night fishing by arrangement with warden
Control:	Private. Tel: 0530 811215
Restrictions:	No night fishing
BK Rating:	Moderate
W/A:	NRA Severn-Trent Region
Comments:	Lake contains a large island around which the fish often congregate; large numbers of water birds

Knossington Carp Lake

Location:	Knossington, near Oakham
Type and Size:	Small lake
How to Find:	West of Oakham
Carp Stock:	Well stocked with plenty of low doubles and fish of 8-9lbs
Category:	Carp Water
Other Species:	Crucians, bream, roach, tench
Permits:	D H Preke. Tel: 066-447-305. Advanced booking only
Cost:	Approx £2 per day (£1 juniors)
Control:	Private
BK Rating:	Easy to Moderate
Restrictions:	No night fishing, no keepnets, no groundbaiting
W/A:	NRA Severn-Trent Region

Launde Abbey Pools

Location:	Launde Abbey, off the Oakham-Leicester road
Type and Size:	Four small Abbey pools, now restored, dredged and stocked
Carp Stock:	Well stocked with commons to doubles
Category:	Mixed Fishery
Other Species:	Tench, roach, rudd, perch and chub
Permits:	Day tickets on bank
Cost:	£3.25; £2.50 for juniors and OAP's. Evening tickets from 5pm at £2.25
Control:	Tel: 057 286 202
Restrictions:	Fishing is dawn to dusk, but there is some night fishing by arrangement. No groundbaiting
BK Rating:	Moderate
W/A:	NRA Anglian Region

Little Pit

Location:	Hinckley
Type and Size:	5 acre clay pit
How to Find:	On Barwell Lane, Hinckley (opposite ASDA superstore)
Carp Stock:	A few carp to a little over 20lbs
Category:	Mixed Fishery
Other Species:	General coarse fish
Permits:	Hinckley and District AC. Secretary: Pat Donnachie. Tel: Hinckley 636121. Also available from Tony Hortons Fishing Tackle, Burbage. Tel: Hinckley 632269
Cost:	£15 per year
Control:	Club
BK Rating:	Difficult
W/A:	NRA Severn-Trent Region
Comments:	Typical deep clay pit, most success to surface and margin fishing

Mallory Park

Location:	Mallory Park Fisheries, Kirkby Mallory LE9 7QE. Tel: 0455 842931
Type and Size:	Several lakes built in 1986 by Roy Marlow
Carp Stock:	Well stocked with carp to 20lbs
Category:	Mixed Fishery
Other Species:	Most coarse fish
Permits:	Marks and Marlow Ltd, 39 Tudor Road, Leicester. Tel: 0533 537714
Control:	Private - two famous anglers, Ivan Marks and Roy Marlow
BK Rating:	Moderate
W/A:	NRA Anglian Region
Comments:	This is a conservation area, with ponds and Nature Reserve. Motor Sport racing, accommodation, buffet and bars nearby. Sponsors invited to help create conservation areas for wildlife

Mill Farm   A

Location:	Gilmorton, 10 miles south of Leicester
Type and Size:	Attractive four acre lake on a farm
How to Find:	Turn right onto the A427 from junction 20 of the M1 going north, then take the first left turn to Gilmorton
Carp Stock:	Fairly well stocked with carp to about 19lbs, many of which are small

Category:	Mixed Fishery
Other Species:	Roach, rudd, bream and tench
Permits:	Day tickets on bank or from the shop - Tel: 0455 552392 for details
Cost:	£3.50 one rod; £5 for two. Concessionary permits
Control:	Private
Restrictions:	Dawn to dusk only. some summer night fishing by arrangement. No particles or groundbait
BK Rating:	Easy
W/A:	NRA Severn-Trent Region
Comments:	Some holiday accommodation at this very attractive lake - details from the phone number above. Bait and refreshments

Mill-on-the-Soar

Location:	Mill-on-the-Soar Hotel, Sutton-in-the-Elms, just off the B4114 road, south west of Leicester
Type and Size:	Three and a half acre lake with large island, fed by the River Soar
Carp Stock:	Quite well stocked with carp to over 20lbs
Category:	Mixed Fishery
Other Species:	Chub, roach, rudd, perch and a few trout
Permits:	£2.50 per day at the hotel reception desk
Control:	Malcolm Cliff. Tel: 0455 282419
Restrictions:	No night fishing - dawn till dusk only; no carp in keepnets
BK Rating:	Moderate
W/A:	NRA Severn Trent Region
Comments:	Some access for the disabled; restocking and dredging is planned

Murphys Lake

Location:	Next to both the Grand Union Canal and a Walkers Crisp Factory. Either down Canal Street, Thurmaston or by the back of Wanlip Country Club
Type and Size:	Large gravel pit of 30 acres
Carp Stock:	Few carp - fish caught to 27.8 - good chance of a 30lb+ fish. Maybe only 25 fish
Category:	Mixed Fishery
Other Species:	Specimen fish of all species
Permits:	Season tickets £25.00 from Alan Smith, Broome AS. Membership open to all, but occasional waiting list for permits
Control:	Club
Restrictions:	None
BK Rating:	Very Difficult - locating fish essential for success
W/A:	NRA Severn-Trent Region
Comments:	Very large open gravel pit, very few features; once located fish are quite catchable. Also contains pike to 26lb+, bream to 10lbs+ and large tench, specimen fish of all species. Used by water skiers

Nanpantan Reservoir

Location:	Nanpantan, near Loughborough
Type and Size:	Reservoir about 5 acres in size
How to Find:	Take the B5350 road to Loughborough to Nanpantan
Carp Stock:	After draining, the lake was stocked with mirror carp many of which are now 5-9lbs, with a few lower doubles and possibly one 20

Category:	Carp Water
Other Species:	Bream, tench, roach and perch
Permits:	W H Wortley, 45 Baxter Gate, Loughborough. Tel: Loughborough 212697
Baits/Methods:	Carp tactics and baits, including sweetcorn and luncheon meat
Control:	Private
Restrictions:	No groundbaiting. Thirty anglers only per day. No night fishing. Barbless hooks. Minimum 8lb line
BK Rating:	Moderate
W/A:	NRA Severn-Trent Region
Comments:	Granite block banks - unhooking mats recommended. Part of the lake is closed to anglers. Toilet block. Permits in advance only from Soar Valley Tackle, Woodbrook Road, Loughborough or W H Wortley. Information on 0509 234901

Peatling Pools

Location:	Peatling Parva, just south of Leicester
Type and Size:	Two small lakes, each with an island
Carp Stock:	Well stocked with carp to over 25lbs
Category:	Mixed Fishery
Other Species:	Chub, roach, bream, rudd, tench and trout
Permits:	On the bank at £3.50 and £4.50 for two rods
Control:	Tel: 0533 478222
Restrictions:	No night fishing - dawn till dusk only
Baits/Methods:	A good water for surface fishing
BK Rating:	Moderate
W/A:	NRA Severn Trent Region

Sheepy Lake

Location:	Sheepy Magna
Type and Size:	Lake of 7 acres
How to Find:	Take the A444 between Sibson and Twycross and then the B585 to Sheepy Parva and Magna villages
Carp Stock:	Well stocked with carp between 5 and 7lbs, mostly mirrors. A few doubles, and one possible 20
Category:	Mixed Fishery
Other Species:	Crucians, and some other coarse fish
Permits:	Day tickets on the bank
Cost:	Approx £1 per day
Control:	Private
BK Rating:	Easy
W/A:	NRA Severn-Trent Region

Spring Grange

Location:	South Croxton, off the A607 north east of Leicester, and between Beeby and South Croxton
Type and Size:	Two small lakes
Carp Stock:	Well stocked with carp to 26lbs
Category:	Mixed Fishery
Other Species:	Bream, tench, roach, rudd, chub and barbel
Permits:	Tickets in advance or on the bank

Cost:	£5 for the large lake; £4 for the smaller. Reductions for OAP's, juniors and the disabled. Reduced rates for evenings
Control:	Tel: 0537 50609
Restrictions:	Barbless hooks only. Groundbait, peanuts, and dogs are banned (presumably all three cannot be used as baits!). No night fishing (dawn to dusk only). 4lb minimum line limit on large lake. Access for the disabled
BK Rating:	Not known
W/A:	NRA Severn Trent Region

Sulby Lily Pond

Location:	Near Welford, on Leics/Northants border
Type and Size:	2 acre silty pool
How to Find:	Sulby is signposted just north of Welford on east side of A50
Carp Stock:	Well stocked, a lot of small carp, but fish go up to about 20lb
Category:	Carp Water
Other Species:	Tench, small pike, roach and perch
Permits:	Hinckley and District AC. Secretary: Pat Donnachie. Tel: Hinckley 636121. Also available from Tony Hortons Fishing Tackle, Burbage. Tel: Hinckley 632269
Cost:	£15 per year
Control:	Private
Restrictions:	No night fishing
BK Rating:	Moderate
W/A:	NRA Severn-Trent Region
Comments:	Very weedy little water with lilies and silkweed

Walif Gravel Pits

Location:	Near Willington
Type and Size:	Large gravel pits
How to Find:	Willington, near Derby
Carp Stock:	Not known — some carp
Category:	Few Carp
Other Species:	Mixed coarse fish
Permits:	Rising Sun public house, Willington
Cost:	Approx £1 per day
Control:	Derby Angling Assocation. J Callaghan, 3 Calvin Close, Alvaston, Derby DE2 OHX
BK Rating:	Insufficient information
W/A:	NRA Severn-Trent Region

Wanlip Country Club

Location:	Wanlip Road, Syston - near Leicester
Type and Size:	Virtually square gravel pit of 8 acres
Carp Stock:	Carp to 27lb - most fish doubles. Possibly 10 twenties
Category:	Mixed Fishery
Other Species:	Tench to 7lb. Roach, perch, pike etc
Permits:	Season tickets £25.00 from Alan Smith. Broome AS - enquire locally for details. Membership open to all, but occasionally waiting list for tickets

Control:	Club
Restrictions:	No restrictions
BK Rating:	Hard
W/A:	NRA Severn-Trent Region
Comments:	Long range tactics essential on this open water. Only features are gravel bars and right in the centre of the lake, the old causeway when it was dug. Water also used by water skiers. Keep rod tips low to avoid being cut off by the speed boats!

Welford Reservoir

Location:	Welford, near Leicester
Type and Size:	20 acre reservoir
Carp Stock:	Quite well stocked with good carp to double figures
Category:	Mixed Fishery
Other Species:	Bream, pike, tench, rudd and roach
Permits:	British Waterways, Willow Grange, Church Road, Watford, or the bailiff, Mr W Williams, Welford Grange Farm, Welford
Cost:	Season tickets only at about £13
Restrictions:	No day tickets, and there may be a waiting list
BK Rating:	Moderate
W/A:	NRA Severn-Trent Region

Willesley Lake

Location:	Near Measham, off the A453
Type and Size:	Estate lake of 23 acres, shallower at one end
Carp Stock:	Large numbers of carp to 23lb, 4 twenties, 2 twenty commons, good head of doubles
Other Species:	Usual coarse fish
Permits:	Day tickets on bank £3.50, or season tickets £20 from local tackle shops
Control:	Club. Tel: 0530 270041 - Measham Tackle
Restrictions:	No night fishing; no floating baits. No day tickets on Sundays
BK Rating:	Easy to Moderate
W/A:	NRA Severn-Trent Region
Comments:	Very heavily fished by match anglers due to large head of bream. No day tickets at weekends. Margin fishing productive in shallows

Willow Farm Carp Pool

Location:	Off Wanlip Road, Systan; through gravel working
Type and Size:	¾ acre pool
Carp Stock:	Plenty of carp to 19lb+, 10-15 doubles
Category:	Carp Water
Other Species:	Usual coarse fish
Permits:	Season tickets £25 on bank or from Michael Winterton. Tel: 0533 600937
Control:	Private
Restrictions:	No restrictions
BK Rating:	Moderate
W/A:	NRA Severn-Trent Region
Comments:	Season ticket covers 10 lakes and several miles of Rivers Soar and Wreake. Most of the other lakes on the complex hold few carp to 20lb+

LINCOLNSHIRE

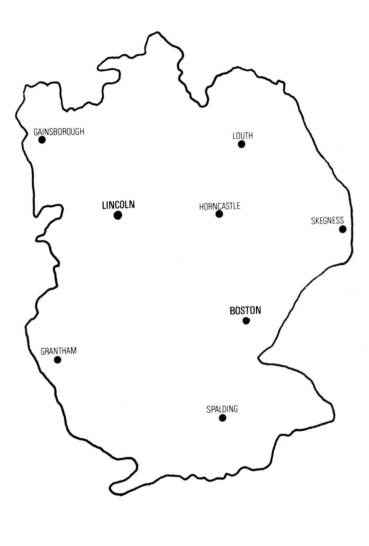

Ashby Park

Location:	Ashby Park, West Ashby, near Horncastle. Tel: 0507 527966 or 0790 53321
Type and Size:	5 lakes - about 15 acres of water
Carp Stock:	Well stocked with carp to doubles
Category:	Mixed Fishery
Other Species:	Chub, rudd, tench, bream, pike, perch, roach and eels
Permits:	From Robin and Margaret Francis at the above address
Cost:	Day - £3; one week - £15
Control:	Private
BK Rating:	Not known
W/A:	NRA Anglian Region
Comments:	Touring caravan site by lake; car parking at swims, ideal for disabled anglers; no close season; camping

Belleau Bridge Lake

Location:	South Thoresby, west of Alford, off the A16 Louth to Spilsby road
Type and Size:	Six acre shallow lake
Carp Stock:	Quite well stocked with carp to about 15lbs
Category:	Mixed Fishery
Other Species:	Roach, tench, bream and eels
Permits:	On the bank at ú5 per day
Control:	Tel: 0507 480225
Restrictions:	No night fishing; no excessive groundbaiting
BK Rating:	Moderate
W/A:	NRA Anglian Region
Comments:	No close season. Cars can be driven to water's edge

Brickyard Fishery   A

Location:	South Somercotes, Louth
Type and Size:	4 acre brick pit
How to Find:	South Somercotes road, to the east of Louth
Carp Stock:	Some carp to about 20lbs
Category:	Mixed Fishery
Other Species:	General coarse fish
Permits:	Day tickets on site
Cost:	Approx £2 per day
BK Rating:	Moderate
Control:	Private
W/A:	NRA Yorkshire Region
Comments:	Small quiet caravan site - static vans for hire. Toilet block. Tourers welcome

Brookside Fisheries   A

Location:	North Scarle, between Lincoln and Newark
Type and Size:	One acre pond with island
Carp Stock:	Well stocked with quite a number of doubles to over 25lbs
Category:	Mixed Fishery
Other Species:	Koi, golden orfe, tench, rudd and roach
Permits:	On bank at £2 per rod

Control:	Tel: 0522 77234
Restrictions:	No night fishing; no keepnets or groundbait
BK Rating:	Moderate
W/A:	NRA Anglian Region
Comments:	No close season; four caravans for hire; disabled anglers can take cars to the bank

Chapel Boating Lake

Location:	Near Skegness
Type and Size:	Lake of 4 acres
Carp Stock:	Well stocked with carp. A 32lbs common was reported in Angling Times, January 1991, on boilie
Category:	Mixed Fishery
Permits:	John Cooke. Tel: 0754 72631
Cost:	£2.70 one rod; £3.80 for two
Restrictions:	Open March 14th to the end of October only; no night fishing
BK Rating:	Moderate
W/A:	NRA Anglian Region

Denton Reservoir

Location:	Denton, near Grantham
Type and Size:	Large reservoir
How to Find:	Off the A607, 4 miles west of Grantham
Carp Stock:	Well stocked with carp to 26lbs
Category:	Mixed Fishery
Other Species:	General coarse fish
Permits:	Enquire locally
Cost:	Approx £7.50 per year
BK Rating:	Moderate
Control:	Not known
Restrictions:	None
W/A:	NRA Severn-Trent Region
Comments:	We have been unable to find out where these permits can be obtained - try local tackle shops

Elmhurst Lake   A

Location:	Horncastle
How to Find:	Elmhurst, near Horncastle
Carp Stock:	Some carp to 15lbs
Category:	Mixed Fishery
Other Species:	Bream and tench
Permits:	Tel: 06582 7533
Cost:	On application
Control:	Private
BK Rating:	Insufficient information
W/A:	NRA Yorkshire Region
Comments:	Caravan site - caravans to let. Lake described as 'picturesque'. No close season. Further information from owners on the number listed above

Golf Lakes

Location:	Golf Club, off the A158 at West Ashby about a mile north of Horncastle
Type and Size:	Two lakes, of five acres and one and a half acres
Carp Stock:	Some carp to 20lbs
Category:	Mixed Fishery
Other Species:	Tench to over 10lbs, roach, chub, bream and perch
Permits:	In advance. Tel: ?507 526800
Cost:	£10 per day
Restrictions:	More than any other water we have! No night fishing (8am till sunset only); no keepnets, carp sacks, bolt rigs or hair rigs; barbless hooks. Float fishing only; no line of less than 5lb B/S
BK Rating:	Not known
W/A:	NRA Anglian Region

Grooby's Pit

Location:	Thorpe Culvert, off the B1195 near Spilsby
Type and Size:	Two acre lake
Carp Stock:	Not many carp, best about 12lbs
Category:	Few Carp
Other Species:	Tench, bream, roach and eels
Permits:	Must be obtained from the house before fishing
Cost:	£1.50 per day; 50p from 5pm to 9pm
Control:	Tel: 0754 880216
Restrictions:	Fishing is 6am to 9pm; no night fishing; no groundbait
BK Rating:	Difficult
W/A:	NRA Anglian Region

Hall Farm Moat

Location:	Hall Farm, Harpswell, near Gainsborough. Tel: 042773 412
Type and Size:	Farm moat of three quarters of an acre
How to Find:	Off the A631 between Corringham and Harpswell
Carp Stock:	Well stocked with carp of all sizes to 20lbs
Category:	Mixed Fishery
Permits:	Day tickets from Hall Farm
Cost:	Approx £1.50 per day
BK Rating:	Fairly Hard
Control:	Private
Restrictions:	No night fishing
W/A:	NRA Severn-Trent Region
Comments:	The carp in this water are still growing - and now we have a moat, a stream and a dock in our guide!

Hill View Lake

Location:	Hogsthorpe, near Skegness
Type and Size:	Three-quarters of an acre man-made lake
How to Find:	Off the A52 road from Skegness to Mablethorpe, near Chapel St. Leonards
Carp Stock:	Heavily stocked with carp, mainly small to 18lbs
Category:	Mixed Fishery

Other Species: Tench and roach
Permits: On site. Details from owner Ken Raynor on Skegness (0754) 72979
Cost: Approx £1.50 per day for one rod; £2.50 for two rods. Juniors, pensioners and disabled £1. After 5pm 80p for all
BK Rating: Easy
Control: Private
Restrictions: Barbless hooks only; no carp to be kept in keepnets
W/A: NRA Anglian Region
Comments: There is also a trout lake on the site. Tackle can be hired. Tea, coffee and snacks. No close season. Owner a National Anglers' Council qualified game fishing instructor. Ideal spot for the holidaymaker

Lake Helen   A

Location: Lake Helen, Mill Lane, Sutterton
Type and Size: Small lake
Carp Stock: Well stocked with carp to upper doubles
Category: Mixed Fishery
Other Species: Usual coarse fish
Permits: Send for brochure. Tel: 0205 460681
Control: Private
BK Rating: Moderate
W/A: NRA Anglian Region
Comments: One lakeside bungalow and caravan only

Lincolnshire Drains

Location: Spalding area
Type and Size: A number of Fen drains, including Vernatts
Carp Stock: Some carp to about 10lbs
Other Species: Pike, perch, rudd, bream and tench
Permits: Spalding Fishing Club - try local tackle shops, such as D T Ball, 1 Hawthorne Bank, Spalding or M Tidwells, Fen Lane, Spalding
Control: Club
BK Rating: Difficult
W/A: Anglian

Lowfields Country Holiday Fishing Retreat   A

Location: Lowfields Grange, Eagle Lane, North Scarle, Lincoln LN6 9EN
Type and Size: 3 small lakes; 2½, 1½ and ½ acres
How to Find: Off the A1133 Newark-on-Trent to Gainsborough road and south west of Lincoln
Carp Stock: Good carp to 20lbs+
Category: Mixed Fishery
Other Species: Perch, roach, bream, tench, eels, rudds and crucians
Permits: LCHFR, Lincoln. Tel: 0522 77717
Cost: On application
Control: Private. Paul and Andrea Anderson
Restrictions: No day tickets; no bivvies
BK Rating: Moderate
W/A: NRA Severn-Trent Region

Comments: Formerly known as the Poplars and now surely our longest title! Self-catering accommodation in beautiful surroundings, including some caravans. Holiday club ownership scheme. Baits on sale

Marshalls Lake

Location:	Fulston, near Louth - enquire locally
Type and Size:	Small farm pond
Carp Stock:	Well stocked with carp to upper doubles
Category:	Mixed Fishery
Other Species:	Roach and rudd
Permits:	Day tickets from bailiff on bank
Control:	Private
BK Rating:	Difficult
W/A:	NRA Anglian Region
Comments:	There is no close season in Lincolnshire; night fishing permitted

North Kelsey Park

Location:	North Kelsey, between Brigg and Caistor
Type and Size:	Small lake
Carp Stock:	Well stocked with commons to 18lbs and mirrors to 20lbs
Category:	Mixed Fishery
Other Species:	Usual coarse fish
Permits:	For day tickets. Tel: 0831 132819
Cost:	£2.50 per day
BK Rating:	Moderate
W/A:	NRA Anglian Region
Comments:	New water opened in October 1991, so not much known

Richmond Lake

Location:	North Hykeham, near Lincoln. Tel: 0522 681329
Type and Size:	Large gravel pit of 80 acres
How to Find:	To west of A46 at Richmond Drive near North Hykeham
Carp Stock:	Plenty of doubles to 23¼lbs
Category:	Carp Water
Other Species:	Double figure bream, tench and rudd
Permits:	On site
Cost:	£2.50 per day approx
BK Rating:	Easy
Control:	Private
Restrictions:	No night fishing
W/A:	NRA Anglian Region
Comments:	No close season

River Glen

Location:	Surfleet, near Boston
Type and Size:	Fens type wide river
Carp Stock:	Some carp to well over 20lbs; a 20lb mirror was caught in July 1992
Category:	Few Carp
Other Species:	Most coarse fish; a noted roach water

Permits:	Try local tackle shops
Control:	Club
BK Rating:	Difficult
W/A:	NRA Anglian Region
Comments:	There is said to be a shoal of carp which includes a number of twenties

River Witham

Location:	Bardney area
Type and Size:	Large 'fen drain' type river, noted for its match fishing
Carp Stock:	Not many, but a record for the river was caught on maggots and light tackle in 1990 - it was a 23½lb mirror
Category:	Few Carp
Other Species:	Bream and most other coarse fish, including zander
Permits:	Lincoln and District AA - enquire locally or in Lincoln
Control:	Club
BK Rating:	Very Difficult
W/A:	NRA Anglian Region

Rossways Water   A

Location:	189 London Road, Wyberton, Boston. Tel: 0205 361643
Type and Size:	One acre clay pit
How to Find:	Main A16 road Boston to Spalding, 1 mile from Boston
Carp Stock:	Well stocked with carp to 25½lbs
Category:	Mixed Fishery
Other Species:	Perch, roach, rudd, tench, bream
Permits:	On site - day tickets by prior arrangement only
Cost:	Approx £2.50 per rod; £4 for 2 rods
BK Rating:	Very Difficult
Control:	Private
Restrictions:	No nuts; no sacking, no groundbait; no particles
W/A:	NRA Anglian Region
Comments:	Rod licences sold on premises. Night fishing by arrangement. Cafeteria, toilets, showers. Tackle and bait for sale. Attractive tree lined pond. Possibly one fish of around 30lbs. Depth of 10-14 feet. Numbers limited, swims bookable. Many carp taken on float tackle near bank. Static caravans on site for holiday stays

Swan Lake Leisure Park   A

Location:	Culvert Road, Thorpe Culvert, Skegness. Tel: 0754 880469
Type and Size:	2½ acre caravan park lake
How to Find:	Take the A52 from Skegness to Wainfleet. At Wainfleet, turn right onto the B1195 towards Spilsby. After about 1½ miles, turn left down a lane and left again at the first crossroads
Carp Stock:	Well stocked with carp, water record 26lbs
Category:	Mixed Fishery
Other Species:	Tench, roach and rudd
Permits:	Weekly or daily, for site residents only
Cost:	£2.50 per rod per day. £10 weekly per rod. £5 per week per rod for children from 12 to 16
BK Rating:	Moderate

Control:	Leisure Park
Restrictions:	No night fishing. No groundbait. No floating baits
W/A:	NRA Anglian Region
Comments:	The park is 7 acres in size with plenty of wildlife, and is only 5 miles from Skegness. There is a launderette and 4 caravans sleeping 7 or 8, and a four bedroomed cottage. Costs from £75 to £165 per week, according to time of year. No close season. Brochure from Mrs Caton

Sycamore Lake Carp Fishery   A

Location:	Willow Lodge, Willow Lakes, Newark Road, Foston, Grantham NG32 2LF. Tel: 0400 82190
Type and Size:	Small and quite new, man-made lake of about three quarters of an acre and up to 7 feet deep
How to Find:	Half a mile off the A1 between Newark and Grantham, and just outside the small village of Foston
Carp Stock:	Well stocked with mirrors and commons between 2lbs and 12lbs
Category:	Carp Only
Permits:	On site
Cost:	£3 per day, £2 for evening, to include two other lakes on site. Reductions for juniors and OAP's, and half price for those staying in the caravans on site
Control:	Private
Restrictions:	Barbless hooks; no keepnets or carp sacks. All nets to be disinfected at start
BK Rating:	Easy
W/A:	NRA Anglian Region
Comments:	Good fun fishery on pleasant site. Separate car park for day ticket anglers. 6 caravans to rent on site, with bait and tackle for sale, and usual caravan site facilities, ideal for a family holiday. Caravan prices from £65 to £113 per week, all with full mains services. No close season

Sycamore Lakes

Location:	Burgh-le-Marsh, off the A158 road from Skegness
Type and Size:	Three small clay pits
Carp Stock:	All three are well stocked with carp to upper doubles
Category:	Mixed Fishery
Other Species:	Tench, rudd, roach, golden orfe and perch
Permits:	Day tickets on site
Cost:	£3.50 or £5 for two rods. Reduced rates for juniors, OAP's and the disabled
Control:	Joy or Jose Giraldez on 0754 810749
Restrictions:	No night fishing; 6am till dusk; no carp to be put in keepnets; all particle baits banned, except for sweetcorn
BK Rating:	Moderate
W/A:	NRA Yorkshire Region
Comments:	No close season; toilets, cafe and camping

Tattershall Park

Location:	Tattershall Park Country Club, off the A153 between Sleaford and Skegness; near Tattershall Castle
Type and Size:	Five acre estate lake
Carp Stock:	Well stocked with carp to doubles
Category:	Mixed Fishery
Other Species:	Rudd and other coarse fish
Permits:	Day tickets from the shop on site. Includes several other lakes and the River Bain
Control:	Tel: 0526 43162
BK Rating:	Moderate
W/A:	NRA Anglian Region
Comments:	There are over 350 acres of water in this country park, with big bream and pike in the other lakes. No close season

Tetford Country Cottages   A

Location:	East Road, Tetford, near Salmonby, off the A158 from Skegness
Type and Size:	1½ acre lake with islands
Carp Stock:	Carp to 24lbs
Category:	Mixed Fishery
Other Species:	Tench, perch, roach and rudd
Permits:	On bank, or from the owners, Peg and Tony Buckman, Manor Farm, East Road, Tetford, near Horncastle LN9 6QQ. Tel: 0507 532276
Cost	Day tickets £2.50. £1.50 for children under 14 and OAP's
Restrictions:	Barbless hooks, not bigger than size 10. No keepnets at present as the water was very low in the summer of 1992
BK Rating:	Not known
W/A:	NRA Anglian Region

Trent Backwater

Location:	Off the A156 road between Gainsborough and Lincoln, at Fosdyke, near Torksey
Type and Size:	Arm of the River Trent, which is tidal
Carp Stock:	Not many, but possibly some large fish
Category:	Few Carp
Other Species:	Pike, roach, bream and eels
Permits:	£1.50 per day on bank
Control:	Worksop and District AA
Restrictions:	No night fishing
BK Rating:	Difficult
W/A:	NRA Severn Trent Region

West Ashby Lakes

Location:	West Ashby, near Horncastle
Type and Size:	Two gravel pits of 5 and 2 acres
How to Find:	On A153 just north of Horncastle
Carp Stock:	Many doubles up to 25lbs. Average 11lbs
Category:	Carp Water
Other Species:	Tench, chub, roach
Permits:	On site - Tel: 0507 600473

BK Rating:	Easy
Restrictions:	No hair rigs; barbless hooks; no boilies; no particles (what is left?)
Control:	Private
W/A:	NRA Anglian Region

Whisby Fishery

Location:	Off the A46, south west of Lincoln
Type and Size:	Two adjacent lakes of two acres and three acres
Carp Stock:	Well stocked with doubles to over 20lbs
Category:	Mixed Fishery
Other Species:	Tench, grass carp, crucians, bream, roach and rudd
Permits:	On bank
Cost:	£2.50 per day; £2 for juniors, OAP's and the disabled; season tickets £55 and £45
Control:	Gary Fasheavrne. Tel: 0522 682208
Restrictions:	Night fishing by arrangement only - normally fishing is 7am until 9pm
BK Rating:	Moderate
W/A:	NRA Anglian Region
Comments:	Good access for the disabled; toilets, cafe and garden centre. No close season

Willow Lakes   A

Location:	Willow Lakes, Newark Road, Foston, Grantham NG32 2LF. Tel: 0400 82190
Type and Size:	Three small lakes - Poplar is 1¼ acres; Willow is one acre
Carp Stock:	Some crucians and other species in Poplar; Willow was stocked with 2,500 small mirrors and commons in 1990; Sycamore - carp to 14lbs
Category:	Mixed Fisheries
Other Species:	Tench, rudd, bream, roach, chub, perch
Permits:	Day tickets on site
Cost:	£3 per day;,£2 for the evening. Reduced price for juniors and OAP's, and half price tickets for those renting the caravans on site
Control:	Private
BK Rating:	Easy
Restrictions:	Barbless hooks; all nets to be disinfected at start
W/A:	NRA Anglian Region
Comments:	There are 6 large caravans close to the lakes for rent, at prices ranging from £65 to £113 a week. They all have mains services and modern equipment, and are available from the middle of March until the end of October. The lakes are reed-fringed and attractive, and there is a further small carp fishery on the site (see separate entry). Tackle and bait available on site. No close season

Woodlands Fishery

Location:	Ashby Road, Spilsby, off the A1115 Skegness road
Type and Size:	Two very small man-made ponds
Carp Stock:	Some small carp
Category:	Mixed Fishery
Other Species:	Crucians, tench, rudd, roach, perch and gudgeon
Permits:	On site at £2 per day; evening tickets in the summer at £1.50
Control:	Marie or Chris Sibley. Tel: 0790 54252
Restrictions:	No night fishing
BK Rating:	Not known
W/A:	NRA Anglian Region

MERSEYSIDE

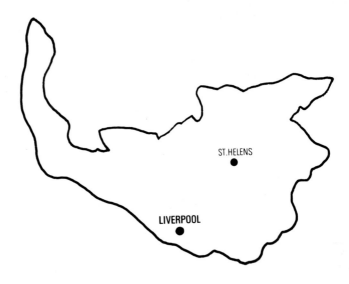

Burton Mere (b)

Location:	Burton Manor, between Chester and Heswall (in the Wirral)
Type and Size:	3½ acre estate lake
How to Find:	9 miles north west of Chester off the A540 raod
Carp Stock:	Heavily stocked with carp to 25lbs
Other Species:	Perch, rudd, roach and tench
Permits:	Tony Dean's Rod and Reel Tackle Shop, Enfield Road, Ellesmere Port. Tel: 051-356 0678
Cost:	Approx £3.50 per day; £2 per half day (weekends only)
Control:	Private
BK Rating:	Easy
W/A:	NRA Welsh Region - purchase rod licence before fishing
Comments:	Former home of Victorian Prime Minister Gladstone - his ghost must haunt the grounds! Mere averages 5 feet in depth. Float fishing close to the bank works well

Church Street Canal

Location:	Church Street, St. Helens
Type and Size:	Industrial area canal; stretch of about 400 yeards
How to Find:	St. Helens is north east of Liverpool
Carp Stock:	Quite well stocked with carp to double figures
Category:	Mixed Fishery
Other Species:	Roach, bream, perch and gudgeon
Permits:	St. Helens Angling Association. Details on bank or from local tackle shops. J Corkish, 65 Laffak Road, Carr Hill, St. Helens WA11 9EH
Control:	Club
BK Rating:	Moderate
W/A:	NRA North West Region
Comments:	There is a warm water outlet from a factory on this stretch and it has become very popular in the winter, when the water is warm enough to paddle in and other local waters are frozen. The canal gets very busy at this time. Plenty of matches but some good carp for pleasure anglers, and well worth a try - if you can get a place to fish - in icy conditions

Figure Eight Pond

Location:	Birkenhead - Hoylake road (Wirral)
Type and Size:	One third of an acre pit
How to Find:	From Birkenhead take the A553. At Bidston roundabout go straight on. You will see the pit on the right in an open field
Carp Stock:	Not many carp but an 18 and a 22 have been caught. No small carp
Category:	Mixed Fishery
Other Species:	Big tench, crucians, perch, bream, rudd
Permits:	Free
Cost:	None
BK Ratings:	Difficult
W/A:	NRA North West Region
Comments:	Early season fishing and night fishing are good

Mill Dam

Location:	Near Kirkby, Liverpool
Type and Size:	Small lake, recently cleared out and restocked
Carp Stock:	Some carp, numbers and sizes not known
Category:	Mixed Fishery
Other Species:	Tench, roach, perch, and (they say) one pike!
Permits:	From bailiff on bank
Cost:	£7 adults; £3.50 juniors
Control:	Kirkby Junior AC - community hall on banks of lake
BK Rating:	Not known
W/A:	NRA North West Region

Newsham Park Lake

Location:	Newsham Park, Tuebrook, Liverpool
Type and Size:	Ancient odd-shaped park lake, about 3 acres
Carp Stock:	Mixed fishery
Other Species:	Tench, roach and perch

Permits:	None necessary - all fishing on the many Liverpool park lakes is free
Control:	Liverpool City Council
BK Rating:	Easy
W/A:	NRA North West Region
Comments:	This lake was de-silted and restocked with over 50,000 fish in 1991. Platforms have been built for disabled anglers

Overflow

Location:	Bidston Docks, Birkenhead (Wirral)
Type and Size:	Formerly a 6 acre dry dock (now freshwater)
How to Find:	Take the A553 from Birkenhead to St. James's Church. Turn right, then first left to Bidston Incinerator, take next entrance and follow dockside - Overflow is the furthest water
Carp Stock:	Carp to 10lbs+
Other Species:	Big perch (3-4lbs) and eels of 4-6lbs
Permits:	Free
Cost:	Nothing
BK Rating:	Moderate
Control:	Docks/British Rail
W/A:	NRA North West Region
Comments:	Carp caught on snaggy tip side - beware sunken cars. Maggots and worm work well on light tackle. Dock is 30 feet deep: we now have a stream and a Dock in our guide!

Peak Forest Canal

Location:	Marple area (Greater Manchester)
Type and Size:	Short, narrow canal
Carp Stock:	Some carp, mainly in lock pools at Marple
Category:	Mixed Fishery
Other Species:	Tench and general coarse fish
Permits:	Try local tackle shops or County Palatine AA
Control:	Club
BK Rating:	Not known
W/A:	North West

Sefton Park Lake

Location:	A park in Liverpool
Type and Size:	4 acre park lake, very busy and public
Carp Stock:	Quite well stocked with small carp
Other Species:	Tench, roach, crucians and perch
Permits:	None necessary - free fishing and in other park lakes containing carp in Liverpool
Control:	Liverpool City Council
BK Rating:	Easy
W/A:	NRA North West Region
Comments:	No close season

NORFOLK

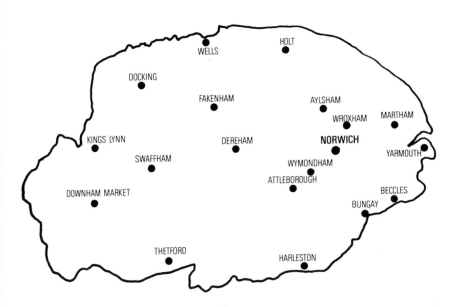

HOLT
WELLS
DOCKING
FAKENHAM
AYLSHAM
WROXHAM
MARTHAM
KINGS LYNN
DEREHAM
NORWICH
SWAFFHAM
YARMOUTH
WYMONDHAM
ATTLEBOROUGH
DOWNHAM MARKET
BECCLES
BUNGAY
THETFORD
HARLESTON

Aldeby Hall Farm Pits

Location:	Aldeby Hall Farm, near Aldeby, Beccles
Type and Size:	Four small pits
How to Find:	Take the A146 from Norwich, and just before Beccles turn left to Aldeby. A mile after the village, find a track on the right going through a fruit farm, which is actually an old railway track; the pits are on the left in half a mile
Carp Stock:	Some mirrors to 20lbs
Category:	Mixed Fishery
Other Species:	Crucians, bream, tench, rudd and roach
Permits:	From bailiff on bank (day tickets), at £3
BK Rating:	Easy
Control:	Private
W/A:	NRA Anglian Region
Comments:	The two pits on the left hold the carp; the others are mainly crucians with some rudd

Bedingham Pit

Location:	Woodton, just off the B1332 between Bungay and Norwich
Type and Size:	5 acre gravel pit
Carp Stock:	Well stocked with quite a few doubles, and a number of 20's to nearly 30lbs
Category:	Carp Water
Permits:	This is a syndicate water, with information hard to obtain, but try local tackle shops in Norwich, Beccles and Bungay
Cost:	Well over £100 per season
Control:	Private
BK Rating:	Moderate
W/A:	NRA Anglian Region
Comments:	It may be possible to get details of how to obtain membership in the village of Woodton. This is a very good carp water, and it would be worth some trouble to get into

Beeston Lake

Location:	Neatishead, near Wroxham
Type and Size:	Shallow three acre Broadland-type lake, with very clear water
How to Find:	Take the A1151 from Norwich, and about a mile past Wroxham, turn right on the Neatishead road. Turn left at the Post Office, and the lake is 300 yards on the right
Carp Stock:	Not many carp to low doubles
Category:	Few Carp
Other Species:	Very big tench and bream (the former British record bream of 13lb 9oz came from here), roach, rudd, eels and pike
Permits:	Day tickets in advance only from the bailiff, A Jeckells. Tel: 0692 630688
Cost:	£1; Only five tickets issued per day
Control:	Private
BK Rating:	Very Difficult
W/A:	NRA Anglian Region

Billingford Pit

Location:	Billingford, near Swanton Morley
Type and Size:	Three acre pit
How to Find:	Take the A1067 from Norwich and turn left to Billingford at Bawdeswell. In the village, turn left towards Swanton Morley, and after 100 yards on the right there is a narrow track leading down to the pit
Carp Stock:	A few big carp
Category:	Few Carp
Other Species:	Roach, perch and pike
Permits:	Day tickets in advance only from local tackle shops, or Dereham District AS, Mr S R Allison, Pound Cottage, Cemetery Road, East Dereham. Tel: Dereham 694428. Membership is £7 for the season, to cover other pits and the river
Cost:	Day tickets £1.50
BK Rating:	Difficult
Restrictions:	No night fishing
Control:	Club
W/A:	NRA Anglian Region

Blickling Lake

Location: Blickling Hall, Aylsham
Type and Size: Estate lake of 20 acres
How to Find: Take the A140 from Norwich to Aylsham. Go through the town and take the Blickling road. Bear right, and this road leads to the car park at the northern end of the lake
Carp Stock: Well stocked with carp to double figures
Category: Mixed Fishery
Other Species: Famous for its big bream, also tench, roach and big pike
Permits: Day tickets from bailiff on the bank. Some season tickets from Mr B Cooper, tel: Aylsham 734181
Cost: Day tickets: £2; season: £25
BK Rating: Moderate
Control: National Trust
W/A: NRA Anglian Region
Comments: In the grounds of a famous stately home, this beautiful lake holds some fine fish

Booton Clay Pit

Location: Near the village of Booton, near Norwich
Type and Size: Clay pit of about 4 acres
How to Find: Take the Reepham road from Norwich and just before Reepham turn right towards Haveringland and Buxton. After a mile and a half you will find the pit on the left behind some trees
Carp Stock: Only very few carp, but they are large. Two 30's were reported from this pit in 1984, but it is not known if these were genuine weights
Category: Few Carp
Other Species: Tench, roach, rudd, pike and bream
Permits: Day and season tickets from the bailiff on the bank
Cost: £2 per rod per day
Control: Private
BK Rating: Difficult
W/A: NRA Anglian Region
Comments: An attractive lake, quite deep, with reeds and sandbars

Bradmoor Lakes

Location: Narborough, near Swaffham
Type and Size: Two gravel pits, one of two acres and the other five acres
How to Find: From Norwich take the A47 to Narborough. Beyond East Dereham and Swaffham, after two bridges over the River Nar, take lane on the right. The lakes will be seen on the left
Carp Stock: Very heavily stocked with mirrors to double figures. The crucian carp record was caught here
Category: Carp Water
Other Species: Crucians, bream, tench, roach and rudd
Permits: Membership of Swaffham Angling Club is necessary to fish this water - no day tickets. The Secretary, 30 Kings Street, Swaffham
Cost: Approx. £5 per person
Control: Club
BK Rating: Easy to Moderate
W/A: NRA Anglian Region
Comments: Very pleasant water, details of rules etc. from the Club Secretary

Bridge Lake

Location:	Lenwade, near Norwich
Type and Size:	Two gravel pits
Carp Stock:	Some carp, sizes not known
Category:	Probably Few Carp
Other Species:	Roach, rudd, bream, tench and pike
Permits:	Limited annual permits from The City of Norwich AC, Mr Tom Boulton. Tel: Norwich 426834. Waiting list
Control:	Club
Restrictions:	Please note that this is a syndicate water, although controlled by the Norwich Club - waiting list for syndicate membership
BK Rating:	Not known
W/A:	NRA Anglian Region

Broadland Nurseries Lake

Location:	Ormesby St. Michael, just past Ormesby Broads
Type and Size:	Lake of 2 acres
How to Find:	Go to Wroxham and take the A1062 to Potter Heigham. Then take the A419 to Ormesby St.Michael. The lake and cafe are on the right just past the Broads
Carp Stock:	Said to contain a 'good stock' of carp to double figures
Category:	Mixed Fishery
Other Species:	Perch, roach, rudd, bream and tench
Permits:	Day tickets in advance only from Mr Millar, Broadland Cafe, Ormesby St. Michael
Cost:	About £2 per day
Control:	Private
BK Rating:	Moderate
W/A:	NRA Anglian Region

Bure Valley Fishery

Location:	Bure Valley Trout Lakes, 4 miles from Aylsham off the B1354 to Saxthorpe
Type and Size:	Two acre gravel pit
Carp Stock:	Quite well stocked with mirrors to over 20lbs
Category:	Mixed Fishery
Other Species:	Roach, perch, rudd and tench
Permits:	In advance only, with booking essential, from David Green on Saxthorpe 666
Cost:	£5 per 12 hour day session
BK Rating:	Moderate
Control:	Private
W/A:	NRA Anglian Region

Chiswick Pit

Location:	Farm near the village of Stow Bardolph
Type and Size:	Small farm pond
How to Find:	A47 from Norwich, then the A1122 to Stradsett. Turn right onto the A134 towards Kings Lynn. At Shouldham Thorpe turn left and a mile

further on take a farm track on the left. The pond is on the left opposite
the farmhouse

Carp Stock:	Numbers not known but said to contain a reasonable number of mirrors and commons to double figures
Category:	Mixed Fishery
Other Species:	Rudd and tench
Permits:	Day tickets must be obtained in advance from Stow Estates Office, Stow Bardolph. Tel: Downham Market 383194
Cost:	Approx. £1 per day
Restrictions:	No night fishing - dawn to dusk only. Only three permits per day are issued
BK Rating:	Moderate
W/A:	NRA Anglian Region

Cobbleacre Lake

Location:	Off the A140 Norwich to Cromer road, nine miles north west of Norwich
Type and Size:	Three and a half acre gravel pit with two islands, up to 18 feet deep in places
Carp Stock:	Well stocked with mirrors and commons to 15lbs
Category:	Mixed Fishery
Other Species:	Bream to over 10lbs, roach, rudd, tench and perch
Permits:	Day tickets on bank
Cost:	£5 per day; £3 from 5pm till dusk; £8 for 24 hours
Control:	Private. Tel: 0605 48305
Restrictions:	Night fishing by arrangement only
BK Rating:	Moderate
W/A:	NRA Anglian Region

Common Lakes

Location:	Common Lane, Lenwade, off the A1067 Norwich - Fakenham road
Type and Size:	Three gravel pits between two and five acres
Carp Stock:	Some commons and mirrors, sizes not known
Category:	Possibly Few Carp
Other Species:	Roach, rudd, tench, perch, pike and bream
Permits:	From bailiff on bank
Cost:	£2 per day
BK Rating:	Not known
Control:	Great Witchingham Fuel Allotment Charity
W/A:	NRA Anglian Region
Restrictions:	No night fishing - dawn to dusk only

Cranworth - Woodrising Carp Lake

Location:	Near Jubilee Farm, Cranworth, Dereham
Type and Size:	Man-made farm pond of about an acre
How to Find:	From Norwich take B1108 road to Watton. After Hingham take road on the right to Shipden. Follow the signs to Cranworth, and the lake is just after Jubilee Farm in the village
Carp Stock:	Well stocked with commons and mirrors, mainly small but up to double figures
Category:	Carp Water

Other Species:	A few tench
Permits:	Day tickets from Mr Bunning at Jubilee Farm
Baits/Methods:	Normal carp fishing baits and methods
Control:	Private Tel: 0362 820702
BK Rating:	Easy
W/A:	NRA Anglian Region
Comments:	Quite shallow, coloured lake, long and narrow

Denver Pit

Location:	Sandy Lane, Denver, near Downham Market (not Denver, Colorado, USA!)
Type and Size:	One and a half acre gravel pit, with two islands and some weed
Carp Stock:	A small number of carp to over 20lbs
Category:	Few Carp
Other Species:	Catfish, tench, bream, roach, rudd and perch
Permits:	In advance only from Bob Riches, 15 Sandy Lane, Denver
Cost:	£2 per day; £3 for two rods
Restrictions:	No night fishing; dawn till dusk only
BK Rating:	Difficult
W/A:	NRA Anglian Region
Comments:	The wels are said to go about 7lbs, but there are reputed to be two other catfish varieties in the lake

Docking Village Pond

Location:	Village of Docking near Fakenham
Type and Size:	Clay pit of about an acre
How to Find:	Take the A1067 from Norwich, and Docking is after Fakenham (A148 - B1454)
Carp Stock:	Quite well stocked with small commons up to 8lbs
Category:	Mixed Fishery
Other Species:	Crucian carp, roach and tench
Permits:	From Roys Shop, close to pond. Day tickets must be bought on the same day
Cost:	Approx £1 per day
Restrictions:	Fishing 8.30am to 11pm only. No Sunday fishing. Eight tickets only issued each day
Baits/Methods:	Normal baits and methods
Control:	Private
BK Rating:	Easy
W/A:	NRA Anglian Region
Comments:	The commons are said to be wild carp, although with crucians present hybrids must be expected

Felmingham Mill Lake

Location:	Felmingham Mill, off the B1145 road near Aylsham, about a mile from the village
Type and Size:	Two small lakes
Carp Stock:	Some double figure mirrors
Category:	Few Carp
Other Species:	Roach, perch, crucians, rudd and tench

Permits:	Day tickets must be obtained before fishing from M Moore at the Mill House near the water. (Tel: Aylsham 735106). Tickets include fishing in the little Mill Stream for roach, trout, pike and a few grayling
Cost:	£2 per day; £1 for children
BK Rating:	Not known
W/A:	NRA Anglian Region
Comments:	No night fishing

Fosters End Pits

Location:	East Winch, near Kings Lynn - the pits are one mile down a track by the church
Type and Size:	8 acre pit and three tiny ponds
Carp Stock:	Carp to double figures
Category:	Few Carp
Other Species:	Pike to over 20lbs, roach, rudd and crucians
Permits:	Members only water of the Kings Lynn AA. Membership costs £12. Details from the Secretary, Mr George Bear. Tel: Downham Market 387114
Control:	Club
Restrictions:	Members only
BK Rating:	Not known
W/A:	NRA Anglian Region

Geens Pit

Location:	Shropham, near Snetterton
Type and Size:	Old pit of about one acre, shallow and wooded along one bank
Carp Stock:	There are said to be only a few carp, but these are very large. A 34 pounder was reported in 1984, and since this is recorded as the lake record, it could well be genuine although we cannot be sure about this
Category:	Few Carp
Other Species:	Roach, rudd, tench and bream
Permits:	Advance booking by telephone only to the owner, Mr Geen, Tel: Caston 735. Day tickets. Cost not known.
Control:	Private
BK Rating:	Difficult
W/A:	NRA Anglian Region
Comments:	We have listed a few waters of this kind, where very large carp have been reported caught. We cannot guarantee that these weights quoted are genuine, especially as all carp anglers know that the weights of many fish reported are exaggerated. If we can prove conclusively that any weights are genuine we will say so

Glen's Pit

Location:	Caston, Shropham, Near Attleborough
Type and Size:	One acre pit, quite deep in places
How to Find:	Caston is just off the B1077 road between Attleborough and Watton. The pit is on the left hand side going into the village from the Attleborough side

Carp Stock: Quite well stocked with about 40 carp, most of which are doubles, with some bigger fish to about 34lbs
Category: Mixed Fishery
Other Species: Roach, rudd, perch, bream and eels
Permits: Syndicate - information from J Green on Caston 735
Control: Private
BK Rating: Very Difficult
W/A: NRA Anglian Region

Granary Lakes   A

Location: Granary Hotel, Little Dunham, near Dereham
Type and Size: 3 small interconnected long narrow lakes, plus a 1 acre lake near the hotel
How to Find: Take the A47 Norwich - Dereham road, and 8 miles from Dereham turn right towards Little Dunham. Turn left, then right in village to the Granary Hotel
Carp Stock: Carp to 20lbs in all lakes
Category: Mixed Fishery
Other Species: Crucians and tench
Permits: Day tickets from hotel. Tel: Fakenham 701310. In advance only
Cost: Approx £3 a rod - on bank for the three lake complex
BK Rating: Moderate
Control: Private
W/A: NRA Anglian Region
Comments: Hotel accommodation with restaurant, swimming, golf, tennis as well as fishing

Great Massingham Village Pond

Location: Great Massingham, between Norwich and Fakenham
How to Find: Take A1067 Fakenham road from Norwich and then B1145 from it at Bawdeswell. Go through Litcham and after 6 miles take the road to Great Massingham. The pond is in the middle of the village
Carp Stock: Well stocked with small commons
Category: Carp Only
Permits: Free fishing
BK Rating: Easy
W/A: NRA Anglian Region
Comments: These fish are said locally to be wild carp, but readers should note that there are very few wildies left in the country. John Wilson has confirmed that these are true wildies

Great Melton Reservoir   A

Location: Lombe Estate, Hall Farm, Great Melton, Norwich NR9 3BW, 6 miles from Wymondham
Type and Size: 5 acre estate lake constructed 16 years ago, alongside a Nature Reserve
Carp Stock: Well stocked with commons to about 10lbs
Category: Carp Water
Other Species: Possibly some brown trout, as it was a trout fishery until 3 years ago
Permits: David Gregory, The Estate Office, address above. Tel: 0603 810135.

These are confined to those who book holiday accommodation on the estate

Control:	Private
Restrictions:	No pets; some areas out of bounds to protect wildlife. Some fishing allowed from punts
BK Rating:	Not known, but probably Easy
W/A:	NRA Anglian Region
Comments:	Three cottages are to rent for self-catering holidays on this attractive estate, with fishing on two carp lakes, and the River Yare at Marlingford. Prices from about £200 per week, fishing included

Gunthorpe Hall Lake

Location:	Gunthorpe Hall, Gunthorpe, near Melton Constable
Type and Size:	2 acre estate lake
Carp Stock:	Some common carp to double figures
Category:	Few Carp
Other Species:	Roach, rudd, perch, pike and tench
Permits:	Day tickets by prior booking only from the Hall. Tel: 0263 861373. Only 7 tickets per day issued
Cost:	£1 50 per day
BK Rating:	Not known
Control:	Private
Restrictions:	No night fishing - dawn till dusk only. No Sunday fishing
W/A:	NRA Anglian Region

Hall Farm Pit

Location:	Hall Farm, Burgh Castle opposite Burgh Hall on the road from Yarmouth
Type and Size:	Half acre pit
Carp Stock:	Well stocked with mirrors to double figures
Category:	Mixed Fishery
Other Species:	Crucians, roach, rudd and tench
Permits:	Day tickets from the farm at the top of the field before fishing
Cost:	£1 50 per day
Control:	Private
BK Rating:	Not known
W/A:	NRA Anglian Region

Haveringland Lake

Location:	Haveringland, near Norwich
Type and Size:	14 acre dammed, shallow lake
Carp Stock:	Carp to double figures
Category:	Mixed Fishery
Other Species:	Rudd, roach, bream, tench and pike
Permits:	Mr K Rustige. Tel: Norwich 871302
Control:	Private. Please note that you can only fish this water if you park a touring caravan on the park by the water
Restrictions:	No fishing except for those with touring caravans on site
BK Rating:	Not known
W/A:	NRA Anglian Region

Hevingham Lakes　　　　A

Location:	Hevingham, 8 miles north of Norwich
Type and Size:	Man-made lakes of which there are two, both quite small
How to Find:	From Norwich take B1149 towards Holt. About six miles from Norwich take the second right turn marked 'Hevingham'. The fishery entrance is on the left about a mile further on
Carp Stock:	Well stocked with carp, many of which are small but there are some doubles and also a few over 20lbs
Category:	Mixed Fishery
Other Species:	Crucians, roach, rudd, tench and bream
Permits:	Day tickets in advance only from the owner who lives in the bungalow at the entrance of the fishery - Mr C J Matthewson. Tel: Hevingham 368
Cost:	Free to those who stay
Baits/Methods:	Normal carp fishing baits and methods
Control:	Private
BK Rating:	Moderate
W/A:	NRA Anglian Region
Comments:	You can holiday here as the owner lets caravans to anglers. There are toilet and shower facilities. Touring caravans and tents are welcome and there is also a farmhouse to let. Prices approx £90 - £135 per week according to season

Holkham Hall Lake

Location:	Off the A149 near Wells-next-the-Sea
Type and Size:	15 acre estate lake in the grounds of a big house which is open to the public
Carp Stock:	Fairly well stocked, mainly with commons to upper doubles
Category:	Mixed Fishery
Other Species:	Tench, roach and perch
Permits:	Day tickets from the Estate Office
Control:	Private Tel: 0328 710227
Restrictions:	No night fishing; dawn till dusk only; much of the bank cannot be fished after August 31st. No camping
BK Rating:	Moderate
W/A:	NRA Anglian Region

Hoveton Hall Lake

Location:	Off the A1151 Norwich road near Wroxham
Type and Size:	Three acre Broadland lake
Carp Stock:	Well stocked with carp from 10lbs to 20lb
Category:	Mixed Fishery
Other Species:	Roach and tench
Permits:	Day tickets on bank
Cost:	£1.50 per day from cottage by lake
BK Rating:	Easy
W/A:	NRA Anglian Region
Comments:	Ideal water for youngsters

Little Lake Land

Location:	Wortwell, Bungay
Carp Stock:	Some carp to double figures
Type and Size:	Half acre lake, depths to 12ft
Category:	Mixed Fishery
Other Species:	Roach, perch, bream tench
Permits:	Mr A Hopkins. Tel: Homersfield 646
Control:	Private
Restrictions:	No fishing except for those who park touring caravans at the lake
BK Rating:	Moderate
W/A:	NRA Anglian Region

Little Melton Reservoir   A

Location:	Marlingford, Wymondham, near Norwich
Type and Size:	Two acre estate lake
Carp Stock:	Fairly well stocked with carp, sizes not known
Category:	Carp Water
Other Species:	Some very large brown and rainbow trout, as this was previously a trout water
Permits:	David Gregory, The Estate Office, Hall Farm, Great Melton, Norwich NR9 3BW. Tel: 0603 810135 - only for those booking the self-catering cottages on the estate
Control:	Private
Restrictions:	No pets; some areas may be out of bounds to protect wildlife. Some boat fishing allowed
BK Rating:	Easy
W/A:	NRA Anglian Region
Comments:	There are 3 cottages as holiday rents on this attractive estate, with prices ranging from £200 per week to only about £250 in August, with fishing on three lakes and the River Yare included

Lyng Easthaugh Pits

Location:	Lyng, near Norwich
Type and Size:	Two acre gravel pit
How to Find:	Take the A1067 Norwich-Fakenham road, and turn left for Lyng at Lenwade village. Pits on the right in 1½ miles
Carp Stock:	Well stocked with carp
Category:	Carp Water
Other Species:	A few coarse fish
Permits:	Season tickets only - Dereham and Dist. A.C. Secretary, S Allinson, Sequenta, Cemetery Road, East Dereham. Tel: Dereham 4828; the farm, Lyng, or local tackle dealers
Cost:	Approx £7 per year
BK Rating:	Easy
Control:	Club
Restrictions:	Members only
W/A:	NRA Anglian Region
Comments:	The ticket includes other pits and river fishing. The big pit alongside may contain a few carp

Marlingford Mere   A

Location: Marlingford, Wymondham, Norwich
Type and Size: 12 acre gravel pit, landscaped and now a fishery and wildlife reserve
Carp Stock: Well stocked with common carp about three years ago, numbers and sizes not known
Category: Carp Water
Other Species: Probably some
Permits: David Gregory, Estate Offfice, Hall Farm, Great Melton, Norwich NR9 3BW. Tel: 0603 810135; fishing only available to those booking the holiday cottages on the estate
Control: Private
Restrictions: No pets
BK Rating: Not known
W/A: NRA Anglian Region
Comments: There are three cottages to rent for holidays on the estate, which is most attractive. Prices range from about £200 to £260 per week, with fishing on 3 carp lakes and the River Yare included. No day tickets or other permits

Martham Pits

Location: Close to the ferry on the River Thurne, near Martham village
Type and Size: A number of small, interconnected pits
Carp Stock: Some carp to double figures
Category: Mixed Fishery
Other Species: Well known as a tench fishery; also pike, bream, rudd, roach and eels
Permits: Molly's Sweet Shop, Black Lane, Martham. Tel: Great Yarmouth 740366. Only 15 issued in advance each day
Cost: £2 per day
Control: Private
BK Rating: Difficult
W/A: NRA Anglian Region

Mere Farm Pond

Location: Mere Farm, Saxthorpe
Type and Size: 1 acre farm pond
How to Find: Take the B1149 Holt road from Norwich to Saxthorpe. In village, cross the River Bure and straight across the crossroads. Mere Farm is one mile ahead on the left
Carp Stock: Well stocked with wild carp to 6lbs
Category: Mixed Fishery
Other Species: Roach and eels
Permits: From farmhouse; Tel: 026387 883
Cost: £1.60 per day
BK Rating: Easy
W/A: NRA Anglian Region
Comments: John Wilson tells us these carp are 'wildies' — and there are very few of those left in this country! Most fish which locals call 'wildies' are just long, thin commons

Nunnery Lakes

Location:	Thetford
Type and Size:	5 gravel pits of 2-5 acres
How to Find:	Enquire from local owner
Carp Stock:	Well stocked with mirrors
Category:	Mixed Fishery
Other Species:	Tench, roach, perch, rudd
Permits:	Annual syndicate only - apply in close season to Mr Lowndes, Nunnery House, Nunnery Place, Thetford with an SAE
Cost:	On application
BK Rating:	Moderate
Control:	Private
Restrictions:	No day tickets
W/A:	NRA Anglian Region

Railway Pit

Location:	3 miles from Attleborough
Type and Size:	Tiny pit of about ¼ acre
How to Find:	Take the A11 from Norwich and 3 miles after Attleborough turn left at Old Buckenham crossroads. Cross the railway line, and the pit is on the left, surrounded by trees
Carp Stock:	Some mirror carp, sizes and numbers not known
Category:	Probably Few Carp
Other Species:	Small tench, roach, perch and pike
Permits:	FREE fishing
BK Rating:	Not known
W/A:	NRA Anglian Region

Reepham Fisheries

Location:	Just outside the village of Reepham, on the left of the road from Norwich
Type and Size:	Three acre ex-trout lake
Carp Stock:	Carp to doubles
Category:	Mixed Fishery
Other Species:	Crucian, rudd and tench. There are also some ghost koi
Permits:	From the bungalow, or on the bank
Cost:	£5 per day
Control:	Private. Tel: Norwich 870829
Baits/Methods:	Float and legering methods both work well
Restrictions:	No night fishing, except by prior arrangement. Fishing from 6am until 10pm only. No keepnets, and carp to be retained for a few minutes in landing nets only for photographs
BK Rating:	Moderate
W/A:	NRA Anglian Region

Ringland Lakes

Location:	Ringland, near Norwich
Type and Size:	Seven gravel pits
How to Find:	From Norwich take A47 Dereham road and after two miles turn right down Longwater Lane by the Roundwell public house. Turn left at

	bottom of the hill, then keep left at the fork and a mile further on you will see a track on the right leading to the fishery
Carp Stock:	Not a large number of carp but are said to be mostly large - from doubles to 30lbs, in the largest lake. This is called Days Waters and is the first along the track on the left
Category:	Few Carp
Other Species:	Perch, pike, bream, rudd, crucians and tench
Permits:	Day tickets and also season tickets from the bailiff on the bank
Cost:	Day tickets: approx £2
Control:	Leisure Sport Angling
BK Rating:	Moderate
W/A:	NRA Anglian Region

River Wensum

Location:	Below the mill in Norwich
Type and Size:	Town river
Carp Stock:	Plenty of carp to well over 20lbs, and 30's - escapees from a local fish farm
Category:	Mixed Fishery
Other Species:	Most coarse fish, including barbel
Permits:	Clubs have some water in this area, but most is free fishing
BK Rating:	Difficult, as fish must first be located, usually in the deeper, slower moving parts of the river
W/A:	NRA Anglian Region
Comments:	It was only a flood which 'stocked' this river with carp, though there is no telling how many will survive. Other fish grow to good sizes in the Wensum, so the carp should do well

Rodally Pit

Location:	In the centre of the village of Old Buckenham which is on the B1077 from Attleborough
Type and Size:	Half acre shallow pond
Carp Stock:	Some small commons
Category:	Mixed Fishery
Other Species:	Rudd and tench
Permits:	FREE fishing
W/A:	NRA Anglian Region

Scottow Pond

Location:	Scottow, near Swanton Abbot, and Coltishall
Type and Size:	5 acre shallow, silty bottomed lake
Carp Stock:	Well stocked with mirrors in 1983 - a rich lake so they should have grown well
Category:	Mixed Fishery
Other Species:	Good tench, pike and eels
Permits:	Members only, no day tickets, from Mr Townsend, Hall Gardens, Scottow. Tel: 069 269671
Cost:	£6 per season
Control:	Private

Restrictions:	Members only
BK Rating:	Not known, although it could be quite hard, as this water is very clear
W/A:	NRA Anglian Region
Comments:	This water is just down the road from RAF Coltishall where PM was stationed during his National Service from 1949-51. He did try fishing it, and found it very difficult.... nothing but blanks!

Shallow Brook Carp Lake

Location:	New Costessey, near Norwich
Type and Size:	2¼ acre lake about 12ft deep
How to Find:	From Norwich take the A47 Dereham road into New Costessey. Turn right at the traffic lights into Norwich Road, and half a mile further on the lake is on the left just after the river bridge
Carp Stock:	Plenty of commons and mirrors to 20lbs
Category:	Mixed Fishery
Other Species:	Roach, perch, tench, crucian carp and rudd
Permits:	Day tickets from farm shop before fishing
Cost:	£5 per day: £3 - half day: £2 - evening. Season tickets also available. For details contact Norwich 742822 (daytime). Norwich 741123 (evenings)
Control:	Private
Restrictions:	No night fishing unless you buy a season ticket; day tickets are from dawn to dusk
BK Rating:	Easy
W/A:	NRA Anglian Region
Comments:	Car park close to lake. Facilities for wheelchair anglers. Permit includes roach, dace and chub fishing in a stretch of the little River Tub nearby

Shropham Pits

Location:	Shropham, near Attleborough
Type and Size:	Two pits, of from 5 to 10ft deep
How to Find:	Take the A11 from Norwich to 4 miles past Attleborough, and pass the White Lodge pub on the left. After another 1½ miles, turn right at a sign marked 'By road'. At the crossroads turn right over a bridge, and take the first road on the left. The pits are 300 yds on the left
Carp Stock:	Some carp to double figures
Category:	Probably Few Carp
Other Species:	Pike, tench, roach, rudd, eels, bream and crucians
Permits:	Members only water of Wymondham and District AC. Membership from The Secretary, Mr T Binks, 25 Rosemary Road, Norwich. Tel: Norwich 405341, or from the bailiff in the house opposite the pit entrance
Cost:	£12 per season
Control:	Club
BK Rating:	Difficult
W/A:	NRA Anglian Region

Stonegate Lake

Location:	Off the B1145 Aylsham to Cawston road, turning left under the old railway bridge. The lake is on the right
Type and Size:	Shallow three acre lake
Carp Stock:	Some mirrors and commons to a good size
Category:	Mixed Fishery
Other Species:	Perch, rudd, crucians, bream and pike
Permits:	Members only water of the Yarmouth, Gorleston and Dist.A.C. Apply to the Chairman, Tony Giacomelli. Tel: 0760 44323, or from Tom Boulton. Tel: Norwich 426834
Cost:	£14 per season, to include fishing at Bawburgh Lake, Granary Lakes, and the Muckfleet Dyke
Control:	Club
W/A:	NRA Anglian Region

Stradsett Lake

Location:	Stradsett, near Kings Lynn - from Stradsett, turn right onto the A134, and the lake is also on the right, one mile further on
Type and Size:	Eight acre lake, about 7ft in depth
Carp Stock:	Some carp, sizes not known
Category:	Mixed Fishery
Other Species:	Bream, perch, pike and tench
Permits:	Members only water, and a specialist syndicate, to which only members of Kings Lynn AC can apply. To join the club, apply to the Secretary, Mr George Bear. Tel: Downham Market 387114
Cost:	Kings Lynn AC costs £12 to join, and then there is an extra fee to join the Stradsett Syndicate
Control:	Club
BK Rating:	Moderate
W/A:	NRA Anglian Region

Swangey Lakes

Location:	Near West Carr, Attleborough
Type and Size:	Two gravel pits of 4½ and 1½ acres
How to Find:	Take the A11 from Norwich, and on the Attleborough by-pass turn right to West Carr. After half a mile turn left when the road forks, and then right in 100 yards, continue through a ford across the river, and the fishery entrance is on the left
Carp Stock:	Well stocked with carp to 20lbs and catfish to 25lbs
Category:	Carp Water
Other Species:	Crucians, tench, rudd, roach, perch, bream
Permits:	Day tickets on bank from bailiff. Further enquiries from M and M Enterprises. Tel 0953 453119
Cost:	£5 per day, half price for juniors
Control:	Private
Restrictions:	No night fishing - fishing is from dawn to dusk only
BK Rating:	Easy
W/A:	NRA Anglian Region
Comments:	The lakes are 30ft deep in places

Swanton Morley Fisheries

Location:	Swanton Morley, near East Dereham
Type and Size:	Gravel pits, 3 lakes totalling 65 acres
How to Find:	From East Dereham take the B1147 road, signposted Bawdeswell past the Papermakers public house and the church. Bear left at the T-junction then sharp right. Pass Waterfall Farm on your left and the entrance to the lakes is 400 yards on the right. Do NOT use the works entrance
Carp Stock:	Not many carp; sizes unknown
Category:	Few Carp
Other Species:	Pike, perch, rudd and tench
Permits:	Day tickets must be obtained in advance from: Rod and Gun, Norwich Street, Dereham; Mrs V Marsham, Waterfall Farm, Swanton Morley (Please enclose SAE). After 8am tickets can be obtained from Waterfall Farm. Season tickets from Waterfall Farm
Cost:	Approx £1 per day (Juniors/OAPs/evening fishing 50p)
Restrictions:	No night fishing. Fishery is open from sunrise to sunset. Do NOT go to the working site or works lake.
Control:	Redland Angling Scheme
BK Rating:	Difficult, as there are few carp
W/A:	NRA Anglian Region

Taswood Lakes

Location:	Flordon, Tasburgh, Norwich
Type and Size:	Five man-made lakes of from one to 3½ acres
How to Find:	From Norwich take the A140 and take the right fork to Flordon in Newton Flotman. After 1½ miles turn left to Tasburgh. The lakes are on the left in 200 yards
Carp Stock:	All the lakes contain some mirrors, the numbers of which are not known. The biggest lake holds some 20's, best weight recorded is 29lbs 10ozs in 1984
Category:	Mixed Fishery
Other Species:	Crucians, roach, rudd, bream, tench, perch, pike, some grass carp in the pond near the house
Cost:	Day ticket cost approx £2
Control:	Private - owner lives on property
BK Rating:	Moderate
W/A:	NRA Anglian Region
Comments:	Owner sells koi carp, goldfish and other pond fish on site

Tatts Pit

Location:	The Willows, Downham Market
Type and Size:	Tree-lined pit of about an acre
How to Find:	Take the A47 Dereham road from Norwich, then the A1122 to Downham Market, then follow the Wisbech road and look out for Downham Tackle on your right. Just before the shop, turn left, and the pit is 100 yards on the left at 'the Willows'
Carp Stock:	Some mirrors, sizes not known
Category:	Possibly Few Carp
Other Species:	Tench and crucians
Permits:	In advance only from Downham Tackle, Railway Road, Downham Market. Tel: 0366 384338

Cost:	£2 per day
Control:	Private
BK Rating:	Not known
W/A:	NRA Anglian Region

Taverham

Location:	Costessey No. 2 and No. 3 pits, Taverham, near Norwich
Type and Size:	Ski Pit (No. 2) - 12 acres, up to 20ft deep. The Carp Lake (No. 3) - 6 acres, and 8 to 15 feet deep
Carp Stock:	No. 2 has a small number of carp to double figures. No. 3 also has very few, but mirrors between 28lbs and 30lbs are caught each season
How to Find:	Take the A1067 Fakenham road from Norwich to Taverham, and turn left at the crossroads into Sandy Lane. Go straight ahead at the next crossroads, and over the River Wensum bridge. The pits are on the left, with the car park by No. 2. No parking on the roadside
Category:	No. 2 - Difficult: No. 3 Very Difficult
Other Species:	Tench, bream, roach, eels, perch and pike to 23lbs
Permits:	Day tickets from tackle dealers, or season tickets from, The Secretary, Mr Cyril Wigg, 3 Coppice Avenue, Norwich. Tel: Norwich 423625, and *must* be purchased in advance — no tickets on the bank
Cost:	Day - £1; Season - £10
Baits/Methods:	Advanced carp fishing baits and techniques needed for these big hard to catch carp
Control:	Club - Norfolk and Suffolk Anglers Consultative Council
Restrictions:	No night fishing
BK Rating:	No. 2 - Difficult; No. 3 - Very Difficult
Comments:	The big carp in No. 3 are well known to carp specialists, so this is very much a specialist's water. Since there are very few of these fish they are obviously very hard to catch. There are some level swims provided near the car park for disabled anglers.

Taverham Mill Lake   A

Location:	Sandy Lane, Taverham, on the right just before the bridge over the River Wensum
Type and Size:	15 acre attractively matured man-made lake, dug in the '40's, with many islands, bays and peninsulas, and up to 12ft in depth. Heavily weeded in summer
Carp Stock:	Plenty of carp, sizes not known
Category:	Mixed Fishery
Other Species:	Tench, big bream and pike, roach and rudd
Permits:	Day tickets limited in advance only from Norwich Angling Centre, Sprowston Road, Norwich. Tel: 400757. Accommodation also available
Cost:	On application
Control:	Private
BK Rating:	Moderate
W/A:	NRA Anglian Region

New and best selling carp videos from Beekay Publishers. See page 19

Thompson Water

Location:	Merton, near Watton, Norwich
Type and Size:	Shallow lake of 30 acres
How to Find:	Take the B1108 road from Norwich to Watton and then the B1110 to Merton and Thompson, Take the track straight on to Peddars Way and the huge lake is on the left
Carp Stock:	There have apparently always been some commons in this big lake, although not very many. It is reported to have been 'heavily stocked' (numbers not known) with mirrors in 1984 and they are also said to be caught in double figures
Category:	Mixed Fishery
Other Species:	Crucians, rudd, roach, bream, tench and pike
Permits:	Day tickets from bailiff on bank. Information about the water from Merton Estate Office, Watton, Thetford IP25 6QJ. Tel: Watton 883370
Cost:	Approx £2 per day
Control:	Private
Baits/Methods:	Usual carp baits and methods, though it may be wise to select baits which are less likely to be taken by the many other fish in the water
BK Rating:	Difficult
W/A:	NRA Anglian Region

Time-Share Lakes A

Location:	Near Norwich
Type and Size:	Large lakes
Carp Stock:	Well stocked with carp to over 20lbs
Category:	Mixed Fishery
Other Species:	Tench, roach, bream and possibly others
Permits:	Tel: 0603 407199 for information and details
Cost:	£5,000! (This is not a misprint — this fishery has been advertised at this cost for *life membership*, which includes 4 weeks fishing and accommodation every year for life
Control:	Private
BK Rating:	Unknown
W/A:	NRA Anglian Region

University Broad

Location:	Norwich University
Type and Size:	Ten acre gravel pit
How to Find:	In Norwich take B1108 Watton road and turn left onto Bluebell Road in Earlham. The lake will be seen on the right
Carp Stock:	Good stock of mirror and koi carp to double figures
Category:	Mixed Fishery
Other Species:	Roach, rudd, tench, bream, and pike
Permits:	Members only - University of East Anglia, Biology Department, U.E.A. Norwich. Annual permits only. Apply in writing with SAE
Cost:	Approx £12 per year
BK Rating:	Moderate
Control:	University
Restrictions:	Not known
W/A:	NRA Anglian Region
Comments:	Only big stillwater within the city - up to 20 feet deep

Wades Pit

Location:	Wymondham, near Norwich
Type and Size:	Weedy pit of about an acre, up to 7 feet deep
How to Find:	Take the A11 from Norwich to Wymondham, and turn left at the traffic lights into the B1135. Take the first left turn after the railway bridge, and the pit is another half mile, on the left
Carp Stock:	Some mirrors to middle doubles
Category:	Few Carp
Other Species:	Roach, perch, tench and crucians
Permits:	Day tickets from bailiff on bank, season tickets and information from:- Mr R Bartlett, 6 Vimy Ridge, Wymondham. Tel:Wymondham 605505
Cost:	70p (Juniors - 35p) for day tickets: £3 (Juniors £1.50) per season
Baits/Methods:	Good float fishing water, ideal for youngsters
Control:	Private
BK Rating:	Easy for most fish, though we suspect harder for the carp, as there are not many of the bigger fish
W/A:	NRA Anglian Region

Walnut Tree Farm   A

Location:	Lyng, off the A1067 Norwich Fakenham road, 12 miles north west of Norwich
Type and Size:	Two recently opened and restored gravel pits of about 35 acres
Carp Stock:	Well stocked with carp to 30lbs
Category:	Mixed Fishery
Permits:	William Bingham on site; enquire locally or at Norwich tackle shops
Cost:	Not known
Control:	Private
BK Rating:	Not known
W/A:	NRA Anglian Region
Comments:	Reported in the angling papers in July 1992 as having already produced a carp of 30lb 11oz in the first week of the season. However, the owners are said to be ready to import carp from Holland of up to 72lbs as soon as they can obtain the permission from MAFF, though the fish will not be eligible for British records. There are 'small lodges' for holidays, but we have been able to discover neither an address nor a phone number

Waveney Valley Lakes   A

Location:	Wortwell, near Harleston, on the Suffolk border
Type and Size:	Six mature gravel pits from 2 — 5 acres in size
How to Find:	Take the A140 from Norwich to Pulham Market, then the B1134 to Harleston and the A143 to Wortwell. The entrance to the lakes is signposted in the middle of Wortwell
Carp Stock:	All the lakes are well stocked with large carp. Plenty of doubles and 20's, and a number of very well authenticated 30's have been taken to 36lbs
Category:	Carp Water
Other Species:	Crucians, tench, roach, rudd, bream, perch, pike and eels
Permits:	Day tickets should be puchased from the site shop if open, if not, bailiffs call around. Day tickets cover 12 hours only. Night fishing allowed but another 12 hour ticket will be needed
Cost:	£3.50 for one rod for 12 hours; two rods £6. Weekly + bivvy £40 for 1 rod; £65 for 2 rods

Control:	Details from shop, or Tony Knox on 0986 86676
Baits/Methods:	Advanced carp fishing rigs and methods and baits are needed at this heavily fished specialist carp water. Many boilies and multiple baits go in every day. Hard boilies, such as Maestros, work best
BK Rating:	Moderate though some of the lakes can be easy for the smaller fish and lower doubles; the really big fish are quite difficult
W/A:	NRA Anglian Region
Comments:	One of the best commercial carp fisheries in the country - and for this reason very well known for its twenties and thirties, and hard fished by many expert carp anglers. Tents can be pitched for long-stay holidays at an extra charge and you can also take your touring caravan. There are luxury lakeside caravans which must be booked well in advance, and these are ideal for a family holiday. There are top class shower and toilet facilities, and the shop sells carp bait, tackle and food. G, E and D lakes are said to be the best for the really big fish, some of which are caught quite often and are well known to the regulars. No dogs. One of the comparatively few carp waters in the country which can be fished by everyone and where you are always in with a chance of a big fish. Caravans about £200 weekly. Sacking for 15 minutes only; unhooking mats compulsory. Day tickets only available on some lakes from November. Holiday cottages also to let in the area. Tel: Fressingfield 395

Wensum Fisheries

Location:	Costessey, near Norwich
Type and Size:	Attractive, wooded, old gravel pits of from 2 to 10 acres in size
How to Find:	Take the A47 from Norwich, and after two miles turn right by the Roundwell public house down Longwater Lane. At the 'T' junction turn left, and then take a right fork in half a mile. The lakes are then 200 yards on the left, behind iron gates
Carp Stock:	Clear Water Lake is well stocked with carp into double figures; Rainbow Pool contains a few carp
Category:	Clear Water - Mixed Fishery; Rainbow - Few Carp
Other Species:	Back Lake (the biggest) - roach, rudd and bream to over 9lbs (no carp); Roach Lake - roach, tench and bream (no carp); Clear Water Lake - tench and bream; Rainbow Pool - roach, tench and bream
Permits:	Members only water of Norwich and Dist.AA. Permits from the Secretary, Mr C Wigg, 3 Coppice Avenue, Norwich. Tel: Norwich 423625 (Includes fishing on River Wensum)
Cost:	On application
Control:	Club
Restrictions:	No night fishing
BK Rating:	Clear Water - Moderate; Rainbow - Difficult
W/A:	NRA Anglian Region

Wereham Pit

Location:	In the village of Wereham, opposite the George and Dragon pub
Type and Size:	Tiny, shallow, quarter of an acre pit
How to Find:	Find Wereham, near Stradsett, off the A134, and then Wereham
Carp Stock:	Plenty of little carp
Category:	Mixed Fishery
Other Species:	Roach and pike

Permits: FREE fishing, ideal for young people
W/A: NRA Anglian Region
BK Rating: Easy

West Lexham   A

Location: West Lexham, near Kings Lynn
Type and Size: Beautiful moat
Carp Stock: Well stocked with carp to over 30lbs
Other Species: General coarse fish
Category: Mixed Fishery
Permits: Sue Allerton. Tel (Swaffham) 0760 755252
Control: Private
Restrictions: No fishing, except to those renting one of the self-catering holiday cottages on the site. Includes fishing on the River Nar
BK Rating: Not known
W/A: NRA Anglian Region

Willsmore Water

Location: Hayes Lane near Fakenham
Type and Size: 1½ acre man-made lake
How to Find: From Fakenham cross the River Wensum at Goggs Mill, then take Sandy Lane and Hayes Lane
Carp Stock: Well stocked with carp to doubles
Category: Mixed Fishery
Permits: Fakenham AC (members only). Membership from G Parsons, 26 St Peters Road, Fakenham. Tel: 4637
Cost: Approx £4 entry fee - £10 per season
BK Rating: Moderate
Restrictions: No keepnets, no groundbaiting
W/A: NRA Anglian Region
Comments: Membership also includes some other lakes and trout and coarse fishing on the River Wensum

Wolterton Park Lake

Location: Wolterton Hall, 5 miles from Aylsham
Type and Size: Attractive estate lake, with an island and very clear water
Carp Stock: Some carp, sizes not known
Category: Few Carp
Other Species: A few big tench, eels and perch
Permits: Day tickets from the Head Gardener's Lodge, just inside the orchard which leads round the Great Hall to the lake
Cost: £2 per day
Control: Private
BK Rating: Very Difficult
W/A: NRA Anglian Region
Comments: A very weedy, clear water which is very difficult to fish, as it seems to be sparsely stocked

Wood Lakes

Location:	Stow, near Kings Lynn
Type and Size:	Six lakes, largest 15 acres
How to Find:	Take the A10 from Kings Lynn and turn right at Stow Bardolph. 500 yards before the bridge carry straight on at sharp bend. The lakes will be seen on the right shortly before Stow Bridge
Carp Stock:	All well stocked with carp to over 25lbs
Category:	Mixed Fishery
Other Species:	Roach, rudd, tench, bream and pike
Permits:	Day tickets from the reception kiosks, or on the banks from the bailiffs if the reception is closed
Cost:	£4.50 per 12 hours (2 rods); £6 for 24 hours
Baits/Methods:	Specialist carp fishing methods and baits needed for the better carp. Night fishing best, when there is less disturbance.
Restrictions:	No winter fishing from November 1st onwards
Control:	Private. Tel: 0533 810414
BK Rating:	Moderate
W/A:	NRA Anglian Region
Comments:	Camping is allowed at extra cost. Touring caravans are also welcomed. Family-type water during the day. Best chance for the specialist is after dark

Worthing Pits

Location:	Dereham,near Norwich
Type and Size:	Two pits of 8 acres and 2 acres, the larger of which is open and has depths of up to 20ft
Carp Stock:	Some carp, numbers and sizes not known
Category:	Few Carp
Other Species:	Roach, tench, perch and pike
Permits:	Day tickets, in advance only, from local tackle shops, or Mr S R Allison, Pound Cottage, Cemetery Road, East Dereham. Tel: Dereham 694828
Cost:	£1.50 per day; Dereham and Dist. AC membership, which includes these waters, several other pits, and stretches of the River Wensum behind the pits; cost £7 per season, half price for juniors
Control:	Club
BK Rating:	Not known
W/A:	NRA Anglian Region

NORTHAMPTONSHIRE

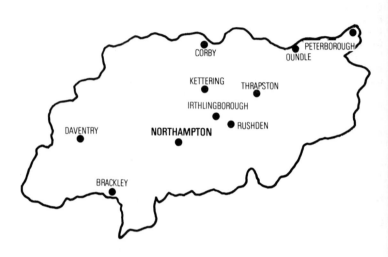

CORBY

PETERBOROUGH
OUNDLE

KETTERING
THRAPSTON

IRTHLINGBOROUGH

DAVENTRY
RUSHDEN

NORTHAMPTON

BRACKLEY

Biggin Lake

Location:	Biggin Estate, Oundle
Type and Size:	6 acre estate lake
How to Find:	Oundle is east of Corby on the A427
Carp Stock:	A few fish under 10lbs, but plenty of doubles; average about 18lbs; said to be a number of twenties, and fish of 36lbs and 34lbs have been reported, though we have no evidence of authenticity
Category:	Carp Only
Other Species:	None
Permits:	B P Tackle, Mill Road, Kettering (Tackle Shop). Season tickets (in advance) only
Cost:	On application
BK Rating:	Moderate
Control:	Private
Restrictions:	No sacking except for quick pics. 72 hour maximum stay
W/A:	NRA Anglian Region
Comments:	Well established, attractive water with plenty of cover on banks. Only fished for the past 6 years so it is thought that some of the big fish have never been caught

Biggin Pit

Location: Oundle Golf Course
Type and Size: Gravel pit of 6 acres
How to Find: On the outskirts of the town of Oundle
Carp Stock: Well stocked with carp to 20lbs
Category: Carp Water
Other Species: Few other fish
Permits: Robin Sharp, B P Tackle, Mill Road, Kettering
Cost: Syndicate - £100 per season and day tickets at £7.50
Control: Private
BK Rating: Easy
W/A: NRA Anglian Region
Comments: Shallow, silty pit said to be good carp fishing. Quiet peaceful lake. Second lake about 3 acres on site also contains many small carp. Day tickets, bookable in advance - a very easy water

Billing Aquadrome

Location: Little Billing, near Northampton
Type and Size: There are a number of lakes on this holiday caravan and leisure complex, but only the Willow Pool (12 acres) is of much interest to carp anglers
How to Find: Take the A45 from Northampton and turn off to the village of Little Billing
Carp Stock: Very few, but have grown to great size in the past. The lake became famous in the 50's and 60's when a huge catch of twenties and a thirty were caught by Bob Reynolds, and in 1966 a 42 pounder was caught by Ray Clay. Still a few big fish but they are rarely caught
Category: Few Carp
Other Species: Pike, perch, roach, tench, bream
Permits: On site. Information - Tel: Northampton 45255
Restrictions: No night fishing. No fishing after mid-October
BK Rating: Super-Difficult
W/A: NRA Anglian Region
Comments: Famous carp water now declined to the extent that carp are almost never caught there - although it was always very difficult. Crowds of thousands at weekends and bank holidays - hundreds of caravans, cafes and amusements etc. There may still be a few big fish and there was a low 30 caught there fairly recently

Boddington Reservoir

Location: Byfield, 7 miles from Banbury
Type and Size: Big reservoir - 65 acres
Carp Stock: Some carp to a good size
Category: Mixed Fishery
Other Species: Pike, bream, perch, roach and tench
Permits: Season tickets from Principal Fisheries Officer, British Waterways, Willow Grange, Church Road, Watford, Herts. Tel: Watford 226422. (There may be a waiting list)
Cost: £17 per season
Control: British Waterways
BK Rating: Not known
W/A: NRA Thames Region

Brightwells Lake

Location:	On the Ringstead to Addington road, between Thrapston and Kettering
Type and Size:	15 acre gravel pit
Carp Stock:	Heavily stocked with many doubles to 24lbs, and several hundred small ones, placed in the water in 1991
Category:	Mixed Fishery
Other Species:	Tench, pike and roach
Permits:	Season tickets only from Irthlingborough DAS; Peter Pratt, 7 The Shortlands, Irthlingborough
Cost:	£13 per season
BK Rating:	Moderate
W/A:	NRA Anglian Region

Castle Ashby Lakes

Location:	Castle Ashby, near Northampton
Type and Size:	Three estate lakes of various sizes
How to Find:	Take a left turn off the A248 Northampton-Bedford road about 7 miles from Northampton
Carp Stock:	Two of the lakes are quite well stocked with carp to mid-doubles
Category:	Mixed Fishery
Other Species:	General coarse fishing
Permits:	Castle Ashby Estate Office, Castle Ashby, Northampton. Tel: 0604 712346. One lake recently opened as a specimen carp water - details from the estate office
Cost:	£1.50 per day
Control:	Castle Ashby Estate
BK Rating:	Moderate. Menagerie Lake - Very Easy for carp to 18lbs
Restrictions:	No night fishing. Fishing is dawn till dusk only
W/A:	NRA Anglian Region

Clarkes

Location:	Clarkes Pick Your Own Farm, Hannington, near Kettering - off the A43
Type and Size:	Small farm lake of about an acre dug for irrigation and 16 feet deep
Carp Stock:	Well stocked with carp to 25lbs, although many are small
Category:	Mixed Fishery
Other Species:	Usual coarse fish
Permits:	Day tickets on site, at £2 per day
Control:	Private
BK Rating:	Moderate
W/A:	NRA Anglian Region

Corby Boating Lake

Location:	On the outskirts of Corby, Cottingham Road
Type and Size:	Town lake of 3½ acres
How to Find:	In Corby
Carp Stock:	Stocked with carp to 20lbs; a 33lb has been reported
Category:	Mixed Fishery
Other Species:	Roach, bream, tench, pike, rudd and catfish
Permits:	Free fishing

Control: Council
BK Rating: Moderate
Restrictions: No night fishing. barbless hooks, no groundbaiting
W/A: NRA Anglian Region

Cransley Hall   A

Location: Off the Broughton bypass, about 3 miles from Kettering on the Northampton road
Type and Size: Estate lake
Carp Stock: Some carp to 20lbs
Category: Mixed Fishery
Other Species: Roach, tench
Permits: Cliff Smart's Angling Holidays, 29 Bridal Road, Burton Latimer, Northants NN15 5QP. Tel: 0536 724226/725453
Control: Bryan Perkins, Cransley Hall
BK Rating: Not known
W/A: NRA Anglian Region
Comments: Bed and breakfast accommodation in 17th century Hall, with croquet, bowls and tennis. Cost about £36 per night, fishing included. Dinners at oak table in ornate dining room

Ditchford Lake

Location: Near Rushden
Type and Size: Two well matured gravel pits of about 6 and 30 acres
Carp Stock: Stocked with commons and mirrors most of which are doubles with a few twenties. Record 26lbs, from small lake; about 12 twenties in big lake with at least 4 twenty pound commons
Category: Mixed Fishery
Other Species: Most coarse fish
Permits: Rushden, High Ferrers and Irchester Angling Club. Season tickets only from Jack Leach Fishing Tackle, Church Street, Rushden
Cost: Approx £10 per season with a number of other good waters on the club ticket
Control: Club
BK Rating: Difficult
W/A: NRA Anglian Region
Comments: Night fishing is allowed

Ecton Lakes

Location: Billing, near Northampton
Type and Size: New gravel pit of 40+ acres
Carp Stock: Low density - about 2 fish per acre, but plenty of 20's caught
Category: Mixed Fishery
Other Species: General coarse fish - some big pike
Permits: Jack Leach Fishing Tackle, Church Street, Rushden, or Northampton Nene AC, M Eaton, 12 Thorne Hill, Briar Hill, Northampton NN4 9SN
Cost: Approx £20 per season
BK Rating: Difficult
Control: Club
W/A: NRA Anglian Region
Comments: Fish kill in 1991 (SVC) reduced stock drastically.

Fineshade Abbey

Location:	On the A43 between Corby and Stamford
Type and Size:	Two small lakes, recently opened
Carp Stock:	Some carp to doubles
Category:	Mixed Fishery
Other Species:	Roach, tench, perch and bream
Permits:	Day tickets on site
Cost:	Weekends 9am to 4.30pm - £5
Control:	Private. Tel: 0780 83284 for bookings and information
Restrictions:	Thought to be no night fishing; restricted fishing on weekdays
BK Rating:	Not known
W/A:	NRA Anglian Region

Flecknoe Farm Fisheries

Location:	Just outside Daventry
Type and Size:	Small farm lake
Carp Stock:	Well stocked with carp to doubles
Category:	Carp Water
Permits:	Season tickets only from Flecknoe Fisheries, 4 Watts Way, Long Buckby NN6 7QX. Tel: 0327 853657
Cost:	£75 per season; numbers limited
BK Rating:	Not known
W/A:	NRA Severn-Trent Region

Foxholes Fisheries

Location:	Crick, Northampton NN6 7US. Tel: 0788 823967. Off the A428 between West Haddon and Crick
Type and Size:	Four small lakes on fish farm. New 2 acre carp lake containing 50 carp from 10lbs to 22lbs
Carp Stock:	Day Ticket Pool - mainly carp to 8lbs; Top Lake - carp only, most from 3-8lbs in weight; Bottom Lake - carp only, 5lbs to 12lbs; Middle Lake - some carp
Category:	Day Ticket Pool - Mixed Fishery; Middle Lake - Mixed Fishery; Top Lake and Bottom lake - Carp Only; New Lake - Carp Only
Other Species:	Day Ticket - crucians and tench; Middle Lake - tench, chub, perch, roach, crucians, bream and barbel
Permits:	From Roger and Joan Chaplin at the above address
Cost:	Day Ticket Pool - £2.50 for one rod, £5 for two rods, issued on bank by bailiff. Season tickets for Top, Bottom, Middle and New Lakes £40 for one weekday; £50 for 2 weekdays; £60 for 4 weekdays; £60 for Saturday plus one weekday; £65 for Sunday plus one weekday; £80 for Saturday and Sunday; £100 for 6 days a week
Restrictions:	Barbless hooks; no keepnets; season ticket waters closed on Tuesdays; day ticket pool open every day; guest tickets allowed to season ticket holders
BK Rating:	Easy
W/A:	NRA Severn-Trent Region
Comments:	Shop and information office; ornamental fish for sale; conference room with seating for 50, and all conference facilities; can be booked for clubs or school trips at about £50 for an afternoon; lectures by staff

at £10 per hour. Bookable on Tuesdays for business entertaining which may include fishing at £100 per day. Bookings also available on other days, with fishing for £50. Matches may be booked at £40 for Sunday mornings (15 pegs on Middle Lake). Leaflet with details on request. Demonstration nettings on some bank holidays at £1 per person. Annual open day with free fishing for tackle shop proprietors and angling correspondents. Fishery management courses... what more can you ask!] We have not been invited to visit this fishery, but after such a good write-up, perhaps we shall be... Yes we were! We even have a free permit, thanks to owner Roger Chaplin

Gayton Pool

Location:	Near Northampton
Type and Size:	Small pool
How to Find:	Enquire from Secretary
Carp Stock:	Well stocked with carp
Category:	Carp Water
Other Species:	Some coarse fish
Permits:	Gayton AC. S Barker, 91 Battmead, Bilsworth, Northants - members only
Cost:	On application
BK Rating:	Moderate
W/A:	NRA Anglian Region

Grand Union Canal

Location:	Leicester Arm, near Watford Gap
Type and Size:	Narrow canal
How to Find:	Near Watford Gap services on M1
Carp Stock:	Plenty of carp to middle doubles
Category:	Mixed Fishery
Other Species:	General coarse fish
Permits:	Coventry AA - try local tackle shops
Cost:	On application
Control:	Club
BK Rating:	Moderate
W/A:	NRA Anglian Region
Comments:	Quite easy once fish are located. Coventry AA - P O'Connor, 48 Doncaster Close, Manor Farm, Wyken, Coventry CV2 1HX

Grendon Lakes

Location:	Grendon, just off the A428 Northampton-Bedford road
Type and Size:	Four lakes; Windsurfing Lake is 26 acres; Club Lake is about 10 acres
How to Find:	From the A428 south of Northampton, turn left at Brafield-on-the-Green and right to Cogenhoe. At the T-junction turn right towards Grendon. Left in the village and left again at the next T-junction. The lakes are signposted on the left in about 400 yards
Carp Stock:	Club Lake well stocked with carp to doubles; Windsurfing Lake - some carp to 20lbs
Category:	Mixed Fishery
Other Species:	Roach, rudd, tench, perch, bream and chub
Permits:	Day tickets on bank

Cost: £2 per day; £1.50 for juniors, OAP's and the disabled. Half season - £35 and £20; season - £55 and £35
Control: Private, some sailing and windsurfing
BK Rating: Moderate
W/A: NRA Anglian Region

Higham Wharf Lake

Location: Off the Higham Ferrers by-pass
Type and Size: 20 year old gravel pit of about 120 acres
How to Find: The entrance is at the Ski Club roundabout on the A45, Wharf Road, in Higham Ferrers and Pine Trees Village in Irthlingborough
Carp Stock: Not known, but not many. Fish to upper doubles caught, but there are probably some bigger fish
Category: Few Carp
Other Species: Roach, tench, bream, rudd, perch and pike
Permits: Irthlingborough AC - from local tackle shops
Cost: £13 per season
BK Rating: Difficult
W/A: NRA Anglian Region
Comments: A night fishing ban, and long walks, make this lake a difficult proposition to all but the most determined

Hinton Fisheries

Location: Hinton-in-the-Hedges, near Brackley
Type and Size: Lake of 1½ acres
How to Find: Take the Hinton-in-the-Hedges road from Brackley
Carp Stock: Well stocked with carp, most fish between 5 and 12lbs, although there are plenty of doubles, and several twenties
Category: Carp Water
Other Species: Tench to 7lbs, crucians, roach, rudd, chub and trout
Permits: In advance in writing only from the owner, Trevor Smith, 24 Red Poll Close, Banbury, Oxfordshire. Information on 0295 264483
Cost: On application
Control: Private
BK Rating: Moderate
W/A: NRA Anglian Region
Comments: A second lake at this very pleasant fishery will be built this year. The fishery is in quiet farmland away from main roads, and is secluded by high hedges and a locked gate, to which only the members have a key. Usual rules, baits and methods. Hinton Fish and Fishing also supply a netting service, and have fish for sale, including double figure carp at very reasonable prices, with occasional twenties. Details from the owner at the number above. Hinton-in-the-Hedges has long been my favourite English place name - now I know what it looks like!

Irthlingborough Main Lake

Location: Irthlingborough - off the A605 Rushden-Kettering road, then turn left on the B751. After about 1½ miles turn left into a new housing estate, and then left again along a rough track, at the end of which is a car park
Type and Size: Typical Northants matured gravel pit of about 10 acres

Carp Stock:	Plenty of carp to about 20lbs
Category:	Mixed Fishery
Other Species:	Pike, bream, tench, roach, hybrids and perch
Permits:	Irthlingborough and District AC. Secretary: Peter Pratt, 7 The Shortlands, Irthlingborough
Cost:	£13 per season to include other waters; juniors and OAP's — £6
Control:	Club
Restrictions:	Members only
BK Rating:	Moderate
W/A:	NRA Anglian Region
Comments:	Attractive, reed-fringed lake, which is not heavily fished, and could contain some very big carp, which have been seen on the surface

Maxey No. 4 Pit

Location:	Deeping St. James, Peterborough
Type and Size:	Gravel pit of 8 acres
How to Find:	Off the A15 north of Peterborough
Carp Stock:	Well stocked with carp to upper double figures
Category:	Mixed Fishery
Other Species:	Bream, tench, roach, pike and catfish
Permits:	Day and season tickets from N Cesare, 55 Cardinals Gate, Werrington, Peterborough. Tel: 0733 70226
Cost:	On application
BK Rating:	Easy
Control:	Deeping St. James Angling Club
W/A:	NRA Anglian Region
Comments:	Good club mixed fishery. An angler had 50 to 9lbs in one session in July 1988!

Mid-Northants Carp Fishery

Location:	Woodford Mill, Addington Road, near Ringstead
Type and Size:	3 lakes of 10 acres, 6 acres and 1 acre; gravel pits
How to Find:	Turn left at the roundabout towards Ringstead from the A605 Higham Ferrers-Thrapston road, and at Ringstead take the left turn towards Great Addington. Woodford Mill will be seen on your right just after the bridge over the River Nene
Carp Stock:	'B' Lake (6 acres) - very well stocked with carp up to 20lbs, with many doubles; 'A' Lake (10 acres) contains about 40 carp of over 20lbs, a number of thirties, and one 40, best known as 'Two-Tone', which has been caught on a number of occasions. Some doubles, but most fish over 20lbs. 'C' Lake (1 acre) is recently dug and contains a number of small carp
Carp Stock:	'B' Lake - Mixed Fishery; 'A' Lake - Carp Water; 'C' Lake - Mixed Fishery
Other Species:	'B' Lake - big tench, double figure bream, catfish to 18lbs; 'C' Lake - grass carp and other species
Permits:	Duncan Kay, 4 Sawyers Crescent, Chelveston, Northants. Tel: 0933 460115. In advance only. No day tickets; season tickets only
Cost:	'B' and 'C' Lakes, half mile of the adjacent River Nene, including membership of Higham Ferrers AC - £107 per year, January to January. 'A' Lake - £250 per season

Kevin Maddocks with a January 40¼ from the Mid-Northants Carp Fishery

BK Rating:	'B' and 'C' Lakes - Easy to Moderate. 'A' Lake - Moderate
Control:	Private (Duncan Kay)
Restrictions:	No long stay fishing, 48 hours maximum, 24 hours at weekends
W/A:	NRA Anglian Region
Comments:	The Mid-Northants Carp Fishery is one of the most famous big fish and carp waters in the country, with many 20's and 30's caught each season, and several 40's, which have even been caught in the winter. The fishery is in a quiet and pleasant situation alongside the River Nene, but because of the huge fish it contains, and the fact that numbers of members are strictly limited, it is very hard to get into, and there is always a waiting list. The 'B' ticket, which includes Lake 'C' and the river is used as a waiting list for Lake 'A', the big carp lake, so you will need to apply for the 'B' ticket membership first, with the idea of hoping to get into 'A', the big carp water later. Full details from Duncan Kay, who controls the fishery, and who is well known as one of the leading big fish anglers in the country. This is private property, *so do not go to the lakes* without permission - if you are caught there without first getting permission to visit from Duncan, you are not likely to be offered membership - you have been

warned! Rule 13 should be carefully noted: 'No climbing the trees is allowed' (there are virtually no trees, except a few saplings to about 5 feet tall!) and also Rule 13b: 'The management takes no responsibility for any injury to members from trees falling on them!' Trees and bushes are being planted, and these will soon improve this already very pleasant fishery

Naseby Reservoir

Location:	Naseby, between Kettering and Rugby, off the A50
Type and Size:	85 acre reservoir
Carp Stock:	Well stocked with carp to over 20lbs
Category:	Mixed Fishery
Other Species:	Tench and rudd, possibly other species including catfish
Permits:	British Waterways, Willow Grange, Church Road, Watford, Herts. Tel: Watford 226422
Cost:	£20 per season per rod. Two rods £30-£50
Control:	British Waterways
Restrictions:	No juniors
BK Rating:	Moderate
W/A:	NRA Severn-Trent Region

Overstone Solarium

Location:	Overstone, near Northampton
Type and Size:	Two estate lakes of 4 acres and 2 acres
How to Find:	Off the A4500 between Northampton and Wellingborough
Carp Stock:	Fairly well stocked to 24lbs, mostly commons
Category:	Mixed Fishery
Other Species:	General coarse fish
Permits:	On site
Cost:	Approx £1 per day
BK Rating:	Moderate
Control:	Private Tel: 0604 645265
W/A:	NRA Anglian Region
Comments:	Night fishing allowed. Day ticket water with caravans etc

Ransome Road Gravel Pit

Location:	Near Northampton
Type and Size:	Large gravel pit, about 30 acres plus
How to Find:	On A508 near motorway junction 15
Carp Stock:	Not many carp to 20lbs plus
Category:	Few Carp
Other Species:	General coarse fish
Permits:	Northampton Nene AC - local tackle shops
Cost:	Approx £10 per season
BK Rating:	Difficult
Control:	Club Tel: 0604 770001
W/A:	Anglian
Comments:	Lake record 29lbs. Matured gravel pit. Details from Jack Leach Tackle, Church Street, Rushden

Red House Farm Fishery   A

Location:	Syresham, off the A43 between Silverstone and Brackley
Type and Size:	Half acre farm pond
Carp Stock:	Well stocked with carp to 18lbs
Category:	Mixed Fishery
Other Species:	Trout and catfish
Permits:	Day tickets from bungalow on site. Tel: 0869 810306 (John Harper)
Cost:	£3 per day
Control:	Private
Restrictions:	Fishing 5am to 11.30pm - no night fishing
BK Rating:	Moderate
W/A:	NRA Severn-Trent Region
Comments:	No close season. 3 self catering cottages to rent on the farm, close to the lake

River Nene

Location:	Northampton, Ditchford, Peterborough, Oundle
Type and Size:	River
How to Find:	The River Nene runs from Peterborough to Northampton
Carp Stock:	In some areas well stocked. Average 11-12lbs. Some fish to 27lbs. Quite a few 20's. Biggest reported 27lbs from Billing stretch
Category:	Mixed Fishery
Other Species:	General coarse fish
Permits:	Various clubs and local tackle shops. Jack Leach, Church Street, Rushden
Cost:	Northampton Club - approx £10; Rushden Club £6
Control:	Clubs
W/A:	NRA Anglian Region
Comments:	Location is the problem, but simple methods and baits such as corn and luncheon meat will enable fish to be caught reasonably easily. Northampton Nene AC - M Eaton, 12 Thorne Hill, Briar Hill, Northampton NN4 9SN. Rushden AA - J Leach, Anglers Dept, Rushden, Northants. Many carp at Wellingborough, Ditchford and Higham areas, average size about 14lbs. Most fish now caught on boilies

Rushton Lake

Location:	Rushton, off the A6003 between Kettering and Corby
Type and Size:	Medium-sized gravel pit
Carp Stock:	Well stocked with small carp to doubles
Category:	Mixed Fishery
Other Species:	Big bream and roach
Permits:	Local club, try local tackle shops in Kettering and Corby. Matches at the lake are booked by telephoning 0536 760986, so you might get some information on this number
Restrictions:	Not known, but possibly no night fishing
BK Rating:	Easy
W/A:	NRA Anglian Region
Comments:	Matches take place each Thursday, with the draw at 5.30pm; entries and details from the phone number above

School Water

Location:	Kimbolton, near Grafham Water
Type and Size:	1½ acres
How to Find:	Near Kimbolton Castle
Carp Stock:	Plenty of small carp to 5lbs
Category:	Mixed Fishery
Other Species:	General coarse fish
Permits:	On site
Cost:	Approx £1 per day
BK Rating:	Easy
Control:	Private
W/A:	NRA Anglian Region

Sibson Fisheries   A

Location:	New Lane, Stibbington, Peterborough
Type and Size:	14 acres of lakes
How to Find:	Just off the A1 between Peterborough and Stamford
Carp Stock:	Well stocked with carp to a good size
Category:	Mixed Fishery
Other Species:	Tench, bream, rudd, roach and trout
Permits:	Details from the above address. Tel: Stamford (0780) 782621. Limited day tickets. Secretary - Sharon Denny. In advance only. Cost approx £3.50 per day, same for night. Season £40, book well in advance
BK Rating:	Insufficient information
Control:	Private
W/A:	NRA Anglian Region
Comments:	Also two miles of river and holiday cottages at £20 per night. Trout lake. Bailiff David Moisey also provides information. Tel: Stamford (0780) 782621 (Monday to Friday 9am to 5pm), 51 Church Lane, Stibbington. Membership limit 50 for coarse waters in advance only. Strict rules

Sulby Reservoir

Location:	Welford, between Kettering and Rugby, off the A50
Type and Size:	Huge reservoir of about 100 acres
Carp Stock:	Well stocked with mirrors to doubles
Category:	Mixed Fishery
Other Species:	Roach and bream
Permits:	British Waterways, Willow Grange, Church Road, Watford, Herts. Tel: Watford 26722
Cost:	Season tickets only (limited) at £17
Control:	British Waterways
BK Rating:	Moderate
W/A:	NRA Severn-Trent Region
Comments:	These big BW reservoirs certainly contain carp, although they may be hard to find in such a huge area. There could well be some very big fish caught from them in the future

Sywell Reservoir

Location:	Sywell Country Park, 6 miles from Northampton off the A45; between Earls Barton and Mears Ashby
Type and Size:	20 acre reservoir
Carp Stock:	Some good carp, numbers and sizes not known
Category:	Mixed Fishery
Other Species:	Famous as a big tench water; also pike over 20lbs, perch and roach
Permits:	Members only water of Wellingborough and District AC. Season tickets about £5 from local tackle shops, or Wellingborough and District AC, Mr H Battison, 36 Church Way, Weston Favell, Northampton
Control:	Club. Tel: 0604 810970
BK Rating:	Difficult
Restrictions:	No day tickets - members only
W/A:	NRA Anglian Region
Comments:	Warden and local tackle shops. Very busy at weekends

Thrapston Gravel Pit

Location:	Thrapston, near Kettering
Type and Size:	Huge gravel pit of 300 acres - 3 miles round
How to Find:	Just off the A605 at Thrapston
Carp Stock:	Unknown - some small fish but a few very big carp; small head of doubles, mostly commons from the river
Category:	Few Carp
Other Species:	General coarse fish
Permits:	Permits from B P Tackle, Mill Road, Kettering
Cost:	£20 per season or £3.50 per day
BK Rating:	Super-Difficult
Comments:	Possibly the biggest gravel pit in the country - and could contain some of the biggest fish. Carp have bred and some small carp have been caught recently. Heavily match fished with many boats. Poor access and very long walks

Weedon Road Gravel Pits

Location:	Weedon Road, Northampton
Type and Size:	Mature lake of about 15 acres
How to Find:	In Northampton
Carp Stock:	Low density - lake record 24lbs, but there are said to be bigger fish
Category:	Few Carp
Other Species:	General coarse fish - large tench
Permits:	Northampton Nene AC - local tackle shops.
Cost:	Approx £10 per season
BK Rating:	Difficult
Control:	Club
W/A:	NRA Anglian Region
Comments:	Northampton Nene AC. Secretary: M Eaton, 12 Thorne Hill, Briar Hill, Northampton NN4 9SN. Permits supplied

NORTHUMBERLAND

BERWICK ON TWEED

BLYTH

Ancroft Ponds

Location: Ancroft, on the B6525, five miles south of Berwick-on-Tweed
Type and Size: Two small ponds
Carp Stock: Some carp, numbers and sizes not known
Category: Mixed Fishery
Other Species: Crucians, roach, perch, tench and eels
Permits: Paul Armstrong. Tel: 091 274 9399
Control: Club - BWAC
Restrictions: Weekly permits available for those residing outside 100 mile radius
                 of Newcastle
BK Rating: Not known
W/A: NRA Northumbrian Region
Comments: As far as we know, this is the most northerly water containing carp in
                 England. Details of all waters in Northumberland, and most in Tyne
                 and Wear and Durham are taken from the Angling Guide of the National
                 Rivers Authority of the Northumbria Region; free copies can be obtained
                 from the NRA at Eldon House, Regent Centre, Gosforth, Newcastle upon
                 Tyne NE3 3UD. Tel: 091 213 0266. This is an excellent guide in a way,
                 but it doesn't give quite enough information; the size of the still waters
                 is not given, the size and numbers of carp present are not mentioned
                 and they don't tell us what BWAC means!

Brenkley Pond

Location:	Near Seaton Burn, between Newcastle and Cramlington
Type and Size:	Small pond
Carp Stock:	Some carp, numbers and sizes not known
Category:	Mixed Fishery
Other Species:	Crucians, roach, perch, bream, tench, rudd and gudgeon
Permits:	Mac Lycett. Tel: 091 237 3361
Control:	Wansbeck and Cramlington AC; members only; details of membership from the phone number listed above
BK Rating:	Not known
W/A:	NRA Northumbrian Region

Dissington Pond

Location:	Ponteland, 7 miles north west of Newcastle, on the A696
Type and Size:	Small pond
Carp Stock:	Some carp
Category:	Mixed Fishery
Other Species:	Roach and perch
Permits:	Paul Armstrong. Tel: 091 274 9399
Control:	Club - BWAC
BK Rating:	Not known
W/A:	NRA Northumbrian Region
Comments:	There may be no close season in this and other ponds in Northumberland, Tyne and Wear, and Durham

NORTH YORKSHIRE

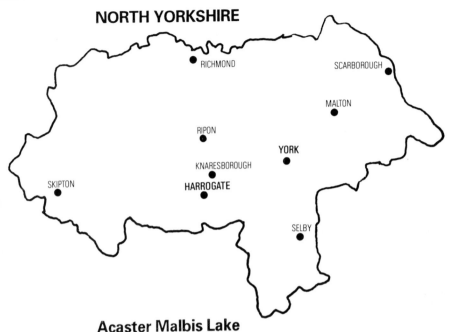

RICHMOND

SCARBOROUGH

MALTON

RIPON

YORK

KNARESBOROUGH

SKIPTON

HARROGATE

SELBY

Acaster Malbis Lake

Location:	Acaster, York
Type and Size:	Lake of 2 acres
How to Find:	Take the A64 south from York to the village of Acaster
Carp Stock:	Quite well stocked with carp to about 20lbs
Category:	Mixed Fishery
Other Species:	Tench, roach, perch and bream
Permits:	Day tickets from the office on the site, which is also a caravan site
Cost:	On application
Control:	Private
BK Rating:	Moderate
Restrictions:	No night fishing; fish from 7am until dusk
W/A:	NRA Yorkshire Region

Balne Lake

Location:	Off the A19 near Whitely Bridge, Selby
Type and Size:	Five acre lake, quite shallow, surrounded by trees, and very weedy
Carp Stock:	Very heavily stocked with mirrors between 5lbs and 10lbs
Category:	Carp Water
Other Species:	Roach
Permits:	Season tickets only from local tackle shops - sometimes on the bank from owner
Control:	Balne Moor AC
Restrictions:	No night fishing; no carp sacks
BK Rating:	Very Easy - multiple catches common
W/A:	NRA Yorkshire Region

Barlow Common Pond

Location:	Barlow, near Selby
Type and Size:	4 acre lake with an irregular bottom, and quite shallow
Carp Stock:	Well stocked with very small carp to about 5lbs, with the occasional double from the original stocking
Category:	Mixed Fishery
Other Species:	Roach, bream and tench
Permits:	Day tickets on bank
Cost:	£1.50 per day
Control:	Private
Restrictions:	No night fishing
BK Rating:	Easy
W/A:	NRA Yorkshire Region
Comments:	This is a very weedy, shallow lake, which is a Nature Reserve, so part of the bank cannot be fished

Birkdale Fishery

Location:	Terrington, near York
Type and Size:	Small, attractive lake in pleasant surroundings
Carp Stock:	Well stocked with carp to 15lbs
Category:	Mixed Fishery
Other Species:	Tench, roach and bream
Permits:	Day tickets on bank, or can be booked on 065 384 301
Cost:	£3 per day plus £1 for extra rod
Control:	Privately run by Wynn Jones
Restrictions:	Night fishing by arrangement only
BK Rating:	Moderate
Comments:	Suitable for disabled anglers

Broken Brea   A

Location:	Off the B6217 at Brompton-on-Swale, near Richmond
Type and Size:	Three acre man-made fishery recently opened; lake up to 15 feet in depth
Carp Stock:	Recently stocked with 6,000 carp to 8lbs
Category:	Mixed Fishery
Other Species:	Roach, tench, bream, perch and gudgeon
Permits:	Day tickets from farm shop
Cost:	£6; £3.50 for a morning or evening session
Control:	Tel: 0748 825647
Restrictions:	No night fishing; barbless hooks; no keepnets
BK Rating:	Easy
W/A:	NRA Yorkshire Region
Comments:	Cottages to rent for holidays; free fishing for those who stay at the cottages

Carlton Towers

Location:	Off the A1041 south of Selby, and close to the M62
Type and Size:	10 acre lake in grounds of a stately home
Carp Stock:	Not many, to upper doubles
Category:	Few Carp
Other Species:	Tench, roach, bream, perch and crucians

Permits: Carlton AC - season tickets only; enquire on 0405 860791
Restrictions: Fishing the field bank only. No night fishing
BK Rating: Very Difficult
W/A: NRA Yorkshire Region
Comments: Not much fished by carp anglers - a very attractive, shallow water with much weed and lilies

Cawood Park A

Location: Cawood, near Tadcaster
Type and Size: Three acre park lake
How to Find: From Tadcaster take the A162 towards Sherburn-in-Elmet, then turn left onto the B1223 towards Selby. After the village of Ryther, the lake will be found just before Cawood, on the right
Carp Stock: Said to be well stocked with carp, sizes not known
Category: Mixed Fishery
Other Species: Large pike, roach, perch, chub, bream, pike, trout and tench
Permits: Day tickets from the site warden
Cost: Day - £2; week - £10; from 5pm onwards - £1; season - £35
Control: Private. Details of fishing and caravans and bungalows to rent from Mr W G Archer, tel: Cawood 450 or Site Warden, tel: Cawood 8865
BK Rating: Not known
Restrictions: No keepnets except in matches. All trout to be returned immediately
W/A: NRA Yorkshire Region
Comments: This is a caravan site and park, with luxury caravans and bungalows to rent. Licensed bar, children's boating pond and amusements. Trout fishing from March 25th

Drax Lake

Location: Drax, near Selby - off the A1041 between Selby and Goole
Type and Size: Attractive, estate type lake of about 10 acres
Carp Stock: Well stocked with carp to upper 20's, heavily weeded and surrounded by trees
Permits: Season ticket only - Mr G Simms, 2 Oaklands, Camblesforth, Selby
Cost: £10 joining fee, then £8 per season - reduced prices for juniors and OAP's
Control: Private
Restrictions: No sacks, weighing slings or radio-controlled boats
BK Rating: Easy
W/A: NRA Yorkshire Region
Comments: A very pleasant water, though weedy and lines of 10-12lbs BS are recommended. All methods are successful including floating baits

Dringhouses Lake

Location: Southern outskirts of York City
Type and Size: 3 acre lake
How to Find: From York take the A1036 Tadcaster road. The lake is about 3 miles from the city centre
Carp Stock: Well stocked with a number of doubles to about 20lbs
Category: Mixed Fishery
Other Species: Pike, roach, rudd, chub and perch

Permits:	Day tickets from house on site, must be obtained before fishing
Cost:	On application - extra cost if not bought before starting to fish
Control:	Private
BK Rating:	Moderate
Restrictions:	Night fishing on car park bank only
W/A:	NRA Yorkshire Region
Comments:	Pleasant water with trees, but quite heavily fished

Elvington Lake

Location:	Elvington, near York
Type and Size:	Lake of 3½ acres
How to Find:	Take the B1228 from York towards Elvington to the south east of the city. The lake is just over 5 miles from York
Carp Stock:	The lake is well stocked with carp, with plenty of small ones but some doubles to about 15lbs. Bigger fish are said to have been caught
Category:	Mixed Fishery
Other Species:	Trout, roach, rudd, tench, chub, perch. There are rumoured to be one or two barbel in the water
Permits:	Day tickets from the house on the property - Mr T Britten, Lake Cottage, Elvington, York. Tel: 0904 608255. £3 for carp fishing
Control:	Private
BK Rating:	Easy
Restrictions:	No night fishing, no groundbait
W/A:	NRA Yorkshire Region
Comments:	No close season

Fairview Lake

Location:	In Broad Lane, Cawood Common, near Selby
Type and Size:	Small lake
How to Find:	Take the B1233 from Selby, and the lake is near the intersection with the B1222
Carp Stock:	Well stocked with carp, sizes unknown
Category:	Mixed Fishery
Other Species:	Tench, rudd, perch and rainbow trout
Permits:	Day tickets from the cottage on the banks of the fishery
BK Rating:	Moderate
Control:	Private
W/A:	NRA Yorkshire Region
Comments:	A pleasant and attractive lake

Gowdall Pond

Location:	New Gowdall, Hemingbrough, near Selby
Type and Size:	Small pond of just over one acre, weedy and shallow
Carp Stock:	Quite well stocked with carp to middle doubles
Category:	Mixed Fishery
Other Species:	Roach and bream
Permits:	Day tickets on site
Cost:	£2 per rod per day
Control:	Private

Restrictions: No night fishing, day tickets only
BK Rating: Moderate
W/A: NRA Yorkshire Region

Grafton Mere   A

Location: Marton-cum-Grafton, Boroughbridge
Type and Size: Man-made lake of 2½ acres, spring fed
How to Find: This village is between York and Ripon. Take the B65265 from Boroughbridge to York. After 3 miles turn right to Grafton
Carp Stock: 8 doubles to 18lbs; 80 of 5-10lbs; 200 of 2lbs+, stocked in 1987
Category: Carp Only
Other Species: None
Permits: Prospect Farm. Tel: 0423 322045 (Roger Naish)
Cost: On application
BK Rating: Easy
Control: Private
Restrictions: Barbless hooks
W/A: NRA Yorkshire Region
Comments: 100 yards from good pub. Bus service to York which is 16 miles. Three holiday cottages and bed and breakfast in 18th century working farm. Ideal centre for family holiday near Yorkshire Moors, dales and coast

Hay-A-Park

Location: On the outskirts of Knaresborough
Type and Size: Small gravel pit in two parts totalling 3 acres
Carp Stock: Reasonable head of carp averaging 10lbs, largest reported to date is 18lbs
Other Species: Bream, roach, rudd, tench, pike and perch
Permits: M and C Johnson Fishing Tackle, Briggate, Knaresborough. Tel: Harrogate 863065. Permits must be obtained before fishing
Control: Private. Knaresborough Piscatorials incorporating Dales AC
Baits/Methods: Normal carp tactics and baits
BK Rating: Fairly Easy
W/A: NRA Yorkshire Region

THE
BEEKAY
GUIDE
TO
1500
BRITISH
& EUROPEAN
CARP
WATERS

Is YOUR Water listed? If so, are the details correct?

If you spot omissions, inaccuracies, or know of any changes, please let us know by filling in the Waters Questionnaire at the back of this guide and return it to us at:

FREEPOST
Beekay Publishers
Withy Pool
Henlow Camp
Bedfordshire
SG16 6EA

Hoxne Farm Pond

Location:	Sheriff Hutton Road, Strensall, York
Type and Size:	Small pond
Carp Stock:	Mirrors and commons to 20lbs
Category:	Mixed Fishery
Other Species:	Usual coarse fish
Permits:	Tel: 0904 490726
Cost:	£2 per day
Restrictions:	Fishing 7.30am till dusk only; barbless hooks
BK Rating:	Moderate
W/A:	NRA Yorkshire Region

Knaresborough Lagoon

Location:	Stockwell Lane, Knaresborough
Type and Size:	Gravel pit of about 55 acres
Carp Stock:	Some carp over 30lbs
Category:	Few Carp
Other Species:	Pike, bream and tench
Permits:	Day tickets from tackle shops in Knaresborough and Harrogate
Control:	Knaresborough Piscatorials incorporating Dales AC
BK Rating:	Very Difficult
W/A:	NRA Yorkshire Region
Comments:	A very clear water, and hard to fish. Recent restocking

Lightwater Valley Lake

Location:	Lightwater Valley Theme Park, near Sheffield
Type and Size:	15 acre lake
Carp Stock:	Well stocked with small carp to doubles
Category:	Mixed Fishery
Other Species:	Roach and bream
Permits:	Day tickets on site at £1 per rod
Control:	Private
Restrictions:	No *day* fishing! Fishing is 6pm to 9am only
BK Rating:	Easy
W/A:	NRA Yorkshire Region
Comments:	Too many people on the park during the day, so only night fishing is allowed. Possibly no close season. Three rods allowed

Lingcroft Farm Pond

Location:	One mile south off the York by-pass on the A19 towards Selby; farm is on the right
Type and Size:	Small farm pond with large island
Carp Stock:	Recently stocked with carp, sizes and numbers not known
Category:	Mixed Fishery
Other Species:	Bream, chub and roach
Permits:	Day tickets from the farmhouse, cost £1.50
BK Rating:	Not known
Control:	Private
Restrictions:	No arrivals before 8am; no night fishing. Barbless hooks and no groundbait

W/A:	NRA Yorkshire Region
Comments:	Much wildlife on this very pleasant fishery, so no litter and no left line, which damages wildlife. All proceeds from the fishery are donated to Fulford Church - this is a new one to us; could it start a trend?

Newhay Lake

Location:	Newhay Carp Farm, near Selby
Type and Size:	2½ acre lake
How to Find:	Take the A63 from Selby, and at Hemingborough turn right to Newhay
Carp Stock:	Well stocked with carp to 23lbs
Category:	Mixed Fishery
Other Species:	Bream, tench, chub, roach and perch
Permits:	Day tickets on site. Details on 0756 638383
Control:	Private
Cost:	£2 for one rod; £2.50 for two and £3 for three
BK Rating:	Moderate
Restrictions:	No night fishing - fishing times are from 8am till dusk; no keepnets or groundbait
W/A:	NRA Yorkshire Region
Comments:	No close season; some night fishing by arrangement

Northingales Fish Ponds

Location:	Cawood, near York
Type and Size:	Two ponds of 2 acres and 1 acre
How to Find:	Take the A19 south from York towards Selby, and turn off on B1222 to Cawood
Carp Stock:	Both lakes contain some carp and the bigger one has fish to about 15lbs
Category:	Mixed Fishery
Carp Stock:	Tench, roach, bream, perch, dace, trout and gudgeon
Permits:	Day tickets from the house at the site, cost approx £1.50. Details from the owner on Cawood 414
Control:	Private
BK Rating:	Moderate
Restrictions:	One rod only. No night fishing. No juniors (under 16) unless accompanied by an adult. No groundbait
W/A:	NRA Yorkshire Region

Oak Mere Fishery

Location:	Hill Farm, Skipwith, between York and Market Weighton
Type and Size:	Pond of less than two acres in size, only dug in 1989
How to Find:	From York take the A19 towards Selby and turn right onto the A163 for two miles. At the crossroads turn left towards Skipwith. Hill Farm is on the right after Skipwith
Carp Stock:	Some carp to over 10lbs
Category:	Few Carp
Other Species:	Tench, rudd, bream and crucians
Permits:	On the bank or from Hill Farm
Cost:	£2.50 per day; £1.50 after 5pm in summer; winter day tickets are £2
Control:	Anthony Patrick. Tel: 0757 288910

Restrictions:	Lots! No night fishing (dawn till dusk only); barbless hooks; one rod only; no groundbait, no keepnets for carp
BK Rating:	Difficult
W/A:	NRA Yorkshire Region - they use this as a stockpond, which is perhaps why there are so many restrictions

Primrose Valley Holiday Camp

Location:	On the A165 Bridlington to Scarborough road
Type and Size:	Small lake
Carp Stock:	Well stocked with carp to 26lbs
Category:	Mixed Fishery
Other Species:	Usual coarse fish
Permits:	On site; all information from Linford's Tackle Shop, Bridlington
Cost:	£1.50 per day
BK Rating:	Moderate
W/A:	NRA Yorkshire Region
Comments:	Shallow boating lake, best fished early and late

Pumping Station Lakes

Location:	Angram, Barlby, near Selby
Type and Size:	Two lakes of about 2 acres each, both of which are fairly deep and weedy
Carp Stock:	Well stocked with carp to double figures
Category:	Mixed Fishery
Other Species:	Coarse fish
Permits:	None necessary — free fishing
Control:	Council
Restrictions:	No night fishing
BK Rating:	Moderate
W/A:	NRA Yorkshire Region

Racecourse Lake

Location:	Near Ripon
Type and Size:	Pit of about 15 acres
How to Find:	The fishery is about 1½ miles south of Ripon
Carp Stock:	Quite well stocked with carp which include a number of doubles. A 28 has been caught
Category:	Mixed Fishery
Other Species:	Bream, rudd, tench, roach
Permits:	Season tickets from Ripon Piscatorial Angling Association. Mainly membership only for locals but some tickets for those from outside the area. Details from the Secretary: Mr R Looney, 12 Lower Street, Agnes St Ripon, or P Godden, 3 Oak Road, Ripon. SAE required. Day tickets about £3 from Ripon Angling Centre, North Street, Ripon
Control:	Club
BK Rating:	Moderate
W/A:	NRA Yorkshire Region

Raker Lake

Location:	Wheldrake, off the B1228 south east of York
Type and Size:	Newly opened fishery of three acres, mixed lake and small specialist carp lake
Carp Stock:	Main lake stocked with carp to 7lb. Carp Lake stocked with carp to 14lbs
Category:	Mixed Fishery
Other Species:	Roach, rudd, bream, tench, chub, dace and perch in main lake
Permits:	From self-service unit in car park at £2.50 per day
Control:	Tel: 0904 448793
Restrictions:	No night fishing; particle baits and keepnets not allowed on carp lake
BK Rating:	Moderate
W/A:	NRA Yorkshire Region
Comments:	Some access for the disabled; toilets

Red House Lagoon

Location:	Close to the River Ouse at Moor Monkton, off the A59 north west of York
Type and Size:	Large lake often flooded from the river
Carp Stock:	Some carp, but few and far between
Category:	Few Carp
Other Species:	Bream, roach, tench, perch and a few pike and chub
Permits:	Day tickets in advance only by sending a SAE to S Tomlinson, 57 Water Lane, Clifton, York YO3 6PW. Tel: 0904 638237
Cost:	£3 per day
Control:	York AA
Restrictions:	No night fishing
BK Rating:	Super-Difficult
W/A:	NRA Yorkshire Region

Ripon Canal

Location:	Near Ripon
Type and Size:	Small narrow canal, with little boat traffic
Carp Stock:	Well stocked with carp to 10lbs
Category:	Mixed Fishery
Other Species:	Usual coarse fish
Permits:	Tel: 0765 607114
Control:	Club
Restrictions:	Possibly no night fishing; used for matches at £1.50 per peg
BK Rating:	Easy
W/A:	NRA Yorkshire Region

Scarborough Mere

Location:	In the town of Scarborough, off the Seamer Road
Type and Size:	18 acre mere
Carp Stock:	Some carp to doubles
Category:	Probably Few Carp
Other Species:	Bream, tench, roach and pike
Permits:	From bailiff on bank, or from Buckleys Tackle Shop, Leading Post Street, Scarborough. Low cost
Control:	Scarborough Mere Angling Club

BK Rating:	Probably Difficult for the bigger carp
W/A:	NRA Yorkshire Region
Comments:	Refreshments on site during summer

Scrapyard Pond

Location:	Drax, between Selby and Goole
Type and Size:	Shallow ballast pit of about 2 acres
Carp Stock:	Not very many, but some doubles to about 20lbs
Category:	Few Carp
Other Species:	Roach, perch and tench
Permits:	British Rail Staff Association - enquire from the scrapyard or try G Harcome, 8 Upper Belmont Road, St. Andrews, Bristol - possibly day tickets
Control:	British Rail
BK Rating:	Very Difficult
W/A:	NRA Yorkshire Region

Shearons Pond

Location:	Goose Hill, Carlton, near Selby
Type and Size:	2 acre lake, specially dug about 25 years ago
Carp Stock:	Very heavily stocked with commons and mirrors from 5lbs to low doubles
Category:	Carp Water
Other Species:	Some coarse fish
Permits:	Free to holders of a Yorkshire W/A licence
Restrictions:	Night fishing is allowed
BK Rating:	Very Easy
Baits/Methods:	Good floater water, but any bait and method works well
Comments:	Good lake all the year round, and ideal for a practice water

Staveley Lakes

Location:	Staveley, between Harrogate and Ripon
Type and Size:	Two lakes of three acres and two acres
How to Find:	Take the A6055 from Knaresborough and turn left going north to Staveley
Carp Stock:	Quite well stocked with carp to about 16lbs with a number of doubles. Fished of over 20lbs rumoured
Category:	Mixed Fishery
Other Species:	Tench, chub, rudd, perch and bream
Permits:	Bradford City Angling Association. Season tickets from Mr H Briggs, 4 Brown Hill Close, Birkenshaw, Bradford, West Yorkshire
Control:	Club
BK Rating:	Moderate
W/A:	NRA Yorkshire Region

Three Lakes

Location:	Selby
Type and Size:	Lake of about 4 acres, two other lakes, 8 acres in all
Carp Stock:	Well stocked with carp to over 20lbs
Category:	Mixed Fishery
Other Species:	Reported are tench to 8lbs, eels to 6lbs, bream to 11lb, large perch, roach and trout
Permits:	Day tickets, details from Paul Howgego. Tel: Selby 706065
Cost:	Approx £2 per day for each lake
Control:	Private
Baits/Methods:	Normal carp fishing baits and methods. Boilies good
Restrictions:	No groundbait, special permission needed for night fishing
BK Rating:	Moderate
W/A:	NRA Yorkshire Region
Comments:	Catches of up to a dozen fish a day reported. many snags and sunken trees. Rumours of bigger fish. Several good 20's reported caught in 1991, and also a thirty

Tollerton Cross Lanes Pond   A

Location:	Just off the A19, 10 miles from York and three miles from Tollerton
Type and Size:	Three small ponds
Carp Stock:	Quite a number of doubles, with the record at 28lbs
Category:	Mixed Fishery
Other Species:	Tench, perch, roach, chub and pike
Permits:	If you arrive before 7am you can start fishing, and pay on the bank; for arrivals after 7am you can buy your day ticket from the house
Cost:	£2.50 per day
Control:	Private; Margaret Wackerman on 03473 336
Restrictions:	No night fishing; dawn till dusk only; no groundbaiting; no keepnets for carp
BK Rating:	Moderate
W/A:	NRA Yorkshire Region
Comments:	Bed and breakfast at £10 per night, to include a day's fishing. Pleasant looking ponds, close together, with reeds etc

Two Otters Fishery

Location:	Womersley, off the A19 Doncaster Whitley road, near a transport cafe
Type and Size:	Small lake, with an island, in private grounds
Carp Stock:	Well stocked with carp, including 50 doubles to over 20lbs
Category:	Mixed Fishery
Other Species:	Crucians, rudd, roach, bream, perch, chub and tench
Permits:	On the bank at £2 per day
Restrictions:	No night fishing; no groundbaiting
BK Rating:	Easy
W/A:	NRA Yorkshire Region

Welham Lake

Location:	Norton Golf Club, Malton
Type and Size:	5 acre lake
How to Find:	Take the Welham road from Malton, and follow the sign to Malton and Norton Golf Club. The lake is in woodland to the right after entering the golf course
Carp Stock:	Stocked with carp in 1988, sizes not known
Category:	Probably Few Carp, though might become a Mixed Fishery
Other Species:	Tench and eels
Permits:	Permits only in advance before visiting. Booking advised, from Mike O'Donnell, Moorland Trout Lake, Pickering. Tel: Pickering 73101
Cost:	£8 per day (24 hours) - one rod only
Control:	Private
BK Rating:	Insufficient information
Restrictions:	8 anglers only per day. No permits on bank. Barbless hooks
Comments:	A famous tench water, and very picturesque

Westerley Lake

Location:	Wheldrake, six miles south east of York, off the B1228 road
Type and Size:	Four acre lake
Carp Stock:	Quite well stocked with carp to lower doubles
Category:	Mixed Fishery
Other Species:	Grass carp, bream, roach, rudd, perch and tench
Permits:	On the bank at £2.50 per day. You can also get permits from the bungalow on the site, or from Springwell Garden Centre nearby
Control:	Bruce Hairsine. Tel: 0904 448500
Restrictions:	No night fishing - dawn to dusk only; no hemp or groundbait
BK Rating:	Moderate
W/A:	NRA Yorkshire Region

Whitfield Reservoir

Location:	Barrows Lane, Steeton, off the A629 Keighley—Skipton road
Type and Size:	Small reservoir
Carp Stock:	Some carp, numbers and sizes not known, but thought to be at least to double figure size
Category:	Few Carp or Mixed Fishery
Other Species:	Pike, roach, tench and perch
Permits:	Keighley Angling Club - members only but open to all - Mr D Ward, 4 Compeigne Avenue, Keighley, North Yorkshire
Control:	Club
W/A:	NRA Yorkshire Region

Willowgarth Fishery

Location:	Carlton Miniott, near Thirsk
Type and Size:	Two acre lake
How to Find:	Turn left off the A19 north of York, go through Thirsk and just after Carlton Miniott turn left
Carp Stock:	Well stocked with carp to mid-doubles; also ghost carp
Category:	Carp Water
Other Species:	Roach, perch and tench, and stocked annually with rainbow trout

Permits: Day tickets on bank
Cost: £5 March to end October; £3 November 1st to end February. Evening tickets half price
Control: Private
BK Rating: Easy
Restrictions: No night fishing - 6am to 9pm only
W/A: NRA Yorkshire Region
Comments: Said to be Yorkshire's prettiest and most heavily stocked fishery. Car park and refreshment bar. One side suitable for disabled anglers. Groundbait, keepnets and nuts as baits are not allowed. No close season. Information from the owner Robin Fletcher. Tel: 0845 522827

Wistow Pit

Location: Broad Lane, Cawood Common, on the A1222 south of York
Type and Size: Very attractive three acre lake
Carp Stock: Well stocked with carp to low doubles, with possibly one or two just reaching 20lbs
Category: Mixed Fishery
Other Species: Tench, roach and bream
Permits: Day tickets on bank
Cost: About £1.50 per rod
Control: Private
Restrictions: No night fishing
BK Rating: Difficult
W/A: NRA Yorkshire Region

Yorkshire Lakeside Lodges

Location: Outskirts of York, formerly known as 'Hoggy's Pond'
Type and Size: Small pool
How to Find: Edge of York
Carp Stock: Well stocked with carp to doubles
Category: Mixed Fishery
Other Species: Tench
Permits: Tel: York 702346
Cost: On application
BK Rating: Moderate
Control: Private
W/A: NRA Yorkshire Region
Comments: Full details from the phone number above

NOTTINGHAMSHIRE

BAWTRY

WORKSOP

EAST
RETFORD

MANSFIELD

NEWARK

NOTTINGHAM

BEESTON

LONG EATON

Arches Lake

Location:	East Retford, off the A638
Type and Size:	Small, attractive lake near town
Carp Stock:	Some carp to over 20lbs
Category:	Mixed Fishery
Other Species:	Roach, tench and bream
Permits:	Sheffield Piscatorial Association; enquire from tackle shops in Sheffield
Control:	Small club, with waters not heavily fished
BK Rating:	Difficult, as there are not large numbers of carp
W/A:	NRA Severn-Trent Region

Attenborough North

Location:	Long Lane, Attenborough, Beeston
Type and Size:	7 gravel pits from 13 acres to 43 acres
How to Find:	Off the A6005 Beeston road through Attenborough village
Carp Stock:	Not known some carp to 13lbs
Category:	Few Carp
Other Species:	General coarse fish
Permits:	Season tickets only
Cost:	£21.00
Other Species:	General coarse fish
Permits:	Season tickets only

BK Rating: Not known
Control: Leisure Sport Angling, Staines Road, Chertsey, Surrey. Tel: 0932 562633
Restrictions: No night fishing
W/A: NRA Severn-Trent Region
Comments: Site of Special Scientific Interest

Attenborough South (River Trent)

Location: Barton Lane, Long Eaton, Nottingham
Type and Size: Gravel pit of 114 acres; 2,500 metres of the River Trent
How to Find: Station Road, Long Eaton. Take New Hythe Street, opposite Horseshoe Sports Tackle Shop for one mile to municipal car park
Carp Stock: There may be no carp in the lake, but carp to 31lbs have been reported from the River Trent area
Category: Few Carp
Other Species: Mixed coarse fish
Permits: Frank Russel 'Wotsits' Tackle Shop, 8 Archer Road, Stapleford, Nottingham. Tel: Nottingham 396096. Day tickets on bank
Cost: £1.50
BK Rating: Very Difficult
Control: Leisure Sport Angling, Staines Road, Chertsey, Surrey. Tel: 0932 562633
Restrictions: No night fishing, dawn to dusk only
W/A: NRA Severn-Trent Region
Comments: Main interest is in the river but it should be noted that this is regarded as a separate fishery, with fishing only allowed when no matches are taking place. Information from Gordon Plummer on 0602 3245

Bestwood Pond

Location: Near Nottingham
Type and Size: Medium sized pool
How to Find: Enquire locally
Carp Stock: Well stocked, sizes not known
Category: Mixed Fishery
Other Species: General coarse fishing
Permits: Notts AA — local tackle shops
Cost: On application
BK Rating: Insufficient information
Control: Club
W/A: NRA Severn-Trent Region
Comments: Try local tackle shops for information, and also Nottingham and District Federation, W Belshaw, 17 Spring Green, Clifton Estate, Nottingham; and Notts AA, E J Collin, 224 Radford Boulevard, Nottingham NG7 5QG. Both supply tickets and information on other carp waters controlled by Nottingham clubs

Bleasby Lake

Location: Off the A38 between Mansfield and Sutton-in-Ashfield
Type and Size: 60 acre ancient lake, with much weed, and very shallow
Carp Stock: Not many carp, but they go to upper 20's

Category:	Few Carp
Other Species:	Most coarse fish
Permits:	In advance only, low cost
Control:	Members only water of Mansfield and District AA. Secretary: A Quick, 138 Huthwaite Road, Sutton-in-Ashfield NG17 2GX
BK Rating:	Very Difficult
W/A:	NRA Severn-Trent Region
Comments:	This is a beautiful lake, but is very hard to fish, and very few carp are caught. In hot weather in the summer the weed makes the lake very difficult to fish, and you should only tackle this one if you are prepared for many long blanks

Butterley Reservoir

Location:	Near Ripley
Type and Size:	Medium sized reservoir
How to Find:	No information. Try local tackle shops
Carp Stock:	Well stocked, sizes not known
Category:	Mixed Fishery
Other Species:	General coarse fish
Permits:	Ripley and District AA. From local tackle shops - day tickets
Cost:	On application
BK Rating:	Moderate
Control:	Club

W/A: NRA Severn-Trent Region
Comments: Little known - try locally, Ripley and District AA - R Turner, 2a Argyll Road, Ripley - ticket supplied

Coach House Pond

Location: The Coaching House, Tickhill, Bawtry
Type and Size: Very tiny estate pond
Carp Stock: Not many carp, but a possible 20
Category: Few Carp
Other Species: Tench and roach
Permits: On application from the house on the property - enquire locally for information
Control: Private
Restrictions: No night fishing, except by arrangement
BK Rating: Difficult
W/A: NRA Severn-Trent Region

Daneshill Lake

Location: Daneshill Road, Torworth, Retford
Type and Size: 21 acre lake
How to Find: Just off the A1 north west of East Retford, near the main railway line
Carp Stock: Stocked in 1984 with 48 carp to 11lbs, but commons to 24¼lbs reported
Category: Mixed Fishery
Other Species: General coarse fish and pike to over 20 pounds
Permits: Day tickets on site
Cost: Approx £2 per day; £15 per season - night syndicate £55
BK Rating: Moderate
Control: Daneshill AC. Tel: 0909 770917 (day) or 0909 565787 (evening)
Restrictions: Night fishing reserved for syndicate. No inflatable boats
W/A: NRA Severn-Trent Region

Erewash Canal

Location: Long Eaton area
Type and Size: 12 mile canal
How to Find: Close to M1 from Long Eaton northwards
Carp Stock: Some good carp
Category: Mixed Fishery
Other Species: General coarse fish
Permits: Local tackle shops
Cost: On application
Control: Long Eaton AA and Long Eaton Victoria AS
BK Rating: Moderate
W/A: NRA Severn-Trent Region
Comments: Once polluted, this canal is now restored and restocked, and it holds some good specimen fish. Long Eaton AA, W Parker, 75 College Street, Long Eaton, Notts; Long Eaton Victoria AS, D Kent, 18 Collingwood Road, Long Eaton, Notts. Permits available from both club secretaries

Grantham Canal

Location:	Bottesford, to the west of Grantham
Type and Size:	Attractive, very narrow and reeded canal stretch, with few boats
How to Find:	Take the A52 Grantham to Bottesford road, then the Easthorpe road to Bottesford
Carp Stock:	Some carp to over 10lbs
Category:	Mixed Fishery
Other Species:	Tench, bream and roach
Permits:	Day and season tickets on bank, or from Matchman Supplies, Nottingham
Cost:	£1.50 per day; £6 per season
Control:	Bottesford DAA - Norman Chenoweth. Tel: 0602 335793
Restrictions:	No night fishing
BK Rating:	Difficult, at least until the carp are located
W/A:	NRA Severn-Trent Region

Hartshill Reservoir

Location:	Hartshill, Worksop, off the A57
Type and Size:	Two lakes of 20 acres and 5 acres, both heavily weeded
Carp Stock:	Both stocked with a few big carp, most of which are doubles
Category:	Few Carp
Other Species:	Most coarse fish
Permits:	Day tickets on bank
Control:	Worksop and District AA. Secretary: R Whitehead, 72 Dryden Vale, Worksop
Restrictions:	No night fishing, and sailing in daytime
BK Rating:	Very Difficult
W/A:	NRA Severn-Trent Region

Iron Mongers Pond

Location:	Wilford, Nottingham
Type and Size:	Small man-made pond
Carp Stock:	Said to be some carp, numbers and sizes not known
Category:	Mixed Fishery
Other Species:	Usual coarse fish
Permits:	Day tickets from bailiff on bank
Control:	Nottingham AA
BK Rating:	Not known
W/A:	NRA Severn-Trent Region

Langold Lake

Location:	Near Worksop
Type and Size:	Big old gravel pit, very attractive, of more than 20 acres in size
Carp Stock:	Not many, but most are doubles with a possible 20
Category:	Few Carp
Other Species:	Most coarse fish
Permits:	Day tickets from bailiff on site
Cost:	£3 per day
Control:	Private

Restrictions: No night fishing; no season tickets; two rods only
BK Rating: Difficult
W/A: NRA Severn-Trent Region
Comments: A busy and heavily fished water, though as there are so few carp there are not many carp anglers

Lound Windsurf Lake

Location: Chainbridge Lane, Lound, East Retford
Type and Size: Large lake
How to Find: Off the A638, north of East Retford
Carp Stock: Some carp to over 20lbs, including commons to 27lbs
Category: Mixed Fishery
Other Species: General coarse fish
Permits: East Midlands Windsurf Centre on lake shore
Cost: About £80 per season
BK Rating: Moderate
Control: Private
Restrictions: None
W/A: NRA Severn-Trent Region
Comments: Obviously, there will be windsurfing on this lake! Weedy at times

Manor House Fishery

Location: North Muskham, near Newark
Type and Size: Three lakes, North Muskham, near Newark and a stretch of the River Trent (largest 12 acres)
How to Find: Find North Muskham, which is north of Newark, near the A1
Carp Stock: Some good bags of small carp of under 5lbs are taken from the Trent in this area though there is always the chance of bigger fish. No. 1 lake to 27lbs
Category: Mixed Fishery
Other Species: Roach, chub, bream, dace, tench, pike, bleak and gudgeon
Permits: Day tickets from the owner at his house on site, Walter Bower - Tel: 0636 702457
Cost: £2 per day
Restrictions: Fishing 6am to 7pm only
Control: Private
W/A: NRA Severn-Trent Region

Newark Dyke

Location: Just north of Newark-upon-Trent
Type and Size: Short cut off the main River Trent, much used for match fishing
Carp Stock: Not many, but fish over 20lbs have been caught
Category: Few Carp
Other Species: Chub, roach, barbel and gudgeon
Permits: Day tickets on bank
Cost: £2 per day - no season tickets
Control: Newark and District AA
BK Rating: Very Difficult
W/A: NRA Severn-Trent Region

Nottingham - Grantham Canal

Location: Winding canal, between both towns - Nottingham and Grantham
Type and Size: Narrow, canal many miles in length
Category: Mixed Fishery
Other Species: Most coarse fish
Permits: Different clubs - enquire from tackle shops in both towns
BK Rating: Difficult, until fish located, but in the heavily stocked areas it is quite easy
W/A: NRA Severn-Trent Region

River Trent

Location: Dunham Bridge
Type and Size: Large river
How to Find: West bank near Dunham Bridge, off the A57 Lincoln-Sheffield road
Carp Stock: All sizes up to 22lbs (commons)
Category: Mixed Fishery
Other Species: General coarse fish
Permits: From local tackle shops. Sheffield and District AA, PO Box 218, Sheffield S1 1BU
Cost: £5 per season
BK Rating: Difficult
Control: Club
Restrictions: Heavily match fished
W/A: NRA Severn-Trent Region
Comments: Tidal water

Sapphire Lake

Location: Norwell Road, Cromwell, near Newark-on-Trent
Type and Size: 12 acre lake
How to Find: On the A1 just north of Newark; the Morwell road
Carp Stock: Heavily stocked with carp to 25lbs, best 30lbs. A 35 pounder is rumoured
Category: Mixed Fishery
Other Species: Bream, perch and eels
Permits: On site. Tel: 0636 821131 or 0860 268177
Cost: Coarse lake - £3 per day, £5 per night; Specimen carp lake - £6 per day or night

BK Rating: Moderate
Control: Private - Ken Barker
Restrictions: Line below 10lbs BS banned in certain areas. Car keys must be left with owners when night fishing
W/A: NRA Severn-Trent Region
Comments: A widely publicised fishery with big catches recorded - many doubles and some twenties. No close season

Shireoaks Hall Lake

Location: Shireoaks, just of the A57 between Worksop and Sheffield
Type and Size: Four lakes of about 2½ acres on estate
Carp Stock: Very heavily stocked with small carp to low doubles
Category: Carp Water
Permits: Day tickets on bank at low cost
Control: Private
Restrictions: No night fishing
BK Rating: Very Easy
W/A: NRA Severn-Trent Region
Comments: Big catches common on standard baits. Bar and cafe on bank; ideal for beginners

South Muskham Fisheries (A1 Pits)   A

Location: South Muskham, near Newark-on-Trent
Type and Size: 6 gravel pits, and stretch of River Trent
How to Find: Turn off the A1 at North Muskham. The entrance is by the rail crossing
Carp Stock: Very well stocked with many carp of up to 25lbs+; many commons
Category: Mixed Fishery
Other Species: General coarse fish, pike to 20lbs and big bream
Permits: On bank
Cost: £2.50 per day and £2 for night. Season - £100
BK Rating: Moderate
Control: Private
Restrictions: None
W/A: NRA Severn-Trent Region
Comments: These big gravel pits flood from the River Trent at times. Holiday accommodation: The Old House, North Muskham, Newark. Tel: 0636 706886. Guest house and self-catering. The 40 acre and 30 acre pits are best for carp. Cars can be driven to the swim. Can be noisy at times

Steetly Pool

Location: The village of Shireoaks, between Worksop and Sheffield
Type and Size: 4 acre quarry, quite attractive
Carp Stock: Well stocked with small carp to about 10lbs, with one or two slightly bigger fish also present
Category: Mixed Fishery
Other Species: Roach, bream and tench
Permits: In advance only from Steetly Concrete Office, Shireoaks
Control: Steetly Concrete Co

Restrictions: No day tickets on bank; no Sunday fishing; one bank private; no night fishing
BK Rating: Moderate
W/A: NRA Severn-Trent Region

Windmill Farm

Location: Windmill Farm, Spalford, near Newark. Tel: 0522 77305
Type and Size: Small farm lakes
Carp Stock: Well stocked with carp to doubles
Category: Carp Water
Other Species: Possibly a few
Permits: From the owner at the address above
Cost: £2 per day - £2.50 for night fishing
Control: Private
BK Rating: Not known
W/A: NRA Severn-Trent Region
Comments: Tents and touring caravans allowed at this fishery - good facilities provided

Windthorpe Pits

Location: Close to the A1, near Newark
Type and Size: 25 acre gravel pit, connected to the River Trent - very deep, with little cover
Carp Stock: Plenty of doubles, and possibly a few twenties
Category: Mixed Fishery
Other Species: Pike, roach, tench, bream and perch
Permits: Day tickets from the house close to the pit
Control: Sheffield Angling Club - season tickets from F Turner, 30 Mather Walk, Sheffield, or 142-144 Princes Street, Sheffield S4 4UW
Restrictions: Night fishing is allowed
BK Rating: Difficult
W/A: NRA Severn-Trent Region

Winthorpe Lake

Location: Off the Newark-Gainsborough road, near Newark
Type and Size: 20 acre gravel pit
Carp Stock: Quite well stocked with carp to 22lbs
Category: Mixed Fishery
Other Species: Usual coarse fish
Permits: Sheffield and District AA. Secretary: F E Turner, 30 Mather Walk, Sheffield S9 4GL, or 142-144 Princes Street, Sheffield S4 4UW
Control: Club
BK Rating: Moderate
W/A: NRA Severn-Trent Region
Comments: This water is very heavily match fished. The permit also includes some good fishing on the River Trent in the same area, with plenty of carp from 8lbs to 22lbs

Woodsetts Pond

Location:	Woodsett, near Dinnington, off the A57 between Worksop and Sheffield
Type and Size:	5 acre sand pit, locally known as 'The Quarry'
Carp Stock:	Quite well stocked with carp to upper doubles
Category:	Mixed Fishery
Other Species:	Tench and roach
Permits:	Day tickets on bank
Control:	Worksop and District AA. Secretary: R Whitehead, 72 Dryden Walk, Worksop
Restrictions:	No night fishing
BK Rating:	Very Difficult
W/A:	NRA Severn-Trent Region
Comments:	This quarry is deep and weedy, which perhaps is why it is so hard, as it is quite well stocked with good sized carp

Woodsetts Quarry Pond

Location:	Off the A57 Worksop to Sheffield road, near Worksop
Type and Size:	Small disused quarry
Carp Stock:	Said to be some carp; numbers and sizes not known
Category:	Mixed Fishery
Other Species:	Roach, bream and tench
Permits:	Day tickets from bailiff on bank
Control:	Worksop and District AA
BK Rating:	Not known
W/A:	NRA Severn-Trent Region

OXFORDSHIRE

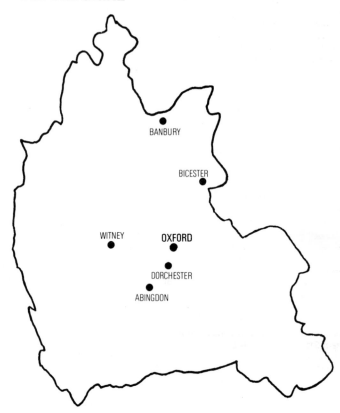

Dorchester Lagoon

Location:	Dorchester Fisheries, Abingdon, Dorchester OX10 7LP. Tel: 0865 341810 (between 9am and 7pm only)
Type and Size:	40 acre gravel pit, with extensive islands
Carp Stock:	Recent restocking included some doubles, and smaller fish. Three upper 30's and many 20's caught
Category:	Mixed Fishery
Other Species:	Tench, roach, bream and pike
Permits:	Day and season tickets from Paul Bray at the address above - £4
Cost:	1 rod - £4, 2 rods - £6
Control:	Dorchester Fisheries, which also include Orchid Lake, Queenford Lagoon, Club Lake and several miles of the River Thame
BK Rating:	Moderate to Difficult
W/A:	NRA Thames Region
Comments:	Under new management - this complex was recently bought from ARC by David DeVere, owner of Old Bury Hill Lake, an excellent water containing big carp, which is near Dorking in Surrey. No close season

Dukes Lake

Location:	Oxford
Type and Size:	4 acre town lake
Carp Stock:	Carp to doubles
Category:	Mixed Fishery
Other Species:	Tench, rudd and pike
Permits:	North Oxford AS - Secretary, P Jackman, 1 Churchill Road, Kidlington, Oxford. Tel: Kidlington 79582
Control:	Club
BK Rating:	Moderate
W/A:	NRA Thames Region

Hardwick Pits

Location:	Hardwick, near Witney
Type and Size:	Hardwick 1 - 70 acre gravel pit; Hardwick 2 - 60 acres
Carp Stock:	One - about 60 carp, sizes not known. Two - said to be only 6 carp!
Category:	Few Carp (very few!)
Other Species:	Record chub and other coarse fish
Permits:	Enquire at tackle shops in Witney and Oxford
BK Rating:	Super-Difficult
W/A:	NRA Thames Region
Comments:	As you can see, we know little about this one, except that the pits do contain a few carp and that some of them might be very big

Horse and Groom Inn   A

Location:	Milcombe, near Banbury
Type and Size:	Small lake
How to Find:	Just off the A361 between Banbury and Chipping Norton
Carp Stock:	Carp to 15lbs
Category:	Mixed Fishery
Other Species:	General coarse fish
Permits:	Horse and Groom Inn, Milcombe. Tel: Banbury 720471
Cost:	On application
Control:	Private
BK Rating:	No information
W/A:	NRA Thames Region
Comments:	16th century inn, bed and breakfast, games room, skittle alley, 220 acres of rough shooting. Edge of Cotswolds

Linch Hill Fishery   A

Location:	Standlake, Stanton Harcourt, near Oxford
Type and Size:	Large gravel pit
How to Find:	West of Oxford
Carp Stock:	Some big carp to 25lbs+
Category:	Mixed Fishery
Other Species:	General coarse fish
Permits:	S D Lawson, Linch Hill Leisure Park, Stanton Harcourt, Oxford. Tel: 882215
Cost:	On application
BK Rating:	Moderate

Control:	Private
Restrictions:	Not known
W/A:	NRA Thames Region
Comments:	Accommodation - Hardwick Park, Downs Road, Standlake, Oxon. Tel: 0993 775278 or 086731 501. Caravan and camping park with a few letting vans, and also 45 acre lake for fishing and sailing

Marlborough Pool

Location:	On the A40 between Witney and Oxford
Type and Size:	Mature gravel pit of 11 acres
Carp Stock:	Well stocked with carp many years ago which have gone to over 20lbs
Category:	Carp Water
Permits:	Oxford Angling and Preservation Society. M Baston, 28 Mayfield Road, Farmoor, Oxford. Tel: 0865 862426
BK Rating:	Moderate
Control:	Club
W/A:	NRA Thames Region
Comments:	Quite a well-known carp water, quite heavily fished and in the past some well-known anglers have fished there

Milton Common

Location:	Just off junction 7 of the M40; can be seen from the motorway
Type and Size:	Three lakes of 3, 2 and 1½ acres
Carp Stock:	Quite well stocked with carp to 24lbs
Category:	Carp Waters
Permits:	From owner on site
Cost:	Approximately £1.50 per rod per day
Control:	Private
BK Rating:	Moderate
W/A:	NRA Thames Region
Comments:	We could find out little about this fishery, so you will need to go to the area which is near Oxford and ask locally. We have heard that this fishery may stay open during the close season

Newlands AC

Location:	Near Witney
Type and Size:	12 acre lake
Carp Stock:	Well stocked with doubles, and there are said to be two thirties, the biggest of which is 36lbs
Category:	Mixed Fishery
Other Species:	Usual coarse fish
Permits:	Said to be a syndicate - enquire at tackle shops in Witney and Oxford
BK Rating:	Difficult
W/A:	NRA Thames Region

Orchid Lake

Location:	Dorchester Fisheries, Abingdon Road, Dorchester OX10 7LP. Tel: 0865 341810 (between 9am and 7pm)
Type and Size:	17 acre gravel pit
Carp Stock:	About 300 carp, most of which are over 20lbs, and 5 thirties. There are now said to be about forty 20's in the lake
Category:	Mixed Fishery
Other Species:	Tench, roach and perch
Permits:	Day and season tickets from Paul Bray at the above address
Cost:	£6 for one rod; £10 for 2 rods
Control:	Dorchester Fisheries, which also includes Dorchester Lagoon, Queenford Lagoon, Club Lake and a stretch of the River Thame
BK Rating:	Moderate
W/A:	NRA Thames Region
Comments:	Under new management - David DeVere, owner of Old Bury Hill Fisheries, bought this complex recently, and the fishing is now managed by a British Carp Study Group member, Paul Bray. A lot of very big carp have been stocked, and this is likely to be one of the top big carp waters during the next few years. No close season. Cafe, toilets, washing facilities. Purpose-built bivvy swims. Concessions for long stay anglers

Oxford Canal

Location:	Banbury
Type and Size:	Midlands canal, quite narrow
How to Find:	On the outskirts of Banbury
Carp Stock:	Plenty of carp to 15lbs+
Category:	Mixed Fishery
Other Species:	General coarse fish
Permits:	Local tackle shops
Cost:	On application
Control:	Club
BK Rating:	Moderate
W/A:	NRA Severn-Trent Region
Comments:	Once you can find an area containing carp, they are not hard to catch. Average 6-8lbs. Good winter fishing. Banbury and District AA, D Brewer, 42 Stanwell Lea, Middleton Cheney, Banbury, Oxon for tickets. A fish kill took place on the canal in the Banbury area in 1991

Oxford Quarry

Location:	Near Stanton Harcourt, Oxford
Type and Size:	Gravel pit of 16 acres
How to Find:	Lake is off the B4449 road between Eynsham and Standlake
Carp Stock:	Small number of carp to about 25lbs
Category:	Few Carp
Other Species:	Rudd, chub, tench, catfish, pike
Permits:	Vauxhall Motors Angling Club, season tickets. Secretary: Mr B Matthews, 88 Langford Drive, Luton, Beds. Tel: Luton 419489
Cost:	On application
Control:	Club

BK Rating:	Difficult
W/A:	NRA Thames Region
Comments:	One side shallow with gravel bars. Carp baits taken mainly by chub. Best method stalking individual fish often close in

Pickford Lake

Location:	Oxford
Type and Size:	Small town lake
Carp Stock:	Well stocked with carp to 10lbs
Category:	Mixed Fishery
Other Species:	Tench
Permits:	North Oxford AS (members only). Secretary: P Jackman, 1 Churchill Road, Kidlington, Oxford. Tel: Kidlington 79582
Control:	Club
BK Rating:	Not known
W/A:	NRA Thames Region

POWYS (Wales)

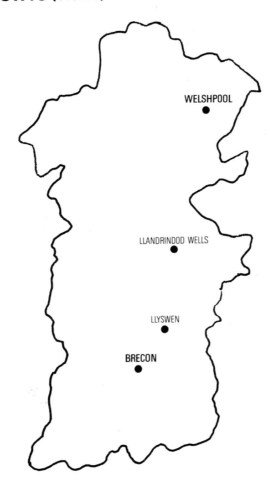

WELSHPOOL

LLANDRINDOD WELLS

LLYSWEN

BRECON

Llandrindod Wells Lake

Location: Edge of the town of Llandrindod Wells, central Wales
Type and Size: Dammed town lake with island, 16 acres
How to Find: Road leading from town centre goes round three sides of the lake
Carp Stock: Very heavily stocked, mostly mirrors. Many doubles and the occasional 20 pounder

Category: Mixed Fishery/Carp Water
Other Species: Roach, bream, pike, eels
Permits: Day and season tickets from the boathouse cafe on the lake. Night syndicate, details from the cafe

Restrictions:	No night fishing unless you are a night syndicate member. No fishing on dam
Cost:	On application
Baits/Methods:	Fairly sophisticated carp methods and boiled baits used, but carp also caught on luncheon meat and floating baits, and on float tackle
Control:	Day and season ticket, local Council
BK Rating:	Moderate
W/A:	NRA Welsh Region
Comments:	Town lake with roads and many walkers, but still attractive. Often fishes well when the boats are being used!

Llyswen Carp Pools   A

Location:	The Dderw, Llyswen, Builth Wells
Type and Size:	Three pools of 3 acres, 2 acres and 2½ acres
How to Find:	Llyswen is on the A470 road between Brecon and Builth Wells
Carp Stock:	The Orchard Pool nearest the farmhouse is quite well stocked with commons to about 10lbs and a few double figure mirrors to 20lbs. The other lakes are very heavily stocked with small commons to about 7lbs
Category:	Carp Waters
Other Species:	Tench, bream, roach, perch
Permits:	Day tickets from the farm: Mr Eckley, The Dderw, Llyswen, Powys. Tel: 0874 754224
Cost:	Orchard Pool £5 per day. Mill Pool and The Pool £4
Control:	Private
BK Rating:	Orchard Pool - Moderate. Mill Pool - Easy. The Pool - Very Easy
Baits/Methods:	Boilies and particle baits; also floaters. Rigs and methods of all types will work and on the other pond the fish will take almost any bait as it is so overstocked
W/A:	Welsh, Wye Area, 4 St. John Street, Hereford. Tel: 0432 276313, or from tackle shops. Senior Coarse Licence approximately £4.10 per season, day licence £2.50
Comments:	The Orchard Pool is a pleasant water surrounded by trees and reeds. The lakes are in the Wye Valley 10 miles south east of Builth Wells. Accommodation in three self-catering studio apartments on site - part of the house, sleeping four, three and two

---

THE BEEKAY GUIDE TO 1500 BRITISH & EUROPEAN CARP WATERS	**Is YOUR Water listed? If so, are the details correct?**
	If you spot omissions, inaccuracies, or know of any changes, please let us know by filling in the Waters Questionnaire at the back of this guide and return it to us at:
	FREEPOST Beekay Publishers Withy Pool Henlow Camp Bedfordshire SG16 6EA

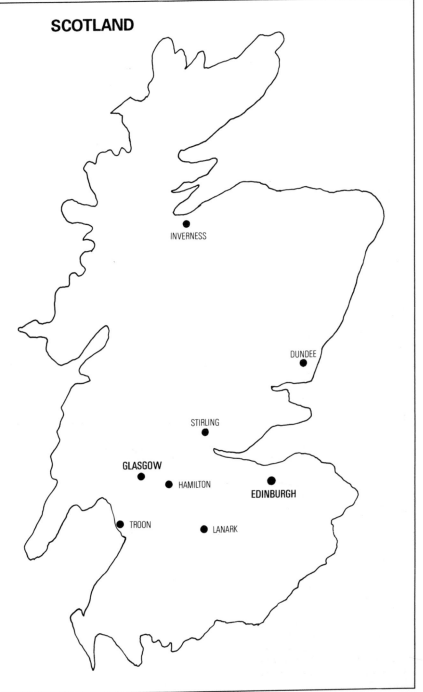

SCOTLAND

INVERNESS

DUNDEE

STIRLING

GLASGOW

HAMILTON

EDINBURGH

TROON

LANARK

Barrhead Reservoir

Location:	Just off the A77 south west of Glasgow, near Newton Mearns (Strathclyde)
Type and Size:	There are several lakes here, and the small one contains carp
Carp Stock:	Mirrors to low doubles
Category:	Mixed Fishery
Other Species:	Some coarse fish and trout
Permits:	None necessary - free fishing
Control:	Glasgow City Council
BK Rating:	Not known
W/A:	NRA Scottish Region
Comments:	No close season; quite a pleasant water which needs investigating

Clatio Loch

Location:	Centre of the town of Dundee (Tayside)
Type and Size:	10 acre town lake
Carp Stock:	Stocked with small carp in about 1988, and there are now fish up to about 6lb
Category:	Mixed Fishery
Other Species:	Roach, bream and perch
Permits:	From Dundee City Council, at no cost
Control:	Council
BK Rating:	Easy
W/A:	Scottish
Comments:	No close season; a match water

Cowans Farm and Guest House   A

Location:	Kirkgunzeon, Dumfries (Dumfries & Galloway)
Type and Size:	1½ acre man-made loch
How to Find:	9 miles south west of Dumfries, off the A711 Dalbeattie road
Carp Stock:	Contains some carp
Category:	Few Carp
Other Species:	Roach, tench and rudd
Permits:	Tel: 038776 284
Cost:	Day permits £2.50 per rod, free fishing to residents
BK Rating:	Insufficient information
Control:	Private
Restrictions:	No keepnets. No groundbaiting
Comments:	Bed and breakfast and evening meal in licensed guest house, 200 yards from loch. Other lochs and sea close by. No close season

Craichlaw Fisheries   A

Location:	Near Newton Stewart (Dumfries & Galloway)
Type and Size:	Lake of 6½ acres. There are 4 other lakes in the fishery, some of which also contain carp
How to Find:	First ask at the owner's: Palakona Guest House, 30/32 Queen Street, Newton Stewart
Carp Stock:	150 fish to 30lbs
Category:	Mixed Fishery

Other Species:	Many tench and some golden orfe and bream
Permits:	Day and weekly permits only from the owner, N Thornton, at Palakona Guest House. No tickets on the bank - you must obtain a permit before fishing
Cost:	£4 per day
Control:	Private
BK Rating:	Not fished enough yet to be sure of a rating, but at present we would guess at Moderate
Comments:	No close season. Comfortable accommodation in the owner's guest house. Tel: 0671 2323. There are very few carp waters in Scotland and this is one of the newest. It should have a good future, as the SW of Scotland has a very mild climate. The lake is very attractive and has a lined bottom, which was built by the monks. In fact, this was a monastery fish pond, and the monks' fish house is still there. There are trees, with an island and a boat house. Depths are from 4 to 11 feet and there is some weed. The water is unfished, as it was only stocked with carp in 1985, so the carp are uncaught

Culcreuch Castle Pool   A

Location:	Fintry, on the B818, 15 miles west of Stirling (Stirlingshire)
Type and Size:	Two small lakes on estate
Carp Stock:	Well stocked with mirrors to about 10lbs, and commons to lower doubles, which are said by locals to be wildies
Category:	Carp Water
Permits:	Scottish Carp Group, 57 Iona Way, Kirkintilloch, Glasgow. Tel: 041-776 7922
BK Rating:	Moderate
Comments:	Attractive lakes in the grounds of an hotel; members only, no day tickets

Duddingston Loch

Location:	City centre of Edinburgh (Lothian)
Type and Size:	50 acre town lake, which is a bird reserve, and belongs to the Crown. Much of the bank cannot be fished
Carp Stock:	Plenty of doubles to about 15lbs
Category:	Mixed Fishery
Other Species:	Roach, bream and perch
Permits:	Available free from Edinburgh City Council, or Mikes Tackle Shop, Portobello, Edinburgh
BK Rating:	Difficult
Comments:	No close season - size and restrictions make it difficult to find fish

Forth and Clyde Canal

Location:	Kelvindale, north west Glasgow
Type and Size:	Very wide, large canal
Carp Stock:	Some very big carp to well over 20lbs
Category:	Few Carp
Other Species:	Roach, bream, perch and pike
Permits:	None necessary - free fishing
BK Rating:	Super-Difficult

Comments: No close season. Fish very difficult to locate in this big canal, but they have certainly never been caught

Glen Esk Caravan Park   A

Location: Glen Esk Caravan Park, Edzell, Angus DD9 7YP, on the B966 eight miles north of Brechin
Type and Size: Three-quarter acre lake
Carp Stock: Well stocked with commons and mirrors to doubles
Category: Carp Water
Permits: On site
Control: Tel: 03564 523/565
BK Rating: Not known
Comments: No close season. Some caravans. Trout and salmon fishing available

Gooseloan Pond

Location: Kilwinning, 10 miles north of Troon, near the west coast (Ayrshire)
Type and Size: Old, deep quarry of about 4 acres
Carp Stock: Over 30 carp to about 20lbs
Category: Carp Water
Permits: Not known; enquire locally, possibly from farmers
BK Rating: Very Difficult

Hogganfield Loch

Location: City centre of Glasgow
Type and Size: 80 acre town lake, very busy and quite dangerous to fish at times!
Carp Stock: Well stocked with carp to about 20lbs
Category: Mixed Fishery
Other Species: Big bream and eels
Permits: None necessary - free fishing
Control: Council
BK Rating: Moderate
Comments: No close season, and night fishing is allowed. Thousands of water birds, and some people of dubious reputation, especially at night!

Lanark Loch

Location: Public park in Lanark, on the A73 20 miles south east of Glasgow
Type and Size: 20 acre public lake
Carp Stock: Stocked with 500 carp of about 5lbs each in 1988
Category: Mixed Fishery
Other Species: Tench and bream
Permits: About £12 per season from Clydesdale District Council and local tackle shops
Cost: About £10 per season. Possible day tickets
BK Rating: Not known, but could be quite hard, as 20 fish an acre is a low stocking density
Comments: No close season - might be a good bet to catch a Scottish carp

Turn Grandad's old tackle into cash see page 287

Loch Libo

Location: Uplawmoor, Barrhead (Renfrewshire)
Type and Size: 20 acre shallow and weedy loch
Carp Stock: Well stocked with doubles to lower twenties, and small commons
Category: Carp Water
Permits: Scottish Carp Group, 57 Iona Way, Kirkintilloch, Glasgow.
Tel: 041-776 7922
Cost: About £30 per year
Control: Scottish Wildlife Trust
Restrictions: No fishing in some areas; limited number of anglers
BK Rating: Difficult
Comments: No close season

Monkland Canal

Location: Coatbridge (Lanarkshire)
Type and Size: Narrow canal
Carp Stock: This canal area was stocked with several thousand small carp recently
Category: Mixed Fishery
Other Species: Most coarse fish
Permits: Scottish Federation of Coarse Anglers, c/o J B Angling, Townhead, Kirkintilloch, Glasgow G66
Control: Local club; details from the Scottish Federation
BK Rating: Easy
W/A: Scottish
Comments: No close season

Strathclyde Water Park

Location: Hamilton (Lanarkshire)
Type and Size: 150 acre lake
Carp Stock: Well stocked with doubles to about 15lbs
Category: Mixed Fishery
Other Species: Roach and bream
Permits: From the Sports Centre at the lake, £4 per day
Control: Private
BK Rating: Moderate
Comments: No close season. Lots of people and match anglers

Torwood House Hotel   A

Location: Glenluce, Newton Stewart, Wigtownshire (Dumfries & Galloway)
Type and Size: Two lochs
How to Find: Newton Stewart is to the west of Dumfries
Carp Stock: Little known, but does contain some carp
Category: Few Carp
Other Species: Tench, bream, roach, perch
Permits: From hotel: Tel: 05813 469
Cost: On application, day tickets
Control: Torwood House Hotel
Comments: Accommodation in hotel, 200 yards from lochs. No close season. Pike and salmon fishing nearby. Some trout fishing

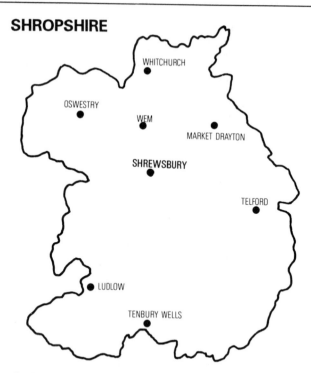

SHROPSHIRE

WHITCHURCH

OSWESTRY

WEM

MARKET DRAYTON

SHREWSBURY

TELFORD

LUDLOW

TENBURY WELLS

Apley Pool

Location:	Near Telford at Lee Gomory
Type and Size:	Small pool
Carp Stock:	Heavily stocked to 10lbs
Category:	Carp Only
Other Species:	None
Permits:	Telford Anglers Association, Malcolm Kelly, Tel: Telford 244272
Cost:	On application
BK Rating:	Easy
Control:	Club
W/A:	NRA Severn-Trent Region

Bache Pool

Location:	Near Ludlow
Type and Size:	1½ acre farm pond
How to Find:	Turn off the B4365 from Ludlow towards Craven Arms and go through some narrow winding lanes, virtually getting lost!
Carp Stock:	Very heavily stocked with many small commons and a few good mirrors and commons to 25lbs
Category:	Carp Water
Other Species:	General coarse fish
Permits:	Day tickets on bank?
Control:	Club

BK Rating:	Easy,though hard for the big fish
W/A:	NRA Severn-Trent Region
Comments:	Heavily fished, long narrow lake with lilies; shallow. Bigger fish very wary. Floaters good. A well known water to many Midlands carp anglers. Very opaque, 'coloured' water. Big torches, Tilley lamps and loud radios common!

Bayliss Pools

Location:	Shifnal, near Telford
Type and Size:	No. 1: 2 acres; No. 2: 2½ acres; No. 3: 3-6 acres
Carp Stock:	No. 1: carp to 16lbs; No. 2: carp to 16lbs; No. 3: recent stocking
Category:	Mixed Fishery
Other Species:	Mixed coarse fish
Permits:	On site. Tel: 0952 503550
Cost:	£2 per day approximately. About £1 (1pm till dark)
BK Rating:	No. 1 - Moderate. No. 2 - Difficult
Control:	Private
W/A:	NRA Severn-Trent Region
Comments:	No. 2 pool is said to be very deep and it fishes well in the winter. Information from Rod & Gun, 3 High Street, Dawley. Tel:0952 503550

Beeches Pool

Location:	Ironbridge, near Telford
Type and Size:	One acre pool
Carp Stock:	Doubles to 16lbs and three twenties
Category:	Mixed Fishery
Other Species:	General coarse fish
Permits:	On site
Cost:	£1.50 per day approximately
BK Rating:	Moderate
Control:	Private
W/A:	NRA Severn-Trent Region
Comments:	Try local tackle shops for permits and more information, such as Rod & Gun, 3 High Street, Dawley. Tel: 0952 503550

Boldings Pool

Location:	Astley Abbotts, off the B4373 near Bridgnorth
Type and Size:	Eight small pools
Carp Stock:	Carp to upper doubles
Category:	Mixed Fishery
Other Species:	Tench, bream, chub, perch, roach and barbel
Permits:	On bank between 6.30 and 8.30am; after 8.30am pay at house
Cost:	£3 per day; £2 for juniors under 16
Control:	Eddie and Sue Turner. Tel: 0746 763255
BK Rating:	Moderate
W/A:	NRA Severn Trent Region

Bomere

Location:	In the town of Shrewsbury
Type and Size:	Attractive lake of about 5 acres
Carp Stock:	Probably only one or two, to upper doubles
Category:	Few Carp
Other Species:	Roach, tench, bream, perch and pike
Permits:	Day tickets from local tackle shops
Control:	Club
Restrictions:	No night fishing
BK Rating:	Super-Difficult
W/A:	NRA Severn-Trent Region

Brockton Grange   A

Location:	Brockton, near Much Wenlock. Tel: Mrs Julia Russell on 0746 36443
Type and Size:	Estate lake of about an acre
Carp Stock:	Well stocked with carp to 20lbs; restocked November 1991
Category:	Mixed Fishery
Other Species:	Some coarse fish, trout fishing also available by arrangement
Permits:	From the Grange
Control:	Private
BK Rating:	Moderate
W/A:	NRA Severn-Trent Region
Comments:	High class bed and breakfast accommodation in fine Victorian country house with 25 acres of attractive grounds and lake. Double £40 per night; single £30 per night. This property is in Corvedale, one of Shropshire's finest dales, and convenient for Ludlow, Church Stretton and Ironbridge

Brown Moss Mere

Location:	Near Whitchurch off the A41
Type and Size:	Lake of about 3 acres, very shallow and weedy
Carp Stock:	Quite well stocked to doubles
Category:	Mixed Fishery
Other Species:	Roach, tench and bream
Permits:	Day tickets on the bank at low cost
Control:	Local club water
Restrictions:	No night fishing
BK Rating:	Moderate
W/A:	NRA Severn-Trent Region

Canal Reservoirs

Location:	Great Sowdley, near Market Drayton
Type and Size:	Small reservoirs off the canal
Carp Stock:	Some carp, most small
Category:	Mixed Fishery
Other Species:	Perch, pike, roach, tench
Permits:	Stoke-on-Trent AS. F Broadgate, 5 Kingsford Oval, Basford, Stoke-on-Trent ST4 6HN
Control:	Club
BK Rating:	Difficult
W/A:	NRA Severn-Trent Region

Castle Pool/Dandy Pool/Wide Waters

Location: LIttle Dawley, near Telford
Type and Size: 3 separate small lakes, 2-3 acres each
How to Find: Details from Telford Anglers Association. Tel:Telford 244272
Carp Stock: Castle and Dandy well stocked with doubles to 20lbs; Wide Waters some carp to 25lbs+
Category: Mixed Fisheries
Other Species: Mixed Coarse Fish
Permits: Telford Anglers Association
Cost: On application
BK Rating: Castle/Dandy - Moderate; Wide Waters - Difficult
Control: Club
W/A: NRA Severn-Trent Region
Comments: We could find out very little about these waters, but the Telford Club Secretary should be able to help

Hawkstone Park Lake

Location: Hawkstone Park, Hodnett, near Wem
Type and Size: Park Lake, very narrow and about 1½ miles long!
Carp Stock: The water is stocked with plenty of doubles and numerous twenties, both commons and mirrors to about 28lbs
Category: Carp Water
Other Species: General coarse fish
Permits: Hawk Lake Trust, Mr P Johnson, 4 Soulton Crescent, Wem SY4 5HY
Control: Hawk Lake Trust
BK Rating: Difficult
Baits/Methods: Normal carp fishing baits and methods
W/A: NRA North West Region
Comments: With such an immensely long lake one of the main problems is obviously to find the fish, and it is this which makes the water hard, although it is quite well stocked with carp

Isle Estate

Location: Shrewsbury
Type and Size: Estate lake of about 5 acres
Carp Stock: One of the most heavily stocked carp waters in the country. Mostly small carp to 6lbs, but some fish present up to 20lbs
Category: Carp Water
Other Species: General coarse fish
Permits: Prince Albert AS, Secretary Mr C Clarke, 2 Avon Close, Upton, Macclesfield, Cheshire. Season tickets only
Cost: About £35 entry fee and approximately £35 per season. Members only
Control: Club
BK Rating: Very Easy
W/A: NRA North West Region
Comments: One of those overstocked waters where the carp breed like rabbits. Fish can be caught by any method, and huge catches are recorded

Kingsnordley Pools

Location:	Quatt, off the A442 just south east of Bridgnorth
Type and Size:	Nine very small pools
Carp Stock:	Well stocked with plenty of doubles to over 20lbs
Category:	Mixed Fishery
Other Species:	Bream, tench, roach, rudd, perch, gudgeon, barbel and goldfish
Permits:	Day tickets from the farmhouse (after 8am) at £3
Control:	Tel: 0746 780247
Restrictions:	No night fishing; no boilies; no groundbait
BK Rating:	Moderate
W/A:	NRA Severn-Trent Region

Kyre Pool

Location:	Tenbury Wells
Type and Size:	Small lake
How to Find:	Near Tenbury Wells
Carp Stock:	Good carp to over 20llbs
Category:	Mixed Fishery
Other Species:	Pike and eels
Permits:	S Lewis Fishing Tackle, Bewdley - day tickets
Cost:	On application
Control:	Private
BK Rating:	Moderate
W/A:	NRA Severn-Trent Region

Middle Pool

Location:	Wombridge, near Telford
Type and Size:	2½ acre pool
Carp Stock:	Carp to 20lbs, numbers not known
Category:	Mixed Fishery
Other Species:	Big bream
Permits:	Season tickets from local tackle shops. No day tickets
Cost:	On application
BK Rating:	Moderate
Control:	Telford Anglers Association. Tel: Telford 244272
Restrictions:	No night fishing. No boilies
W/A:	NRA Severn-Trent Region

Mildenham Fishery   A

Location:	Near Tenbury Wells
Type and Size:	Disused canal, with no boats
Carp Stock:	Some carp, numbers and sizes not known
Category:	Mixed Fishery
Other Species:	Rudd, roach, chub, dace and perch
Permits:	Tel: 0299 250021 for details
Control:	Private
BK Rating:	Not known
W/A:	NRA Severn-Trent Region
Comments:	Accommodation in Victorian farmhouse; some private river fishing also

Moss Pool

Location:	Forton, near Newport, Telford
Type and Size:	Pool of about 2 acres
Carp Stock:	Good head of doubles to 28lbs
Category:	Mixed Fishery
Other Species:	Bream and tench
Permits:	On bank
Cost:	Approximately £2 per day
BK Rating:	Very Difficult
Control:	Private
W/A:	NRA Severn-Trent Region
Comments:	Try local tackle shops for permits and details. Rod & Guns, 3 High Street, Dawley. Tel: 0952 503550

Neen Sollars Bungalow   A

Location:	Between Cleobury Mortimer and Tenbury Wells
Type and Size:	Estate lake of about an acre
Carp Stock:	Some carp to about 10lbs
Category:	Mixed Fishery
Permits:	Fishing only available to those who rent the bungalow from the owner. Mr S R Jennings, 26 Moorpool Avenue, Harborne, Birmingham B17 9HN. Tel: 021 429 3262, weekdays after 7pm
Other Species:	Roach, rudd and bream
Control:	Private
Restrictions:	Barbless hooks only; no keepnets
BK Rating:	Not known
W/A:	NRA Severn-Trent Region
Comments:	The accommodation is a chalet type self-catering bungalow with two double bedrooms, and a pull-down bed in dining room; sitting room, small kitchen and shower room etc. Covered verandah and summer house. Large garden, aviary and swing. Electricity included in price. Some acres of beautiful private woodland and pasture with the lake and Mill Brook, with some stream fishing. 18 acre wildlife sanctuary with walks, and wildlife pool with log benches for picnics. Ideal for a holiday with children. Cost from £150 to £200 per week according to season. Only guests have access to the land and fishing, which is included in the price. Private property - do not visit without permission

Nordley Ponds

Location:	Nordley, near Bridgnorth
Type and Size:	Three ponds of about an acre each
Carp Stock:	Recently stocked with mixed coarse fish including some small carp
Category:	Mixed Fishery
Other Species:	Roach, bream and perch
Permits:	Birmingham Anglers Association; members only
Restrictions:	Probably no night fishing
BK Rating:	Not known
W/A:	NRA Severn Trent Region

New and best selling carp videos from Beekay Publishers. See page 19

Oswestry Lakes

Location:	On the River Mor, near Oswestry
Type and Size:	Small pools
Carp Stock:	Well stocked with carp, sizes not known
Category:	Mixed Fishery
Other Species:	Most coarse fish
Permits:	Oswestry AA, M J Shilton, 24 Windsor Close, Oswestry SY11 2UY. Tickets available for visitors. Details also from J E Ellis, Regal Stores, Oswestry; Morton Lodge Hotel, Morton
Cost:	Season tickets; at £6.50 - no day tickets
Control:	Club
BK Rating:	Not known
W/A:	NRA Severn-Trent Region

Patshull Park   A

Location:	Patshull Park, Pattingham, Shropshire WV6 7BR
Type and Size:	Large estate lakes; Great Pool is 75 acres
Carp Stock:	Well stocked with carp to over 20lbs
Category:	Mixed Fishery
Other Species:	Tench, bream, roach, perch and some pike to over 30lbs. Usual coarse fish and some trout fishing
Permits:	All information from the Patshull Park Hotel at the address above. Tel: 0902 700100; information on fishing from Dave Tooth. Tel: 0902 700774. Day tickets at £2.50
BK Rating:	Moderate
W/A:	NRA Severn Trent Region
Comments:	48 bedroom hotel, golf, tennis and gymnasium; special breaks and conferences. Lakeside restaurant and coffee shop. Swimming and Beauty Centre(!) 280 acres of parkland not far from Wolverhampton

Rosehill Fishery

Location:	Off the A41 at Rosehill, just south of Market Drayton
Type and Size:	Two pools of 6 acres and two acres
Carp Stock:	Some carp to middle doubles in large pool; carp to lower doubles in the newer small pool
Category:	Mixed Fishery
Other Species:	Crucians, roach, bream and perch in the large pool; barbel in the smaller pool
Permits:	Day tickets on bank
Cost:	£3.50 per day
BK Rating:	Moderate
W/A:	NRA Severn-Trent Region

Shropshire Carp Syndicate

Location:	Undisclosed
Type and Size:	Small, attractive, secluded lake
Carp Stock:	Well stocked with mirrors and commons to over 20lbs
Category:	Mixed Fishery
Other Species:	Ghost carp and big perch

Permits:	Experienced anglers only can obtain details by telephoning 0909 450354 (daytime) or 074 636 443 (evenings)
BK Rating:	Not known
W/A:	NRA Severn Trent Region
Comments:	Sounds like a pleasant syndicate; hot sandwiches and punt available. Night fishing allowed

Stirchley Pools

Location:	Hinkshay, near Stirchley
Type and Size:	Two pools of 1½ and 2½ acres
How to Find:	These waters are near Dawley
Carp Stock:	Small pool - carp to 10lbs; larger pool - some doubles to over 20lbs
Category:	Mixed Fisheries
Other Species:	Tench
Permits:	Dawley Anglers Club. Tel: Telford 592899
Cost:	About £1 per day
BK Rating:	Moderate
Control:	Club
W/A:	NRA Severn-Trent Anglers
Comments:	All information from Dawley Anglers. Tickets from Rod & Gun, 3 High Street, Dawley

Trench Pool

Location:	Trench, near Telford
Type and Size:	Large lake of 30 acres
Carp Stock:	Some carp to over 20lbs
Category:	Mixed Fishery
Other Species:	Big pike, bream and tench
Permits:	Free
Cost:	None
BK Rating:	Moderate
Control:	Not known
W/A:	NRA Severn-Trent Region
Comments:	There are not many lakes where the fishing is free! Information from Rod & Gun, 3 High Street, Dawley. Tel: 0952 503550

Walcot East Lake

Location:	Near Lydbury North, Ludlow
Type and Size:	7 acre lake
How to Find:	Take the A49 Craven Arms road from Ludlow, and turn left on the B4368 to Little Brampton. Then take the right turn (B4385) to Lydbury North, and turn left into the estate at the Powis Arms
Carp Stock:	A few carp to about 10lbs
Category:	Few Carp
Other Species:	Bream, roach, perch
Permits:	Birmingham Anglers Association, 100 Icknield Port Road, Rotton Park, Birmingham B16 OAP. Tel: 021-454 9111. 9.30am to 1.30pm 7pm to 9pm, weekdays. (Members only)
Cost:	About £13 a season, which includes all other BAA waters
BK Rating:	Difficult, as there are few carp

Control:	B.A.A.
Restrictions:	No groundbait of any kind
W/A:	NRA Severn Trent Region
Comments:	Not worth considering unless you want a general fishing day with the chance of a carp

Whitchurch Lake

Location:	Near Whitchurch
Type and Size:	Small lake
Carp Stock:	Well stocked with carp to about 10lbs
Category:	Mixed Fishery
Other Species:	Usual coarse fish
Permits:	From J E Windsor, Black Park, Whitchurch
Cost:	£5 per season
Control:	Private
BK Rating:	Not known
W/A:	NRA Severn-Trent Region

Withy Pool

Location:	In the town of Telford
Type and Size:	Medium sized town park lake
How to Find:	Telford town park
Carp Stock:	Carp to over 30lbs. Numbers not known
Category:	Mixed Fishery
Other Species:	General coarse fish. Catfish to over 20lbs
Permits:	Dawley Anglers Club and Rod & Gun, 3 High Street, Dawley.
Cost:	On application
BK Rating:	Difficult
Control:	Club
Restrictions:	No night fishing. No boilies
W/A:	NRA Severn-Trent Region
Comments:	This lake could produce both big carp and catfish. Contact Mr A Buttery, of Dawley AC. Tel: Telford 592899

Woodcote Hall Pool

Location:	Newport, near Telford
Type and Size:	3 acre estate lake
Carp Stock:	Well stocked with carp to upper 20's
Category:	Carp Water
Other Species:	Roach, bream, rudd, perch and tench
Permits:	Season tickets only. Tel: 0952 503550
Control:	Private
BK Rating:	Moderate
W/A:	NRA Severn-Trent Region
Comments:	Heavily fished water, said to be the best carp water in this area. Try Rod & Gun, 3 High Street, Dawley. There may possibly be some day tickets at £3 per day

SOMERSET

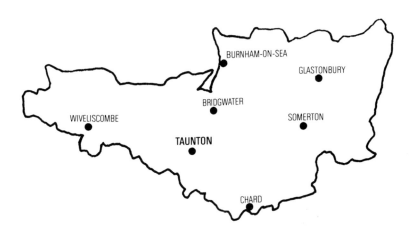

BURNHAM-ON-SEA

GLASTONBURY

BRIDGWATER

WIVELISCOMBE

SOMERTON

TAUNTON

CHARD

Apex Pond

Location: Burnham-on-Sea
Type and Size: Old pit of about 5 acres
How to Find: Go through Burnham-on-Sea and you will see the lake to the left of the road near houses
Carp Stock: Said to be well stocked with commons to about 6lbs
Category: Mixed Fishery
Other Species: Tench, rudd and pike
Permits: North Somerset Association of Anglers, and on the same tickets as Newton Pond and Hutton Pond. Secretary, R Newton, 64 Clevedon Road, Twickenham, Clevedon, Avon
Restrictions: No night fishing
Control: Club
BK Rating: Fairly Easy
W/A: NRA Wessex Region
Comments: We cannot find out much about this water since it was drained and restocked by the local Council, but we think it might serve as a fun fishery

Bridgwater Bay Holiday Park   A

Location: End of the Esplanade, Burnham-on-Sea
Type and Size: Small lake on holiday park
Carp Stock: Some mirror carp to 10 lbs+
Category: Mixed Fishery
Other Species: Roach, rudd, tench and bream
Permits: Residents only, weekly tickets from reception at low cost

Control:	Private
Restrictions:	No close season fishing allowed
BK Rating:	Moderate
W/A:	NRA Wessex Region
Comments:	Large holiday camp with lodges, chalets, apartments and caravans. All modern facilities, including outsoor heated swimming pool, boating lake, snooker and pool room, tennis courts, shops, bars etc. etc. Details and bookings from Hoseasons Holidays, Sunway House. Lowestoft NR32 3LT. Tel: 0502 500500

Bridgwater - Taunton Canal   A

Location:	Bridgwater to Taunton, exit 24 of the M5
Type and Size:	Narrow canal
How to Find:	See local maps
Carp Stock:	Some carp, mostly doubles to over 20lbs
Category:	Mixed Fishery
Other Species:	General coarse fish
Permits:	Local tackle shops in Bridgwater and Taunton. Bridgwater AA has some of the water
Cost:	£1.50 per day in advance only
BK Rating:	Difficult
Control:	Club
W/A:	NRA Wessex Region
Comments:	There are some big fish in this weedy canal. Near and between locks is often best. Could produce an upper 20. Self catering cottages on the banks of the canal. Tel: 0278 662783 (Mrs Day)

Combwich Pond

(pronounced Come-itch — or something similar!)

Location:	Combwich, near Bridgwater
Type and Size:	Old clay pit of about 25 acres
How to Find:	From Bridgwater take the A39 Minehead road and turn right at the War Memorial, Cannington. After about 1¼ miles you will see a track on the right, opposite Bowlan Farm, which leads to the car park
Carp Stock:	Well stocked with both commons and mirrors which are said to average more than 15lbs in weight. There are many upper doubles and a number of 20's, some of which are commons. Several lower 30's have been reported
Category:	Carp Water
Other Species:	Tench, roach, rudd, pike and many thousands of eels
Permits:	Bridgwater Angling Association - same ticket as for Dunwear Ponds, from local tackle shops, Veals of Bristol, and the Secretary, 7 Webbers Way, Puriton, Bridgwater, Somerset
Cost:	£11.50 per year, open to all
Control:	Club - Bridgwater Angling Association
BK Rating:	Very Difficult
Baits/Methods:	All the most advanced baits, rigs and methods needed for this very hard water. Pastes and boilies are eaten by eels and it has been said that you may easily hook at least 100 eels per season, and lose many hooks in the snags and excessively irregular bottom of this lake, which was flooded at different times. Multiple (particle) baits are said to work best

W/A:	NRA Wessex Region
Comments:	A very hard water where nearly all the success goes to long-stay carp specialists, although you can do a season there without catching a fish! If you do get one it is likely to be big, with a very good chance of a 20, though fish are reported 'going back' in 1991

Dunwear Ponds

Location:	Dunwear Lane on the edge of the town of Bridgwater
Type and Size:	Three clay pits known as the North Pond (about 4 acres); the South Pond (about 2 acres) and the Large Pond (about 20 acres)

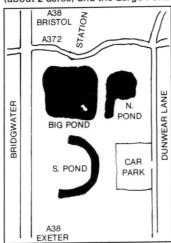

How to Find:	Turn off the A38 at the traffic lights towards Bridgwater Station (Westonzoyland Road). After nearly a mile turn right into Dunwear Lane and the car park will be seen only 400 yards along the lane on the right hand side. This is the ONLY entrance to the lakes
Carp Stock:	North Pond well stocked with carp to about 18lbs, although a fish of about 24lbs has been reported from this lake. South Pond contains a few carp but most are doubles, and there is one very big fish which has been caught more than once at over 30lbs. Large Pond has a big stock of commons to about 8lbs and a few mirrors, which are very hard to locate, to about 19lbs
Category:	North Pond - Carp Water, South Pond - Mixed Fishery, Large Pond - Mixed Fishery
Other Species:	Roach, rudd, tench, pike, bream
Permits:	Season tickets for this club water of the Bridgwater Angling Association are obtainable from the Secretary, 7 Webbers Way, Puriton, Bridgwater, Somerset, or from local tackle shops in Bridgwater and from Veals Fishing Tackle, Old Market, Bristol. Membership is open to all
Cost:	£11.50 per season which includes other waters
Restrictions:	No entry to water by any roads other than from the car park. No fishing on north bank of Large Pond
BK Rating:	North Pond - Moderate; South Pond - Moderate; Large Pond - Fairly Easy for the small commons. Difficult for the mirrors
Control:	Club

Baits/Methods: Modern advanced carp rigs, methods and baits needed for most of these fish
W/A: NRA Wessex Region
Comments: The Bridgwater club is an excellent club owning most of its own fisheries, but rules are strict, and anglers would do well to observe them. Best swim on the South Pond is the one next to the houses, past which you cannot go. This and the North Pond are hard fished by carp specialists, many of whom come from other parts of the country and spend days and nights in bivvies. Water is very busy during summer and crowded with children etc. Autumn fishing is much more peaceful. The Large Pond has islands and is split up by many reed beds which grow out into the lake along old, now flooded, paths. It is also very weedy with a thick growth of weed over most of the bottom. The club also has other ponds containing carp

Howley Street Pond

Location: Howley Street, near Chard
Type and Size: Half acre pond
Carp Stock: Some carp to about 10lbs
Category: Mixed Fishery
Other Species: Tench, bream, roach and perch
Permits: Day tickets from Chard Angling Centre, The Old Bakehouse, 2 Holyrood Street, Chard
Cost: £2
Control: Club
BK Rating: Not known
W/A: NRA Wessex Region

Newtown Pond

Location: Centre of the town of Highbridge, west of A38
Type and Size: Clay pit of 7 acres
How to Find: Take the Burnham-on-Sea road from Highbridge, turn first left into housing estate; lake is on the left surrounded by houses
Carp Stock: 50 doubles, mostly mirrors. One or two lower 20's. 150 commons, mostly under 10lbs; fish said to be going back
Category: Carp Water/Mixed Fishery
Other Species: Pike, roach, rudd, bream, eels
Permits: Newsagent in Highbridge High Street, Veals of Bristol, Old Market, Bristol
Cost: Approximately £12.50 per season
Baits/Methods: Boilies and multiples. Normal carp legering methods and rigs
Control: Club. North Somerset Association of Anglers. Open to all
Restrictions: No night fishing between 10.30pm and 5.30am; one rod only; no floating crust
W/A: NRA Wessex Region
BK Rating: Moderate
Comments: Town water quite noisy and busy, mostly 10-15 feet deep; little weed. Club Secretary: Mr R F Newton, 64 Clevedon Road, Tickenham, Clevedon, Avon, who will supply all information and possible details of day tickets

Oxenleaze Farm A

Location:	Wiveliscombe
Type and Size:	2 farm ponds of an acre and ½ an acre
How to Find:	From Taunton take the A361 (B3227) road west, where you will see a right turn to Wiveliscombe, by the Rock Inn to Waterrow - follow the fish sign for 4 miles
Carp Stock:	Good number of carp to 20lbs
Category:	Mixed Fishery
Other Species:	Tench, roach, rudd and bream
Permits:	Free fishing to those who stay in one of the six caravans on the site. Information from Mrs Rottenbury on 0984 23427 (caravan site open Easter until end of October). Day permits for non-residents
Control:	Private
BK Rating:	Moderate
W/A:	NRA South West Region - rod licences on sale at farm

Perry Street Pond

Location:	Perry Street, near Chard
Type and Size:	1¼ acre matured pit
Carp Stock:	Well stocked with carp, including a number of doubles to about 17lbs
Category:	Mixed Fishery
Other Species:	Tench, roach, rudd, bream and perch
Permits:	Season tickets only from Chard Angling Centre, The Old Bakehouse, 2 Holyrood Street; Chard Cycle Centre, Holyrood Street
Control:	Club
BK Rating:	Difficult
W/A:	NRA Wessex Region
Comments:	A pleasant little pond, but the doubles have been hooked a lot, and are not easy to catch

River Parrett A

Location:	Upstream from Bridgwater
Type and Size:	Short river
How to Find:	Bridgwater to Somerton
Carp Stock:	Unknown but commons caught recently to 21½lbs
Category:	Few Carp
Other Species:	Most coarse fish
Permits:	Bridgwater Angling Club - local tackle shops
Cost:	On application
BK Rating:	Difficult due to location problems
Control:	Club
W/A:	NRA Wessex Region
Comments:	This river, the Huntspill, the King Sedgemoor Drain, and other rivers in the area all contain carp to about 25lbs - if you can find them! Try backwaters, mill pools, islands or any other features - and be prepared to do some walking! Try also the Milk Factory at Bason Bridge on the River Bure; Mark; and Edington. Holiday accommodation: self-catering lodges alongside River Huntspill, also bed and breakfast in main house with bar. Tel: 0278 781612 or 784264 for details and brochure

Screech Owl Ponds

Location: Close to the M5, and next to the River Parret, just outside Bridgwater
Type and Size: Small interconnected clay pits, heavily reeded
Carp Stock: In the past, carp to 20lbs have been reported
Category: Mixed Fishery
Other Species: Rudd, tench, bream and eels
Permits: From local tackle shops and Bridgwater AC, 7 Webbers Way, Puriton, Bridgwater, Somerset TA7 8AS
Cost: About £12 per year, to include Dunwear Ponds and Combwich
Control: Club
BK Rating: Difficult
W/A: NRA Wessex Region
Comments: A hard to fish water because of the profuse reed hedges which split up the water areas. A Nature Reserve, with one bank out of bounds to anglers

Thorney Lakes A

Location: Thorney Farm, Muchelney, Langport
Type and Size: Two small lakes
Carp Stock: Well stocked with carp to 18lbs
Category: Mixed Fishery
Other Species: Trout and some other coarse fish
Permits: Ann and Richard England, at the above address. Tel: 0458 250811
BK Rating: Moderate
W/A: NRA Wessex Region
Comments: Camping and touring caravans; one free permit for each caravan

Viaduct Fishery

Location: Cary Valley, Somerton TA11 6LJ. Tel: 0458 74022
Type and Size: Two lakes of 5 acres
Carp Stock: Some carp to double figures
Category: Mixed Fishery
Other Species: Bream, tench, rudd, roach and perch
Permits: Restricted membership obtainable from Tim and Lisa Chapman at the address above. Write or phone for brochure
Cost: £3 per day; £2 - half day; £12 for 5 days; season - £35; weekday season - £20
Control: Private
BK Rating: Not known
W/A: NRA Wessex Region
Restrictions: No nuts or boilies. Barbless hooks; no keepnets
Comments: There is a lodge, where drinks and refreshments are sold, as well as fresh and smoked trout, and pick your own strawberries! There are also two trout fly lakes, and one novices any-method trout pond. The trout fisheries are open all the year; normal close season applies for the carp fishing. Best trout to date is 9lbs 3ozs

Walrow Ponds

Location:	Near Bridgwater
Type and Size:	Small pits
Carp Stock:	Well stocked with carp to 10lbs or so
Category:	Mixed Fishery
Other Species:	Bream, roach, rudd, tench and perch
Permits:	From local tackle shop. Secretary, Bridgwater AA. L A Williams, 7 Webbers Way, Puriton, Bridgewater TA7 8AS
Cost:	About £11 per season, to cover all the other Bridgwater club fisheries, most of which contain carp
Control:	Club
BK Rating:	Easy
W/A:	NRA Wessex Region

Westhay Lake

Location:	Between Westhay and Shapwick, off the B3151 road near Glastonbury
Type and Size:	3½ acre lake
Carp Stock:	Well stocked with carp to 28lbs
Category:	Mixed Fishery
Other Species:	Tench, roach, rudd and crucians
Permits:	All information and permits from Alan Tedder on 0278 456429
Cost:	£4 per day; £3 per night
Control:	Private
BK Rating:	Not known
Comments:	This new fishery opened on June 16th 1991. Many of the fish came from a water called The Beeches, near Bridgwater, which is now closed;

SOUTH GLAMORGAN (Wales)

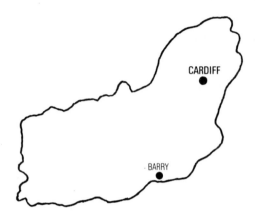

Barry Reservoir

Location: Barry Docks, Barry, near Cardiff
Type and Size: 5 acre shallow lake with reeds but little weed
Carp Stock: Well stocked with small commons, and a few double figure mirrors
Category: Mixed Fishery
Other Species: Eels, roach and rudd
Permits: Members only water of Glamorgan AC. Secretary: P Mason, 8 Denys Close, Dinas Powis, South Glamorgan
Cost: About £30 per season
BK Rating: Fairly Hard
Restrictions: No night fishing; no day tickets
W/A: NRA Welsh Region

Cafarfatha Park Lake

Location: Brecon Road, Merthyr Tydfil
Type and Size: Three acre town park lake with islands
Carp Stock: Well stocked with small carp, and a few upper doubles
Category: Mixed Fishery
Other Species: Eels, rudd and roach
Permits: Day tickets from bailiff on bank. Season tickets from local tackle shops
Cost: £1.50 per day; £10 per season
Restrictions: No night fishing; fishing from one bank only
BK Rating: Easy
W/A: NRA Welsh Region

Hendre Lake

Location: Hendre Road, Cardiff, off the A48
Type and Size: Six acre town lake with island
Carp Stock: Quite well stocked with doubles to about 20lbs

Category:	Mixed Fishery
Other Species:	Roach, tench and bream
Permits:	Day tickets from Gary Evans Fishing Tackle, Cardiff or Newport, in advance only. Night syndicate, members only
Cost:	£1.40 per day; £12 per season
Control:	Private
Restrictions:	No night fishing for non-members
BK Rating:	Easy
W/A:	NRA Welsh Region

Kenfig Lake

Location:	Kenfig, between Port Talbot and Porthcawl
Type and Size:	90 acre lake
Carp Stock:	Some carp to over 10lbs
Category:	Mixed Fishery
Other Species:	Pike, bream, tench, roach, rudd, brown and rainbow trout
Permits:	Kinfig Hill and District AA. A Waite, 16 Marlas Road, Pyle, Glamorgan
Cost:	£3 per day; £15 per season
Control:	Club
BK Rating:	Difficult, as this is a very big lake
W/A:	NRA Welsh Region

Marshfield Reens

Location:	Near Cardiff
Type and Size:	Small lake
Carp Stock:	Well stocked with carp to over 10lbs
Category:	Mixed Fishery
Other Species:	Tench and some other coarse fish
Permits:	Bute AA - season tickets from L V Powell, 176 Clare Road, Grangetown, Cardiff
Control:	Club
BK Rating:	Moderate
W/A:	NRA Welsh Region

Roath Park Lake

Location:	Roath Park, Cardiff
Type and Size:	Park Lake of about 4 acres
Carp Stock:	Quite well stocked with carp to upper doubles
Category:	Mixed Fishery
Other Species:	Tench, roach, rudd
Permits:	On bank
Control:	Cardiff Corporation
BK Rating:	Moderate
Restrictions:	No night fishing
W/A:	NRA Welsh Region

SOUTH YORKSHIRE

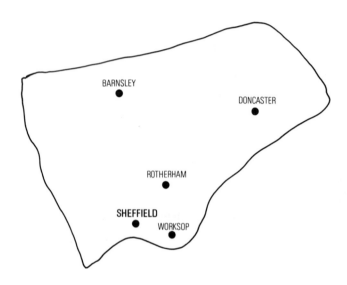

BARNSLEY
●

DONCASTER
●

ROTHERHAM
●

SHEFFIELD
●   WORKSOP
●

Askern Lake

Location:	Askern, near Doncaster
Type and Size:	Park lake of 8 acres with an island
How to Find:	Take the A19 from Doncaster to Askern. The lake is by the road on the right, in the town centre
Carp Stock:	Lakes 1 and 2 contain a fair number of smaller carp. Lake 3 which is 8 acres, is well stocked with good carp to 29lbs
Category:	Mixed Fishery
Other Species:	Perch, roach, tench, crucians and pike
Permits:	From bailiff on site
Cost:	£1.10 per day, half price for juniors and OAP's. Boat hire at £2.15 for four hours
BK Rating:	Moderate
Control:	Council
Restrictions:	No night fishing
W/A:	NRA Yorkshire Region
Comments:	A busy town park lake, with tarmac banking which is very suitable for disabled anglers. Fishing allowed from boats

Bank End Coarse Fisheries

Location:	Blaxton, near Doncaster
Type and Size:	Two lakes of 4½ and 3½ acres
How to Find:	Take the A614 Bawtry to Thorne road, then the B1396 from Blaxton. The lakes are on the right about 1½ miles from Blaxton
Carp Stock:	These lakes were stocked in 1989 with carp to 12lbs; there are also carp to 20lbs
Category:	Smaller lake - Carp Water; larger lake - Mixed Fishery
Other Species:	Bream, tench, roach, rudd and perch
Permits:	Day tickets on site
Cost:	£3 per day
BK Rating:	Insufficient information
Control:	Private. Tel: 0302 770224
Restrictions:	No night fishing. No hemp or tares
W/A:	NRA Severn-Trent Region
Comments:	There are big tench and bream here, so every take will not be from a carp. Car parking on banks, with swims built to allow wheelchairs for the disabled. Tackle shops in Doncaster have details

Beedom's Fishery

Location:	South Yorkshire, undisclosed location
Carp Stock:	Carp to well over 20lbs - at least five 20's and a thirty
Control:	Club
Comments:	Those who control this water do not want publicity, so no further details can be published. For information and an introduction to the controlling body, please contact Mr M A Beedom, 1 Martindale Walk, Carcroft, Doncaster DN6 8BX. Tel: Doncaster 330749

Blacker Dam

Location:	Blacker Green Lane, Silkstone, near Barnsley, off the A628 Manchester road
Type and Size:	Small attractive pond
Carp Stock:	Thought to be quite well stocked
Category:	Moderate
Other Species:	Tench
Permits:	Leeds and District ASA, members only but open to all - Secretary, Leeds and District ASA, c/o Leeds Anglers Club, Stoney Rock Lane, Leeds 9
Control:	Club
W/A:	NRA Yorkshire Region

Bolton Brickponds

Location:	Goldthorpe, Bolton-upon-Dearne, near Barnsley
Type and Size:	3 lakes, covering about 10 acres in all
How to Find:	In Bolton-upon-Dearne, opposite the Council offices
Carp Stock:	Well stocked with mirror and common carp to over 20lbs
Category:	Mixed Fishery
Other Species:	Pike, bream, tench, roach, perch, chub and trout
Permits:	From the fishing hut on site, to be purchased before fishing. Only £3 per

year, but day tickets needed in the trout season

BK Rating:	Moderate
Restrictions:	Night fishing by arrangement, but during the close season daytime only, and only using fly, worms, maggots or casters
Control:	Community Miners Welfare. Tel: 0709 895263
W/A:	NRA Yorkshire Region
Comments:	Toilets on site. Good facilities for disabled anglers

Bullhole

Location:	Barnby Dun, near Doncaster
Type and Size:	Offcut of the River Dun, about 3½ acres in size
How to Find:	Go through Barnby Dun towards the power station. The pond is on the left beside the banks of the Don
Carp Stock:	Some carp to double figures
Category:	Mixed Fishery
Other Species:	Most coarse fish
Permits:	Mr J Thornton. Tel: 0302 886126
Cost:	£8.50 per year, which includes three other ponds
BK Rating:	Difficult
Control:	Club
W/A:	NRA Yorkshire Region
Comments:	No close season

Campsall Country Park

Location:	Campsall, Askern, near Doncaster
Type and Size:	Clay pit of about 11 acres
How to Find:	Take the A19 from Doncaster to Askern, then a left fork to Campsall. Turn left to the lake before the Sports Centre
Carp Stock:	Stocked with carp to mid-doubles
Category:	Mixed Fishery
Other Species:	Bream, tench, perch and rudd
Permits:	Day tickets on bank
Cost:	£1.10, half price for juniors and OAP's
BK Rating:	Not known
Control:	Council
Restrictions:	No night fishing
W/A:	NRA Yorkshire Region
Comments:	This is a park fishery stocked in 1982. It is very deep and has an island. Many fishing platforms, and good for the disabled. Askern Miners Welfare actually control the water

Carlton Mill Pond

Location:	Carlton-in-Lindrick, on the A609 just north of Worksop
Type and Size:	3 acre mill pond — enquire locally for exact venue
Carp Stock:	Some carp to over 20lbs reported caught
Category:	Mixed Fishery
Other Species:	Usual coarse fish, including tench
Permits:	Enquire locally or on bank — small local angling club, but we have no further details
BK Rating:	Not known
W/A:	NRA Severn-Trent Region

Crookes Valley Lake

Location:	In the centre of Sheffield, at Crookesmoor
Type and Size:	City park lake
Carp Stock:	Some mirrors to about 12lbs
Category:	Few Carp
Other Species:	Tench, roach, perch and pike
Permits:	On bank
Control:	Sheffield City Council
BK Rating:	Difficult as there are not many carp
W/A:	NRA Yorkshire Region
Comments:	Flat concrete banks like many park lakes. Rowing boats etc

Cumwell Canal Pond

Location:	Cumwell Lane, between Thurcroft and Bramley
Type and Size:	2 acres of canal-like open water
Carp Stock:	Some carp to over 20lbs, number and sizes not known
Other Species:	General coarse fish
Permits:	Day tickets on bank at low cost
Control:	Local council
Restrictions:	No night fishing
BK Rating:	Moderate
W/A:	NRA Yorkshire Region
Comments:	Public area; a bit like a rubbish tip!

Cusworth Hall Lakes

Location:	Cusworth House, Cusworth, near Doncaster
Type and Size:	Two estate lakes of about 4 acres each
How to Find:	Take the A638 from Doncaster for about 1½ miles, and follow the signs for Cusworth Hall
Carp Stock:	Well stocked with carp to 22lbs
Category:	Mixed Fishery
Other Species:	Crucians, roach, perch, rudd and tench
Permits:	Day tickets on bank
Cost:	£1.30 per day, half price for juniors and OAP's
BK Rating:	Easy
Control:	Doncaster and District AA
Restrictions:	No night fishing
W/A:	NRA Yorkshire Region
Comments:	Fine country house and grounds, with museum. Toilet facilities, a picnic area and good for the disabled

Delves Lakes

Location:	Thorne, near Goole, off the A614
Type and Size:	Two small lakes
Carp Stock:	Quite well stocked with carp to mid-doubles
Category:	Mixed Fishery
Other Species:	Tench, roach, perch, bream and a few crucians
Permits:	On the bank at £1 per day; £5 per year

Control:	Charles Gaston. Tel: 0405 812828/816605. Thorne and Moorends AC
BK Rating:	Moderate
W/A:	NRA Yorkshire Region

Elsecar Reservoir

Location:	Elsecar Park, Hoyland Nether, near Barnsley
Type and Size:	Medium-sized reservoir
How to Find:	Take junction 36 from the M1 to Hoyland, then follow the signs for Elsecar. Turn left at the T-junction, and at the Market Hotel turn right towards Wentworth
Carp Stock:	Carp to over 20lbs
Category:	Mixed Fishery, although possibly Few Carp
Other Species:	Pike, bream, roach and tench
Permits:	Day permits from bailiff on bank. Low cost, reduced prices for disabled and free to pensioners
BK Rating:	Not known
Control:	Elsecar Main Colliery Angling Society. Secretary: Mr W Turner, 14 Eaden Crescent, Hoyland, near Barnsley. Tel: Barnsley 746002
Restrictions:	No night fishing. No fishing from the parkside foreshore
W/A:	NRA Yorkshire Region
Comments:	Costs for these reservoirs and other waters in Yorkshire seem to be very low, so Yorkshire looks like a good county for anglers

Flash Lane Pond

Location:	Flash Lane, Wickersley, Rotherham
Type and Size:	Small lake of about two acres
Carp Stock:	Some carp to about 20lbs
Category:	Few Carp
Other Species:	Roach, rudd, tench and perch
Permits:	Enquire from local tackle shops or ask on bank
Control:	Small local club
BK Rating:	Difficult
W/A:	NRA Yorkshire Region

Fleets Dam

Location:	Smithies Lane, off the A61 one mile north of Barnsley
Type and Size:	10 acre attractive reed-fringed lake
Carp Stock:	Well stocked with carp, about three years ago, and now caught to 10lbs
Category:	Mixed Fishery
Other Species:	Tench, roach, perch and pike
Permits:	Day tickets on the bank
Cost:	£3.50 adults, £2.50 juniors; evening tickets from 4pm £2.50. Season £50
Control:	Allan Hanson, Stanborough Fisheries. Tel: 0226 29579 or 0924 367424
Baits/Methods:	Luncheon meat, sweetcorn and bread all work well, with standard methods, especially float fishing close in
BK Rating:	Easy
W/A:	NRA Yorkshire Region
Comments:	This is mainly a match fishery, with big weights taken, and many anglers are broken in carp whilst pole fishing. Most matches take place on Tuesdays, Wednesdays, Saturday and Sunday, on about half the lake

Graves Park Pond

Location: Left side of the A61, travelling south from Sheffield City centre
Carp Stock: A few carp to about 7lbs
Category: Few Carp
Other Species: Roach and perch
Permits: From bailiff on bank
Control: Sheffield City Council
BK Rating: Difficult
W/A: NRA Yorkshire Region
Comments: Good for disabled anglers, with a cafe nearby

Hoyle Mill Dam

Location: Kinsley, Hemworth, near Pontefract. Find Hoyle Mill Road, near Hemsworth Water Park
Type and Size: Large lake
Carp Stock: Carp to double figures
Category: Mixed Fishery
Other Species: Roach, tench, bream, chub and big eels
Permits: Day tickets from bailiff on bank, at £2 each
Control: Hemsworth and District AA. Open to all. Details and membership from Stan Pollington, 2 Common Road, Kinsley, Pontefract. Tel: Hemsworth 612556
BK Rating: Not known
W/A: NRA Yorkshire Region

Lindholme Lake Fisheries

Location: Sandtoft, near Doncaster
Type and Size: One and a half acre carp lake
How to Find: The complex is off the Sandtoft road, 14 miles from Doncaster and 7 miles from the M18 junction
Carp Stock: Well stocked with carp - sizes not quoted in brochure
Category: Carp Only
Permits: On site
Cost: Day - £3.50; evening from 5pm - £2; some season tickets at £40
Control: Brian Lindley on site or Tel: 0427 872015
Restrictions: No night fishing - open 8am to 10pm, or one hour after sunset; no keepnets; one rod only; children under 14 must be accompanied by an adult
BK Rating: Insufficient information
W/A: NRA Yorkshire Region
Comments: Some places for disabled anglers; toilets, washroom; free hot drinks. Rod and line hire; tuition by arrangement. Food can be arranged. Rod licences sold. There is also an 18 acre general coarse lake, open from 16th June to 31st October and a four acre trout lake, open March to September (fly only)

Long Pond

Location: Barnby Dun, near Doncaster
Type and Size: Offcut from River Don, about half a mile long
How to Find: Near Thorpe Marsh power station, which is just across the canal

Carp Stock: through Barnby Dun
Well stocked with carp to over 20lbs, and several thirties are rumoured to have been caught recently
Category: Mixed Fishery
Other Species: Most coarse fish
Permits: On the same permit as Bullhole - Mr I Thornton. Tel: 0302 886126
Cost: £8.50 per year, which includes three other ponds
BK Rating: Difficult
Control: Club
W/A: NRA Yorkshire Region
Comments: No close season

Pool Bridge Farm
Location: Crockey Hill
Type and Size: Small lake, long and narrow with island
Carp Stock: Well stocked with carp to 20lbs
Category: Mixed Fishery
Other Species: Chub, roach, perch, tench, rudd, dace and crucians
Permits: Day ticket on bank at £2
Control: Ron Fletcher. Tel: 0904 637854
Restrictions: No night fishing, no keepnets; no sweetcorn or hemp (what will they ban next!)
BK Rating: Moderate
W/A: NRA Yorkshire Region
Comments: A new lake is being constructed, and will be stocked with carp to over 20lbs

Rother Valley Country Park
Location: Killamarsh, Sheffield
Type and Size: Public country park lake of about 20 acres
Carp Stock: Some carp stocked to about 2lbs
Category: Few Carp
Other Species: General coarse fish
Permits: Day ticket on bank at low cost
Control: Private
BK Rating: Very Difficult
W/A: NRA Yorkshire Region
Comments: Many members of the public, boats and water-ski-iers; no night fishing

Roundwood Pond
Location: The Mill, Aldwalk, Rotherham
Type and Size: Mill dam of about 10 acres
Carp Stock: Quite a few doubles to about 20lbs
Category: Mixed Fishery
Other Species: Usual coarse fish
Permits: British Rail - try BR Staff Association, 8 Upper Belmont Road, St. Andrews, Bristol, or enquire from tackle shops in Rotherham
BK Rating: Moderate
W/A: NRA Yorkshire Region
Comments: This water was stocked with about 50 good carp in the early 70's, and there could be some even better fish than the 20's reported caught

Sheffield Canal

Location:	Tinsley, in the centre of Sheffield
Type and Size:	Typical city canal
Carp Stock:	The carp were put in 1979, and there are plenty of small fish, with the occasional double and 20
Category:	Mixed Fishery
Other Species:	Roach, pike, rudd and bream
Permits:	Local club - enquire at tackle shops. Day tickets on bank in some areas
BK Rating:	Moderate - Easy in the locks
W/A:	NRA Yorkshire Region
Comments:	Usual problems associated with fishing in cities and towns - most of them caused by other people!

Thurnscoe Reservoir

Location:	Opposite Hickleton Main Colliery, off the A635 Barnsley-Doncaster road at Thurnscoe
Type and Size:	Small reservoir
Carp Stock:	Fairly well stocked with carp, sizes not known
Category:	Mixed Fishery
Other Species:	Pike, roach, tench and bream
Permits:	From bailiff on bank
Cost:	About £2 per *season*
Control:	Hickleton Main Angling Cub
BK Rating:	Not known
W/A:	NRA Yorkshire Region

Tyram Lakes   A

Location:	Off the A614 at Hatfield Woodhouse, near Doncaster
Type and Size:	Three lakes of 30 acres, 25 acres and one acre
Carp Stock:	All well stocked with carp to mid-doubles
Category:	Mixed Fishery
Other Species:	Roach, bream, tench and perch
Permits:	Details from the William de Lindholme Hotel on site
Cost:	£4 per day
Control:	Colin Clegg, Tel: 0302 840324 or Chris Moore, Tel: 0302 842382
BK Rating:	Easy
W/A:	NRA Yorkshire Region
Comments:	Accommodation, food and drinks at hotel. No close season. No bait bans

Underbank Reservoir

Location:	Stocksbridge, Sheffield
Type and Size:	60 acre reservoir, very deep
Carp Stock:	A few carp, some doubles and the odd 20
Category:	Few Carp
Other Species:	Trout and some coarse fish
Permits:	Day tickets on bank at low cost
Control:	Council
BK Rating:	Very Difficult
Restrictions:	No night fishing
W/A:	NRA Yorkshire Region

William De Windholme Lake

Location:	On the A64 8 miles SE of Doncaster, between Hatfield Woodhouse and Bawtry
Type and Size:	10 acre lake
Carp Stock:	Well stocked with carp between 5lbs and 15lbs
Category:	Carp Water
Permits:	Annual only from Neville Fickling, 27 Lodge Lane, Upton, Gainsborough DN21 5NW
Cost:	£50 for 12 months
BK Rating:	Easy
W/A:	NRA Severn-Trent Region
Comments:	Close season fishing allowed within NRA rules; a good water to learn on. Water sports centre, can be busy at weekends

Willow Garth Fishery

Location:	Shaftholme Lane, Arksey, near Doncaster
Type and Size:	4 acre lake
How to Find:	From Doncaster take the A19 to Bentley, then turn right onto Arksey Lane and Marsh Lane
Carp Stock:	Well stocked with carp to mid-doubles
Category:	Carp Water
Other Species:	Roach, perch and tench, and stocked annually with rainbow trout
Permits:	Day tickets on bank
Cost:	£2 dawn till dusk; £1.30 4pm till dusk; £2.50 per night
BK Rating:	Moderate
Control:	Private
W/A:	NRA Yorkshire Region
Comments:	Very pleasant water, sometimes heavily fished. Car park and refreshment bar. One side suitable for disabled anglers. Groundbait, keepnets and nuts as baits not allowed. No close season. Information from the owner, Keith Davis. Tel: Doncaster 974258

Wintersett Reservoir

Location:	Two miles from Crofton village in between Wakefield and Doncaster
Type and Size:	Wintersett is the small lake next to Wintersett Reservoir. The fishery also includes Cold Hindley Reservoir
How to Find:	Take the A638 Doncaster road from Walkefield. About about 2½ miles, take a right turn down Lodge Lane to Crofton village. The lakes are about two miles beyond the village
Carp Stock:	Quite well stocked with plenty of doubles, and mirrors to 27lbs
Category:	Mixed Fishery
Other Species:	Roach, perch, tench, bream and pike from the small Wintersett lake. Crucians from Cold Hindley
Permits:	From bailiff on bankside
Control:	Coal Industries Social Welfare Organisation
BK Rating:	Moderate
W/A:	NRA Yorkshire Region

Wombwell Dam

Location:	Wombwell, three miles south east of Barnsley
Type and Size:	Five acre lake
Carp Stock:	Well stocked with doubles and smaller fish, with a few to nearly 30lbs
Category:	Mixed Fishery
Other Species:	Roach, bream and rudd
Permits:	Day tickets on the bank
Cost:	£2.50 for adults; £2.50 for juniors, OAP's and the disabled
Control:	Wombwell Angling Centre, Tel: 0226 750659 or Barnsley Angling Centre, Tel: 0226 742859
Restrictions:	No night fishing; no boilies or nuts(!)
BK Rating:	Easy
W/A:	NRA Yorkshire Region

Worsborough Reservoir

Location:	Worsborough, near Barnsley
Type and Size:	Large reservoir
Carp Stock:	Not many carp, but some big ones
Category:	Few Carp
Other Species:	Bream, tench, roach, bream/tench hybrids, crucians, perch, pike, eels and trout
Permits:	On bank
Cost:	£1.50 per day
Control:	Barnsley DAS. T Eaton, 60 Walton Street, Barnsley
Restrictions:	No night fishing; no keepnets; Sunday fishing for members only; no live baiting, hempseed, bloodworm or jokers(!)
BK Rating:	Very Difficult
W/A:	NRA Yorkshire Region
Comments:	Since there is no close season, the adventurous might like to try it, but carp are few and far between, and are rarely seen

---

STAFFORDSHIRE

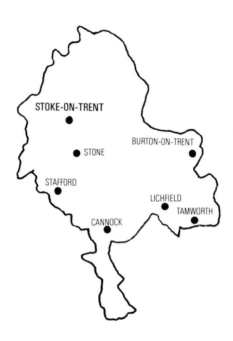

STOKE-ON-TRENT
●

BURTON-ON-TRENT
● STONE ●

STAFFORD
●

LICHFIELD
● TAMWORTH
CANNOCK ●
●

Amington (Pigs)

Location:	Near Tamworth
Type and Size:	40 acre natural lake
How to Find:	Near Shuttington village
Carp Stock:	Well stocked with small carp, but fish up to possible 30lb
Category:	Mixed Fishery
Other Species:	General coarse fish
Permits:	Birchmoor Angling Club. Secretary: Peter Mason, c/o Game Cock Inn public house. Tel: 0827 895144. Also day tickets available for small part of lake from Pritty Pigs public house on bank
Cost:	£7 per year
Control:	Club
Restrictions:	No fishing from one bank
BK Rating:	Easy for small fish, large fish - Difficult, due to quantity of small ones
W/A:	NRA Severn-Trent Region
Comments:	Lake formed by land subsidence and is mostly very shallow, river runs along one margin. Stalking best bet to sort out better fish

Betley Mere

Location:	Betley, on the A531, between Newcastle-under-Lyme and Nantwich
Type and Size:	Ten acre shallow mere; a very attractive lake
Carp Stock:	Well stocked with carp to about 25lbs
Category:	Mixed Fishery
Other Species:	Big pike, bream, tench and roach
Permits:	From the house at the lake, or on the bank at weekends
Cost:	£3 per day
Control:	Frank Speed. Tel: 0270 820229
Bait/Methods:	Boilies best for carp; long stay fishing often needed for success
BK Rating:	Difficult
W/A:	NRA Severn Trent Region
Comments:	Night fishing is only allowed by special arrangement

Canwell Pool

Location:	Canwell estate
Type and Size:	5 acre estate lake
How to Find:	Off the A453 Tamworth to Sutton Coldfield road
Carp Stock:	Well stocked with carp to mid-20's
Category:	Mixed Fishery
Other Species:	General coarse fish
Permits:	Sutton Coldfield AS. Secretary: Don Jones, Bricklyn House, Bulls Lane, Wishaw, Sutton Coldfield B76 9QN
Cost:	£25 + possible joining fee
Control:	Private
BK Rating:	Fairly Hard
W/A:	NRA Severn-Trent Region
Comments:	There is a long waiting list to join SCAS. A very quiet and attractive water

Chasewater Lake

Location:	Chasewater Park, Brownhills, Cannock
Type and Size:	20 acre lake
Carp Stock:	Not many carp, but possibly a couple of 20's
Category:	Few Carp
Other Species:	Roach, rudd, bream, tench, perch and pike
Cost:	About £2 per day
Control:	Private
BK Rating:	Very Difficult
W/A:	NRA Severn-Trent Region
Comments:	A public water, and very busy. Only worth a try if you fancy something really hard, as this is certainly not a carp water

Cudmore Fishery

Location:	Whitmore, near the M6 and Newcastle-under-Lyme; the sign to the fishery will be seen 1½ miles from Whitmore on the Keele road
Type and Size:	Two medium-sized man-made lakes
Carp Stock:	Milo Pool - well stocked with carp to 20lbs; Avaco Pool has small carp
Category:	Milo - Carp Only; Avaco - Mixed Fishery
Other Species:	Chub, tench, roach and possibly some barbel

Permits:	Day tickets on site, in advance only
Cost:	£2.50 for two rods
Control:	Cyril Brewster. Tel: 0782 680919
Restrictions:	Lots....! No boilies, barbed hooks or hemp, no pole fishing (!); anglers must 'book in' and 'book out' even if they catch nothing
Baits/Methods:	Sweetcorn and maggots, legered or float fished, and floaters also work well
BK Rating:	Milo - Easy; Avaco - Moderate
W/A:	NRA Severn-Trent Region
Comments:	A new venue recently opened

Deep Hay Pool

Location:	Near Leek
Type and Size:	Two small pools
Carp Stock:	Carp to about 15lbs
Category:	Mixed Fishery
Other Species:	Roach, rudd, bream and tench
Permits:	Members only water of Leek and Morland Fishing Club. H Emery, 20 Osbourne Street, Leek; or enquire from local tackle shops
Restrictions:	No day tickets; no night fishing
BK Rating:	Moderate
W/A:	NRA Severn-Trent Region

Ellenhall Pools

Location:	Eccelshall, near Stone
Type and Size:	4 small farm pools
Carp Stock:	Some carp, numbers and sizes not known
Category:	Mixed Fishery
Other Species:	Roach, tench, bream and perch
Permits:	N Dale Tackle Shop, Albert Street, Stone
Control:	Stone and District AS
BK Rating:	Not known
W/A:	NRA Severn-Trent Region

Fisherwick Fly Fishing Lakes

Location:	Whittington, near Lichfield. Tel: 0543 472515/472934
Type and Size:	The Long Stream (500 yards); the Pump Pool (¼ acre); the Small Pool (¼ acre)
Carp Stock:	Well stocked with carp to double figures
Category:	Mixed Fishery
Other Species:	Roach and perch
Permits:	On site at the address above - discounts for annual membership
Control:	Midland Game Fisheries
BK Rating:	Not known
W/A:	NRA Severn-Trent Region
Comments:	There are also three fly fishing lakes of 12 acres, 5 acres and 3 acres, and the Short Stream (fly fishing) - brown and rainbow trout in all these. Boats, tackle, rod licences, refreshments etc

Fradley Canal

Location:	Burton-on-Trent
Type and Size:	Small canal
How to Find:	Near Burton-on-Trent
Carp Stock:	Plenty of carp when located - stocked with 5,000 small carp in 1990
Category:	Mixed Fishery
Other Species:	General coarse fish
Permits:	Enquire in local tackle shops
Cost:	On application
BK Rating:	Easy, when fish are located
Control:	Club
W/A:	NRA Severn-Trent Region
Comments:	An early season catch last year was reported as 7 fish to 12lbs in 4 hours, on legered boilies, using a 4lb line. For information try Burton-on- Trent AA - D J Clark, 7 Denton Rise, Burton-on-Trent DE13 0QB

Hanley Park Lake

Location:	Cauldon Road, Stoke-on-Trent
Type and Size:	Shallow, three acre town park lake, attractive with two islands
Carp Stock:	Some carp to doubles; double figure commons
Category:	Mixed Fishery
Other Species:	Roach, perch and bream
Permits:	On bank
Cost:	Half day £1.55 for adults; £1.25 juniors; season £13.60 and £8. Reductions for the disabled and unemployed
Control:	Stoke-on-Trent Council, Leisure and Recreation Dept. Tel: 0782 202312
Restrictions:	Dawn till dusk only; no night fishing
BK Rating:	Moderate
W/A:	NRA Severn Trent Region

Hopton Pools

Location:	Hopton, near Stafford
Type and Size:	Small lakes
Carp Stock:	Some carp, sizes not known
Category:	Mixed Fishery
Other Species:	Tench and other coarse fish
Permits:	Day and weekly tickets - Izaak Walton (Stafford) AA - T H Babbs, 4 Fieldside, Wildwood, Stafford
Control:	Club
BK Rating:	Not known
W/A:	NRA Severn-Trent Region

Lawton Hall Pool

Location:	Off the A34 near Church Lawton, Kidsgrove
Type and Size:	Very attractive estate lake
Carp Stock:	Well stocked with carp to 28lbs
Category:	Mixed Fishery
Other Species:	Tench, bream, roach, perch and pike
Permits:	Day tickets from Nick's Tackle Supplies, Kidsgrove or Anglers Den, Newcastle-under-Lyme; Tel: 0782 715155 or 0782 775871

Cost:	£10 for a 24 hour ticket; some day tickets at £3; season £55 for dawn to dusk fishing. There is also a carp syndicate at £160 a year
BK Rating:	Moderate
W/A:	NRA North West Region

Pool House Farm

Location:	Hunts Green, Tamworth
Type and Size:	Old established one acre pool
How to Find:	Off the A4091 towards Tamworth from Junction 9 on the M42
Carp Stock:	Well stocked with many doubles
Category:	Mixed Fishery
Other Species:	Rudd, roach, tench and crucians
Permits:	Day tickets in advance only from Mr C Heys, Pool House Farm, Brick Kiln Lane, Middleton, Tamworth B78 2BA. Tel: 0827 874856
Cost:	£4 per day
Control:	Private
Restrictions:	Fishing 7am till dusk only; barbless hooks; no groundbait; no nuts
BK Rating:	Moderate
W/A:	NRA Severn Trent Region
Comments:	An attractive pool with 21 fishing stages. Car park only 20 yards from bank. Also suitable for contests

Serpentine Reservoir

Location:	Knypersley, Stoke-on-Trent
Type and Size:	Reservoir of 50 acres
How to Find:	Knypersley is north of Stoke-on-Trent about half-way between Stoke and Congleton on the A27
Carp Stock:	Not many carp in a very large water, but there are one or two big fish of well over 20lbs
Category:	Few Carp
Other Species:	General coarse fish
Permits:	Cheshire Anglers' Association - members only. Secretary: G Brassington, 12 Highfield Drive, Nantwich, Cheshire
Control:	Club
BK Rating:	Very Difficult
W/A:	NRA Severn-Trent Region
Comments:	Waters of this kind, which are large and contain only a very few big carp, are only recommended for experienced and successful carp anglers prepared to spend very long periods without catching, for the sake of a very big fish

Shredicote Pools

Location:	Mitton, just west of Penkridge off the A449
Type and Size:	Two small attractive pools with trees, lilies etc
Carp Stock:	Well stocked with carp to about 15lbs
Category:	Mixed Fishery
Other Species:	Tench, roach, perch and crucians
Permits:	On the bank at £1 per day
Restrictions:	None, and night fishing is allowed
BK Rating:	Moderate
W/A:	NRA Severn Trent Region

Shuttington Pool

Location:	Near Tamworth
Type and Size:	11 acre natural lake
How to Find:	Near Shuttington village
Carp Stock:	Well stocked to mid-20's
Category:	Mixed Fishery
Other Species:	General coarse fish
Permits:	Lambs Angling Club. Secretary: Mr Ghent, Hopleys, Ingram Pit Lane, Amington, Tamworth, Staffs B77 3JA. Tel: 0827 51033
Cost:	£17 + £5 joining fee
Control:	Club
Restrictions:	See club book
BK Rating:	Unknown
W/A:	NRA Severn-Trent Region
Comments:	May be a very long waiting list to join Lambs AC

Staffs-Worcester Canal

Location:	Cross Keys, Penkridge, off the A449 between Stafford and Wolverhampton. The stretch is near the Cross Keys pub, off Filance Lane
Type and Size:	Narrow canal with some boat traffic
Carp Stock:	Quite well stocked with carp to doubles
Category:	Mixed Fishery
Other Species:	Perch, eels, tench, bream, crucians, chub and gudgeon
Permits:	On bank at £1 per day
Control:	Broomhill AS - Tony Cunningham. Tel: 0543 271775. Club membership at £5 (£2 juniors); from P Eldershaw Butchers on the A449, or from Tight Lines Fishing Tackle, Penkridge
BK Rating:	Moderate
W/A:	NRA Severn Trent Region

Stowe Pool

Location:	Lichfield
Type and Size:	Town lake of 4 acres
How to Find:	In the centre of Lichfield
Carp Stock:	Some carp to over 20lbs
Category:	Few Carp
Other Species:	General coarse fish
Permits:	Day tickets on bank
Cost:	£1.50 per day approximately
Control:	Council
BK Rating:	Difficult
W/A:	NRA Severn-Trent Region
Comments:	A busy town lake

Westbridge Park Canal

Location:	Weaver's Lane Bridge, Trent and Mersey Canal; off the A34 road between Stoke-on-Trent and Stone
Type and Size:	Wide canal with some boat traffic
Carp Stock:	Well stocked with carp to upper doubles
Category:	Mixed Fishery

Other Species:	Crucians, bream, roach, ruffe, gudgeon and chub
Permits:	In advance only from Neil Dale Fishing Tackle, Albert Street, Stone. Tel: 0785 813708
Cost:	£1 per day; weekly - £2; monthly - £5; annual - £12, to include three pools
BK Rating:	Moderate
W/A:	NRA Severn Trent Region

Westport Lake

Location:	Tunstall, Stoke-on-Trent
Type and Size:	Small lake between the railway and a canal
How to Find:	Take the Tunstall-Burslem road from the A500 Stoke ring road, then the A527 at roundabout. The entrance to the lake is just along this road on the left hand side
Carp Stock:	Well stocked with carp to about 25lbs
Category:	Mixed Fishery
Other Species:	Big tench, bream and pike and some good roach
Permits:	Day tickets on bank
Cost:	£1.70 per day. Season tickets for 12 waters at about £14, £8 for juniors and £3.25 for the unemployed and the disabled
Control:	Stoke-on-Trent Council control all these waters
BK Rating:	Moderate
W/A:	NRA Severn Trent Region

SUFFOLK

Barham Pits

Location:	Claydon, near Ipswich
Type and Size:	2 pits of 20 acres and 4 acres
How to Find:	At Barham, 5 miles north of Ipswich, off the A45 Ipswich-Norwich road; Pest House Lane
Carp Stock:	Some good carp in both waters
Category:	Mixed Fishery
Other Species:	General coarse fish; big pike
Permits:	Members only. Gipping Angling and Preservation Society. Membership from G Alderson, 19 Clover Close, Chantry Estate, Ipswich
Cost:	About £20-£25
BK Rating:	Moderate
Control:	Club
W/A:	NRA Anglian Region
Comments:	The big lake is very attractive, with islands and bays. The club has other lakes and 10 miles of the River Gipping

Brandon Lake

Location:	Close to the Little Ouse in Brandon, near Thetford
Type and Size:	Man-made lake of about three acres
How to Find:	In Brandon - Remembrance Park
Carp Stock:	Some carp to double figures
Category:	Mixed Fishery
Other Species:	Roach, perch and bream
Permits:	Day tickets before fishing from the Rod'n'Line tackle shop, Thetford. Tel: 0842 752930
Cost:	£2 per day
BK Rating:	Moderate
Control:	Club
W/A:	NRA Anglian Region

Broome Pits

Location:	Near Bungay, about a mile off the B1332 from Norwich
Type and Size:	Four pits from one to four acres
Carp Stock:	Mirrors to 20lb in Pit C and Pit D
Category:	Mixed Fishery
Other Species:	Crucians, roach, pike and big bream
Permits:	Day tickets on bank
Cost:	£1 per day: weekly tickets on application
Control:	Bungay Cherry Tree AC - membership at £10 per season open to all, including numerous other waters in the area. Details from the Secretary, Mr I Gosling, 37 St.Mary's Terrace, Bungay. Tel: Bungay 2982. Pit administrator is Mr R Patrick. Tel: Bungay 4371
BK Rating:	Moderate
W/A:	NRA Anglian Region
Comments:	The Club Secretary has a leaflet on these waters. The two bigger pits are about ten feet in depth about one rod length from the bank

Bures Lake

Location:	Bures, near Colchester
Type and Size:	Beautiful wooded gravel pit of 4½ acres
How to Find:	Take the B1508 into Bures from Colchester, and after the river bridge turn right past the church and along the Nayland road; 500 yards further on you will see the LAA entrance sign and gate
Carp Stock:	A small number of big carp to over 20lbs
Category:	Few Carp
Other Species:	Many big tench to 6lbs, bream to 8lbs, roach, rudd, perch and pike
Permits:	A members only water of the London Anglers Association - no day or season tickets, so to fish you will have to join the LAA, or one of the affiliated clubs. Details from LAA, Hoe Street, Walthamstow, London E7
Cost:	£15 a year, to include many other fine waters all over the country
Restrictions:	Members only
Control:	LAA
BK Rating:	Difficult
W/A:	NRA Anglian Region
Comments:	This water became well known to carp anglers some years ago when a carp of well over 30lbs was reported from it, though most carp anglers I have spoken to did not believe that the weight was genuine

Colston Hall Ponds

Location:	Colston Hall, Dennington, near Harleston
Type and Size:	Two irrigation reservoirs of about an acre each
How to Find:	From Harleston take the B1116 to Dennington, and turn left onto the A1120. In two miles turn down a lane to Colston Hall
Carp Stock:	The pond nearest the house contains some carp. The other is about 6ft deep and is well stocked with mirrors to double figures
Category:	Pond near house - Mixed Fishery; Other Pond - Carp Only
Other Species:	Tench and rudd in the Mixed Fishery pond
Permits:	Members only water of the Framlingham and Dist AA. Open to all for an annual subscription of £9 (£5 juniors) with several other local ponds and fishing on the River Deben. Details from the Secretary, Mr Brian Finbow, Saxmundham Angling Centre, Market Place, Saxmundham. Tel: Saxmundham 3443
Control:	Club
BK Rating:	Moderate
Restrictions:	Members only
W/A:	NRA Anglian Region

Diss Mere

Location:	In the town of Diss
Type and Size:	4 acre mere
How to Find:	Take the A140/A1066 from Norwich to Diss
Carp Stock:	Some mirrors to double figures
Category:	Mixed Fishery
Other Species:	General coarse fish
Permits:	Diss AC members only. Membership from 'Catch 22' Tackle shop, 23 Victoria Road, Diss. Tel: 3272
Cost:	About £7 per year
BK Rating:	Difficult
Control:	Club
W/A:	NRA Anglian Region

Ditchingham Pit

Location:	Bungay Common
Type and Size:	3 acre gravel pit
How to Find:	Bungay Common, off the B1332 alongside the River Waveney
Carp Stock:	Well stocked with carp to doubles
Category:	Mixed Fishery
Other Species:	General coarse fish
Permits:	Bungay Cherry Tree AC members only. Membership from Mr I Gosling, 37 St Mary's Terrace, Bungay. Tel: 2982
Cost:	About £10
BK Rating:	Moderate
Control:	Club
W/A:	NRA Anglian Region
Comments:	Attractive lake. This club has much other fishing in the area

Flood Park

Location:	Haverhill
How to Find:	Opposite Sainsbury's superstore in Haverhill
Type and Size:	2½ acre clay pit
Carp Stock:	About 50 fish to upper doubles
Category:	Mixed Fishery
Other Species:	Very large perch, roach, rudd and bream
Permits:	Haverhill AC. Permits available from J & A Tackle. £11 per season. £7 Juniors and OAP's free
BK Rating:	Moderate
W/A:	NRA Anglian Region
Comments:	Carp are doing well and twenties are expected soon

Glemsford Lake

Location:	Near Sudbury and Long Melford
Type and Size:	3 gravel pits of 18, 14 and 3 acres
How to Find:	Take the A1092 from Long Melford and then to Cavendish. The lakes are on the left, opposite Glemsford Road
Category:	Few Carp
Other Species:	General coarse fish
Permits:	London Anglers Association - members only, open to all. Join through affiliated clubs or the LAA, Hoe Street, Walthamstow, London E17
Cost:	About £12 a year
BK Rating:	Difficult
Control:	Club
Restrictions:	No night fishing
W/A:	NRA Anglian Region
Comments:	The LAA has many waters all over the south of England, including Bures Lake near Nayland, which contains a few 20lb carp

Great Lodge Farm Ponds

Location:	Great Lodge Farm, Dennington, near Harleston
Type and Size:	4 small farm ponds on private estate
How to Find:	Take the B1116 from Harleston to Dennington, then left onto A1120. In 2 miles turn right onto the B1120 and a mile further on turn right down a track to the farm
Carp Stock:	Mirrors to doubles
Category:	Mixed Fisheries
Other Species:	General coarse fish
Permits:	Framlingham and Dist AC. (members only). Open to all. Apply to the Secretary, Mr B Finbow, Saxmundham Angling Centre, Market Place, Saxmundham. Tel: 3443
Cost:	About £9 a year
BK Rating:	Moderate
W/A:	Anglian
Comments:	Membership also includes other local ponds and a stretch of the River Debden

Guildhall Carp Lake

Location:	Hadleigh, 10 miles west of Ipswich; just off the A1071
Type and Size:	Eight acre estate lake, very attractive, and often referred to as a 'typical' carp water
Carp Stock:	Well stocked with carp to 28lbs; many doubles
Category:	Carp Water
Other Species:	Large tench; some roach
Permits:	Guildhall Estate Office on site. Some day tickets in summer only; most fishing is by season ticket, with limited numbers
Cost:	Current charges not known, but thought to be quite low
Control:	Private estate
Restrictions:	No bent hooks or permanently fixed leads; no peanuts
BK Rating:	Easy for the doubles and smaller fish; Moderate for the twenties
W/A:	NRA Anglian Region
Comments:	A beautiful, 'old fashioned' carp lake, not well known, and therefore not heavily fished. Catches of several 20's in one session have been reported. Catches must not be publicised. Night fishing by arrangement

Gunssons Lake

Location:	White House Farm, Sibton
Type and Size:	One acre pond
How to Find:	Off the A120, south-west of Southwold
Carp Stock:	Well stocked with mirrors to doubles
Category:	Carp Water
Other Species:	Some tench and bream
Permits:	Season tickets only from Mr Kitson. Tel: Peasenhall 260
Cost:	On application
BK Rating:	Moderate
Control:	Private
Restrictions:	Season tickets and touring caravanners only
W/A:	NRA Anglian Region
Comments:	Shallow, coloured water, mainly for touring caravanners

Gunton Hall Lake   A

Location:	Corton, near Lowestoft
Type and Size:	Two acre lake
How to Find:	From Lowestoft take the A12 towards Great Yarmouth: Gunton Hall is on the right, just before Corton
Carp Stock:	Some mirrors to double figures
Category:	Mixed Fishery
Other Species:	Tench, roach, rudd
Permits:	Day tickets from Reception at Hall - must be booked in advance. Summer season and winter season tickets
Cost:	On application. About £4 a day
BK Rating:	Moderate
Control:	Gunton Hall. Tel: Lowestoft 720288
W/A:	NRA Anglian Region
Comments:	This is a holiday centre; golf, tennis, archery and clay pigeon shooting for residents. For details telephone Gunton Hall. Attractive, weedy lake, quite shallow

Henham Dairy Pond

Location:	Henham Park Estate, near Brampton
Type and Size:	One acre estate lake only about 3 feet deep
How to Find:	From Beccles take the A145 to Blythburgh. Go through Brampton and after 2 miles turn left into Henham Park Estate. The pond is on the left hand side
Category:	Mixed Fishery
Other Species:	Crucians, tench, roach and rudd
Permits:	Day tickets from the farmhouse before fishing
Cost:	Approximately £1 per day
Restrictions:	No night fishing; one rod only; limited number of tickets
Control:	Henham and District Angling Club (details from farm)
BK Rating:	Easy
W/A:	NRA Anglian Region

Holmans Pits

Location:	Northfield Farm, Southery, near Downham Market. The pits are on the left off the B1386 Southery road, and probably just in Norfolk!
Type and Size:	Three shallow pits of one to three acres
Carp Stock:	Some carp, sizes not known
Category:	Mixed Fishery
Permits:	Members only water of Kings Lynn AC. Membership £12 to include many other local waters, from the Secretary, Mr George Bear. Tel: Downham Market 387114
Other Species:	Roach, rudd, bream, tench, perch and pike
Control:	Club. Southery is is Norfolk, so the pits may also be Norfolk
Restrictions:	Members only
BK Rating:	Difficult
W/A:	NRA Anglian Region

Ickworth Lake

Location:	Horringer, near Bury St. Edmunds, in the middle of the village
Type and Size:	5 acre estate lake
Carp Stock:	Some carp, sizes not known
Category:	Probably Few Carp
Other Species:	Roach, rudd and tench
Permits:	From bailiff on bank
Cost:	£2 per day
Control:	National Trust
BK Rating:	Difficult
W/A:	NRA Anglian Region

Lakeside Caravan Park   A

Location:	Saxmundham
Type and Size:	Three acre lake
How to Find:	Find Harleston and take the B1116 to Framlingham, then the B1119 Saxmundham road. At Rendham you will see signs on the left to the caravan park and lake
Carp Stock:	A good head of mirror carp to double figures

Category:	Mixed Fishery
Other Species:	Roach, bream, perch and tench
Permits:	Day tickets from bailiff who calls round. Information from the Manager. Tel: 0728 3344
Cost:	About £2 per day
Control:	Caravan site
BK Rating:	Moderate
W/A:	Anglian
Comments:	Campers and touring caravans welcome

Long Pond

Location:	Stoke-by-Clare
How to Find:	Alongside road between Cavendish and Clare
Type and Size:	2 acre clay pit
Carp Stock:	Well stocked with fish to upper doubles
Category:	Mixed Fishery
Other Species:	Roach, rudd, crucians, bream and tench
Permits:	Enquire locally
BK Rating:	Easy
W/A:	NRA Anglian Region
Comments:	An idyllic lake

Oulton Water

Location:	Near Ipswich
Type and Size:	Medium-sized reservoir
Carp Stock:	Not many carp, but there are some big fish to well over 20lbs
Category:	Few Carp
Other Species:	Usual coarse fish
Permits:	Try local tackle shops for information
Control:	Not known
BK Rating:	Very Difficult
W/A:	NRA Anglian Region

Redgrave Lake

Location:	Redgrave Park, Botesdale, near Norwich
Type and Size:	Huge estate lake with open bank - wooded at the dam end
Carp Stock:	Only a few, but some big ones
Category:	Few Carp
Other Species:	Many bream to 8lbs, tench, roach, perch, eels and pike to 25lbs
Permits:	Members only water. Apply to Redgrave Park, Redgrave. Tel: 0379 898206
Cost:	£29.50 per year
Control:	Private
Restrictions:	Members only - no day tickets
BK Rating:	Difficult
W/A:	NRA Anglian Region

Reydon No.1 Pit

Location:	Lakeside Park Development, near Southwold off the A1095
Type and Size:	Three acre reed-fringed gravel pit
How to Find:	Take the A1095 from Southwold, and after going over a bridge, turn into the Lakeside Park estate road. The car parking area is behind the pit.
Carp Stock:	Some carp to 20lbs
Permits:	Purdy's Newsagents, 31 High Street, Southwold. Tel: Lowestoft 724250. In advance only
Cost:	£2 per day
Control:	Southwold and Dist. Freshwater Angling Preservation Society, Secretary, Mr Barry Reid. Tel: Lowestoft 518198
Restrictions:	No night fishing. One rod only. No Sunday fishing. No fishing until 9am
BK Rating:	Not known
W/A:	NRA Anglian Region
Comments:	This lake is over 20ft deep in places. The club also has other waters. Half price for juniors. A new fishery has been constructed nearby, especially as a carp fishery, and known as Reydon No.4 Pit. Permits as above, and the water has been stocked with mirrors and commons to double figures

Roydon Sand Pit

Location:	Roydon, near Diss
Type and Size:	Little three-quarter acre pit, 25 feet deep in places
How to Find:	From Diss take the A1066 to Roydon. Just before the service station, turn left down a lane to the house
Carp Stock:	Small carp
Category:	Mixed Fishery
Other Species:	Tench, rudd, crucians
Permits:	From the house next to the pit; Mrs Alasia. Tel: Diss 4409
Cost:	About £2 per day
BK Rating:	Easy
Control:	Private
Restrictions:	Not known
W/A:	NRA Anglian Region

Rushbrooke Lake

Location:	Near Bury St. Edmunds
Type and Size:	3 acre lake
How to Find:	Take the A45 from Bury towards Ipswich. In 2 miles turn right, then second right to Wellnethan. The lake is on the left
Carp Stock:	Carp to over 20lbs
Category:	Mixed Fishery
Other Species:	Tench, bream, roach
Permits:	Members only - yearly from N Bruton. Tel: Bury St. Edmunds 66074 or local tackle shops
Cost:	On application
BK Rating:	Moderate
Control:	Private
Restrictions:	No night fishing
W/A:	NRA Anglian Region

Comments:	Membership also entitles members to fish West Stow Country Park, an 18 acre pit, which is a bird sanctuary (no night fishing) containing some carp to doubles - this water is near Lackford, off the A1101

Slaters Pit

Location:	Near Oulton Broad, which is close to Lowestoft
Type and Size:	Small pit
Carp Stock:	Well stocked with carp to about 15lbs
Category:	Mixed Fishery
Other Species:	Roach and tench
Permits:	Not known - try local tackle shops
BK Rating:	Thought to be Easy
W/A:	NRA Anglian Region
Comments:	We have not been able to find out much about this one... except that it is there, and it contains carp; any help would be appreciated

Starfield Pit

Location:	Long Melford, near Sudbury
Type and Size:	Gravel pit about 6 acres
How to Find:	Take the A134 from Sudbury to Rodbridge Corner and turn left here towards Foxearth. Go through Liston and to the right of the chemical factory and take a track on the right through Liston Gardens. The pit is on the right at the bottom of the track
Carp Stock:	Quite well stocked with mirrors to double figure size
Category:	Mixed Fishery
Other Species:	Bream, roach and pike
Permits:	Day tickets in advance only from Mr N Mealham, 6 Springfield Terrace, East Street, Sudbury. Tel: Sudbury 77139. Season ticket/Club membership costs approximately £12 from the Club Secretary as above
Cost:	About £1.50 per day. Approximately £12 per season for club membership
Control:	Long Melford and District Angling Association
BK Rating:	Moderate
W/A:	NRA Anglian Region
Comments:	Irregular shaped pit with some weed of 2-10 feet deep, with islands

Suffolk Stour

Location:	Off the A137 near Manningtree
Type and Size:	Wide shallow river, not far from the estuary
Carp Stock:	Not many, but some up to 20lbs
Category:	Few Carp
Other Species:	Tench, roach and bream
Permits:	On the bank at £2 per day. In advance at £1.50 from Viscount Tackle, Ipswich or Bridge Garage, Manningtree
Control:	Lawford AS. Richard Harbach. Tel: 0206 394452
BK Rating:	Very Difficult
W/A:	NRA Anglian Region

The Deep Hole

Location:	Frostend, one mile from Wrentham, near Lowestoft
Type and Size:	Small clay pit between 14ft and 20ft deep
How to Find:	Take the A12 from Lowestoft, go through Wrentham, and turn right just before the Wangford Plough pub. Pit is one mile, on the right
Carp Stock:	Some mirrors to double figures
Category:	Possibly Few Carp
Other Species:	Perch, chub, roach, rudd
Permits:	Members only water of the Southwold and Dist. Freshwater Preservation Society. To join apply to the Membership Secretary, Mr Barry Reid, 19 Sussex Road, Lowestoft. Tel: Lowestoft 518198
Cost:	£14 a year, and £8 joining fee (juniors half price), which includes 5 other ponds
Control:	Club
Restrictions:	Members only
BK Rating:	Not known
W/A:	NRA Anglian Region

Thorpeness Mere

Location:	Thorpeness, near Leiston
Type and Size:	Huge lake with many islands
How to Find:	Norwich - Bungay - Halesworth, then the A12 to Yoxford. Take the B1122 to Leiston, and the B1353 to Thorpeness
Carp Stock:	Some commons to 10lbs
Category:	Few Carp
Other Species:	Roach, rudd, eels
Permits:	Free (100 yards only)
Cost:	None
BK Rating:	Difficult
Control:	Thorpeness Estate Office. Tel: Aldeburgh 3555
Restrictions:	No fishing on most of the bank. No night fishing
W/A:	NRA Anglian Region
Comments:	This is a 'children's playground' with 150 boats for hire - might do for a family day out. The lake is very shallow, only up to 2½ feet deep

Welmore Lake

Location:	Near Downham Market
Type and Size:	Two acre pond
How to Find:	From Downham Market take the A1122, going west, and in Salters Lode, take the left turn and cross the Old Bedford River and the Old Delph
Carp Stock:	Some carp to about 10lbs
Category:	Mixed Fishery
Other Species:	Roach, bream, perch and pike
Permits:	In advance only from B Riches, 15 Sand Lane, Denver, Downham Market. Tel: 0366 383291
Cost:	£2 per day
Control:	Private
BK Rating:	Moderate
W/A:	NRA Anglian Region
Comments:	Usual baits successful. Surface fishing good in summer. Pleasant pond with an island, reeds and lilies

West Stow Country Park

Location: Just off the A1101 Bury St. Edmunds-Mildenhall road. Just after the bridge over the River Lark, the country park will be seen on the right

Type and Size: 18 acre pit in a bird sanctuary. The lake has three islands and depths of up to 25ft

Carp Stock: Some double figure carp

Category: Probably Few Carp

Other Species: Tench, roach, perch, bream and pike

Permits: Members only. Permits from local tackle shops or from Mr N Bruton. Tel: Bury St. Edmunds 66074

Cost: £12 per year, juniors half price. Also includes Rushbrooke Lake

Control: Club

Restrictions: No night fishing

BK Rating: Not known

W/A: NRA Anglian Region

Weybread Gravel Pits

Location: Weybread near Harleston, and quite near Waveney Valley Lakes

How to Find: Take the A140 from Norwich, and at Pulham Market take the B1134 to Harleston. Then take the road to Weybread and after crossing the river the pits will be seen on either side of the road

Type and Size: Five gravel pits, one of which is very big

Carp Stock: The middle pit is very well stocked with mirrors; many are doubles and there are also some 20's. Club only pit is also well stocked with carp

Category: Middle Pit — Carp Water

Other Species: Crucians, roach, perch, tench, bream and pike

Permits: Day tickets in advance only from G Denny, The Tackle Shop, Harleston. Tel: Harleston 852248; and the Cherry Tree public house in Harleston. Club membership Harleston and District Angling Club - details from tackle shop. Club Secretary: J Adamson, Yew Villa, Roydon, Diss - tickets

Cost: Day tickets £2.50, which includes the 4 pits but not the small club carp water. Club membership £7 per year (small club pit plus several miles of the Waveney), and an EXTRA £8 a year to include all 5 pits and the river

Restrictions: Club pit cannot be fished on a day ticket. Night fishing in all pits is for CLUB MEMBERS ONLY

BK Rating: Moderate

Baits/Methods: Advanced carp methods, baits and rigs usually needed for the larger carp

W/A: NRA Anglian Region

Comments: Good gravel pit club fishery, with 20's possible. Worth joining the club for the small pit and the night fishing

White House Farm

Location: White House Farm, Rendham

Type and Size: Shallow half acre lake

Carp Stock: Some mirrors to 10lbs

Category: Mixed Fishery

Other Species: Roach, perch, crucians, and small tench

Permits: Mr Tate. Tel: Renham 485

Control: Private

Restrictions: No fishing, except for those parking touring caravans on the land
BK Rating: Not known
W/A: NRA Anglian Region

Wickhambrook Lake

Location: Wickhambrook, Suffolk
How to Find: About 2 miles outside village towards Newmarket
Type and Size: Narrow 2 acre clay pit
Carp Stock: Very heavily stocked with carp to mid—doubles
Category: Carp Water
Other Species: A few roach, rudd and bream
Permits: £7.50 on the bank per 12 hours for 2 rods
BK Rating: Very Easy
W/A: NRA Anglian Region
Comments: Very prolific, 100 pound catches common, ideal water for beginner

Wickham Market Reservoir

Location: Near Wickham Market
Type and Size: 1½ acre lake
How to Find: From Harleston, take the B1116 to Framlingham and Wickham Market. The lake is visible from the road, on the left just before the town
Carp Stock: Some carp to double figures
Category: Mixed Fishery
Other Species: Roach, rudd, perch
Permits: Day tickets - Rod and Gun, Woodbridge. Tel: 03942 2377
Cost: On application - about £1.50 per day
BK Rating: Moderate
Control: Woodbridge Angling Club
Restrictions: Tickets in advance only. No night fishing
W/A: NRA Anglian Region
Comments: Small weedy water

Wickham Skeith Mere

Location: Village common of Wickham Skeith
Type and Size: Small common pond
How to Find: A140 from Norwich to Stoke Ash (27 miles) then turn right to Wickham Skeith
Carp Stock: Well stocked with small carp
Category: Carp Water
Other Species: Small pike
Permits: Free
BK Rating: Easy
W/A: NRA Anglian Region
Comments: A free fishery ideal for youngsters or the family. Shallow and weedy

SURREY

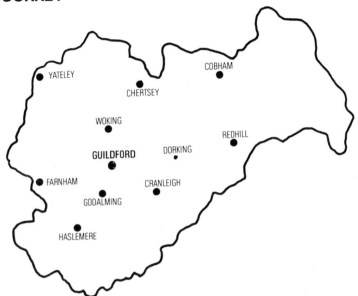

Ash Vale

Location:	Lakeside Road, Ash Vale, Aldershot
Type and Size:	Gravel pits. Lake 1 - 3 acres; Lake 2 -1¼ acres; Lake 3 - 7½ acres
How to Find:	From the A30 at Camberley, go to Frimley, then Frimley Green on the A321. After 3 miles take the Ash Vale road (A3013) then turn right onto Lakeside Road. The entrance to the fishery is under the railway bridge on the left
Carp Stock:	Carp to 20lbs
Category:	Mixed Fishery
Permits:	Leisure Sport Angling, Thorpe Park, Staines Road, Chertsey, Surrey. Tel: Chertsey 64872. Season tickets only - no day tickets. Send for permit application form and enclose when sending in the form two passport size photographs of yourself. Ash Vale is included under 'unrestricted single water' permits. If you want to fish a number of Leisure Sport waters under this category, you can apply for a Group Water Permit to include all 21 of their waters
Cost:	Single Water Permit, Ash Vale - About £14. Junior/OAP/disabled - £7, Group Water Permit for 21 venues (65 lakes and 15 stretches of river) - £29. Junior/OAP/disabled — £14.50
Restrictions:	No fires, no camping, no radios, no bright lights. Night fishing is allowed
Other Species:	Crucian carp, tench, roach, rudd, perch. Pike in Lake 1
Control:	Leisure Sport
BK Rating:	Moderate
W/A:	NRA Thames Region
Comments:	Send to Leisure Sport for the rule and guide book. Rules are strict in Leisure Sport waters and you will lose your membership if you break them

Badshot Lea Pond

Location:	Badshot Lea, Farnham
Type and Size:	Small pond
How to Find:	Badshot Lea is on the outskirts of Farnham, about 3 miles from the centre of town, north of the Hogs Back
Carp Stock:	Heavily stocked with carp of 10lbs, with a few doubles
Category:	Carp Water
Other Species:	General coarse fish
Permits:	Farnham Angling Society. Secretary: 70 Prince Charles Crescent, Farnborough, Hants
Cost:	On application
Control:	Club
BK Rating:	Easy
W/A:	NRA Thames Region

Beaver Farm

Location:	Off the A22 Eastbourne road, Newchapel, Lingfield, near East Grinstead
Type and Size:	Two lakes - Snipe Lake (2½ acres) and West Lake (small)
Carp Stock:	Snipe Lake well stocked with carp, sizes not known; West Lake also has carp
Category:	Mixed Fisheries
Other Species:	Pike, rudd, roach and tench
Permits:	From Beaver Farm
Cost:	£5 per day, second rod £2; under 15's and OAP's half price weekdays only
Control:	Private
Restrictions:	No night fishing (8am to sunset); no keepnets, no radios
BK Rating:	Not known
W/A:	NRA Southern Region

Brittens Pond

Location:	Jacobs Well, near Guildford
Type and Size:	Old pond of about 4 acres, recently dredged and stocked
How to Find:	Find Salt Box Road, Jacobs Well, Guildford, off the A320 towards Woking
Carp Stock:	About 300 fish to 19½lbs, some doubles, mostly small fish. Many of the carp are commons
Category:	Carp Water
Other Species:	Roach, rudd, tench and crucians
Permits:	Guildford Angling Society. Secretary: G Pank, 72 St. Phillips Avenue, Worcester Park, Surrey. Day tickets from Guildford Angling Centre. Tel: 0483 506333
Cost:	£30 per season. Day tickets about £3 per day
Control:	Guildford Angling Centre
BK Rating:	Easy
W/A:	NRA Thames Region
Comments:	A heavily fished water. No floating baits; no night fishing - dawn to dusk only. Barbless hooks, size 12 or larger. Unhooking mat compulsory. No carp to be retained

Broadwater Lake

Location:	Near Godalming
Type and Size:	Lake of about 10 acres
Carp Stock:	Very heavily stocked with many carp. Huge bags of small carp to 8lbs possible. Some doubles up to 20lbs
Category:	Carp Water
Other Species:	General coarse fish
Permits:	Godalming Angling Society. Secretary: A Johnson, 86 Peper Harrow Road, Godalming, Surrey. Very long waiting list though juniors should get in at once
Cost:	On application
Control:	Club
BKRating:	Easy
W/A:	NRA Thames Region
Comments:	A very easy water for small carp; it is hard to get through the small fish to catch the bigger ones, which are there. Club membership is hard to obtain

Chertsey

Location:	Thorpe Road, near Chertsey
Type and Size:	Gravel pit, 4½ acres
How to Find:	Take the M25 to Staines and turn off at the A30 roundabout onto the A320 Staines-Chertsey road. Go to Egham, then Chertsey and take the right turn to Thorpe at the small roundabout. The entrance is on the right just before the M3 flyover
Carp Stock:	Not known - the Leisure Sport guide book reports 'carp in excess of 20lbs'. We will assume it to be...
Category:	Few Carp
Other Species:	Bream, perch, roach, pike
Permits:	Season tickets only from Leisure Sport, Thorpe Park, Staines Road, Chertsey, Surrey. Tel: 0932 64872
Cost:	£20 per season. Juniors/OAP/disabled £10
Restrictions:	No night fishing. No trespassing onto Thorpe Park property. No parking on M3. Cars must not be driven round lake
BK Rating:	Difficult
Control:	Leisure Sport Angling
W/A:	NRA Thames Region

Cobham Lake

Location:	Cobham, near Walton-on-Thames
Type and Size:	Small lake
Carp Stock:	Well stocked with carp
Category:	Mixed Fishery
Other Species:	Pike, tench and bream
Permits:	A members only water of Walton-on-Thames AS. Secretary: A Finlayson, 14 Harrow Road, West Bedfont, Feltham, Greater London
Cost:	Season - £25
BK Rating:	Not known
W/A:	NRA Thames Region

Cutt Mill

Location:	Elstead, near Farnham
Type and Size:	Estate lake of about 7 acres
How to Find:	Elstead is on the B3001 between Farnham and Milford
Carp Stock:	About 200 carp, mostly doubles, and some twenties; lake record is 29lbs 12ozs
Category:	Carp Water
Other Species:	Mixed coarse fish
Permits:	Farnham Angling Society - season tickets only. Secretary: 70 Prince Charles Crescent, Farnborough, Hants
Cost:	About £20 per year plus a joining fee. Details on application
Control:	Club
Restrictions:	No long stay fishing - 48 hours maximum
Baits/Methods:	You will need all the modern rigs, such as hair and bolt rigs and the most sophisticated baits and methods on this hard-fished carp water
BK Rating:	Moderate
W/A:	NRA Thames Region
Comments:	This is quite a well-known carp water and is heavily fished by carp specialists. It is sometimes hard to find a place to fish as there are only about 20 swims on the lake; there are many trees and a marshy area. Recommended mainly for experienced carp anglers. It is a pleasant and attractive lake

Cutt Mill House

Location:	Between Guildford and Farnham
Type and Size:	Beautiful 7 acre lake next to Farnham AA's well known Cutt Mill
Carp Stock:	Well stocked with carp to over 30lbs
Category:	Mixed Fishery
Other Species:	Pike, tench, bream, roach, rudd and perch
Permits:	In advance only from Mrs R Skinner, Cutt Mill House, Puttenham GU3 1BG. Tel: 0252 702229
Control:	Private
BK Rating:	Moderate
W/A:	NRA Thames
Comments:	This water, always known to contain big carp, was only opened in 1990. A very recent rumour is that this lake has been netted and there are few carp left

Epsom Stew Pond

Location:	Off the B280 between Kingston and Epsom
Type and Size:	Small, shallow, weedy pond
Carp Stock:	Quite well stocked with small carp of about 3lbs, with a few up to 10lbs
Category:	Mixed Fishery
Other Species:	Tench, roach, perch, bream and pike
Permits:	Day tickets on bank
Cost:	£3 for adults; juniors and OAP's £1.50
Control:	CALPAC; season and day tickets from J Killick, 22 Shawley Crescent, Epsom Downs. Tel: 0737 352178. Season ticket (£15) includes other waters
BK Rating:	Moderate
W/A:	NRA Thames Region

Firs Farm Lake

Location:	Near Cranleigh
Type and Size:	Newly dug lake of about 4 acres with two islands
How to Find:	From Guildford take the A281 for 8 miles to a left turn into Wildwood Lane, then turn right at the T-junction into Knowle Lane. In a mile you will see the Firs Farm on the right
Carp Stock:	Some small carp to about 7lbs - recently stocked
Category:	Mixed Fishery
Other Species:	Chub, perch, bream and some trout, as this was formerly a trout fishery
Permits:	Day tickets on bank
Cost:	£5 per rod, dawn till dusk; £3 for juniors, OAPs and the disabled
Control:	W Welch. Tel: 0403 822878
Restrictions:	No night fishing; no boilies
BK Rating:	Not known
N/A:	NRA Thames Region

Frensham Great and Little Ponds

Location:	Frensham, between Farnham and Aldershot
Type and Size:	Big Pond is a very old, large lake of about 30 acres; Small Pond about 5 acres
Carp Stock:	Both quite well stocked - the Big Pond did have carp in it until recently to well over 30lbs, but most of these fish died in the late 80's
Category:	Mixed Fishery
Other Species:	Most coarse fish
Permits:	From The Creel, Station Road, Aldershot
Cost:	Day - £3; season - £26 + £2 joining fee
Control:	Farnham and District AS
BK Rating:	Difficult
N/A:	NRA Southern Region

Goldsworth Water Park

Location:	Goldsworth Park, Woking - off the A425 near Knaphill
Type and Size:	20 acre lake on a housing estate
Carp Stock:	Some carp to doubles
Category:	Few Carp?
Other Species:	Roach, tench, bream, chub and perch
Permits:	Day tickets on bank, dawn till dusk only
Cost:	£3 for one rod, and £4.50 for two rods, with reductions for juniors, OAP's and the disabled; annual permits at £25, or £35 to include night fishing
Control:	Woking Water Activity Centre; Head Bailiff Brian Rich. Tel: 0483 764836 after 6.30pm. Other details from Woking Tackle Shop
Restrictions:	No night fishing on day tickets; no bloodworm (!); only 50 boilies per session (I expect they count them!)
BK Rating:	Moderate to Difficult
N/A:	NRA Thames Region

Hawley Lake

Location:	Near Camberley
Type and Size:	25 acre gravel pit
Carp Stock:	Well stocked with carp - plenty of twenties and a few thirties
Category:	Mixed Fishery
Other Species:	Bream, tench, roach, perch and big eels
Permits:	Belongs to the army; day tickets and annual permits at £17.50
BK Rating:	Moderate
W/A:	NRA Thames Region
Comments:	All information on this water, including location, can be obtained from Noel's Tackle, Tel: Camberley 32488

Hungerford Lake

Location:	Near Redhill, just off the M25
Type and Size:	Medium sized lake, much used for match fishing
Carp Stock:	Very heavily stocked with small carp to about 10lbs; hundreds in the 2-3lb range
Category:	Carp Water
Other Species:	Tench and roach
Permits:	Local tackle shops
Control:	Club, but we are not sure which - enquire locally
BK Rating:	Very Easy - small carp caught on match tackle
W/A:	NRA Thames Region

Lodge Pond

Location:	Off the A325 Farnham-Bordon road
Type and Size:	Lake of about 3 acres
How to Find:	Take the A325 from Farnham
Carp Stock:	About 100 carp up to around 17lbs
Category:	Carp Water
Other Species:	General coarse fish
Permits:	Farnham Angling Society. Some temporary membership (day) tickets from local tackle shops; day tickets on bank
Cost:	£5 for 1 rod; £10 per 2 rods. Farnham AS membership about £22 per season plus an entry fee
Control:	Club. Tel: 0420 89694 - T Tarling
BK Rating:	Easy
W/A:	NRA Thames Region
Comments:	A pleasant lake on Forestry Commission land

Newdigate

Location:	New Barn Lane, Newdigate, near Dorking
Type and Size:	Clay pits. Lake 1 - 8½ acres; Lake 2 - 3½ acres
How to Find:	Take the A24 from Dorking, turn left onto Newdigate Road, then take left fork to T-junction in Newdigate village. Turn right, then first left at church. Bear left at next fork and the lakes are about 400 yards on the right, park in car park only
Carp Stock:	Good catches of carp reported to 8lbs (Lake 2); 5½lbs (Lake 1). Much larger carp have been seen in Lake 1

Category:	Carp Waters
Other Species:	None listed in guide book
Permits:	Season tickets only from Leisure Sport, Thorpe Park, Staines Road, Chertsey, Surrey. Tel: Chertsey 64872
Cost:	£20 per season, junior/OAP/disabled - £10
Restrictions:	Night fishing permitted. Usual rules apply. No swimming or boating
BK Rating:	Easy. Guide book reports 'extremely good catches'
Baits/Methods:	Normal carp methods and baits
Control:	Leisure Sport Angling
W/A:	NRA Thames Region
Comments:	Looks like a good water for some fairly easy catches of small carp, with the chance of something much bigger

Old Bury Hill

Location:	Lake View, Old Bury Hill, Dorking
Type and Size:	12½ acre estate lake 200 years old, deep at one end, with lilies at the other
How to Find:	Near Dorking, just off the A25 Dorking-Guildford road
Carp Stock:	Plenty of mid-doubles; some good low 20's; best fish 30lbs
Category:	Mixed Fishery
Other Species:	Tench, bream, rudd, crucians, perch, roach, pike and zander
Permits:	Day tickets on bank; season tickets - Lake View, Old Bury Hill, Dorking. Tel: Dorking 883621 (9am to 7pm) (Mike Ewin)
Cost:	One rod £6; two rods £10; juniors £3 and £5 respectively
BK Rating:	Moderate
Control:	Private.
Restrictions:	No night fishing; no sacking; no particles
W/A:	NRA Thames Region
Comments:	An attractive, fairly shallow lake. Large, hard boilies needed to avoid the big tench. Boats can be hired, but must be booked in advance. Refreshments and toilets on bank. No close season

Priory Lake (a)

Location:	Near Redhill
Type and Size:	Large estate lake
Carp Stock:	Well stocked with carp to upper doubles
Category:	Mixed Fishery
Other Species:	Tench and other coarse fish
Permits:	Seasonal membership. Tel: 0737 823304 for details
Control:	Private club
BK Rating:	Moderate
W/A:	NRA Southern Region

Priory Lake (b)

Location:	Priory Farm, Nutfield
Type and Size:	Lake of 2½ acres
Carp Stock:	Well stocked with carp to doubles
Category:	Mixed Fishery
Other Species:	Rudd, perch, roach and tench
Permits:	Day tickets on bank - Tuesdays only

Cost:	£4.50 from 7am till dusk; £2.50 from 4pm
Control:	Private
Restrictions:	No night fishing; tickets limited on certain days; no wading and anglers must fish from allocated pegs
BK Rating:	Easy
W/A:	NRA Thames Region
Comments:	This is mainly a match water, but good carp are caught close to the bank, or by the islands

River Valley Fishery

Location:	River Valley, Sandhurst Road, Yateley, Camberley
Type and Size:	Gravel pit of 16 acres
How to Find:	This lake is in the same road as Tri-Lakes and the Leisure Sport Lakes
Carp Stock:	Well stocked with carp to 30lbs
Category:	Mixed Fishery
Other Species:	Rudd to 3½lbs; perch, pike, tench
Permits:	On site. Day and night permits
Cost:	About £2.50 per day; approximately £3.50 per night
BK Rating:	Difficult
Control:	Private
Baits/Methods:	Usual carp baits and methods
W/A:	NRA Thames Region
Comments:	Season tickets at about £25 for day; £35 for night. Very deep 47 year old lake, oldest in area, attractive with trees, bushes etc. For information telephone 0252 873865. There are also two smaller lakes and 1½ miles of the River Blackwater containing trout and chub

River Wey

Location:	Byfleet and Wisley
Type and Size:	Tributary of the River Thames
Carp Stock:	Some fish to around 20lbs
Category:	Few Carp
Other Species:	Pike, dace, roach, chub, barbel, bream and perch
Permits:	Byfleet AA - Mrs B Stilwell, 15 Rutson Road, Byfleet
Cost:	£20 per season
Control:	Club
BK Rating:	Very Difficult
W/A:	NRA Thames Region

Send

Location:	Send, near Woking
Type and Size:	Two pits
Carp Stock:	Well stocked with carp to over 30lbs
Category:	Mixed Fishery
Other Species:	Tench and perch
Permits:	A members only water of Woking and District AA - new members welcome. Details from the Secretary: D Powell, Maymont, Guildford Road, Knaphill, Woking
Control:	Club

Restrictions: Members only, though some guest tickets for members' friends
BK Rating: Very Difficult
W/A: NRA Thames Region

Shalford Park

Location: Ferry Lane, near the Ship Inn, off the Guildford to Godalming road
Type and Size: Canal-like stretch of the River Wey, with backwater and a joining stream
Carp Stock: Not many, sizes unknown
Category: Few Carp
Other Species: Chub, roach, perch, bream, pike, gudgeon and trout
Permits: On bank at £3 per day
Control: Guildford AS. Secretary: L Yarrow. Tel: 0483 574462
BK Rating: Very Difficult
W/A: NRA Southern Region

Stillwater Lake

Location: Ash Vale, off the A321 about half a mile after Ash Vale station
Type and Size: Five acre lake, quite shallow
Carp Stock: Well stocked with carp to over 20lbs
Category: Mixed Fishery
Other Species: Bream, roach and tench
Permits: In advance only from Raison's Tackle Shop, 2 Park Road, Farnborough. Tel: 0252 543570
Restrictions: No night fishing; some bait restrictions
BK Rating: Moderate
W/A: NRA Thames Region
Comments: Entry is through locked gate; you will be given a key when you buy your permit from Raison's

Surrey Lake

Location: Ten minutes from Junction 6 on the M25, near Reigate
Type and Size: Attractive lake of about two acres
Carp Stock: Well stocked with carp to 25lbs
Category: Mixed Fishery
Other Species: Tench
Permits: All details and permits on 081-644 3669
BK Rating: Moderate
W/A: NRA Thames Region

TriLakes

Location: Yateley Road, Sandhurst
Type and Size: Two gravel pits of about 14 acres
How to Find: Take the Sandhurst road and turn into Yateley Road, at Yateley. Fishery is on the right just after the entrance to Yateley (Match Lake)
Carp Stock: Not very heavily stocked with carp, but there are a number of 20's and thirties, with the best mirror caught over 35lbs
Category: Mixed Fishery
Other Species: Tench, roach, rudd, perch, bream, chub, pike, trout
Permits: Must be obtained before fishing from the fishing hut by the entrance -

£5 per rod per day. C Homewood, TriLakes, Yateley Road, Sandhurst. Tel: Aldershot 873191

BK Rating: Difficult
Restrictions: No night fishing - open 7am to sunset
W/A: NRA Thames Regions
Comments: This is a well-known commercial fishery which is often heavily fished, especially at weekends. It is quite a pleasant water with many trees and bushes around the banks, and with islands. There are toilets, and a shop which sells bait, drinks, snacks and sweets and a licensed restaurant. A number of very big carp are caught each season. Fishing continues during the close season under special rules. Although most anglers are not carp specialists, the lake is fished by hard-line, and some well-known carp anglers, in the hope of a thirty. Long spells without takes can be expected

Twynersh Fishery

Location: Chertsey, near Thorpe Park, off Junction 11 on the M25
Type and Size: Two newish gravel pits containing carp
Carp Stock: Pit One - well stocked with small carp to 5lbs; Pit Two has carp to 20lbs
Category: Mixed Fisheries
Other Species: Tench, perch, roach, bream and pike
Permits: At the entrance gate
Cost: £4 per day for one rod; two rods is £6. Juniors £2.75 and OAP's £3
Control: Paul Rogers. Tel: 0931 570156
Restrictions: Fishing from two banks only. All carp to be returned at once; no night fishing; no nuts
BK Rating: Easy
W/A: NRA Thames Region
Comments: There is another coarse lake on site, a trout lake, and a short stretch of the River Bourne

Willingshurst Lake

Location: Near Guildford, exact location not known; enquire locally
Type and Size: Small lake
Carp Stock: Well stocked with carp to about 14lbs, most of which are small
Category: Mixed Fishery
Other Species: Tench, roach and perch
Permits: Try local tackle shops for permits and information
BK Rating: Easy
W/A: NRA Thames Region

Willow Pond

Location: Beaver Farm, A22 Eastbourne road, Newchapel, Lingfield, near East Grinstead. Tel: 0342 833144
Type and Size: Half acre specialist carp fishery
Carp Stock: Well stocked with carp, sizes not known
Category: Carp Only
Permits: Day tickets from Beaver Farm
Cost: £5 per day, second rod £2
Control: Private

Restrictions:	No night fishing; no keepnets
BK Rating:	Not known
W/A:	NRA Southern Region
Comments:	Publicity from Beaver Farm gives no information on the sizes of the fish in their three ponds - there is a third one acre fishery on the farm which is stocked with perch, pike, bream and roach

Windhams Pool

Location:	Off the A30 near Yateley
Type and Size:	Two acre lake
Carp Stock:	About 50 doubles
Category:	Mixed Fishery
Other Species:	Crucians, roach, tench and perch
Permits:	In advance, book by phone. Tel: Camberley 874346
Cost:	£3.50 to £4 per day
Restrictions:	No night fishing
BK Rating:	Difficult
W/A:	NRA Thames Region
Comments:	Information from Noel's Tackle. Tel: Camberley 32488

Wisley Common Ponds

Location:	Wisley and Ockham Commons, Wisley
Type and Size:	Several small common ponds
Carp Stock:	Quite well stocked with carp, mostly small
Category:	Mixed Fisheries
Other Species:	Pike, perch and roach
Permits:	FREE fishing
BK Rating:	Easy
W/A:	NRA Thames Region

Yateley

Location:	Sandhurst Road, Yateley, near Camberley
Type and Size:	14 gravel pits varying in size from 3/4 acre to 12 acres
How to Find:	Take the A30 from London to Camberley, then the A327 to Yateley, and turn right at the Royal Oak public house onto Sandhurst Road. Entrance to the west lakes is on the left and the car park to the east lakes is on the right
Carp Stock:	Most of the lakes contain good carp. Lake 11, known as the Match Lake, has plenty of doubles and 20's. Lake 12, known as the Copse Lake, has a small number of big carp including a 30 which has been caught at 35lbs. On the west side of the road, the Car Park Lake (Lake 9) has produced a fish of 42lbs, and the North Lake (Lake 4) contains a small number of large carp, including the 45.12 caught by Ritchie McDonald, which was the second biggest carp ever landed in this country
Category:	Carp Waters/Mixed Fisheries
Other Species:	Crucians, tench, roach, rudd, pike and bream
Permits:	This is a Leisure Sport Angling Special Venue. Season tickets only available, and they are limited, and issued on a 'first come - first served' basis. Apply to LSA, Thorpe Park, Staines Road, Chertsey, Surrey. Tel: Chertsey 64872

Cost:	£28 per season, juniors/OAP/disabled - £14
BK Rating:	The waters vary but most must be regarded as Fairly Hard
Baits/Methods:	Since these waters contain big fish, most of which have been caught a number of times, you will need all the most advanced carp fishing techniques and baits
Control:	Leisure Sport Angling
W/A:	NRA Thames Region
Comments:	Whilst some of these pits are really mixed fisheries, and some contain few carp, we have marked them as mainly carp waters, because of the huge size of some of the fish. Carp specialists fish these waters knowing that they may have very long waits, but may catch a very big fish. Because of the size of these fish, Yateley has become known as one of the top big carp fisheries in the country. It is fished by leading carp specialists, and in most cases long stay fishing and much patience is needed. Some of the lakes are actually just across the border in Hampshire

TYNE & WEAR

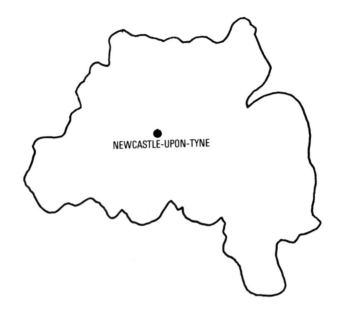

NEWCASTLE-UPON-TYNE

Big Water

Location: Seaton Burn, off the A1 just north of Newcastle
Type and Size: Not given in the W/A Guide; we assume it is a lake
Carp Stock: Some carp; commons, mirrors and crucians, numbers and sizes not known
Category: Mixed Fishery
Other Species: Roach, rudd, tench, bream, eels and perch
Permits: Paul Armstrong. Tel: 091 274 9399
Control: Club - BWAC
Restrictions: Weekly permits for those living more than 100 miles radius from Newcastle
BK Rating: Not known
W/A: NRA Northumbrian Region

Big Waters

Location: Wide Open, Newcastle-upon-Tyne
Type and Size: 20 acre shallow lake
Carp Stock: Well stocked with doubles to about 23lbs, both commons and mirrors
Category: Mixed Fishery
Other Species: Bream, tench and eels
Permits: Big Water Angling Club, Newcastle. Try local tackle shops for information
Cost: About £20 a season
BK Rating: Moderate
W/A: NRA Northumbrian Region
Comments: Not carp fished much

Fellgate Fishery

Location:	Near Gateshead
Type and Size:	Three acre lake
Carp Stock:	Well stocked with commons, mirrors and leathers, doubles to 14lbs
Category:	Mixed Fishery
Other Species:	Dace, tench, roach, perch
Permits:	Steve Sloan. Tel: 091-489 6919
Cost:	About £2 per day
Control:	Day ticket
Restrictions:	No night fishing
BK Rating:	Moderate?
W/A:	NRA Northumbrian Region

Leazes Park Lake

Location:	Leazes Park, near the football ground, Newcastle
Type and Size:	Small public boating lake of about 2 acres in size, with an island
Carp Stock:	Well stocked with carp to about 12lbs
Other Species:	Road and rudd
Permits:	Day tickets from Roberts Tackle Shop, Newcastle
Control:	Council
BK Rating:	Moderate
W/A:	NRA Northumbrian Region

Little Big Water

Location:	Wide Open, off the B1318, just north of Gosforth
Type and Size:	Pond of some kind - the NRA Guide doesn't say!
Carp Stock:	Some commons and mirrors
Category:	Mixed Fishery
Other Species:	Roach, rudd, tench, bream, crucians, perch and eels
Permits:	Paul Armstrong. Tel: 091 274 9399
Control:	Club - BWAC
BK Rating:	Not known
W/A:	NRA Northumbria Region

Marden Quarry

Location:	Whitley Bay, near Newcastle
Type and Size:	Five acre pit
Carp Stock:	Plenty of small commons and mirrors, up to about 15lbs
Category:	Mixed Fishery
Other Species:	Roach, rudd and perch
Permits:	Big Water AC - day tickets from local tackle shops
Cost:	£20 per season; day ticket £1.50
BK Rating:	Easy
W/A:	NRA Northumbrian Region
Comments:	No close season

Ryton Willows

Location:	Ryton, west of Newcastle
Type and Size:	Pond, lake or pit, who knows! ?
Carp Stock:	Some carp
Category:	Mixed Fishery
Other Species:	Roach and perch
Permits:	Limited day tickets available free from Ryton Public Library (also books!)
Control:	Mr C Wouldhave (not Paul Armstrong this time!). Tel: 091 423 4603. Tyne Anglers Alliance
BK Rating:	Not known
W/A:	NRA Northumbria Region

Silksworth Lake

Location:	Sunderland
Type and Size:	Large lake?
Carp Stock:	Some carp
Category:	Mixed Fishery
Other Species:	Tench, bream, roach, rudd and perch
Permits:	Some day tickets from nearby Ski Centre
Control:	Sunderland FWAC; Mr Gordon Bennet. Tel: 091 536 9755 or Mr Tony Kidd, 25 Toronto Close, Sunderland. Tel: 091 522 9070
BK Rating:	Not known
W/A:	NRA Northumbria Region

Stargate Pools

Location:	In the centre of Newcastle
Type and Size:	Two very small pools, which have heavy weed
Carp Stock:	A few to over 20lbs
Category:	Few Carp
Other Species:	Roach, rudd and tench
Permits:	None necessary - free fishing, with no restrictions
W/A:	NRA Northumbrian Region

THE BEEKAY GUIDE TO 1500 BRITISH & EUROPEAN CARP WATERS

Is YOUR Water listed? If so, are the details correct?

If you spot omissions, inaccuracies, or know of any changes, please let us know by filling in the Waters Questionnaire at the back of this guide and return it to us at:

FREEPOST
Beekay Publishers
Withy Pool
Henlow Camp
Bedfordshire
SG16 6EA

WARWICKSHIRE

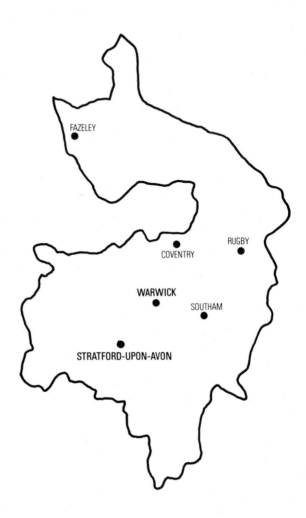

FAZELEY

RUGBY

COVENTRY

WARWICK

SOUTHAM

STRATFORD-UPON-AVON

Bishops Bowl Lakes

Location: Bishops Itchington, Southam
Type and Size: 6 small pools
How to Find: Off the B4451 south east of Leamington Spa
Carp Stock: Dinosaur's Dip - small carp; Mitre Pool - some carp; Blue Pool - carp to 20lbs
Category: Mixed Fisheries
Other Species: General coarse fish, and some trout. Big pike, bream and tench
Permits: On site. Tel: 0926 613344

Cost:	£3.50 per day approximately (6am to just after sunset); about £2 for a half day
BK Rating:	Moderate
Control:	Private
Restrictions:	No night fishing
W/A:	NRA Severn-Trent Region
Comments:	Best known for its trout lake, but the ponds mentioned are worth a try for carp. Matured limestone quarries, now a Nature Reserve. Mitre Pool 40 feet deep in places. Very pleasant surroundings

Foxholes Fishery

Location:	Crick, near Rugby
Type and Size:	3 lakes
How to Find:	Off the A428 Rugby-Northampton road
Carp Stock:	Some carp, sizes not known
Category:	Mixed Fishery
Other Species:	General coarse fish including tench
Permits:	R Chaplin, Great Arbour Close, Kenilworth. Information also from Banks and Burr, 27 Claremont Road, Rugby
Cost:	On application
BK Rating:	Insufficient information
Control:	Private
W/A:	NRA Severn-Trent Region
Comments:	Rugby Federation of Anglers also has some carp in Newbold Quarry (20 acres) near town centre. Tickets from Banks and Burr

Freemans Lake

Location:	Wolvey, on the B4109 south of Hinckley
Type and Size:	Small lake
Carp Stock:	Heavily stocked with small carp, mostly commons
Category:	Mixed Fishery
Other Species:	Crucians, roach and big perch
Permits:	Try tackle shops in Hinckley and Nuneaton
Control:	Club
BK Rating:	Easy
W/A:	NRA Severn-Trent Region

Kingsbury Water Park, Gibsons Lake

Location:	Fazeley, near Tamworth
Type and Size:	Several old pits, one a specialist carp fishery of about 3 acres
How to Find:	Follow the Tamworth road from Birmingham and take the road signposted 'Bodymoor Heath'. After one mile along this lane the fishery is on your left
Carp Stock:	Few carp in some of the lakes. Carp lake well stocked with about 100 carp, plenty of doubles to over 20lbs
Category:	Carp Water
Other Species:	Tench, roach, rudd, bream, perch, pike
Permits:	County Council Offices, Shire Hall, Warwick. No day tickets
Cost:	Season tickets about £35 which cover 6 other gravel pits, including a good pike water

Control: County Council
BK Rating: Moderate
W/A: NRA Severn-Trent Region
Comments: This water has been developed as a carp fishery since 1980, and the fish are said to be still growing well. Quite a pleasant setting

Napton Reservoir

Location: Napton, near Southam, Coventry
Type and Size: Two lakes, 20 acres and 4 acres
How to Find: Take the A425 from Warwick to Southam and then to Napton
Carp Stock: Few but large. Mirrors to over 20lbs
Category: Few Carp
Other Species: Bream, roach, tench and perch
Permits: From bailiffs on bank
Baits/Methods: Normal carp methods and baits
Control: Club - Coventry and District Angling Association, Secretary: P O'Connor, 48 Loxley Close, Wood End, Coventry. Tel: Coventry 612880
BK Rating: Difficult
W/A: NRA Severn-Trent Region
Comments: Most of the bigger carp are caught from the smaller lake, but both have a reputation as hard waters, probably because the carp stock is not large

Newbold Quarry

Location: On the edge of Rugby, about 1½ miles from town centre
Type and Size: 25 acre quarry
Carp Stock: Well stocked with carp to double figures
Category: Mixed Fishery
Other Species: Tench and pike
Permits: From bailiffs on bank, or from Banks and Burr, 17 Claremont Road; C Donald, 155a Bilton Road
Cost: Day tickets £1; season tickets £12 (£2 juniors)
Control: Club; Rugby Federation of Anglers, G Lawrence, 53 Manor Road, Rugby
BK Rating: Moderate
W/A: NRA Severn-Trent Region

Warwick Canal

Location: South of Warwick
Type and Size: 12½ miles of Grand Union Canal
How to Find: South of Warwick and Leamington Spa
Carp Stock: Good carp in reasonable numbers
Category: Mixed Fishery
Other Species: General coarse fish
Permits: Royal Leamington Spa AA. E G Archer, 9 Southway, Leamington Spa, and from local tackle shops
Cost: Day tickets about £1
BK Rating: Moderate
Control: Club
Restrictions: Not known
W/A: NRA Severn-Trent Region
Comments: Carp are in this area in the River Leam, details from local tackle shops

WEST MIDLANDS

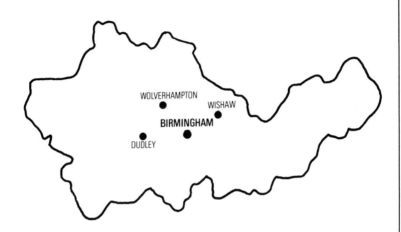

Blackhills Lake

Location:	Wombourne, off the B1477 just south of Wolverhampton - enquire locally for exact location
Type and Size:	4 acre lake on the edge of the golf course
Carp Stock:	Very heavily stocked with small carp, and the occasional lower double
Category:	Carp Water
Permits:	Day tickets from the site office
Cost:	About £2 per day
Control:	Private
BK Rating:	Easy
W/A:	NRA Severn-Trent Region

Blackroot 20 Carp

Location:	Sutton Park, near Birmingham
Type and Size:	Estate lake of 12 acres
How to Find:	Six miles north of Birmingham on the A38 road to Lichfield
Carp Stock:	Quite well stocked with carp which includes several 20's and two fish over 30lbs each
Category:	Mixed Fishery
Other Species:	Good pike and other coarse fish
Permits:	From bailiffs on bank
Control:	Private
BK Rating:	Very Difficult
W/A:	NRA Severn-Trent Region

Bonehill Mill

Location:	Lichfield Street, Fazeley, Tamworth, B78 3QQ. Tel: 0827 288482
Type and Size:	Three lakes totalling 20 acres
How to Find:	Take the A5 to Tamworth and Fazeley village will be found just to the south of the town
Carp Stock:	Very heavily stocked with many small commons mostly in the 2-5lbs range, with the occasional double figure fish. Some 20's to 25lbs
Category:	Mixed Fisheries
Other Species:	Bream, roach, pike, perch
Permits:	Day tickets on bank
Control:	Private
Restrictions:	No night fishing; no nets or sacks; no groundbait, peanuts or tiger nuts; barbless hooks
BK Rating:	Easy
W/A:	NRA Severn-Trent Region
Comments:	Under new management - V Martin

Bracebridge Lake

Location:	Sutton Park, Birmingham, off the A38 Lichfield road
Type and Size:	4 acre park lake close to Blackroot 20
Carp Stock:	Few carp, but possibly some big ones
Category:	Few Carp
Other Species:	Tench, roach, bream and pike
Permits:	Day tickets from bailiff on bank
Cost:	About £2 per day
Control:	Private
BK Rating:	Very Difficult
W/A:	NRA Severn-Trent Region

Bridge Pool

Location:	Patshull Park, Wolverhampton
Type and Size:	Three acre lake next to the Great Lake at Patshull Park
How to Find:	Take the A454 from Wolverhampton, turn right to Pattingham; take the Burnhill Green Road and you will see the fishery on the right in 1½ miles
Carp Stock:	Quite well stocked with carp to doubles, many of which came from the Great Lake
Permits:	Day tickets from the lodge on site before fishing
Cost:	£2.50 per day; £1.50 for juniors - 7.30am till dusk
Control:	Patshull Park
BK Rating:	Moderate
Restrictions:	No night fishing; no groundbait or hemp
W/A:	NRA Severn-Trent Region
Comments:	Easy access for disabled anglers; good float fishing water, with sweetcorn as bait - 4 feet to 9 feet deep, and separated from the big lake by a narrow causeway

Calf Heath Reservoir

Location:	Junction 12 of the M6
Type and Size:	Reservoir of 50 acres
How to Find:	Come off the M6 at junction 12 and take the A5 road towards Telford
Carp Stock:	Stocked by the club with thousands of carp. Several 20's and a 30 have been reported recently
Category:	Carp Water
Other Species:	Some coarse fish
Permits:	Annual permit available from the bailiff's house on the A5 bank
Cost:	On application
Control:	Club
BK Rating:	Fairly Easy
W/A:	NRA Severn-Trent Region
Comments:	This water is being developed as a carp fishery and is not far from the centre of Birmingham

Church Pool

Location:	Patshull Park, Wolverhampton
Type and Size:	Old pit, about 12 acres
How to Find:	From Wolverhampton, take the A41 road west and then turn onto the A464. After the village of Tettenhall turn left to Pattingham. Here turn right to Patshull
Carp Stock:	Well stocked with mirrors and commons to 25lbs. Many of the bigger fish are commons - which is rare! Mixed Fishery but almost reaches Carp Water status
Category:	Mixed Fishery
Other Species:	Bream, roach and tench, all of which reach large sizes
Permits:	Lakeside Lodge Hotel, Patshull Estate. Tel: Pattingham 700100. Pattingham Anglers
Baits/Methods:	Modern advanced carp fishing methods. Recent summer success has been with floating pet foods such as Pedigree Chum Mixer. Boilies are also good, especially later in the year
Control:	Private
Restrictions:	No keepnets
BK Rating:	Moderate
W/A:	NRA Severn-Trent Region
Comments:	This water has not been open long and is producing fine catches of big carp to specialist carp anglers. It is in a very attractive setting but is quite hard fished. There are lilies and some weed, and some of the banks are tree-lined. The lake is over 15 feet deep in places. Good chance of a 20

Coleshill Pool

Location:	Coleshill, near Birmingham
Type and Size:	2 acre lake
Carp Stock:	Quite well stocked with carp to 14lbs
Category:	Mixed Fishery
Other Species:	Tench, roach and bream
Permits:	Telephone 021 3511907
Control:	Private
BK Rating:	Not known, but used for match fishing
W/A:	NRA Severn-Trent Region

Cuttle Mill

Location:	Wishaw, Sutton Coldfield, Birmingham (Cuttle Mill Lane)
Type and Size:	Carp pool 3.2 acres, coarse pool 2.75 acres
How to Find:	Off the A4091 towards Tamworth, near the National Golf Centre
Carp Stock:	Very heavily stocked with many doubles and many twenties. In 1991 3,111 doubles and 440 twenties were reported; plus three thirties
Category:	Carp Water. Long Pool is Mixed Fishery
Other Species:	Tench and roach
Permits:	Day tickets from the owner, Tony Higgins, at the above address. Tel: 0827 872253
Cost:	£10 per day for two rods, £8 from 25th October. Coarse pool £4.50 per day
Restrictions:	No night fishing - fishing is from 7am till dusk. No barbed hooks. No keepnets. No seed, nut bean or pea baits are allowed
Baits/Methods:	Advanced carp rigs and methods needed. Recent successes have been on high protein boilies fished on the hair rig, and floating baits
Control:	Private
BK Rating:	Moderate
W/A:	NRA Severn-Trent Region
Comments:	This is one of the best known commercial carp fisheries in the country, where anglers have a good chance of landing 20's and probably 30's. Up to 31 doubles in a day have been reported, and as this is a commercial fishery it is obviously heavily fished. The house of the owner is right on the bank, and a small mill stream leads from the lake, which is in peaceful surroundings. Alongside the carp lake is another lake of 2.75 acres which is a Mixed Fishery. It contains plenty of carp to over 20lbs, and tench, roach, perch, chub, bream and dace. Details from the owners. Until recently Cuttle Mill was not open in winter

Earlswood Lakes

Location:	Earlswood, Birmingham
Type and Size:	Three estate lakes - 85 acres in all
Carp Stock:	Two of the lakes contain some carp; sizes not known
Category:	Mixed Fishery
Other Species:	Big eels, roach, perch, bream, pike and tench
Permits:	From bailiff on bank
Control:	Private - information from Mrs Palmer, The Bungalow, Valley Road, Earlswood, Birmingham. Tel: Earlswood 2436
BK Rating:	Difficult
W/A:	NRA Severn-Trent Region

Edgbaston Reservoir

Location:	Reservoir Road, Rotton Park, Birmingham
Type and Size:	20 acre reservoir in the city
How to Find:	Turn into Monument Street from the A456 Hagley road in Ladywood, south west Birmingham. Reservoir Road is the fifth turning on the left
Carp Stock:	Some carp to 20lbs
Category:	Few Carp?
Other Species:	Roach, perch, bream and pike
Permits:	Day tickets on bank; season tickets
Cost:	£1.50 (£1 for unemployed)

Control:	Birmingham City Council, Recreation Dept - Tel: 021 4464659
BK Rating:	Difficult
W/A:	NRA Severn-Trent Region
Comments:	Cafe and other town facilities

Fen Pools

Location:	North View Drive, Pensnett, near Brierley Hill
Type and Size:	3 lakes, two quite large
How to Find:	West Birmingham, near Dudley
Carp Stock:	Some carp to over 20lbs, in Middle Pool and also some carp in Grove Pool
Category:	Mixed Fishery
Other Species:	Tench, bream and eels
Permits:	Free fishing
Control:	Private
BK Rating:	Difficult
W/A:	NRA Severn-Trent Region
Comments:	Unpleasant surroundings, between a factory and a housing estate!

Heron Brook Fishery

Location:	Near Wolverhampton, off the A41 near Tettenhall
Type and Size:	Three acre lake with the River Penk flowing through the middle
Carp Stock:	Some carp in the main lake, and the rest in the adjoining carp pool. These fish are mostly doubles
Category:	Coarse Lake - Mixed Fishery; Carp Pool - Carp Only
Permits:	Day tickets *in advance only* from Nigel Williams Fishing Tackle, Wolverhampton. Tel: 0902 744824 - phone call essential, or you may not be able to fish when you get there. Only 4 anglers a day on the Carp Pool
Control:	Private
Baits/Methods:	Boilies, luncheon meat and sweetcorn all do well on standard methods; floaters also take fish
BK Rating:	Moderate
W/A:	NRA Severn-Trent Region

Himley Island Pool

Location:	Himley Park, Dudley
Type and Size:	Small estate lake
How to Find:	Himley Park, near Wombourne
Carp Stock:	Well stocked with carp to 20lbs
Category:	Mixed Fishery
Other Species:	Tench, crucians, bream and roach
Permits:	Beddows Tackle Shop, Wombourne. Day tickets and night syndicate vacancies
Cost:	On application
Control:	Private
BK Rating:	Moderate
W/A:	NRA Severn-Trent Region
Comments:	Night carp syndicate members claim carp to mid-twenties

Lady Barbara's Pool

Location:	Patshull Park, Pattingham, Wolverhampton
Type and Size:	6 acre estate lake, and very attractive
Carp Stock:	Plenty of doubles and a few 20's
Category:	Mixed Fishery
Other Species:	Tench, roach, bream and eels
Permits:	Season tickets from Pattingham AC only - enquire locally
Control:	Club
Restrictions:	No day tickets; no night fishing
BK Rating:	Moderate
W/A:	NRA Severn-Trent Region

Lifford Reservoir

Location:	Tunnel Lane, Lifford, Birmingham
Type and Size:	Small open reservoir
How to Find:	Take the A441 from the centre of Birmingham, then Lifford Lane and Tunnel Lane
Carp Stock:	Well stocked with carp to 20lbs
Category:	Mixed Fishery
Other Species:	Pike, roach, bream and perch
Permits:	On bank
Cost:	£1.40 per day; 90p for juniors
BK Rating:	Moderate
W/A:	NRA Severn Trent Region
Comments:	Car park close to lake, and easy access for the disabled

Makin Fisheries

Location:	Wolvey, north west of Birmingham
Type and Size:	Five lakes with a total area of about 20 acres
How to Find:	Turn off the M6 at Junction 2 and go through Anstey and Shilton to Wolvey. In the village, turn into Bulkington Road, and you will see the signposts to the fishery in just under a mile
Carp Stock:	Heavily stocked with carp to about 25lbs
Category:	Mixed Fishery
Other Species:	Tench, chub, barbel, dace, roach, golden orfe and trout
Permits:	Day tickets on site
Cost:	£5 per day; juniors - £3; OAP's and the disabled - £2. Reductions for winter fishing
Control:	Private
Restrictions:	Barbless hooks; no keepnets; no night fishing
BK Rating:	Moderate
W/A:	NRA Severn Trent Region
Comments:	Snack bar and toilets; big fish of most species. Lakes One and Two open for trout fishing (fly and legered worm) from March 29th to June 15th

Netherton Reservoir

Location: Housing estate in Dudley
Type and Size: 10 acre public lake, with water ski-ing and many boats
Carp Stock: Not many carp, but those reported caught were doubles
Category: Few Carp
Other Species: Mixed coarse fish
Permits: Day tickets on the bank at low cost
Restrictions: No night fishing
Control: Private
BK Rating: Very Difficult
W/A: NRA Severn-Trent Region

Packington

Location: Packington, near Meriden, Coventry
Type and Size: Two pits, Molands Mere and Gearys Level, totalling 35 acres
How to Find: Take the A45 from Birmingham and turn right at the sign for Maxstoke. Entrance is on your right
Carp Stock: Both waters are well stocked with doubles up to 28lbs
Category: Carp Water
Other Species: Large pike, roach, bream and rudd
Permits: Day tickets from the Lodge near the entrance before fishing. Season tickets. Tel: 021-742 2682
Cost: £4 per day, £60 per season; some summer evening and half day tickets
Control: Private
Restrictions: Night fishing for season ticket holders only
BK Rating: Fairly Hard
W/A: NRA Severn-Trent Region
Comments: Well-known water, quite heavily fished and publicised

Park Lime Pits

Location: Near Walsall
Type and Size: Small disused pits
Carp Stock: Some carp, number and sizes not known
Category: Mixed Fishery
Other Species: Bream, roach, perch and pike
Permits: Walsall and District AS - day and season tickets, 38 Lichfield Road, Bloxwich, Walsall
Cost: Cheap tickets
Control: Club
BK Rating: Not known
W/A: NRA Severn-Trent Region

Penns Hall Lake

Location: Sutton Coldfield, Birmingham
Type and Size: Long, narrow lake of about 10 acres
How to Find: Behind Penns Hall Hotel, Penns Lane, Sutton Coldfield
Carp Stock: Not many carp, doubles up to mid 20's
Category: Mixed Fishery
Other Species: Mostly bream and tench

Permits:	Ansells Angling Club. Secretary: Mrs Rogers, Tel: 021-748 1200. Must join Ansells Sports and Social Club first
Cost:	Ansells AC £14 per year, Ansells S & S Club £8 per year
Control:	Private
BK Rating:	Difficult, because small numbers of carp
W/A:	NRA Severn-Trent Region
Comments:	Town water, very popular with walkers

Pool Hall

Location:	Lower Penn, near Wolverhampton
Type and Size:	25 acre lake
How to Find:	Take the Wolverhampton to Bridgnorth road and follow the signs to Lower Penn
Carp Stock:	Heavily stocked with many small carp, mostly commons, but a good number of doubles and twenties to 30lbs
Category:	Carp Water
Permits:	Day ticket on bank
Cost:	About £3 for 24 hours
Control:	Private
Baits/Methods:	All types of carp fishing baits and methods will catch on this easy water
BK Rating:	Very Easy
W/A:	NRA Severn-Trent Region
Comments:	Popular, heavily fished water

Powells Pool

Location:	Sutton Park, Birmingham
Type and Size:	Large lake, also used for sailing
How to Find:	Take the A5217 north from Junction 6 of the M6. Turn left onto the A452 at Erdington, and right on the B4531 Boldmere road at the first roundabout. The entrance to the park is opposite, with the pool and car park on the left
Carp Stock:	Few large carp
Category:	Few Carp
Other Species:	Bream, roach, perch, tench, chub and big pike
Permits:	On bank
Cost:	£1.40 per day; 90p for juniors, OAP's and the unemployed
Control:	Birmingham City Council
BK Rating:	Difficult
W/A:	NRA Severn Trent Region

Salford Park

Location:	In Birmingham, near Spaghetti Junction
Type and Size:	12 acre reservoir
How to Find:	On the A38 towards the centre of Birmingham, close to junction 6 of the M6
Carp Stock:	About 100 carp which average about 13lbs. There are several fish over 20lbs
Category:	Mixed Fishery
Other Species:	Roach, perch and tench
Permits:	Day tickets available on bank; season tickets

Cost:	£1.50 per rod
Control:	Council. Tel: 021-446 4659
Restrictions:	No night fishing
BK Rating:	Fairly Hard
W/A:	NRA Severn-Trent Region
Comments:	Hard fished and busy town fishery

Shatterford Fishery

Location:	Arley, near Kidderminster
Type and Size:	3 small lakes
How to Find:	Take the Bridgnorth road to Arley
Carp Stock:	Eric's - some carp; Stuart's - carp to 20lbs; Knight's Folly - one acre lake stocked with doubles and contains fish to 25lbs+
Category:	Eric's and Stuart's - Mixed Fisheries; Knight's Folly - Carp Only
Other Species:	Mixed coarse fish in Eric's and Stuart's
Permits:	On site - day tickets
Cost:	On application
Control:	Private
BK Rating:	Moderate
W/A:	NRA Severn-Trent Region
Comments:	Knight's Folly is advertised as 'expecting to contain some very big carp' We have heard that their waters have been netted and may not now contain carp

Soho Loop

Location:	Loop of the Birmingham canal, near Dudley Road Hospital
Type and Size:	Narrow and quite attractive canal arm
How to Find:	Take the A45 Dudley Road, left into Winson Green Road, past the prison, then right into Lodge Road, and turn into the entrance on the right past the hospital
Carp Stock:	Some carp to double figures
Category:	Few Carp
Other Species:	Roach, bream, tench, gudgeon and perch
Permits:	Day tickets on bank at 70p
Control:	Fisherman's Friend Tackle Shop in Birmingham
BK Rating:	Difficult
W/A:	NRA Severn-Trent Region

Sutton Bank Fisheries

Location:	Near Birmingham
Type and Size:	Several small lakes
Carp Stock:	Well stocked with carp to 20lbs
Category:	Carp Water
Permits:	Day tickets. Tel: 0952 811048
Cost:	£6 to include a pub meal(!)
BK Rating:	Moderate
W/A:	NRA Severn Trent Region

Walsall Arboretum

Location: In the centre of Walsall
Type and Size: 4 acre lake with islands etc
Carp Stock: Some carp to upper doubles, but fish hard to find
Category: Few Carp
Other Species: Roach, bream and tench
Permits: Day tickets at the lake
Control: Private
BK Rating: Difficult
W/A: NRA Severn-Trent Region
Comments: A town lake not much fished for carp, but it could produce the odd good fish

Ward End Lake

Location: Ward End Park, off the A47 Heath Road, three miles east of Birmingham centre
Type and Size: Narrow, shallow park lake of about three acres
Carp Stock: Quite well stocked with carp to upper doubles
Category: Mixed Fishery
Other Species: Bream, tench, roach and perch
Permits: On bank; £1.40 per day and 90p for juniors
Baits/Methods: Boilies best for the carp
BK Rating: Moderate
W/A: NRA Severn Trent Region
Comments: Busy public park lake with much bankside disturbance

---

THE BEEKAY GUIDE TO 1500 BRITISH & EUROPEAN CARP WATERS

Is YOUR Water listed? If so, are the details correct?

If you spot omissions, inaccuracies, or know of any changes, please let us know by filling in the Waters Questionnaire at the back of this guide and return it to us at:

FREEPOST
Beekay Publishers
Withy Pool
Henlow Camp
Bedfordshire
SG16 6EA

WEST SUSSEX

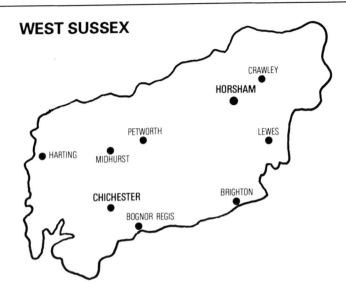

Borde Hill Lake

Location:	Borde Hill Lane, two miles north of Haywards Heath, off the B3206
Type and Size:	New three acre lake
Carp Stock:	Some carp to lower doubles
Category:	Few Carp
Other Species:	Tench, perch and rudd
Permits:	From the Fishery Kiosk
Cost:	£5 per day; £2 for an extra rod
Control:	David Buckley. Tel: 0444 417620
Restrictions:	Fishing is sunrise to 11pm only
BK Rating:	Difficult
N/A:	NRA Southern Region
Comments:	Special facilities for the disabled, including reduced price weekday tickets and car park near lake. Contact Basil Farmer on 0444 247378 for disabled details

Buchan Park Fisheries

Location:	Off the A246 Crawley to Horsham road, about 1½ miles from Crawley
Type and Size:	Two lakes, one of which, Douster Pond, is about 5 acres and is very attractive, surrounded by trees and rhododendrons; this lake is 40 feet deep in places
Carp Stock:	Well stocked with carp to doubles
Category:	Mixed Fishery
Other Species:	Bream, tench, roach, perch, pike, crucians and sunfish
Permits:	Day tickets on bank
Cost:	£3, or £2 in advance from Jack Frost Tackle, Crawley; or Ash Tackle, Horsham
Control:	Crawley AS. Secretary: Mr Kichols, 24 Rillside, Furness Green, Crawley, West Sussex

Restrictions:	No night fishing - dawn till dusk only
BK Rating:	Moderate
W/A:	NRA Thames Region

Chichester Canal

Location:	Near Chichester - runs from Chichester to Birdham Locks
Type and Size:	Narrow disused canal about 10 miles long
Carp Stock:	Well stocked with carp to about 10lbs, most of which are commons
Category:	Mixed Fishery
Other Species:	Tench, perch, pike and roach
Permits:	Details from Mr Snook of Portsmouth and District AS, and also from Chichester Angling Association, Mr J Cooper, 'Jaspers', Coney Road, East Wittering, nr Chichester, West Sussex
Control:	Club
BK Rating:	Moderate
W/A:	NRA Southern Region
Comments:	PM claims the distinction of having stocked this part of the canal between 1946 and 1949! At the age of 16, this was the first water where he caught carp in any quantity. At the time, the lower part of the canal, known as Birdham Locks, was separated from the upper part towards Hunston and Chichester by a dam, constructed when the top lock collapsed. Fish could not get into the upper part, as it was at a higher level. The upper part was said to be almost devoid of fish, since pollution from Chichester Canal Basin killed them during the 1939-45 war. The Birdham Locks section was packed with small commons, said by locals to be 'wildies', though I don't think they were! They had never been caught by 1946, as far as I know, as they were considered in those days to be 'uncatchable'. Once PM got them going on floating crust, which took 6 weeks, they were easy, and he caught up to 18 carp a day, mostly between 2lbs and 5lbs, with his best at 8lbs 3ozs. No-one else fished for carp. He put about 50 of these fish in the upper part of the canal, and is sure that the present stock descended from these fish, though he never fished the upper part of the canal. Later it was said that the Birdham Locks section was also polluted, and the fish had died, so whether there are still carp in the lower section we don't know - on the last visit a few years ago the water looked and smelt unpleasant, and there was no sign of any fish... though carp are notoriously hardy...

Crayfish Farm

Location:	Pound Hill, Crawley
Type and Size:	Four acre lake
How to Find:	Ordnance Survey Sheet No. 187; Reference 307 375
Carp Stock:	Well stocked with carp; quite a number of doubles to about 23lbs
Category:	Carp Only
Permits:	The Owner, Old Hollow, Pound Hill, Worth, West Sussex. Season tickets only
Cost:	About £150 per season
Control:	Private syndicate
BK Rating:	East
W/A:	NRA Southern Region

Comments: An attractive water, membership of which the owners were asking for £250 for the 1985 season, although it is rumoured that this will be down to £150 for 1991

Ditchling Pond

Location: Ditchling Common
Type and Size: Small pond on common land
How to Find: Take the B2112 from Haywards Heath towards Burgess Hill - pond is just before the B2113
Carp Stock: Small head of carp
Category: Few Carp
Other Species: General coarse fish
Permits: Free fishing
Cost: None
BK Rating: Insufficient information
W/A: NRA Southern Region
Comments: Very weedy free fishery

Furse Farm

Location: Rudgwick, on the B2128, six miles north of Billingshurst
Type and Size: Small lake
Carp Stock: Well stocked with small carp to about 10lbs
Category: Mixed Fishery
Other Species: Tench, chub, perch, roach
Permits: For all information and permits, Tel: 0403 822878; match bookings available
Cost: £5 per day, juniors £3
Control: Private
BK Rating: Not known
W/A: NRA Southern Region

Harting Coombe Pond

Location: Harting, near Petersfield
Type and Size: 4 acre woodland lake
How to Find: Enquire from Portsmouth AS Secretary
Carp Stock: Well stocked with carp, sizes not known
Category: Mixed Fishery
Other Species: Tench, roach, rudd, bream and pike
Permits: Portsmouth and District AS. Mr R Snook, 86 Carnarvon Road, Copnor, Portsmouth PO2 7NL. Tel: Portsmouth 662986
Cost: On application - new members about £45 per year
BK Rating: Not known
Control: Club
W/A: NRA Southern Region

Hawkins Pond

Location: Hammer Pond Road, Horsham
Type and Size: Clay pit and former tin mine of 15 acres
How to Find: In the town of Horsham - find Hammer Pond Road
Carp Stock: Reasonable number of small carp, and about 30 doubles. Probably 3

carp to 28lbs, one of which is a common

Category:	Mixed Fishery
Other Species:	Big pike, tench, bream, roach, rudd, perch, chub
Permits:	Horsham and District AA. Secretary: G Kempson, 11 Clarence Road, Horsham, West Sussex
Cost:	About £28 a season - includes all club waters
Baits/Methods:	All baits but floaters good in summer. Hair rig best
Control:	Club
Restrictions:	No night fishing except for permit holders - fishing is from 4am to 11pm. No prebaiting. No litter
BK Rating:	Moderate
W/A:	NRA Southern Region
Comments:	A beautiful lake surrounded by woodland. Average depth 8 feet

Hortons Pond

Location:	Small Dole, near Henfield
Type and Size:	Quarry of about 3½ acres, fringed by reeds
Carp Stock:	A few mirrors and commons, and many ghost carp
Category:	Mixed Fishery
Other Species:	Roach, rudd, tench and bream
Permits:	Blue Circle AC; ask for details at Cowfold Angling Centre, Henfield
BK Rating:	Not known
W/A:	NRA Southern Region
Comments:	Good club water for beginners and juniors

Ivy Lake

Location:	Wyke, Chichester, just off the Chichester by-pass
Type and Size:	5 acre matured gravel pit
Carp Stock:	Quite well stocked with carp, including some doubles and a few 20's
Category:	Mixed Fishery
Other Species:	Roach, rudd, bream, tench and crucians
Permits:	Day tickets on bank
Control:	Private - Tel: Chichester 787715
BK Rating:	Moderate
W/A:	NRA Southern Region

Mill Farm Pool

Location:	Off the A29 three miles south west of Pulborough
Type and Size:	Fairly new man-made lake of about four acres, opened in 1992
Carp Stock:	Very well stocked with small carp up to 10lbs
Category:	Mixed Fishery
Other Species:	Crucians, bream, roach and gudgeon
Permits:	Day tickets on bank
Cost:	£5 and £2.50 for an extra rod; £3 from 5.30pm till dusk
Control:	Tel: 0798 831617
Restrictions:	Fishing 7am till dusk only; no barbed hooks, boilies, groundbait or keepnets
BK Rating:	Easy
W/A:	NRA Southern Region

Milton Mount Lake

Location:	Three Bridges, Crawley
Type and Size:	Small lake
How to Find:	Off junction 13 of the M23
Carp Stock:	Well stocked with carp
Category:	Carp Water
Other Species:	Some other coarse fish
Permits:	Crawley AS. Mr Kichols, 24 Rillside, Furness Green, Crawley
Cost:	Season tickets approximately £20. Some day tickets at about £2
BK Rating:	Moderate
Control:	Club
W/A:	NRA Thames Region
Comments:	Crawley AS also has carp in Tittermus Lake, Roffey Park Lake, Colgate, Buchan Park Lake and New Pond (listed). It is rumoured that this lake has been closed, so you will need to check locally

Newells Lake

Location:	Monks Gate, Horsham
Type and Size:	Clay pit of 4½ acres
How to Find:	Take the A281 from Horsham towards Brighton and after 3 miles the lake will be seen from the road
Carp Stock:	Stocked in 1982 with 220 mirrors to 7lbs. Fish to 19lbs have been caught since
Category:	Carp Water
Other Species:	Tench, pike, roach and rudd
Permits:	Season tickets only from the owner, Mr T Cotton, Newells Pond House, Newells Lane, Lower Beeding, Horsham. Tel: 040376 424
Cost:	£30 per season
Baits/Methods:	Boilies on hair and bolt rigs
Control:	Private
BK Rating:	Easy
Restrictions:	No keepnets or sacks. No particle baits. No Kamatsu hooks
W/A:	NRA Southern Region
Comments:	No weed, open water, with an average depth of about five feet. Several carp a day possible, mostly small fish. Anglers' hut provided with book to record catches

New Pond

Location:	Pease Pottage, near Crawley
Type and Size:	Small tree-lined lake
How to Find:	Near Crawley, off the A23
Carp Stock:	Some carp, to mid doubles
Category:	Mixed Fishery
Other Species:	General coarse fish
Permits:	Crawley AS, Mr Kichols, 24 Rillside, Furness Green, Crawley
Cost:	Season - about £28
BK Rating:	Moderate
Control:	Club - no day tickets
W/A:	NRA Thames Region
Comments:	Crawley AS also has other waters containing carp. No keepnets

Nunnery Lake

Location:	Wyke, Chichester; part of the Chichester gravel pits, just off the by-pass
Type and Size:	10 acre matured gravel pit, with very clear water
Carp Stock:	Well stocked with small carp and doubles to about 20lbs
Category:	Mixed Fishery
Other Species:	Roach, rudd, bream, pike and tench
Permits:	Day tickets on bank
Cost:	£3 per day
Control:	Club
BK Rating:	Moderate
W/A:	NRA Southern Region
Comments:	A heavily fished water, and so not very easy to catch the fish, although they take well on the surface at times

Passies Pond

Location:	Coombes, near Shoreham and Steyning
Type and Size:	Recently dug two acre pond with island
How to Find:	Take the A27 from Worthing, and turn left towards Coombes at Lancing. The lake is signposted on the right in about a mile
Carp Stock:	Very heavily stocked with carp to about 12lbs. Many small fish
Category:	Mixed Fishery
Other Species:	Tench, roach, rudd, crucians, chub and perch
Permits:	Day tickets on site from service machine; evening tickets
Cost:	£5 per day for two rods; juniors £3
Control:	Private
Restrictions:	Lots! No night fishing except for local club members; barbless hooks only; no boilies (the best food ever for bigger fish: banning bread would make more sense as this is much poorer food value!); no hemp; no keepnets for large fish
BK Rating:	Moderate
W/A:	NRA Southern Region
Comments:	Some swims reserved for disabled anglers. Good baits are sweetcorn and luncheon meat

Petworth Park

Location:	Petworth Park, Petworth
Type and Size:	Seven acre estate lake in the grounds of a stately home
Carp Stock:	A small number of carp to over 20lbs
Category:	Few Carp
Other Species:	A few big pike, tench, roach and perch
Permits:	Portsmouth and District AS. Mr R Snook, 86 Carnarvon Road, Copnor, Portsmouth PO2 7NL. Tel: Portsmouth 662986
Control:	Club
Restrictions:	Fishing 9am till dusk only. Only 20 anglers per day. Members of Portsmouth and District AC must book by telephone before fishing - details and phone number from Mr Snook or Petworth Park Estate Office
BK Rating:	Difficult
W/A:	NRA Southern Region
Comments:	This is a very beautiful Estate, and the mansion is often open to the public; details from the Estate Office

Rivers Arun and Adur

Location:	Arun from Pulborough northwards, Adur from Henfield near Brighton northwards
Type and Size:	Some big carp
How to Find:	The Arun runs from Littlehampton through Arundel to Pulborough; and Adur from Hove northwards
Carp Stock:	Not known
Category:	Few Carp
Other Species:	General coarse fish
Permits:	Local angling clubs and tackle shops
Cost:	On application
Control:	Clubs, CALPAC has fishing on these rivers and others, also canals and lakes. Send SAE to CALPAC, 93 Chapel Way, Epsom Downs, Surrey KT18 5TD
BK Rating:	Very Difficult
W/A:	NRA Southern Region
Comments:	As usual with rivers, location is the main problem. Try slower stretches, backwaters and bays. Carp to 20lbs+ have been taken in the middle and upper reaches of both rivers. Try also Pulborough AS. M Booth, 5 South Lane, Houghton, Arundel, West Sussex (Arun). Bines Bridge stretch good on River Adur - many big carp seen basking in weed. Floating crust good. Best legering results from 'Snatcher's Hole', above Bines Bridge

River Ouse

Location:	Barcombe Mills, near Lewes
Type and Size:	33 mile long river
Carp Stock:	A few good carp reported to about 20lbs, in the Barcombe Mills area, and possibly in other sections of the river
Category:	Few Carp
Other Species:	Sea trout (believe it or not!) and some big ones too; perch, bream, roach, dace, chub and pike
Permits:	Old Mill Farm, Barcombe has day tickets. Other tickets from Ouse APS, Dr J L Cotton, Down End, Kingston Road, Lewes
Control:	Private and Club
Restrictions:	Some areas reserved for sea trout fishing; season tickets limited on club stretches
BK Rating:	Very Difficult
W/A:	NRA Southern Region

Roosthole

Location:	Hammer Pond Road, Horsham
Type and Size:	Clay pit of 3½ acres
How to Find:	The lake is in the town of Horsham, find Hammer Pond Road
Carp Stock:	Quite well stocked with small carp and about 20 doubles, best fish 26lbs mirror
Category:	Mixed Fishery
Other Species:	Pike, bream, roach, rudd, perch
Permits:	Season tickets from Horsham and District Angling Association. Secretary: G Kempson, 11 Clarence Road, Horsham
Cost:	About £28 per year to include other club waters

Baits/Methods:	Normal carp methods and all types of baits. Floaters work well
Control:	Club
BK Rating:	Very Difficult
Restriction:	No night fishing, fishing 4am till 11pm. Prebaiting banned. No litter
W/A:	NRA Southern Region
Comments:	Very clear water and depths to 22 feet. Many snags. A peaceful lake, not heavily fished. Much larger carp are said to be in the water, but have not been caught, and the 22lb mirror has only been taken once in the last 5 years

Rother A.C. Lakes

Location:	Near Midhurst
Type and Size:	3 lakes and River Rother
How to Find:	Enquire locally
Carp Stock:	Some carp
Category:	Mixed Fisheries
Other Species:	General coarse fish
Permits:	Day tickets from Rice Bros, West Street; The Rother Inn, Lutener Road
Cost:	Annual subscription about £10 with a £6 entry fee. Secretary: D Merritt, 17 Sandrock, June Lane, Midhurst
BK Rating:	Insufficient information
Control:	Club
W/A:	NRA Southern Region

Soake Pond

Location:	Denmead, near Chichester
Type and Size:	A very rich and attractive two acre lake
Carp Stock:	A good number of carp to over 20lbs
Other Species:	Roach, perch, pike, tench and rudd
Permits:	Portsmouth and District AS. Mr R Snook, 86 Carnarvon Road, Copnor, Portsmouth PO2 7NL. Tel: Portsmouth 662986
Control:	Club
BK Rating:	Moderate
W/A:	NRA Southern Region
Comments:	This water has been run as a specimen fishery for nearly 20 years, so it should contain some very big fish. All information from Mr Snook

Southern Leisure Centre

Location:	Wyke, near Chichester
Type and Size:	3 fair sized gravel pits
How to Find:	On the A27 from Chichester, to the south of the city
Carp Stock:	Ivy, Nunnery and Triangle Lakes contains plenty of carp, up to upper doubles
Category:	Mixed Fishery
Other Species:	General coarse fish
Permits:	On site. Tel: Chichester 787715
Cost:	Approximately £2-£3 per day
Control:	Southern Leisure Centre

BK Rating: Moderate
W/A: NRA Southern Region
Comments: Very heavily fished in summer, and fishing can be difficult at times. Now taken over by Chichester DAS

Stemps Wood Pond

Location: On a farm near Bognor Regis
Type and Size: One acre farm pond in woodland
Carp Stock: Some commons, sizes not known
Other Species: Tench, rudd and crucians
Permits: Details from Mr R Snook, 86 Carnarvon Road, Copnor, Portsmouth PO2 7NL. Tel: Portsmouth 662986
Control: This pond is controlled by Bognor Regis AC, a member of the Hants and Sussex Anglers Alliance - details from Mr Snook above
BK Rating: Not known
W/A: NRA Southern Region
Comments: A newly opened water, rebuilt and stocked from an overgrown derelict farm pond by the hard work of members of the Bognor club

Tilgate Park Lake

Location: Crawley
Type and Size: Estate type of lake of 10 acres
How to Find: Ordnance Survey Sheet No. 187. Reference: 278 345
Carp Stock: Many small commons and a few double figure mirrors to about 22lbs
Category: Mixed Fishery
Other Species: General coarse fish, including large pike
Permits: From park keepers on bank - day tickets at £4
Control: Council
Restrictions: No night fishing
BK Rating: Very Difficult
W/A: NRA Thames Region
Comments: A 'public' water; windsurfers, canoeists and dog walkers. There is even said to be a ghost which joins you in your bivvy! You need to find out the movements of the carp for success, not too easy with a casual approach

Triangle Lake

Location: Chichester gravel pits, just off the by-pass
Type and Size: 6 acre pit
Carp Stock: Well stocked with carp to about 17lbs
Category: Mixed Fishery
Other Species: Roach, crucians, rudd, bream and pike
Permits: Day tickets on site at low cost
Control: Private
Baits/Methods: Quite hard fished water, so sophisticated methods and baits needed; fixed lead methods and pop-ups work well
BK Rating: Moderate
W/A: NRA Southern Region

Wyke Lake

Location: On the Chichester by-pass
Type and Size: Gravel pit of about 8 acres
How to Find: From Bognor Regis, take the Chichester road and turn right towards Portsmouth at the roundabout just before Chichester. The lake will be seen on the right - it is the third lake along
Carp Stock: Quite well stocked with carp to upper twenties, and one known 30
Category: Mixed Fishery
Other Species: Most other coarse fish to a good size
Permits: Chichester and District Angling Society. Membership Secretary: Mr C Few, Fisherman's Den, 5 Canada Grove, Bognor Regis, West Sussex. Season tickets only. Membership includes 3 other lakes and some stretches of river. The lakes all contain carp
Cost: £12 annual subscription plus a £10 entry fee. Juniors/OAPs about £6 entry fee and approximately £5 annual subscription. OAPs about £3 annual subscription only
Control: Club
BK Rating: Moderate
W/A: NRA Southern Region
Comments: Chichester, Bognor Regis and Portsmouth clubs all have gravel pits in this area, most of which contain carp, including the Southern Leisure Centre. Enquire from tackle shops. Chichester AS also has Westhampnett lake, on the A27, a good doubles water

WEST YORKSHIRE

Brookfoot Lake

Location:	Brighouse, off the A6025 Brighouse-Elland road - parking at the Grove Motel
Type and Size:	Small lake
Carp Stock:	Well stocked with carp, to about 20lbs
Category:	Mixed Fishery
Other Species:	Rudd, tench, perch, roach and pike
Permits:	Day tickets from Calder Angling Supplies, Gooder Lane, Brighouse and Pondworks Angling Supplies, 364 Bradford Road, Bailiff Bridge, Brighouse at £1.50; 75p for juniors
Control:	Brighouse Angling Association. M Riley, 30 Ravenstone Drive, West Vale, Greetland, Halifax. Tel: 0484 711063
BK Rating:	Very Easy
Restrictions:	No Sunday fishing; limited numbers. Carp must not be kept in nets
W/A:	NRA Yorkshire Region

Clayton Ponds

Location:	Clayton Wood Road, Leeds
Type and Size:	Two small ponds
How to Find:	Off the Leeds ring road
Carp Stock:	Some carp to double figures
Category:	Few Carp
Other Species:	Tench, roach, perch and big eels
Permits:	Day and season tickets at low cost from Abbey Match Anglers, Commercial Road, Kirkstall, Leeds; and Headingly Angling Centre, Headingly
Control:	Fox and Hounds Angling Club
BK Rating:	Difficult
W/A:	NRA Yorkshire Region

DAF Trucks Pond

Location:	Mirfield, just south of Dewsbury
Type and Size:	Small pond
Carp Stock:	Well stocked with small carp
Category:	Mixed Fishery
Other Species:	Usual coarse fish
Permits:	Enquire locally, or from tackle shops in Dewsbury
BK Rating:	Easy
W/A:	NRA Yorkshire Region

Doe Park Reservoir

Location:	Denholme, between Halifax and Keighley
Type and Size:	20 acre reservoir
How to Find:	Take the A629 from Halifax towards Keighley, and the fishery is at Denholme, on the right hand side of the road
Carp Stock:	Some carp, sizes not known
Category:	Few Carp
Other Species:	Bream, tench, roach, rudd, pike, chub and trout
Permits:	Day tickets from the keeper's house at Doe Park, and from Richmonds, 110 Morley Street, Bradford
Cost:	£2.20 per day
Control:	Bradford City Angling Association. Secretary: H Briggs, 4 Brown Hill Close, Birkinshaw, Bradford, West Yorkshire
BK Rating:	Difficult, as there are not many carp
Restrictions:	No night fishing (starts 7am). Fishing is from June 1st until the end of February. Entrance only from the marked gates
W/A:	NRA Yorkshire Region
Comments:	Bradford City AA issues tickets for other lakes, the canal and rivers

Flanshaw Dam

Location:	Flanshaw Lane, Flanshaw, Wakefield
Type and Size:	Tiny park pond of about half an acre
Carp Stock:	Quite well stocked with carp to about 10lbs
Category:	Mixed Fishery
Other Species:	Bream, tench and roach
Permits:	Day tickets from clubhouse on site; £1
Control:	Wakefield Angling Club. Tel: 0924 827401 or 0924 369556 (clubhouse)
Restrictions:	No night fishing; barbless hooks
BK Rating:	Not known
W/A:	NRA Yorkshire Region

Hemsworth Water Park

Location:	Kinsley, near Wakefield, off the B6273
Type and Size:	Two lakes of 4½ and 1½ acres
Carp Stock:	Some carp to doubles
Category:	Mixed Fishery
Other Species:	Bream, tench, roach and chub
Permits:	£1.30 per day on site
Control:	Hemsworth Water Park. Michael Skues. Tel: 0977 612274

BK Rating: Insufficient information
W/A: NRA Yorkshire Region
Comments: Special stands for disabled anglers. Larger lake used for water sports

Hill Top Reservoir

Location: Longlands Road, Hill Top, near Huddersfield
Type and Size: 11 acre reservoir
How to Find: Off the A62, seven miles south west of Huddersfield
Carp Stock: Some carp
Category: Few Carp
Other Species: Roach, perch, bream and pike
Permits: Day tickets from the Albion Inn, Longroyd Bridge, Slaithwaite
Control: Slaithwaite and District Angling Club
BK Rating: Difficult
W/A: NRA Yorkshire Region

Horbury Quarry

Location: Horbury Junction, near Wakefield
Type and Size: 15 acres, very deep sand quarry
Carp Stock: Not many, but they go to upper doubles
Category: Few Carp
Other Species: Roach, bream, perch and pike
Permits: Season tickets only from Wakefield AC. Secretary: B D Harper, 29 Victoria Crescent, Horsforth, Leeds
Control: Club
BK Rating: Very Difficult
W/A: NRA Yorkshire Region

Kettlethorpe Hall Lake

Location: Kettlethorpe Hall, near Wakefield
Type and Size: Small estate lake of about 2 acres, very attractive, with islands
Carp Stock: Heavily stocked with commons and mirrors average size about 4lbs, but possibly one or two of 10lbs or just over
Category: Carp Water
Other Species: Roach and pike
Permits: Season tickets from local tackle shops
Control: Wakefield AC. B D Harper, 29 Victoria Crescent, Horsforth, Leeds
BK Rating: Very Easy
Restrictions: No night fishing
W/A: NRA Yorkshire Region
Comments: A good, easy water to start carp fishing on, in spite of the fact that it is hard fished

Kippax Pond

Location: Brigshaw Lane, Kippax, Leeds
Type and Size: Small marshland pond
Carp Stock: Very well stocked with carp to upper doubles
Category: Mixed Fishery

Other Species: Roach and other coarse fish
Permits: Leeds and District ASA, members only, but open to all - The Secretary,
                    Leeds and District ASA, 75 Stoney Rock Lane, Beckett Street, Leeds
                    LS9 1TB - £24 per season
BK Rating: Easy
Restrictions: No night fishing; no day tickets; no Chum Mixers or similar baits (!)
Control: Club
W/A: NRA Yorkshire Region

Knotford Lagoon

Location: 1½ miles from Otley, near Leeds
Type and Size: Large lake
How to Find: The fishery is just off the A659 Otley-Pool road
Carp Stock: Not many carp, but a few large fish to well over 20lbs
Category: Few Carp
Other Species: Tench, roach, chub, perch and trout
Permits: Day tickets from Angling and Countrysports, Pool Road, Otley and
                    Leeds tackle dealers
Control: Club
BK Rating: Very Difficult
W/A: NRA Yorkshire Region

Leeds to Liverpool Canal

Location: Three miles between Lodge Hill Bridge and Swine Lane Bridge
Type and Size: Narrow canal
Carp Stock: Well stocked with carp, mostly small, but some to doubles
Category: Mixed Fishery
Other Species: Bream and roach
Permits: Members only water of Marsden Star AC, Colne (try local tackle shops
                    for permits and details)
Cost: £12 per season, members only
Control: Club
BK Rating: Easy
W/A: NRA Yorkshire Region

Magdale Dam

Location: Honley, near Huddersfield, off the A616 Huddersfield-Holmfirth road
Type and Size: Medium-sized dam
Carp Stock: Plenty of carp to double figures
Category: Mixed Fishery
Other Species: Crucians, perch and rudd
Permits: Apply to Peter Budd, 39 Derwent Road, Honley, near Huddersfield.
                    Tel: Huddersfield 660258
Cost: £8 for the season, £4 for juniors. Free to registered disabled persons
Control: Holme Valley Piscatorials Association
BK Rating: Moderate
W/A: NRA Yorkshire Region
Comments: This is a purpose-built fishery, with ramps and stands for disabled
                    anglers. Club membership is open to all

New Miller Reservoir

Location: Off the A61 at Kettlethorpe, near Wakefield
Type and Size: About 70 acres, very pleasant but busy
Carp Stock: Not many carp, but some 20's
Category: Few Carp
Other Species: Most coarse fish, and some trout
Permits: Season tickets only, from local tackle shops
Control: Wakefield AC. B D Harper, 29 Victoria Crescent, Horsforth, Leeds
Restrictions: No night fishing
BK Rating: Super-Difficult
W/A: NRA Yorkshire Region

Nostell Priory   A

Location: Nostell Priory, near Wakefield
Type and Size: 3 lakes of 26 acres, 7 acres and 6 acres
How to Find: Just off the A638 Wakefield to Doncaster road
Carp Stock: All 3 lakes are well stocked with carp and fish of over 20lbs have been reported from all 3 lakes
Category: Mixed Fishery
Other Species: Bream, perch and pike to over 30lbs
Permits: Day tickets and season tickets from the fishery shop. Information from John Austerfield or Tony Frost on 0924 863562
Cost: £3 per day. £2 for half day, from 7am to 1pm or 1pm till dusk. Season tickets £30 for top or bottom of lake, or £60 for all three
Control: Head Bailiff, Foulby Lodge, Foulby, Wakefield. Tel: Wakefield 863562
BK Rating: Moderate
Restrictions: No keepnets; no night fishing, except by arrangement on Upper Lake
W/A: NRA Yorkshire Region
Comments: In the grounds of a stately home owned by the National Trust. Fishing shop on lakeside. Touring caravans and tents welcome on the adjacent 30 acre woodland park. Tel: 0924 863938. Some close season fishing. Fish tackle and baits on sale

Nunroyd Pond

Location: Guiseley; Nunroyd Park, Guiseley - off the A65 Leeds-Ilkley road
Type and Size: Small park lake
Carp Stock: Some carp, sizes not known
Category: Few Carp
Other Species: Roach, tench
Permits: Membership from Abbey Match Anglers, Commercial Road, Kirkstall, Leeds
Control: Aireborough and District AA. Members only, open to all
BK Rating: Difficult
Restrictions: No night fishing. Barbless hooks
W/A: NRA Yorkshire Region

Oulton Hall Pond

Location: Rothwell Sports Centre, off the M62 at junction 20, following the Rothwell-Oulton signs. In the grounds of Oulton Hall

Type and Size: New 1½ acre pond

Carp Stock: Plenty of commons and mirrors

Category: Mixed Fishery

Other Species: Crucians, bream, tench, roach, rudd, perch, gudgeon and pike

Permits: Day tickets from Rothwell Sports Centre, opposite the fishery

Control: Leeds City Council Leisure Services

BK Rating: Not known

Pastures Pond

Location: Allerton Bywater, just off the A639, between Castleford and Leeds, and close to the river

Type and Size: Shallow, 5 acre lake

Carp Stock: A very small number, though a common of over 30lbs has been reported

Category: Few Carp

Other Species: Most coarse fish

Permits: From tackle shops in Castleford and Leeds

Control: Private

BK Rating: Very Difficult

Restrictions: Fishing from one bank only (nearest garage)

W/A: NRA Yorkshire Region

Comments: No close season; very snaggy and difficult water

Pugney's Lake

Location: Crofton, near Wakefield

Type and Size: Very large, open park lake

How to Find: Take junction 39 from the M1, and at the roundabout take the Wakefield road, then the second right to Crofton; Pugney's Country Park

Carp Stock: Some carp, sizes not known

Category: Few Carp or possibly Mixed Fishery

Other Species: Bream, tench and perch

Permits: From reception at the entrance to the park - low cost day tickets

Control: Wakefield Metropolitan District Council

BK Rating: Not known

Restrictions: No night fishing

W/A: NRA Yorkshire Region

Comments: There is windsurfing and sailing on the big lake. Club matches can be booked

Roberts Pond

Location: Behind Roberts Dye Works, Beechcliff, Keighley, off the Keighley to Skipton road

Type and Size: Small pond

Carp Stock: Some carp, number and sizes not known

Category: Probably Few Carp

Other Species: Bream, tench, roach, perch and pike
Permits: Keighley Angling Club, members only but open to all - Mr D Ward, 4
Compeigne Avenue, Keighley
Control: Club
W/A: NRA Yorkshire Region

Roundhay Park Lakes

Location: Roundhay Park, 4 miles from Leeds
Type and Size: Two lakes, both of which contain some carp
Carp Stock: Some carp in both lakes, sizes not known
Category: Mixed Fishery
Other Species: Pike, perch, roach, tench, bream
Permits: Leeds and District AA. Secretary: G Copley, Anglers Club, Becket
Street, Leeds LS9 1TB
Cost: On application
BK Rating: Moderate
W/A: NRA Yorkshire Region

Southern Washlands

Location: Outskirts of Wakefield
Type and Size: Two small lakes created by Wakefield District Council on a recently
reclaimed site
Carp Stock: Some carp
Category: Mixed Fishery
Other Species: Bream, perch, roach and gudgeon
Permits: Day tickets from The Match Anglers Shop, off Westgate, Wakefield
Cost: £1.50 per day
Control: Wakefield MDC and Eastmoor AC - information on Eastmoor
membership from Carl Young, 210 Stanley Road, Wakefield.
Tel: 0924 373286
BK Rating: Not known

Sugden End Reservoir

Location: Crossroads, Keighley
Type and Size: Large reservoir
How to Find: Off the A60 Bradford-Skipton road
Carp Stock: Some big carp
Category: Mixed Fishery
Other Species: General coarse fish; large tench
Permits: Keighley AC. L Brocklesby, 11 Eelholme View Street, Keighley
(information only)
Cost: Day tickets - about £2. Season - approximately £10. From local
tackle shops
BK Rating: Moderate
Control: Club
W/A: NRA Yorkshire Region
Comments: The Keighley club also has other waters containing carp

Ulley Country Park

Location: Near Rotherham, off the A618 Pleasley Road
Type and Size: Large reservoir, 30 acres and very deep
Carp Stock: Some carp, to mid-doubles
Category: Mixed Fishery
Other Species: Bream, roach, perch, pike and trout
Permits: Tickets from a vending machine in the car park (I expect they have robot bailiffs also!)
Control: Rotherham MBC. Information on 0709 365332
BK Rating: Very Difficult
Restrictions: No night fishing
W/A: NRA Yorkshire Region
Comments: This is part of Ulley Country Park, which is a nature reserve. Anglers leaving litter will be ordered by the rangers to leave the fishery; sailing on the lake

Wentworth Fishery-Greasborough Dam

Location: East Lodge, Greasborough
Type and Size: Two small estate lakes
How to Find: Take the B6089 from Rotherham and after Greasborough, turn left at East Lodge and the fishery is 300 yards
Carp Stock: Well stocked with carp to upper 20's
Category: Mixed Fishery
Other Species: Big bream and tench, roach, big perch and trout to 10lbs
Permits: Season tickets only. Applications in writing only to: Fitzwilliam Wentworth Amenity Trust, Estate Office, Clayfields Lane, Wentworth, Rotherham S62 7TD
BK Rating: Not known
Control: Estate
W/A: NRA Yorkshire Region
Comments: A pleasant water with lilies and easy access. There is also a fly only trout lake on the site

Whitefields Reservoir

Location: Near Keighley
Type and Size: Reservoir
How to Find: Off the A60 Bradford-Skipton road near Keighley. Enquire at tackle shops
Carp Stock: Some carp in both waters
Category: Mixed Fisheries
Other Species: Tench, roach, perch, pike
Permits: Keighley AC. L Brocklesby, 11 Eelholme View Street, Keighley (information only)
Cost: Approximately £2 per day; about £10 per season. Tickets from local tackle shops
BK Rating: Moderate
Control: Club
W/A: NRA Yorkshire Region
Comments: Large carp also in Sugden End Reservoir, Keighley AC

Workshop Lake

Location: Fairburn, off the A1 near Castleford; correct name is Newton Lane Pond
Type and Size: 4 acre snaggy lake
Carp Stock: Very well stocked with over 150 carp to low doubles, and a 20lb 10oz mirror caught in November 1991
Category: Mixed Fishery
Other Species: Usual coarse fish
Permits: Tel: 0924 863618. £13 + £5 for special carp permit
Control: Walton AC. Season tickets only; night fishing for members only. Tel: 0226 724771 (L Gray).
Restrictions: All carp to be returned immediately. Waiting list for carp fishing
BK Rating: Easy
W/A: NRA Yorkshire Region

Workshop Ponds

Location: Charles Roberts Factory, Horbury Junction, near Wakefield
Type and Size: Three acre weedy lake used as a water supply for the factory
Carp Stock: Quite well stocked to lower doubles
Category: Mixed Fishery
Other Species: Roach, rudd and bream
Permits: Charles Roberts Angling Club, hard to obtain - enquire locally
BK Rating: Moderate
W/A: Yorkshire
Comments: A heavily weeded works pond, attractive and used by match anglers

Yeadon Tarn

Location: Cemetery Road, Yeadon, between Bradford and Harrogate
Type and Size: Large lake
Carp Stock: Quite well stocked with carp to double figures
Category: Mixed Fishery
Other Species: Tench, roach, bream, trout
Permits: Day tickets from Abbey Match Anglers, Commercial Road, Kirkstall, Leeds. Tel: 744562; The Sweet Shop, Albert Square, Yeadon and Tobacconist, High Street, Yeadon
Control: Aireborough and District Angling Association
Restrictions: No night fishing. No fishing from the Sailing Club jetty whilst sailing is taking place
Baits/Methods: Luncheon meat said be good for the bigger carp
BK Rating: Moderate
W/A: NRA Yorkshire Region
Comments: Big open lake, used also for sailing. Level banks ideal for the disabled

New and best selling carp videos from Beekay Publishers. See page 19

487

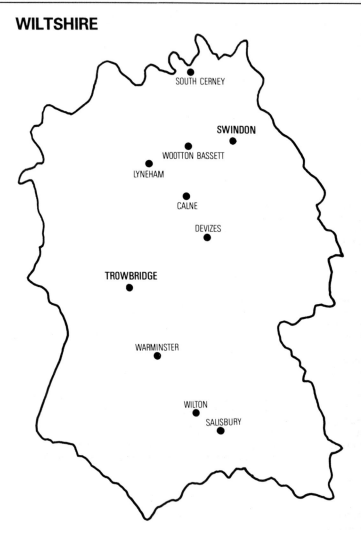

WILTSHIRE

SOUTH CERNEY

SWINDON

WOOTTON BASSETT

LYNEHAM

CALNE

DEVIZES

TROWBRIDGE

WARMINSTER

WILTON

SALISBURY

Barn Moor Lake

Location:	Witherington Farm, Downton, Salisbury
Type and Size:	1½ acre lake
How to Find:	Take the right hand Alderbury turn off the A36 Salisbury-Southampton road. Take the first right turn and the farm is three miles further on, on the right hand side
Carp Stock:	Well stocked with mirrors to 10lbs, and commons to 15lbs
Category:	Mixed Fishery
Other Species:	Tench and roach
Permits:	Day tickets from owner on bank
Cost:	£3. 50 per day - half price for junior and OAP's
Control:	Private

Restrictions: No keepnets; no boilies or high protein baits(!)
BK Rating: Moderate
W/A: NRA Wessex Region

Bowood Lake

Location: Bowood, near Calne
Type and Size: 20 acre estate Lake
How to Find: Bowood Estate near Calne
Carp Stock: Some carp, including doubles
Category: Few Carp
Other Species: General coarse fish
Permits: Bowood Estate, Bowood, Calne
Cost: On application
BK Rating: Difficult
Control: Private
Restrictions: No fishing at the north end of the lake
W/A: NRA Wessex Region
Comments: This beautiful lake contains big pike, and possibly a few big carp

Coate Water

Location: Coate Water Country Park, Marlborough Road, Swindon
Type and Size: Large old lake of about 70 acres
How to Find: Southern outskirts of Swindon
Carp Stock: Few original fish up to 23lbs. Recently stocked with a number of small carp. A 28 was caught in 1988
Category: Mixed Fishery
Other Species: Large bream, tench, roach, pike perch
Permits: On bank; ticket machine
Cost: £1.20 per day - season night tickets for Swindon residents
Control: Thamesdown Borough Council, Euclid Street, Swindon. Tel: 0793 490150
BK Rating: Difficult
W/A: NRA Thames Region
Comments: A big lake made famous by the writings of naturalist Richard Jefferies who lived on the bank. Boats and people - a 'public' water

Flamstone Cottage

Location: Bishopstone, near Salisbury
Type and Size: Small stream fed pool
How to Find: South West of Salisbury off the A354
Carp Stock: Well stocked with carp to 19lbs
Category: Carp Water
Other Species: Brown trout to 12lbs; tench, orfe, chub, roach and grayling - all large
Permits: Ealing Angling Centre. Tel: 081-567 3101
Cost: On application
Control: Private
Restrictions: Barbless hooks no larger than size 12, no keepnets
BK Rating: Easy
W/A: NRA Wessex Region
Comments: An exclusive private specimen fishery. Standard baits. Carp by the island, near rushes

Hunters Moon Lodges   A

Location:	Henford Marsh, Warminster
Type and Size:	Pleasant, small farmland lake
Carp Stock:	Said to be some carp, number and sizes not known
Category:	Mixed Fishery
Other Species:	General coarse fish, and some trout
Permits:	Fishing for residents only
Cost:	On application at reception
Control:	Private
BK Rating:	Not known
W/A:	NRA Wessex Region
Comments:	There are a number of well equipped timber built lodges for rent on the site round the lake. Prices vary from £125 to £300 per week. Booking details from Hoseasons Holidays, Sunway House, Lowestoft NR32 3LT. Tel: 0502 500500

Longleat

Location:	Longleat, near Warminster
Type and Size:	Three estate lakes
How to Find:	Off the Warminster - Frome road
Carp Stock:	Some carp to over 20lbs - stocked with 6,500lbs of small carp to 7lbs in 1990 - Top Lake; other lakes have very small carp
Category:	Mixed Fishery
Other Species:	General coarse fish
Permits:	The Bailiff, Parkhill Cottage, Longleat Estate or on bank at £3
BK Rating:	Moderate
Control:	Longleat Estate, contact Pete Bundy. Tel: 0985 215082
Restrictions:	No peas, beans or nuts. No boilies on middle or bottom lakes
W/A:	NRA Wessex Region
Comments:	Watch out for the 'Lions of Longleat!'

Lower Foxhangers   A

Location:	Lower Foxhangers Farm, Rowde, Devizes, Wilts. Tel: 0380 828245
Type and Size:	This farm/guesthouse does not actually have its own fishing, but it is on the edge of the Kennet and Avon Canal, which contains some carp in this area
How to Find:	Take the A361 from Devizes, and the road to the farm will be seen on the right after a few miles
Carp Stock:	Canal contains plenty of common and mirror carp to about 20lbs
Category:	Mixed Fishery
Other Species:	Roach, perch, tench, crucian carp
Permits:	Devizes Angling Association, Secretary, T.W. Fell, 21 Cornwall Crescent, Devizes
Cost:	Day and weekly tickets on application, and also from local tackle shops
BK Rating:	Fairly Hard
Control:	Club
W/A:	NRA Wessex Region
Comments:	Bed and Breakfast accommodation at farm, with good facilities - £28 per night for two. There are also 4 mobile homes to rent close to the canal, each of which sleeps four, and costs from £110 to £160 per week according to the time of year. Enquire from Colin and Cynthia Fletcher at the farm

Old Warden Castle

Location:	Near Tisbury
Type and Size:	Castle lake
How to Find:	Tisbury, near Wilton; off the A30 six miles west of Wilton
Carp Stock:	Some carp
Category:	Mixed Fishery
Other Species:	General coarse fish
Permits:	Tisbury AC, P Lever, 1 Maypole Bungalow, Ansty, Tisbury
Cost:	On application
BK Rating:	No information
Control:	Club
Restrictions:	Not known
W/A:	NRA Wessex Region

Petersfinger Lakes

Location:	Two miles east of Salisbury just off the A36 Warminster road
Type and Size:	Two large estate lakes in nature reserve
Carp Stock:	Well stocked with good carp to 24lbs, including commons and mirrors
Category:	Mixed Fishery
Other Species:	Bream to 8¾lbs, tench, perch and pike
Permits:	Salisbury and Dist. Angling Club (members only). Membership Secretary, 29 New Zealand Avenue, Salisbury, Wilts SP2 7JX
Cost:	£43 plus £10 registration fee - reduced prices for local OAP's, juniors and members' wives
Control:	Club
BK Rating:	Moderate
W/A:	NRA Wessex Region
Comments:	This well known and very pleasant fishery is partly surrounded by trees and the surrounding nature reserve is owned by the club

Rowde Lake

Location:	In the village of Rowde, near Devizes
Type and Size:	Small pond of about an acre
Carp Stock:	Fairly well stocked with carp to lower doubles
Category:	Mixed Fishery
Other Species:	General coarse fish, including large crucians
Permits:	From house at lake, which is a caravan site
Cost:	Day tickets to about £1 per day
Control:	Private
BK Rating:	Easy
W/A:	NRA Wessex Region

Silverlands Lake

Location:	Lacock, near Chippenham
Type and Size:	5 acre open gravel pit
How to Find:	Off the A350 between Chippenham and Melksham
Carp Stock:	In the past, very few to 26lbs, but was restocked in 1987 - a 26 pounder was reported in late 1990
Category:	Mixed Fishery

Other Species:	Tench, roach, bream, pike
Permits:	Robs Tackle, 22 Marshfield Road, Chippenham
Cost:	Day and night - approximately £3.00; season about £45
Control:	Private
Restrictions:	Night fishing now allowed
BK Rating:	Moderate
W/A:	NRA Wessex Region
Comments:	A long walk - nearly a mile! - across fields. PM's 25¼ caught here in 1971, is now dead - and the walk nearly killed him too!! A 27 was reported from here in 1991. (Late news is that you can now drive to within 50 yards of the lake).

Steeple Langford Lakes

Location:	Steeple Langford, near Warminster
Type and Size:	Gravel pits
How to Find:	Off the A36 ten miles north west of Salisbury
Carp Stock:	Well stocked with carp to over 20lbs
Category:	Carp Water
Other Species:	General coarse fish
Permits:	From bailiff on site. Salisbury and District AC, R W Hillier, 29 New Zealand Avenue, Salisbury
Cost:	On application
BK Rating:	Difficult
Control:	Club
Restrictions:	Not known
W/A:	NRA Wessex Region
Comments:	Salisbury AC also has other good carp waters

Tockenham Reservoir

Location:	Tockenham, near Lyneham
Type and Size:	Reservoir of 8 acres, recently dredged
How to Find:	Off the main Lyneham - Wootton Bassett road. Turn left just outside Lyneham. Down land about 150 yards on right
Carp Stock:	Stocked with about 600 carp of 2-4lbs and about 30 bigger fish to 20lbs. Good head of doubles including commons
Category:	Carp Water
Other Species:	Tench, bream, roach
Permits:	Bristol and District Amalgamated Anglers, membership open to all: Season only. Secretary, J Parker, 16 Lansdowne View, Kingswood, Bristol BS14 4AW
Cost:	About £15 per season
Restrictions:	No night fishing
Baits/Methods:	Normal carp fishing methods, boilies and floaters
Control:	Club
BK Rating:	Easy
W/A:	NRA Wessex Region
Comments:	A very pleasant club water but hard fished especially during the summer. Carp harder to catch as season progresses. Stock fish said to be growing well and now averaging about 8lbs in weight

Wick Water

Location:	Near South Cerney
Type and Size:	Gravel pit of 7 acres
How to Find:	Take the Cerney Wick road from South Cerney and turn right onto the Spine Road at the first crossroads. Wick Water is on the left shortly after the turn
Carp Stock:	About 100 carp to low twenties
Category:	Mixed Fishery
Other Species:	General coarse fish
Permits:	South Cerney Angling Club. Secretary, Fisherman's Rest, Broadway Lane, South Cerney (Send SAE)
Cost:	£13 per season
Restrictions:	No night fishing
Control:	Club
BK Rating:	Fairly Hard
W/A:	NRA Thames Region

Wootton Bassett Lake

Location:	Wootton Bassett, near Swindon
Type and Size:	Small pond of about 1 acre
Carp Stock:	Quite well stocked with carp to low doubles
Category:	Mixed Fishery
Other Species:	General coarse fish
Permits:	Wootton Bassett Angling Club; members only, and you will need to live in the Wootton Bassett area. Secretary, T Strange, 15 Shakespeare Road, Wootton Bassett, Swindon, Wilts.
Control:	Club
BK Rating:	Easy
W/A:	NRA Thames Region

THE BEEKAY GUIDE TO 1500 BRITISH & EUROPEAN CARP WATERS

Is YOUR Water listed? If so, are the details correct?

If you spot omissions, inaccuracies, or know of any changes, please let us know by filling in the Waters Questionnaire at the back of this guide and return it to us at:

FREEPOST
Beekay Publishers
Withy Pool
Henlow Camp
Bedfordshire
SG16 6EA

EUROPEAN SECTION

On our last revision, we resisted the temptation to start listing waters in other European countries but during the last three years so many anglers have been fishing for carp in these countries that we decided to start a small European section.

Needless to say, information has been hard to obtain, and we are very grateful to those who have helped, especially to Bill Turner, Marc Ponsot, Sven Heininger who supplied the section on Germany, and Norman Smith who wrote the section on Spain.

If you know of any waters in any other country you would like listed please let us know about them in time for the next edition of this book.

We would urge all those who go to fish in other countries to remember that *they* are the foreigners, and that they should behave well at all times. Buy all the licences, and keep to all laws and rules; this way, you will help to give English anglers a good name. In some European countries, laws and rules are especially strict, and may be enforced by armed police and rangers.

Already some English carp anglers have become unpopular in France, especially at Lake Cassien, where many English anglers have ignored the rules, and have been caught and had their tackle confiscated. They have also upset local anglers, and have caused trouble in other ways. We have a picture of huge piles of 'English' litter left by English anglers at Lake Cassien, whilst in Holland, the Dutch, who are some of the most pleasant and friendly people we have ever met, already have a bad opinion of some English anglers, and are reluctant to have them on their waters. This especially applies to the lakes, where, so we are told by the Dutch, English anglers often 'bivvy up' for days, weeks, and in some cases, even for months, thus spoiling the fishing for the locals, and often drinking too much and behaving like English football hooligans.

If you cannot behave, and keep to all rules and laws when fishing abroad, you should not go to other countries; if you do, be well-behaved and friendly to local people and anglers, and you will help to restore the good name of English anglers - don't forget, it is *their* country, and whether or not you agree with their laws and rules, you *must* accept them and keep to them whilst you are there. Many fish in European countries are killed and eaten for food (just as English anglers kill sea fish and eat them!) and some English anglers even kill pike in England without even the excuse that they are to eat. If it is the custom to kill fish for food, then it is best to say nothing about it, however much you dislike the idea.

BELGIUM

A Government National Licence is essential to fish nearly all waters. Generally no night fishing but some night fishing is allowed on private waters and there is no close season

DENMARK

There is no close season for carp in Denmark, but there might be restrictions on a chosen water to protect other species.
From 1 January 1993 all who go fishing with rod and line in fresh or saltwater, must have a national licence (Fisketegn). The licences costs 100 dkr (£10) for a year, 75 dkr (£7) for a week and 25 dkr (£2) for a day. This licence does not in itself give permission to fish any water. There is no rod limit.

The licence is obtained at the Post Office and from selected fishery managers and is strictly personal.

In some cases a licence is not required. This applies if the water has no connection to stream, river or beach which fish can pass, as often in trout fisheries with stocking of rainbow trout. People under 18 years and over 67 years do not need a licence.

To fish in freshwater in Denmark, you will need permission, a ticket or membership. If you don't know who to talk to about it, try to ask the local tackle shop/petrol station/grocery or tourist office. Do not just fish, because there are no signs! ("Fiskeri Forbudt"). Very often a water is rented out to hunters who do not take any disturbance lightly.

There is not, as in France and Holland, a large number of public owned waters that a general licence can be bought for.

Catapults of any kind are forbidden to possess or use without permission from the police. The catapult is considered as a weapon and the permission costs approximately 900 dkr! Throwing sticks are legal without permission.

To bivvy up is considered as camping, and requires special permission from the water administrator. Normally there are no problems in private waters. Night fishing is allowed but always check it out, as there might be a ban on a chosen water (often in trout waters).

Carp fisheries as known in England, do not exist in Denmark. The demand is simply not big enough.

Take all the extra carp tackle you need from home. Shops with a decent selection of carp tackle only exist in few numbers, mainly in Copenhagen.

Danish carp fishers return all their fish and use proper slings, sacks and unhooking mats. But still there are holiday anglers who consider all fish as food, especially in mixed trout/carp fisheries, where small carp are stocked.

Any baits can be used. Danish carp fishers use HNV boilies a lot. In heavily fished waters, birds have learned to eat boilies, so be warned! There is often a ban on baiting up in trout fisheries to protect the trout or to make the sport harder. In this case use stringers.

Normally the season starts in May and ends in October, depending on the winter. The last mild winters have provided carp fishing all year round.

The Danish carp are of all kinds, both wild and king, and in all varieties. A standard Danish carp weighs between 5 and 10 kgs, but fish up to 16 kg have been caught and there are rumours about a 20 kg fish. Among Danish carp fishers the presumed maximum weight is 25 kg. As the fishing pressure is very low on most of the waters no one really knows what is out there!

FRANCE

You must have a French National Licence, available from all fishing tackle shops to fish nearly all waters in France. Some are private and an extra permit will be required. Night fishing is not allowed by law on nearly every water in France, although there are a few exceptions. Many of the successful and well known English anglers who caught big fish at Lake Cassien 'made their names' with 50, 60 and 70 pounders.

GERMANY

German anglers have to take a long written examination to obtain a fishing licence, but this is waived for foreigners. A Government licence is normally obtained by all before fishing - this costs about £6 a year from Post Offices. There is no night fishing by law although owners of private waters can allow it, and many fish are killed and eaten. German rules and laws in relation to angling are very strict, so make sure you know what they are and that you keep to them. However, one law that you might choose to break is that *all* fish caught must be killed - the Green Party has managed to get laws passed that fishing is a cruel sport and all fish should be killed and not tortured by returning them alive! Most German anglers, unless fishing for food, do not agree with this law and return the fish alive; the choice is yours!

HOLLAND

You must not fish anywhere in Holland unless you hold a 'Sportvisakte', the national licence which enables you to fish the whole year with two rods. You can fish most Dutch waters with this alone. It can be purchased at all Post Offices and most tackle shops. It only costs about £4 per year. For private waters, you may need another permit, from the club which controls it, or the person who owns the water. If you see the sign 'Verpacht Viswater' the water is *private* and you must get another permit. There is no close season in Holland

Night fishing is normally allowed by law during June, July and August. On many waters you cannot night fish in the other months. Some clubs allow night fishing outside the months listed.

The small private lakes in Holland rarely contain the big fish, and as they are private you should *not* fish this type of water. Many of the big Dutch carp are caught in canals and rivers, and as these are also the most heavily stocked carp waters in Holland, it is these you should fish.

A good map will show large expanses of water to the north of Utrecht, Den Haag (The Hague), and Amsterdam.

All are excellent areas for carp, but the majority of Dutch stock are of the same strain, stocked year after year. this carp strain has about 25 per cent of 'wild blood' in it, which leads to a slower growth rate. This was caused by a group of anglers about 10 to 15 years ago, who said big mirrors and commons were too easy to catch, and that all the lakes should be stocked with wildies!

As a result, the OVB (the Dutch organisation responsible for the stocking of *all* the waters in the country) has stocked with carp of this kind for the last 15 years. Luckily, about a year ago this policy was reversed, and the OVB started stocking again with 'Redmire-type' mirrors.

In short, most Dutch carp are now commons, and the majority of waters do contain beautiful long fish which will easily reach the 20lb mark, but will not often exceed 25lbs.

Catching a bigger fish is difficult, as most of these are quite old, and are normally found only in the bigger lakes, canals and rivers.

Our Dutch informant tells us that ALL waters in Holland contain carp!

SPAIN

Unfortunately the licensing situation in Spain is rather complex. National licences are no longer available and a different licence is required for each of the autonomous regions which also impose their own regulations. ICONA is the body responsible for issuing the licences although in Andalucia (comprising most of the south of Spain) this function is undertaken by IARA.

Tourist licences are available in most areas and although prices vary from region to region one can expect to pay about 1500 pesetas (£8). At the time of applying for one's licence it is also worth asking for a copy of the Boletin Oficial de las norma para la pesca. It is worth struggling through this paper, which is only available in Spanish, as it details all the current regulations regarding angling in that particular area. Local tourist offices often have a leaflet available in English which will give an extract of the more important rules. General rules normally applied include: Two rods per person; fishing is allowed from one hour before dawn to one hour after sunset (this means no night fishing), no camping is permitted on lake or river banks. The night fishing rule is relaxed in some ares but only for the pursuit of Wels catfish (Silurus glanis); this does not apply to carp anglers. In some areas fishing in rivers a close season from April 15th to May 15th is imposed. Generally, carp fishing is carried out in the reservoirs or embalses and we do not know of any area that imposes a close season for coarse fishing here. Controlled fisheries or Cotos do exist and for these it is normally necessary to purchase an additional permit in advance. Elsewhere fishing is generally free. On Cotos the fisheries are controlled by bailiffs or Guardas, elsewhere licences are checked by the Guardia Civil who are armed police and do not take "No" for an answer. Treat them with the utmost respect and do exactly as they say or you could be in big trouble... They are likely to check you at any time of the day or night; you have been warned!

The address of the local licensing authority can be supplied by either the local Tourist Office or police station or can be found in the Yellow Pages (Paginas Amarillas). When applying for the licence you will need to present your passport and the licence will normally be ready for collection the following day, sometimes later the same day.

The Spanish list is only a small selection of the many hundreds of waters available, most of them totally unexplored by carp anglers. We have included some waters well known to British anglers and some that are so far totally unknown except to the locals. We would be grateful if carp anglers visiting Spain would send us details of where they fished and what they caught so we can extend this section in later issues.

AUSTRIA

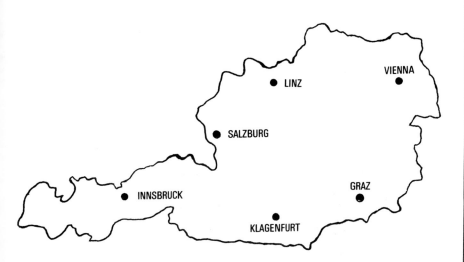

Gosselsdorfer See

Location:	Off the A2 South Motorway at Kärnten, near Klagenfurt
Type and Size:	Old 80 acre lake, very weedy
Carp Stock:	Very well stocked with carp to 40lbs
Category:	Mixed Fishery
Other Species:	Tench, grass carp and catfish
Permits:	Wallerwirt, Seestrasse, Gosselsdorf. Tel: 04236 2168
Cost:	150 Austrian crowns per day; 350 per week
Control:	Private
BK Rating:	Very Difficult
Comments:	Boat fishing essential; lake is full of lilies and is very difficult to fish. Night fishing is allowed. Austrian record carp of about 55lbs was caught from this lake

Irrsee

Location:	Off the A1 motorway at Oberhofen, Oberösterreich
Type and Size:	147 acre lake
Carp Stock:	Well stocked with carp to over 20lbs
Category:	Mixed Fishery
Other Species:	Pike and zander
Permits:	J Hufnagl, Laiter 9, 4894 Oberhofen
Cost:	180 Austrian crowns per day; weekly permits also available
Restrictions:	No night fishing, three rods allowed
Comments:	Famous pike water; best pike caught is 57lbs. No livebaiting

Keutschacher See

Location:	Kärnten, Klagenfurt, off the A2 road
Type and Size:	Lake of 110 acres
Carp Stock:	Well stocked with carp to 35lbs
Category:	Mixed Fishery
Other Species:	Bream, tench, pike and catfish
Permits:	Franzwagner, Plescherken
Restrictions:	No livebaits; two rods allowed; night fishing is permitted
Comments:	Very deep, warm water, with big, powerful fish

Millstatter See

Location:	Off the A2 motorway at Kärnten, near Klagenfurt
Type and Size:	180 acre lake
Carp Stock:	Well stocked with carp to over 40lbs
Category:	Mixed Fishery
Other Species:	Most coarse fish
Permits:	Verkehrsburo Radentheim 9545, Haupstrasse 65. Tel: 04246 2288 or Verkehrsburo Dobriach 9873, Hauptpl 6. Tel: 04246 7727
Cost:	250 Austrian crowns per week; bank fishing, nights allowed. Boat fishing also available, daytime only
Comments:	Biggest known carp caught is over 50lbs

Ossiacher See

Location:	Kärnten, Klagenfurt, off the A2 road
Type and Size:	370 acre lake
Carp Stock:	Well stocked with carp to over 40lbs
Category:	Mixed Fishery
Other Species:	Most coarse fish and large catfish
Permits:	Divided into sections, and permits; from Gerhard Kleindienst, Bodensdorf, Bundesstrasse 6. Tel: 09293 361
Cost:	60 to 100 Austrian crowns per day; also weekly permits
Restrictions:	Night fishing is allowed; two rods; no livebaits
Comments:	Well known as a big catfish water; carp fishing is more recent

Zeller See

Location:	Off the A1 motorway near Salzburg
Type and Size:	120 acre lake
Carp Stock:	Well stocked with carp to over 30lbs
Category:	Mixed Fishery
Other Species:	General coarse fish, with big pike
Permits:	Stadtgem, Zell-am-See, Rathaus 2115 (We think this means the Town Hall!)
Control:	Council
Cost:	100 Austrian crowns per day; guest permits for two weeks
Comments:	Two rods are allowed. Most fishing is for pike, and this is regarded as one of the carp waters of the future in Austria. Best carp to date is about 40lbs

BELGIUM

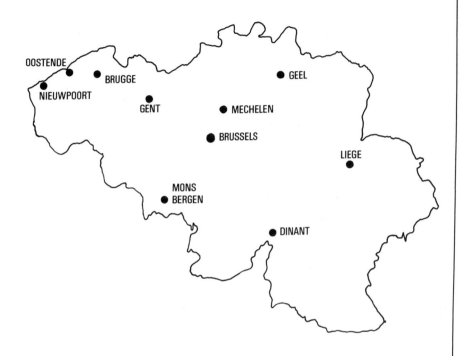

OOSTENDE

BRUGGE

GEEL

NIEUWPOORT

GENT

MECHELEN

BRUSSELS

LIEGE

MONS
BERGEN

DINANT

Eghlegemvyver

Location:	Hombeek, near Mechelen, a city about 40 miles north of Brussels
Type and Size:	92 acre rectangular sandpit
How to Find:	Take the motorway from Ostend to Gent, then the road marked 'Brussels'. Near Brussels follow the ring road, and take the Mechelen exit. At Mechelen take the Hombeek exit
Carp Stock:	Plenty of small carp, and a good number of 20's; best mirror taken was 31lbs and the best common 30lbs
Category:	Mixed Fishery
Other Species:	Pike to 41lbs, bream and big eels
Permits:	On site
Cost:	Day tickets £1.50 per rod; season - £18
Control:	Private
Restrictions:	You can only normally fish from March to the end of September, but the Chairman, Mr R Van Lint, may be able to give permission for fishing at other times. Night fishing only allowed at weekends in May and June
Comments:	This big lake is not far from the pleasant city of Mechelen, and is not a long drive - nearly all motorway - from the port of Ostend

Steve White with a 22.6 from Restaurant de Goorhoeve, near Geel, Belgium

Kalkaert

Location:	Between Middelkerke and Oostende
Type and Size:	Chalk pit of about 20 acres
How to Find:	Follow the coast road from Calais to Ostend
Carp Stock:	Fairly heavily stocked with carp to 38lbs
Category:	Mixed Fishery
Other Species:	Big bream (to which our Belgian correspondent adds '... and I know that carp anglers love them!')
BK Rating:	Moderate
Control:	Private
Permits:	On site
Restrictions:	Long stay fishing not allowed, though you may be able to make an arrangement with the bailiff, to stay longer; night fishing allowed (which is rare in Belgium)
Comments:	Can be fished the whole year, but it is a busy camping site

Montreal

Location:	In the outskirts of the city of Mechelen, which is about 40 miles north of Brussels
Type and Size:	Pleasant town park lake of 5 acres, very busy at most times
Carp Stock:	Said to be the most heavily stocked water in Belgium, with up to 10 doubles caught in a day, and plenty of twenties and smaller carp
Category:	Mixed Fishery
Other Species:	Roach and bream

Permits: Enquire locally, possibly from the restaurant called Montreal, which is on the banks of the lake
Control: Local club - day tickets issued
BK Rating: Very Easy (though PM had a blank there when he fished for a day in January!)
Comments: Plenty of members of the public, dog walkers and water birds, but an attractive, heavily stocked lake where you can hardly fail to catch - or so we're told!

Plassendaalse Vaart

Location: Near Nieuwpoort, in the Ostend area
Type and Size: Big canal, but the best carp area is near the sluices at Nieuwpoort
How to Find: Take the Nieuwpoort road, close to the coast from Calais or Ostend
Carp Stock: Well stocked with carp to all sizes; best caught so far was 47lbs(!)
Category: Mixed Fishery
Other Species: Roach, rudd, bream and eels
Permits: Government licence from any Post Office
Cost: £6 per season
Control: Government
BK Rating: Moderate
Restrictions: Night fishing during June, July and August only
Comments: Rod pods needed for the hard banks. Not a pleasant environment with many tourists. There are many similar canals in Belgium, of which this is a typical example; the canals go from the coast to Brussels, out towards the German border and back via Antwerp to Brugge (Bruges)

Restaurant de Goorhoeve

Location: One mile from Geel, which is 20 miles east of Antwerp
Type and Size: Four lakes
Carp Stock: Heavily stocked with carp to over 30lbs
Permits: Day and night tickets available on the bank
BK Rating: Easy
Comments: The third lake is usually the best, with a good chance of catching many fish

Vossem

Location: Near Zaventem, the Brussels airport
Type and Size: Town park lake of about 45 acres
How to Find: From Brussels take the Zaventem road, and follow the signs to Vossem
Carp Stock: Many very small carp, with a few big ones to 30lbs
Category: Carp Water
Other Species: Some coarse fish
Permits: On site
Cost: £5 per day
Control: Private
BK Rating: Very Easy for the small fish, but Difficult for the big ones
Restrictions: No night fishing
Comments: Long range fishing not necessary — the closer you fish, the bigger fish you are likely to catch

Watersportbaan

Location: Gent, which is south east of Bruges towards Brussels, and is on the motorway
Type and Size: Not very large, long and narrow like a canal
Carp Stock: Heavily stocked with carp, including plenty of 20's
Category: Mixed Fishery
Other Species: Most coarse fish
Permits: Government licence at £6 from any Post Office
Control: Government
Restrictions: No night fishing
BK Rating: Fairly Hard

Please remember –
litter loses fishing.

Take any you find
home with you.

DENMARK

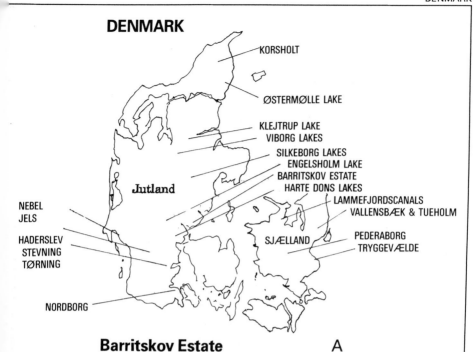

KORSHOLT

ØSTERMØLLE LAKE

KLEJTRUP LAKE
VIBORG LAKES
SILKEBORG LAKES
ENGELSHOLM LAKE
BARRITSKOV ESTATE
HARTE DONS LAKES
LAMMEFJORDSCANALS
VALLENSBÆK & TUEHOLM

Jutland

NEBEL
JELS

HADERSLEV
STEVNING
TØRNING

SJÆLLAND

PEDERABORG
TRYGGEVÆLDE

NORDBORG

Barritskov Estate   A

Location:	25km east from Vejle (E45) in Jutland
Type and Size:	Three very small shallow lakes. Approximately one acre each
How to Find:	Take the road 23 from Vejle and look for the road signs after 25km
Carp Stock:	Lots of small mirrors with some bigger to 25lbs. Average 4lbs
Other Species:	In some other ponds there is a mixed carp/trout fishery
Permits:	On the estate
Cost:	250 kr (£23)/24 hours and 80 kr (£8)/day in trout fishery
Control:	Private, estate office. Tel: 75 69 11 77
Restrictions:	None in carp lakes
Baits/Methods:	Anything that lands in the water
BK Rating:	Easy
Comments:	Accommodation in small cabins around the lakes. Not a decent carp water. Mostly for inexperienced who don't mind easy fish in very small waters

Engelsholm Lake

Location:	Near Nørup, 20 km west of Vejle in Jutland
Type and Size:	80 acres
How to Find:	From Vejle (E45) drive west of the road 28, until sign for Nørup
Carp Stock:	Unknown, but old
Other Species:	Pike to 35lbs, eels to 7lbs, trout
Permits:	From the Q8 gas station in Nørup
Cost:	50 kr (£5) per day
Control:	Nørup-Randbøl Angling Club
Restrictions:	No fishing in bird sanctuary and in marked areas
Comments:	A water unfished by carp anglers. The stream Vejle Å starts here

A well-known Danish carp angler with a big common from a water in Denmark

Haderslev Lake

Location: At Haderslev in southern Jutland
Type and Size: Large 1100 acres mill lake. Many reed beds
How to Find: Located west of Haderslev City
Carp Stock: Unknown but old
Other Species: Pike, eels, bream, roach and perch
Permits: From Sportsmagasinet, Apotekergade 5 in Haderslev. Tel: 74 52 19 55
Cost: 25 kr (£2) per day and 100 kr (£10) per month
Control: Haderslev and Omegn Angling Club
Restrictions: Only bank fishing from public owned bank in eastern part. The areas are pointed out when obtaining the permit
Comments: The local carp fishing takes place in Stevning and Tørning lakes as they are considered the only ones worth trying

Harte-Dons Lakes, Nørre Lake

Location: Near Kolding in Jutland
Type and Size: 90 acres. Very green water (algae)
How to Find: Use junction 63 on the E45/E20 and drive for Dons. Lake on your left
Carp Stock: Mirrors up to 25lbs but not many
Other Species: Pike, roach, tench, eel, perch and bream
Permits: From Steens Jagt and Fiskeri in Kolding, Helligkorsgade 1, 6000 Kolding. Tel: 75 52 85 88. Permit covers three connected lakes
Cost: 30 kr (£3) per day, 150 kr (£14) per week, 300 kr (£28) per year

Control: Kolding Angling Club
Restrictions: Only bank fishing. No fishing for eels
Comments: Some carp fishing has been done here by locals for a number of years

Jels Lakes, Midt-Lake and Neder Lake

Location: Near Jels in southern Jutland
Type and Size: Midt-Lake 60 acres and Neder-Lake is 120 acres. Both are up to 30 feet deep but average is 15 feet. There is also a third smaller lake, that is closed for fishing
How to Find: The lakes are situated just outside the town of Jels
Carp Stock: Mirrors to 30lbs, but otherwise unknown
Other Species: Pike, perch, zander, trout, roach and bream
Permits: From Hotel Jels, Torvet 1, Jels, and from the tourist bureau (Tel: 74 55 21 10) and from the inn "Voldstedet" on the lake bank. From the last place, good advice from the landlord is given
Cost: 40 kr (£4) per day, 125 kr (£12) per week and 250 kr (£24) per year
Control: Jels Fishing Club. Werner Smith. Tel: 74 55 22 23
Restrictions: No returning of roach and bream. If disposal of fish is a problem contact the inn "Voldstedet" who will contact the controllers. The ban is due to a lake rescue programme that removes nuisance fish to restore a healthy balance in the lakes. Programmes like this are normal in Denmark and successful. Carp are not killed in these programmes
Comments: Not much carp fishing is being done here, but the rumours about them have travelled widely. Possibly a number of German anglers have discovered the lake

Klejtrup Lake

Location: North/east of Viborg and west of Hobro
Type and Size: Shallow 300 acre lake. Depth 10 feet
How to Find: 30 km from Viborg and 15 km from Hobro (E45). Drive to the town Klejtrup at the lake. Use road 579 from Hobro and go west until diversion to Klejtrup
Carp Stock: Unknown but old
Other Species: Pike, eel, perch and roach
Permits: Klejtrup kiosk, Viborgvej 3 in Klejtrup
Cost: 25 kr (£2) per day and 100 kr (£10) per year
Control: Klejtrup Fishing Association
Restrictions: Only bank fishing
Comments: This water has received no carp fishing pressure

Korsholt Put and Take

Location: Near Sindal, near Hjørring in north Jutland
Type and Size: A number of small lakes. Maximum three acres
How to Find: Take the E39 to Hjørring, then road 35 to Sindal. Drive through and turn left for Mosbjerg. The fishery is located at Mosbjergvej 135, on your left
Carp Stock: Good head of commons to 25lbs. Mostly smaller fish. The bigger ones live in a separate lake that special permission is needed for
Other Species: Pike and trout
Permits: On the estate

Cost:	125 kr (£12) per day per rod
Control:	Private. Hans Olesen. Tel: 97 93 01 90
Restrictions:	Not known, but some due to the trout fishing
Baits/Methods:	All
Comments:	Some very nice commons have been caught (eg see picture in ABU's Tight Lines from 1990)

Lammefjords Canal

Location:	In the north western part of Sjoelland, near Holbæk
Type and Size:	Two canals. North canal approx 13 miles long and 7-10 yards wide. South canal approx 9 miles long and 10-15 yards wide. Depth from two to five feet. The canal surrounds a very large area of dried out seabed. They end in the sea, protected by sluices
How to Find:	Use road 21 from Holbæk and drive north. The road passes the dam on the seaside
Carp Stock:	North Canal: Many wildies from 1-6lbs, some fish up to 20lb. South Canal: Not so many fish but larger, from 2-12lbs, some fish up to 25lbs
Other Species:	Eels, rudd to 3lbs, roach to 2lbs and ide
Permits:	From the grocery at Audebo (by the south canal on the main road) and from the tackle shop 'Lystfiskeren' in Holbæk in Algade (main street)
Cost:	25 kr (£2) per 24 hours and 200 kr (£19) per year
Control:	Odsherreds Angling Club. Inge Christens. Tel: 53 45 91 87, Nattergalevej 1, 4571 Grevinge
Restrictions:	Maximum two rods. No bivvy on the dam. Only fishing from the dam bank. No digging in dam! No open fires. The rules are necessary to protect the grass and in turn the dam
Baits/Methods:	All methods work well. Float fishing often the best. Sometimes lots of weed and weed cutting. Flow changes all day
BK Rating:	Easy
Comments:	The canals are visited by many anglers, but because of their size fishing pressure is very low, and in some areas nobody comes. Catches of 10 to 30 carp a day is normal. Fish tend to form small shoals

Nebel Lake   A

Location:	Near Vester Nebel, near Esbjerg in southern Jutland
Type and Size:	One larger and three smaller connected dug-out waters. In all 10 acres. Clear water. Mainly a trout fishery
How to Find:	Take the E66 from Esbjerg and after approx 8 km, turn left for Vester Nebel. Drive to the town and ask your way the last 1 km
Carp Stock:	Some fish up to 30lbs, both mirrors and commons. The number of fish is probably very low, perhaps only 20
Other Species:	Trout
Permits:	On site
Cost:	Approx 100 kr (£10) per day per rod
Control:	Private. Aksel Jensen, Vestervadvej 17, 6715 Esbjerg N. Tel: 75 16 94 95
Restrictions:	Carp must be returned. No night fishing. No pre-baiting
Baits/Methods:	Boilies work well
BK Rating:	Difficult
Comments:	The water has its number of regulars who catch well. As the fishing is very expensive very few fish only for carp. There is accommodation in cabins at the lakeside

Nordborg Lake

Location:	Near Nordborg on the island Als east of southern Jutland
Type and Size:	Long and narrow lake of 150 acres. Deep water close to the bank
How to Find:	Drive to Sønderborg and proceed to Nordborg. There are signs all over. Lake is situated on the north side of the town
Carp Stock:	Unknown, but an old stock has been supplemented recently
Other Species:	Pike, roach and bream
Permits:	From Nordals tourist office (in Nordborg). Tel: 74 45 05 92
Cost:	30 kr (£3) per day and 100 kr (£10) per week
Control:	Nordborg Angling Club
Comments:	The water is well known among match fishers but the carp fishing is very limited

Østermølle Lake

Location:	Just outside Dronninglund town in north Jutland, approx 30 km north/east of Ålborg
Type and Size:	Five acre man-made lake with three islands. Depth from 2 to 6 feet
How to Find:	Lake situated just west of town. Small road leads by
Carp Stock:	Mostly commons to 20lbs but some mirrors to 22lbs. Many fish around 10lbs
Other Species:	Grass carp to 10lbs, crucian carp and eels
Permits:	From the tourist office in town and from Metax-Benzin, Slotsgade 55, Dronninglund
Cost:	20 kr (£2) per day and 100 kr (£10) year
Control:	Klokkerholm Angling Club
Restrictions:	Grass carp must be returned. Out of bounds areas marked on ticket
Baits/Methods:	All methods. Boilies work well
BK Rating:	Easy
Comments:	A fairly new water, that has already seen some action, also from locals who eat the carp and see nothing good in returning them. This part of the country is in many ways rather marginal! Birds love boilies. Carp anglers from all over Denmark visit the lake and the carp are beginning to be wary

Pedersborg Lake

Location:	Sorø in the south/west part of Sjoelland
Type and Size:	Long lake of 40 acres with depths up to 20 feet
How to Find:	Take the E20 road to Sorø. The lake is situated in the north/west part of the town. There are two other and much larger lakes around the city
Carp Stock:	Unknown, but some mirrors to 14lbs and a few to 24lbs.
Other Species:	Pike, zander, perch, eel, roach and bream
Permits:	From Boldhuset, Boldhusgade 1 (Tel: 53 63 24 94) in Sorø and from Krebsehuset, Ringstedvej 87 (on the E20) and from the local camping site
Cost:	25 kr (£2) per day
Control:	Sorø Angling Club
Baits/Methods:	All methods
Comments:	These waters are still lightly fished. Carp have been present in the last 300 years together with catfish, but not much is known about the stocks

Silkeborg Lakes

(Silkeborg Langsø, Brassø, Juul sø)

Location:	Around Silkeborg, 40 km from Århus (E45) in Jutland. The lakes are just a small part of a very big lake district all situated around Silkeborg. Maps on site will help you
Type and Size:	It's hard to be precise, but the lakes cover thousands of acres of water and some lakes are deep (100 feet). Don't let the size of these lakes put you off
How to Find:	See location
Carp Stock:	Unknown but old. Mirrors to 22lbs have been caught recently. Not many fish
Other Species:	Pike, perch, zander, trout, turbot, roach, bream, eel
Permits:	From Silkeborg tourist office, Torvet 9, Silkeborg (Tel: 86 82 19 11)
Cost:	35 kr (£3) per day and 95 kr (£9) per week
Control:	Silkeborg Angling Club
Restrictions:	Only fishing from public banks
Baits/Methods:	Boilies work well
BK Rating:	Difficult
Comments:	The lake district around Silkeborg is every year visited by a very large number of British anglers; not carp anglers though. The waters are therefore well investigated by British anglers

Tørning and Stevning Lakes

Location:	West of Haderslev in southern Jutland
Type and Size:	Mill ponds. Shallow and green. 80 acres in all
How to Find:	From E45 take the junction 68 and drive west for Hammelev. Turn left and down in the valley
Carp Stock:	Fish to 30lbs. Mirrors. Not many but high average weight
Other Species:	Pike, eel, roach, bream
Permits:	From the Tørning water mill and from Harry Simonsen (Tørningvej 3, Vojens) who lives at the lake
Cost:	Low
Control:	Haderslev and Omegn Angling Club
Restrictions:	No fishing in the woods
Baits/Methods:	Boilies work well
BK Rating:	Moderate
Comments:	The waters have some fishing pressure, but are still not over-run by carp anglers

Tryggevælde Stream

Location:	South of the city Køge on Sjoelland at Strøby Egede
Type and Size:	Stream, slow current. 15 yards wide. Average depth six feet. Very rich water
How to Find:	Use the E20 or E47/E55 to get to Køge. From there use road 209/261 to get to Strøby Egede, where the stream meets the sea. On this relatively wide beat nearly all fishing is done
Carp Stock:	Unknown, but few fish to at least 18lbs. The stream receives water from carp farms, and therefore also carp fry
Other Species:	Perch to 4lbs, pike to 30lbs, sea trout to 20lbs, bream to 8lbs, roach to 3lbs and ide to 7lbs. Best time is from September till November and from February till May

Permits:	From grocery in Strøby Egede (100 metres from water)
Cost:	35 kr (£3) per day
Control:	Køge Angling Club
Restrictions:	None in carp fishing
Baits/Methods:	All
BK Rating:	Difficult
Comments:	Carp fishing is very hard and the fish landed are very few

Vallensbæk and Tueholm Lakes

Location:	West of Copenhagen near Albertslund (Near Tåstrup)
Type and Size:	Two shallow man-made lakes, fed by rainwater. Weed is scarce. Water colour green. Max depth 7 feet, average 4 feet. Vallensbæk lake is 27 acres and Tueholm lake is 30 acres
How to Find:	The E4 motorway cuts the joined lakes in two. Use the 'Albertslund' junction and drive west. On the north side of the motorway there is an entrance to the car park. The lakes are the largest in the area, so they should be easy to locate
Carp Stock:	The carp were stocked several times starting in the early seventies. Nearly all fish are mirrors but some commons are present. Best fish around 30lbs. The stock consists of a older part with an average of 20lbs and a young part with an average of 10lbs
Other Species:	Grass carp to 18lbs. Pike to 20lbs. Roach, bream, eel, perch, and crucian carp to 5lbs
Permits:	From Shell Service, Albertslundvej 21 and Vestegnens Jagt & Fiskeri in Albertslund city, and from the cafeteria at the lakeside. No permits on bank!
Cost:	10 kr (£1) per day per rod
Control:	VSS Fishing Clubs. Contact: Jørgen Krog. Tel: 43 62 37 25
Restrictions:	Maximum 3 rods per angler. All kinds of carp must be returned. No use of bread. No fishing in certain areas (see map on ticket). No open fires and no fishing from boats
Baits/Methods:	All methods works well
BK Rating:	Moderate
Comments:	This water is birthplace of many Danish carp anglers, and is therefore most heavily fished. The fish however are not as shy as one could fear. Beware that other kinds of anglers also fish here and that the large

number of anglers attract thieves! As the noise from the motorway can be high, don't expect silence. Best places to fish are the areas where the fish can find some rest. Lot of boilie eating birds! You must often walk a long distance as no cars are allowed, so bring a trolley

Viborg Lakes (Nørre and Sønder Lake)

Location:	In Viborg town in Jutland
Type and Size:	Nørre lake is 280 acres and Sønder lake is 300 acres. Deep lakes with green water (algae) and large areas of lilies
How to Find:	Easy location in town
Carp Stock:	Old stock with a small number of fish to 40lbs. Average 15lbs. Both mirrors and commons
Other Species:	Roach, bream, eels, pike
Permits:	None necessary. Free fishing
Cost:	None
Control:	Viborg Tourist Office/the public
Restrictions:	Only fishing from public banks. No camping, but night fishing is allowed
Baits/Methods:	Boilies and particles work well
BK Rating:	Difficult
Comments:	A water with a long history of carp fishing. Most fishing takes place in Sønder lake (the southern one) in the areas with lilies. Many English and German carp anglers visit the water

FRANCE

CALAIS

CHERBOURG

LE HAVRE

ST. MALO

DINAN

RENNES

DREUX

PARIS

CHALONS

METZ

TROYES

CHAUMONT

ORLEANS

NANTES

TOURS

DIJON

NEVERS

CHALON-SUR-SAONE

ARGENTON

TOURNUS

MACON

LYON

BORDEAUX

BISCARROSSE

MIMIZAN

RODEZ

MILLAU

TOULOUSE

MONTPELLIER

MARSEILLE

CANNES

Bazouges Sous Hédé

Location:	Bazouges, Hédé, about 25 miles south of St Malo, near Combourg
Type and Size:	Lake of about 40 acres
Carp Stock:	Well stocked with carp with many upper twenty pound commons; best reported is 36lbs
Category:	Mixed Fishery
Other Species:	Usual coarse fish
Permits:	We are told that this lake is 'on the Brittany licence', but you will have to enquire locally, as Brittany is not a French 'departément', and we cannot find out which 'county' this lake is in
BK Rating:	Moderate
Comments:	The fish are localised and you may not catch unless you locate them. The dam and south west bank by the lilies are the best are. Open all year. May, June, September and October are the best months. Fish not hard to catch once located, as the water is not heavily carp fished

Blois Lake

Location:	Near Blois, 16 miles south west of Orleans
Type and Size:	Natural lake of about 30 acres
How to Find:	From Blois take the 765 road south towards Romorantin. About 3 miles out of Blois turn left towards Barcieux. Before entering the village, take the second dirt track on the right, a rough track which leads to the lake
Carp Stock:	Quite heavily stocked with doubles and twenties
Permits:	From tackle shops in the Market Square at Blois; French national licence
BK Rating:	Easy
Comments:	A good fun water, not suited to the ultra-serious specimen hunter. Crayfish and snaggy areas full of trees can be a problem

Alan Taylor, a regular visitor to France, with a 42 pounder

Bort-les-Orques

Location:	About 40 miles south west of Clermont Ferrand
Type and Size:	Several rivers dammed forming a lake of approximately 1000 acres
How to Find:	Take the E70 out of Clermont heading south west for about 20 miles, then turn left onto the 922 road and the lake can be seen at Bort
Carp Stock:	Reasonable head of carp to at least 45lbs
Permits:	Normal French national licence required
BK Rating:	Moderate
Comments:	Little is known about this water except that it holds huge carp. A lot of potential for the pioneering type of carp angler

Chalet Lake A

Location:	Metz, 20 miles south of St. Avold
Type and Size:	Two very attractive lakes of about 18 acres and 6 acres
Carp Stock:	Heavily stocked with common and mirror carp up to 35lbs. Carp growing at 5-7lbs per season
Category:	Mixed Fishery
Other Species:	Big stocks of grass carp up to 35lb, Koi to over 20lb and loads of catfish to 55lb
Permits:	The fisheries are run by Carp Fishers Abroad and are exclusively let to

small parties. Complete holiday arrangements and permits strictly in advance from 'Carp Fishers Abroad', Rose Cottage, Rodington Heath, near Shrewsbury, Shropshire SY4 4RB. Tel: 0952 770771

BK Rating: Moderate

Comments: Carp Fishers Abroad have the complete package, beautiful and secluded lakes, a chalet on stilts standing in the water and heavy stocks of big carp and catfish. Night fishing and bivvies are no problem whatsoever. The lakes are let to small parties of anglers but can still cope with individuals. This is a water where one phone call will bring you all the directions, information, ferry tickets needed for a really memorable holiday. The lakes do get booked up well in advance so book early. Biggest catch in 1992, 55 carp over 15lbs incuding 34 twenties to two anglers in 6 days

Châteaux du Lorey   A

Location: Normandy, in northern France

Type and Size: Four small lakes on private estate

Carp Stock: Well stocked with carp to over 40lbs; record is 42lbs

Permits: Tel: 010 33 33 45 68 51 (France; English spoken)

Cost: About £35 per person per day, to include accommodation

Restrictions: Little fished; limited to six anglers

BK Rating: Moderate

Comments: Ideal for a family holiday. Accommodation in house - all rooms with private bathroom and food included. Tranquil surroundings, and not far from the ferry ports

Etang de Biscarrosse et Parentis

Location: Biscarrosse, close to the west coast about 40 miles south west of Bordeaux. Shown on all road maps

Type and Size: Dammed river forming a huge reservoir of several thousand acres. Sandy bottomed lake used for drinking water

Carp Stock: Quite well stocked with long lean commons to about 40lbs, plenty of 20's

Permits: French National licence from local tackle shops

BK Rating: Moderate

Comments: This water is partly on an air force base, and is regularly patrolled at night by military police

Etang de Boulet

Location: Feins, about 20 miles north of Rennes in northern France
Type and Size: Dammed river forming a very large, wedge-shaped lake
How to Find: The lake is on the D20, just off the N175 between Rennes and Mont St. Michel
Carp Stock: Lightly stocked with carp averaging over 20lbs; English anglers have had carp to at least 47lbs
Permits: Available from the cafe at Feins - French national licence
BK Rating: Difficult
Comments: A huge boom prevents windsurfers from entering the lake margins, but also causes problems where it is anchored to the bottom. Deeper areas produce the better fish. Hard boilies recommended because of crayfish. There was a fish kill in 1990, but it is still worth fishing

Etang de cloyes sur Loire

Location: About 8 miles south from Châteaudun and 40 miles from Chartres
Type and Size: Old gravel pit of 60 acres near the river Loire
How to Find: Take the D955 from Alençon to Châteaudun
Carp Stock: Well stocked with commons and mirrors and a lake record of 51lbs (common carp)
Other Species: Coarse fish with very big zander over 25lbs
Permits: National French licence plus a day-ticket available on the site
BK Rating: Easy to Moderate
Comments: A lovely lake with a lot of nice commons. Carp fishing is allowed until 11pm

Etang d'Ecluzelles

Location: About 4 miles south of Dreux and 55 miles west of Paris
Type and Size: Dammed stream forming a lake of about 325 acres with varying depths
How to Find: Take the N12 from Alençon to Dreux
Carp Stock: Lightly stocked with some big carp to over 45lbs
Other Species: Coarse fish with big pike and big zander
Permits: French national licence required plus a day ticket from fishing tackle shops in Dreux
BK Rating: Moderate to Fairly Hard
Comments: A beautiful lake with big fish and not far away from Paris. Night fishing is not allowed

Etang d'Entressen

Location: Istres, north west of Marseilles (Bouche du Rhone)
Type and Size: Two lakes of 30 acres and 70 acres, both over 30 feet deep
Carp Stock: Well stocked with carp
Category: Mixed Fishery
Other Species: Tench, zander, gudgeon, roach, rudd, pike, perch and eels
Permits: AAP d'Entressen. Try locally or the Fed Departmentele des AA, 30 Boulevard de la Republique 13100, Aix-en-Provence
Comments: Easy access and little weed. Also very good for pike, perch and zander

S THIS YOUR FORTÉ

40+   **40+**   **40+**

40+   **40+**   **40+**

40+   **40+**   **40+**

── HOOKLENGTHS ARE OURS!! ──

KRYSTON® ADVANCED HOOKLENGTHS – ONCE AGAIN THE NATION'S No. 1 CHOICE

ter records throughout the country have once again tumbled to the leading and thinking anglers who place their faith in our anced lines and hooklengths. Kryston has once more swept the honours field with its unrivalled and unparalleld success. By ducing the largest and greatest range of specialist braided hooklengths in the World our fingers are well and truly on the se of the carp world. Whatever the type of presentational techniques you may wish to pursue we can offer you a specialised to meet those exact requirements. Having pioneered and led the field we have single handedly changed the face of cialist braided lines as we knew them. Kryston have brought them out of the dark ages by utilising ultra modern materials pled with the use of high technology.

♪ SOMETHING IN THE WAY IT MOVES – 'da de da da da de da da' ♪
(With apologies to Shirley Bassey)

SHOULD YOU REQUIRE...

nething that will truly present your bait in a totally realistic and natural manner. Something with such a low diameter that it kes a mockery of conventional breaking strains. Something that would give you choices of buoyancy: neutral, below neutral, ibove neutral. Something that will give you incredible softness and suppleness. Something who's many users would read like 'Who's Who,' and the Hall of Fame of Carp Fishing. Something with an unequalled track record second to non... And finally most importantly! Something which will not immediately sink like a stone and without any doubt whatsoever will not control, ier, or restrict the freedom of your carefully critically balanced preparation...

...THEN WE HAVE THAT SOMETHING... SOMETHING SPECIAL
IT'S CALLED KRYSTON AND IT'S SIMPLY THE BEST!

SILK-WORM **MULTI-STRAND** **MERLIN** **SUPER-SILK** **QUICK-SILVER**

PROVEN BY RESULTS ~ TRIED ~ TESTED ~ TRUSTED

KRYSTON® ADVANCED ANGLING PRODUCTS
Bolton Enterprise Centre, Washington Street, Bolton BL5 5EA
Telephone (0204) 24262   Tel/Fax: (0204) 364283

Etang de Huelgoat

Location:	Huelgoat to the east of Brest and south of Morlaix (Finistere)
Type and Size:	40 acre lake
Carp Stock:	Very well stocked with carp
Category:	Mixed Fishery
Other Species:	Pike, perch, trout, eels and roach
Permits:	Day tickets on site
Control:	Societé Hydroelectrique des Monts d'Arree. Try Fed Dep des AAP, 1 rue de Poher, 29000 Quimper

Etang de Kerlouan

Location:	To the north of Brest (Finistere)
Type and Size:	Shallow lake of 30 acres
Carp Stock:	Heavily stocked with carp
Category:	Mixed Fishery
Other Species:	Roach, tench, bream, eels, pike, dace
Permits:	AAPP de Brest-lesneven; try the Fed Dep des APP, 1 Rue de Poher, 2900 Quimper
Comments:	Rowing boats allowed

Etang de Miallet

Location:	Miallet, on the River Cole, east of Nontron (Dordogne)
Type and Size:	Long, narrow lake, about 35 acres in size
Carp Stock:	Very well stocked with carp
Category:	Mixed Fishery
Other Species:	Tench, chub, bream, eels, roach, pike and zander
Permits:	Day and weekly tickets locally
Control:	The local angling association is at: Residence St-Front, Rue de Lys, BP33, 24002 Périgueux. Tel: (53) 53 44 21
Comments:	Wooded banks, but easy access; motor and rowing boats

Etang de la Gr de Cazine

Location:	On the east side of la Souterraine between Châteauroux and Limoges
Type and Size:	A dammed river forming a lake of about 100 acres
Carp Stock:	Well stocked with doubles and 20s with a sprinkling of 30s and the odd 40
Permits:	Normal French national licence required, available from tackle shops in La Souterraine
BK Rating:	Easy
Comments:	This lake has been carp fished for some time now by French anglers so advanced rigs and baits are most successful

Etang de la Vallée

Location:	About 22 miles east of Orléans in the forest of Orléans
Type and Size:	Beautiful lake of about 170 acres with a maximum depth of 16 feet
How to Find:	At Orléans take the N152 along the river Loire until Châteauneuf sur Loire, then take the D10 until Combreux and turn left, you will see the lake in about a mile
Carp Stock:	Lightly stocked with a good head of magnificent heavily scaled mirrors. An old record for the lake is 46lbs
Other Species:	Bream, tench, pike and big zander over 22lbs, small catfish

Permits: French national licence obtainable in the local fishing tackle shops
BK Rating: Moderate to Difficult
Comments: Very hard boilies needed to beat the small catfish (Bullheads of America). The forest of Orléans is very beautiful. You can also fish the canal of Orléans with a number of carp to 20lbs and the nearby river Loire which is heavily stocked with commons and mirrors to 30lbs

Etang de Pirot

Location: In the Forest of Troncais, west of Moulins (Allier)
Type and Size: Very deep lake of about 200 acres, with the River Marmande flowing through it
Carp Stock: Very well stocked with carp
Category: Mixed Fishery
Other Species: Tench, roach, perch, pike and zander
Permits: Day, week and annual permits from local shops, cafes and tackle shops
Control: AAAP 'La Fraternelle' de Cerilly
Comments: Privately owned. Easy access by car, and camping on the bank. Pleasant surroundings

Not much time for Kevin Maddocks to photograph this 37½ pounder - he caught 21 over 20 pounds in a little over 12 hours! This was another occasion when the fish just couldn't resist those Honey Necta boilies!

Etang de Souston

Location:	About 100 miles south of Bordeaux
Type and Size:	1000 acres of natural lake near the Atlantic in the south west of France
How to Find:	From Bordeaux take the N10 to Magescq, then take the D116 to Souston
Carp Stock:	Lightly stocked
Category:	Mixed Fishery
Other Species:	Coarse fish with very big zander
Permits:	French national licence taken in fishing tackle shop in the area
BK Rating:	Fairly Hard
Comments:	In a very touristic area; July and August are not the best for big carp fishing

Etang de Vert le Petit

Location:	About 35 miles south of Paris and 10 miles from Corbeil-Essonnes
How to Find:	Take the A6 from Paris to Corbeil-Essonnes, then the N191 to La Ferte-Alais
Carp Stock:	Heavily stocked. An estimation of about 10 forties, 80 thirties and 200 twenties is not exaggerated. The lake records for 1991 are a leather of 44lbs, a mirror of 42lbs and a common of 40lbs
Other Species:	Coarse fish with zander over 25lbs
Permits:	National French licence and a day ticket available on site (19 francs in 1992)
BK Rating:	Easy to Moderate (more and more difficult since 1990)
Comments:	There are three lakes at Vert le Petit with big carp over 40lbs in all three. There are also beautiful carp in the River Essonne; a magnificent koi of 27lbs was caught in this river in 1991

A 44 pounder
from Vert le Petit

Etang du Puits

Location:	About 14 miles south of Gien (45 miles from Orléans)
Type and Size:	Beautiful lake of about 400 acres
How to Find:	At Gien, take the D940 to Argent sur Sauldre, then turn right and take the D948, about 4 miles after you will see the lake
Carp Stock:	Lightly stocked with many thirties and a lake record of 41lbs, but bigger carp are living in this lake

Other Species:	Bream, roach, tench and big pike
Permits:	Available from tackle shop at Argent sur Sauldre, French national licence required
BK Rating:	Moderate to Easy
Comments:	A very beautiful lake in the forest with a maximum depth of about 30 feet. Possibility to fish in the nearby canal of Sauldre with carp to 25lbs

Etang du Touroulet

Location:	Touroulet, near Chalais, north east of Nontron (Dordogne)
Type and Size:	Small lake of about 10 acres, up to 15 feet deep
Carp Stock:	Heavily stocked with carp
Category:	Mixed Fishery
Other Species:	Roach, bream, tench, chub, perch and pike
Permits:	Day and weekly tickets on site
Control:	Private
Restrictions:	Three rods only; bank fishing only; open from April to September

Etang St-Andre-des-Eaux

Location:	North west of St Nazaire (Loire-Atlantique)
Type and Size:	15 acre lake up to 40 feet deep, and weedy
Carp Stock:	Very good carp water, heavily stocked
Category:	Mixed Fishery
Other Species:	Roach, tench, pike, eels, bream and zander
Permits:	AAPP de St Nazaire; try Fed Dep des APP, 2 boulevard des Anglais, 44100 Nantes

Etang Tremelin

Location:	Near Rennes, in Brittany
Type and Size:	Lake of over 100 acres
How to Find:	At Montfort, west of Rennes, take the D30 to Iffendic, then the D61 south towards Phelan. The lake is 1½ miles from Iffendic
Carp Stock:	Lightly stocked with carp to 50lbs, average 20lbs
Permits:	On site
BK Rating:	Moderate
Comments:	A holiday-type complex, and quite busy at times. Other water sports take place, but there is a fishing only area

---

THE BEEKAY GUIDE TO 1500 BRITISH & EUROPEAN CARP WATERS

Is YOUR Water listed? If so, are the details correct?

If you spot omissions, inaccuracies, or know of any changes, please let us know by filling in the Waters Questionnaire at the back of this guide and return it to us at:

FREEPOST
Beekay Publishers
Withy Pool
Henlow Camp
Bedfordshire
SG16 6EA

Fishabil   A

Location: Loscouet-sur-Meu, Brittany

Type and Size: Originally a dammed stream built by monks, but in 1990 the lake was increased in size to about 80 acres and the stream diverted. Most of the water is shallow, only 3-6 feet deep.

Bob Baldock, Kevin Maddocks and Allan Parbery with three 20s from Fishabil Lake, Brittany. This was part of a catch of over 950 pounds of carp in three days fishing. All the fish were taken on KM Maestro Bird Spice and Honey boilies and are featured in the 'Euro Carp Quest' video

How to Find: Close to Rennes - as you approach Lascouet-sur-Meu the Fishabil centre is clearly signposted

Carp Stock: Originally there were only a few carp present to about 30lbs but in 1990 more than 35 tons of fish was stocked and most of these were carp. The majority are 15-25lbs with the occasional 30 and 40. One or two of over 50lbs have also been put in!

Permits: Available from the office on site. This is a private water so the normal French national licence is not required. Cost is £24 for 24 hours for 4 rods - a bit expensive but this water is only about an hour's drive from the ferry at St. Malo. Petrol costs are low, and there are no toll roads on this route.

Category: Mixed Fishery

Other Species: Catfish from Russia to over 200lbs have been stocked, with a number of 50-80 pounders; pike, zander, tench and black bass.

BK Rating: Easy

Comments: Late in 1989 Fishabil S.A. purchased the property with the intention of creating a first class fishery, with no expense spared. Bore holes were drilled to obtain high quality water, and as the lake is privately owned it is one of the very few in France which you can legally night fish. The lake is managed by carp angler Raphael Farragi, who speaks good English and is extremely helpful to visitors. High quality accommodation is available by the lakeside, there is a tennis court, an anglers' cinema, horse riding and a coffee shop (no cooked meals).

In 1991 Fishabil was the scene for the highly acclaimed 'Euro Carp Quest' video, featuring Kevin Maddocks, Allan Parbery and Bob Baldock. In three days more than 900lbs of carp including many 20's were caught and anyone contemplating a visit would find the video extremely helpful.

To book a room in advance write to: Fishabil, Le Lac, 22230 Loscouet-sur-Meu, Brittany, France. Tel: 010 33 96252766.

You might encounter one of these monster catfish of 200 pounds plus at Fishabil!

La Ballastière de Laveyssière

Location:	15 miles south from Paris along the river Seine
Type and Size:	Old gravel pit of 70 acres with a maximum depth of 21 feet
How to Find:	From Paris take the N7 to Draveil
Carp Stock:	Well stocked with very big fish. A 56lb mirror was caught in 1991
Other Species:	Coarse fish with big pike and big zander to 30lbs. Small catfish
Permits:	Available from tackle shop in Draveil and Viry Chatillon. French national licence required
BK Rating:	Moderate
Comments:	Very hard boilies are needed to beat the small catfish. Along the River Seine the big carp come in to spawn. Possibility to fish the nearby River Seine where there are some very big carp. A carp of 33lbs is not a big fish for this area

Lac d'Aydat

Location:	On the south west outskirts of Clermont Ferrand
Type and Size:	A dammed river forming a lake of about 200 acres
How to Find:	A little south of the N89/E70 road, about 30 minutes drive from Clermont
Carp Stock:	Well stocked with all sizes of carp up to 55lbs
Permits:	Day and week tickets available at shop on waterside
BK Rating:	Easy
Comments:	An ideal place to take the family. Pedaloes for hire and plenty of nearby campsites. Quite a popular water

Lac de Chambon

Location:	Eguzon, near Argenton-sur-Creuse
Type and Size:	Dammed section of the River Creuse, several hundred acres
Carp Stock:	Lightly stocked, fish to over 50lbs have been caught
Permits:	French national licence, available from tackle shops
BK Rating:	Difficult
Comments:	The best areas are supposed to be where the river opens out into the lake. The depth fluctuates and some banks are steep

Lac de Chaumont

Location:	East of the E17 road, just south of St. Dizier, between Chalons and Chaumont
Type and Size:	Natural looking lake of over 100 acres
Carp Stock:	A good head of doubles and twenties, and there are certain to be fish of over 45lbs, though little is known of bigger fish
Permits:	Available from the tackle shop in Chaumont; normal French national licence is needed
BK Rating:	Moderate
Comments:	As with all large waters, fish location is important, as they do tend to shoal. Multiple baits work well. Other water sports take place on this big lake

Lac de la Chaume

Location:	About 30 miles south of Argenton-sur-Creuse
Type and Size:	Lake of about 150 acres
How to Find:	Follow the N20 south of Argenton, then take the D70 eastwards to Jeux. Half a mile from Jeux turn right down a track which leads to the lake
Carp Stock:	Fairly heavily stocked with small fish but a good sprinkling of 30-40 pounders
Other Species:	Coarse fish and some catfish
Permits:	Available from the Mairie (Town Hall) at Azerables - about £12 for 24 hours with three rods
BK Rating:	Easy to Moderate
Comments:	Night fishing is permitted. Closed between November and March. Used for other water sports, but these are not a serious problem

Lac de la Foret d'Orient

Location:	East of Troyes, to the south east of Paris (Aube)
Type and Size:	Lake of over 5,000 acres which feeds a canal
Carp Stock:	Heavily stocked with carp; excellent fishing
Category:	Mixed Fishery
Other Species:	Pike, tench, bream, perch, bleak, trout, chub, eels, roach
Permits:	AAAP, 10-12 Rue Francois-Gentil, 10,000 Troyes, City of Paris; day, week and annual permits
Restrictions:	Boats allowed, but not with motors. Open from the first Saturday in April to 11th November
Comments:	An excellent fishing lake, although a bit large by English standards. It is said to be dangerous for boats near the western outlet

Lac de Lavuad-Gelade

Location:	Four miles from Royere, south west of Aubusson (Creuse)
Type and Size:	Big lake of over 600 acres
Carp Stock:	Heavily stocked with carp
Category:	Mixed Fishery
Other Species:	Tench, perch and a few trout and pike
Permits:	Enquire locally; the address for the local angling federation is: Maison de la Peche, 60 Av Louis-Laroche, BP 182, 23012 Gueret Cedex. Tackle shop: Sainte-Cricq, 65 Grande Rue, Aubusson
Restrictions:	Rowing boats allowed. Maggot fishing permitted

Lac de Monampteuil

Location:	To the south of Laon, in north France near the Belgian border (Aisne)
Type and Size:	Artificial lake of 70 acres which feeds two canals
How to Find:	Eight miles south of Laon
Carp Stock:	Very well stocked with carp
Category:	Mixed Fishery
Other Species:	Pike, zander, perch, eels and other coarse fish
Permits:	Association de Pêche et de Pisciculture, Laon, 4 Rue d'Ardon, 02000 Laon. Tel: (23) 20 23 23
Comments:	Heavily stocked public water with very good fishing. Fishing from boats is allowed

KM Maestro Wild Strawberry accounted for this magnificent 46 pounder for John Baker

Lac de Pres de St. Jean (Lake Zup)

Location: In the centre of Chalon-sur-Saone
Type and Size: Town park lake of about 60 acres
Carp Stock: Lightly stocked with carp to 40lbs, with 30's not uncommon. Stock also includes 'Mamur Carp' to about 100lbs, average weight about 10lbs
Permits: From Jackie Greset's tackle shop in the town. This is the only public water where you can night fish in France, and you must request a free night permit when obtaining your licence
BK Rating: Difficult
Comments: No boats present; has an overrated reputation, but it does give you somewhere to night fish legally when you are in the area

Typical low twenties from Lake Salagou

Lac de Salagou

Location: West of Montpellier, in the south of France
Type and Size: A dammed river forming an irregular-shaped lake about 4 miles in length
How to Find: Turn off the A9/E15 motorway at the southern, last, Montpellier exit. Follow the signs for Millau/Lodeve on the 109 road. Just past the junction with the E9 (5 miles before Le Lodeve) you will see the signposts to the lake
Carp Stock: Heavily stocked with thousands of commons and mirrors. The average size is 20lbs, with plenty of twenties and thirties. Some 40's and a chance of a fifty. Full potential not known
Other Species: Large trout, bream, pike and zander
Permits: French national licence from the tackle shop just over the first bridge as you enter Lodeve
BK Rating: Easy to Moderate

Comments: Location is very important in this huge water. Mussels are a problem, and some areas are very snaggy. Other places have shelving bottoms which are 'stepped' and these have proved difficult to fish. Hard boilies such as Maestros, are recommended, popped up. A boat is very useful - take your own if possible, as they are very expensive to hire, and are not designed for carp anglers! Most of the lake is accessible from tracks. The ground is very rocky, making bivvy erection difficult. Because of the many snags, a good supply of terminal tackle is essential. Several videos featuring this lake are available

Lac des Closiers

Location:	Dept of Loiret; north of Montargis, to the east of Orléans
Type and Size:	Thirty acre lake
Carp Stock:	Well stocked with carp to over 20lbs
Category:	Mixed Fishery
Other Species:	Roach, perch, bream, tench
Permits:	This private lake is open to holders of a departmental permit; try the Federation départementale des AAPP, 144 Rue des Anguignis, 45100 Orléans. Tel: 56 62 69
BK Rating:	Moderate
Comments:	There may be night fishing as this is not a public water

Lac de St. Cassien

Location: About 10 miles west of Cannes and the Mediterranean coast

Type and Size: Dammed streams forming a lake of about 1,500 acres, which is made up of three sections, south, north and west arms. Depths to 60 feet in the west and south arms, and more than 100 feet in the north arm

How to Find: The lake is close to the north side of the E80/A8 motorway and is shown on all road maps

Carp Stock: Lake Cassien probably holds more big carp than any other lake in the world. Thirty pounders are 'small' by Cassien standards, with 40's, 50's and 60's being the target. Several carp over 70lbs have been caught, and there is little doubt that carp approaching 90lbs exist in the lake. It was first stocked in 1964, and fish of a good size are put in every year

Category: Carp Water

Other Species: A few catfish and one, estimated to weigh about 150lbs, was caught by English angler Johnny Allen; also tench, pike and black bass

Permits: From Chez Pierre's restaurant on the banks of the southern arm, or from tackle shops in Cannes. Normal French licence required

BK Rating: Difficult

Comments: As far as English anglers are concerned, this mecca of carp waters was 'discovered' by Kevin Maddocks and Paul Regent in September 1984. Most English anglers who visit Cassien feel that they have to break the rules to catch fish. Night fishing is against the law and the French authorities have found it necessary to employ *armed* rangers to stop visitors from breaking the rules. Most people, if careful, get away with night fishing, but many have been caught and had their tackle confiscated.

Shortly after the lake was 'discovered' by Kevin Maddocks and Paul Regent, hundreds of English anglers visited the lake, and some historic catches were made.

The English were followed by the Dutch (as usual!) and then the Germans. In recent years the fishing has become much harder and now the water receives much less pressure. The next few years will see only the more serious and dedicated carp anglers visiting the water, and more big catches will be made - but the best time has gone! For full details on Cassien, including an aerial photograph of the lake, see the book 'Carp Fever' by Kevin Maddocks

Lac de St. Croix

Location: About 80 miles north of the Mediterranean coast, and north west of Cannes

Type and Size: A huge lake of more than 10,000 acres, formed by the damming of the River Verdon

Carp Stock: Lightly stocked with some very large fish, which have been caught to over 60lbs. Potential unknown

Permits: French national licence from tackle shops

BK Rating: Difficult

Comments: Very busy with holidaymakers. Lots of snags, but lots of potential also

Lac de St Pardoux

Location:	About 15 miles north of Limoges
Type and Size:	A dammed river forming a lake of about 600 acres
How to Find:	Close to the west side of the N20 main road which runs from Limoges to Châteauroux
Carp Stock:	Well stocked with carp to at least 40lbs
Permits:	Normal French national licence required
BK Rating:	Moderate
Comments:	This water has great potential as it has been fished hardly at all by English anglers

Lac de Vouglans

Location:	Close to the Swiss border, north west of Lyon
Type and Size:	The dammed River Ain, about 20 miles long
How to Find:	Take the N78 from Chalon-sur-Saone to Lons Le Saunier, and after 15 miles you will see the north end of the lake
Carp Stock:	Lightly stocked with some very big carp - commercial fishermain claim carp to 90lbs!
Permits:	French national licence from tackle shops
BK Rating:	Difficult
Comments:	Lots of snags and very steep banks in places. It is advisable not to fish until carp are located, and although it is difficult you could get a very big fish

Lac du Der-Chantecoq

Location:	On the south west outskirts of St Dizier, about 120 miles east of Paris
Type and Size:	A huge reservoir of more than 4000 acres
How to Find:	Take the D384 south west from St Dizier and the lake is situated on the right about 8 miles out
Carp Stock:	Well stocked with carp to over 50lbs. Plenty of 30s
Permits:	Normal French national licence required. Available from local tackle shop at Braucourt and other towns
Restrictions:	No night fishing,regular checks by guards
BK Rating:	Moderate
Comments:	A couple of years ago this place produced some incredible carp catches and is still quite easy today, although it is rapidly becoming more popular with English anglers. Fluctuates in size by more than 1000 acres throughout the year - full in the spring, low in the autumn. For further information on this water see the video 'French Carping 2 Ton-Up at Lac du Der' featuring Alan Taylor when more than 60 thirties were caught

Bicester tackle shop proprietor Joe Taylor with one of his scores of French 30 pounders

Lac du Mignon

Location:	La Greve-sur-Mignon, north east of La Rochelle (Charente Maritime)
Type and Size:	Small shallow lake of about 12 acres
Carp Stock:	Very well stocked with cap
Category:	Mixed Fishery
Other Species:	Roach, tench, bream, rudd, eels, perch and pike
Permits:	AAAP de La Greve - enquire locally
Control:	Information from the Fed Dep des APP, 43 Av Emile-Normandin, 17000 La Rochelle
Comments:	Heavily stocked water, good fishing and much smaller than most French lakes. Rowing boats allowed

Lac Liton Rouge

Location: La Puisayé, Normandy, northern France
Type and Size: Small estate lake
Carp Stock: Well stocked with big carp to 51lbs
Category: Mixed Fishery
Other Species: Grass carp and catfish
Permits: Jean Louis Bunel, 35 Boulevard Arago, 75031 Paris. Tel: 010 331 43366821
BK Rating: Not known
Comments: Night fishing is allowed

La Darce

Location: Macon, on the Saone
Type and Size: This 'lake' is part of the River Saone, and is over 40 acres in size
How to Find: Going south, go through Macon on the main road. Just before the end of the town turn left into the industrial estate
Carp Stock: Variable, as this depends on conditions in the river. When the river is highly coloured and fast, it is quite common for hundreds of carp to enter the Darce, and this also happens at spawning time, so the Darce always contains carp to over 40lbs - sometimes a few, sometimes many hundreds!
Other Species: Catfish to over 100lbs
Permits: French national licence from tackle shops
BK Rating: Moderate
Comments: Not a very attractive place as it is in the middle of an industrial estate, but many of the fish are commons of over 30lbs. Multiple (particle) baits work well

La Fert Vidame (Etang de Rouge)

Location: Puissay, west of Dreux, in Normandy
Type and Size: Dammed stream of about 12 acres
How to Find: Turn off the N12 at Verneuil, which is between Dreux and Alencon. Head south for about 5 miles to La Ferte Vidame
Carp Stock: Fairly heavily stocked with many doubles, quite a few twenties, some thirties and an occasional forty
Other Species: Some coarse fish, including grass carp to 30lbs
Permits: Available on site, or from J L Bunel's tackle shop in Paris
BK Rating: Easy
Comments: Night fishing is allowed, and the French licence is not required, as this is a private water. A nice looking lake, where the average angler can catch some good fish

La Folie   A

Location: Excideuil, Perigord Vert, Dordogne; 20 miles north east of Perigueux
Type and Size: Lake of two and a half acres, spring fed, on private estate
Carp Stock: Well stocked with carp to 40lbs
Category: Carp Water
Permits: Colin Maclean, Exclusive Angling Holidays, 422 Whaddon Way, Bletchley, Milton Keynes MK3 7LA. Tel: 0908 368220/616886
BK Rating: Moderate

Comments: Small bungalow to rent, with fishing included; the house is right at the side of the lake and there is another five acres of land, with woodland and an orchard. Sleeps four in two bedrooms. Exclusive and peaceful holiday with good carp fishing, but La Folie is only available to those who respect the fish, the natural environment, and the French countryside and its people. Beautiful grape-growing region with a very warm climate and plenty of sun. Carp fishing English owners

Lake Aiguebelette

Location: In the French mountains, about 10 miles from Chambery
Type and Size: About 1350 acres with a maximum depth of 250 feet! It's one of the bigger natural French lakes
Carp Stock: Lightly stocked with mirrors and commons. The lake record is a nice common carp caught in the 70's; 57lbs (110 cm long)
Other Species: Coarse fish with big pike to over 40lbs and big lake trout
Permits: Available from the tackle shop in the town of Aiguebelette
BK Rating: Moderate to Difficult
Comments: A big mountain lake, very deep with warm springs, very good for carp fishing

Lake Aussonne

Location: Eight miles from Toulouse in southern France
Type and Size: 20 acre lake
Carp Stock: Recently stocked with two and a half tonnes of carp from 20lbs to 40lbs in weight
Category: Carp Water
Permits: BBS European Leisure Ltd, 46 Beechwood Avenue, Ruislip, Middx HA4 6EJ. Tel: 0895 630516. Bookable in advance only by the week
Cost: £125 per week, or £200 for two weeks, from Saturday noon to Saturday 10am. Accompanied juniors £75 or £125 for two weeks. £25 a week for non-fishing guests. Please note that this does not include accommodation, so you will need to take bivvies
Restrictions: Three rods only. Night fishing allowed, as the lake is private. No sacking in the heat of the day; bivvy areas must be kept clean
BK Rating: Not known
Comments: Send to BBS for brochure and booking form. Restaurant and bar (open until 2am) on lake. English breakfasts. Washing and toilet facilities. Opened on May 30th 1992. Transport provided from local airport/railway station. Summer temperatures can reach 40 degrees C!

Lake Carces

Location: About 27 miles west from the Lake Cassien in the south of France
Type and Size: A lake of 235 acres formed by the damming of the River Caramy
Carp Stock: Lightly stocked with a good head of big fish. A 66lb carp was caught in 1983!
Other Species: Coarse fish with big zander to 25lbs
Permits: Available from tackle shop in Carces
BK Rating: Moderate
Comments: The warm climate of the south of France ensures a fast growth rate in this area

Kevin Maddocks with one of his many French 30's which have fallen to the ever-reliable Honey Necta boilies

Lake de Mervent

Location:	About 5 miles north of Fontenay Le Comte
Type and Size:	A lake of 300 acres formed by the damming of river Vendée
How to Find:	From Fontenay Le Comte, take the D65
Carp Stock:	Lightly stocked
Other Species:	All coarse fish
Permits:	From tackle shop at Fontenay Le Comte. French national licence
BK Rating:	Fairly Hard

Lake de Saint-Etienne Cantalès

Location:	About 15 miles south west of Aurillac in the middle of France
Type and Size:	A big lake of 1400 acres, formed by the damming of the river Cère
How to Find:	Take the N122 from Clermond-Ferrand to Aurillac, then take the N120
Carp Stock:	Well stocked with mirrors and commons
Other Species:	All coarse fish with big zander and pike
Permits:	French national licence from fishing tackle shop at Aurillac
BK Rating:	Fairly Hard
Comments:	Beautiful lake with big fish. A carp over 60lbs has been caught in the past year

Lake des Fades

Location:	In the middle of France, about 20 miles north-east of Clermont-Ferrand
Type and Size:	Lake of 1000 acres, very deep in some places, formed by the damming of the river Sioule (maximum depth of 180 feet)
Carp Stock:	Lightly stocked
Other Species:	Coarse fish and big predatory fish
Permits:	French national licence taken in tackle shop in the area
BK Rating:	Difficult
Comments:	A very beautiful lake

Lake des Vezins

Location:	About 15 miles south east of Avranches, 10 miles off the Atlantic coast and "Le Mont Saint-Michel"
Type and Size:	About 100 acres formed by the damming of the river Sélune, a good French salmon river
How to Find:	From Avranches, take the N175, then at Pontaubault turn left and take the N176 to Ducey and take the D178 to Vézins
Carp Stock:	Lightly stocked
Other Species:	Coarse fish with big zander
Permits:	French national licence from fishing tackle shop at Avranches
BK Rating:	Fairly Hard
Comments:	A lot of common carp. Carp fishing is not very easy on the banks of this lake, it is easier with a boat

Lake de Villeneuve De La Raho

Location:	Three miles south of Perpignan in the south of France near the Spanish border
Type and Size:	About 400 acres in size, near the sea
Carp Stock:	Well stocked with a lot of twenties and thirties
Other Species:	Coarse fish. Big black bass
Permits:	In the fishing tackle shop
BK Rating:	Moderate
Comments:	Very touristic area for family holidays

Lake of Apremont

Location:	10 miles from the Atlantic coast. 10 miles from La Roche sur Yon
Type and Size:	Lake of 320 acres formed by the damming of the River Vie. Maximum depth is about 22 feet
How to Find:	From Nantes take D178, at Aizenay take D107
Carp Stock:	Well stocked with big carp to over 45lbs
Other Species:	Coarse fish
Permits:	Available from Aizenay and La Roche sur Yon. French national licence required
BK Rating:	Easy to Moderate
Comments:	Not far away from the French Atlantic coast; a good place for family holidays

Lake of Bourdon

Location:	About 35 miles south west from Auxerre
Type and Size:	About 475 acres with an average depth of 18 feet
How to Find:	From Auxerre, take the D965 to St Fargeau
Carp Stock:	Heavily stocked with carp to 40lbs
Other Species:	All coarse fish and small catfish
Permits:	Available from tackle shop in St Fargeau
BK Rating:	Easy
Comments:	Lovely lake. Very hard boilies, such as Maestros, are needed to beat the small catfish

Lake of Eguzon

Location:	About 13 miles south from Argenton sur Creuse. About 32 miles from the big town of Châteauroux in the centre of France
Type and Size:	About 625 acres, formed by the damming of the River Creuse, with a maximum depth of 100 feet
How to Find:	From Argenton sur Creuse, take the D913 to Eguzon
Carp Stock:	Well stocked with big carp to over 45lbs
Other Species:	All coarse fish with big zander to over 25lbs
Permits:	Available from tackle shop in Eguzon. French national licence required
BK Rating:	Moderate
Comments:	The banks of this lake are very difficult. A boat is most useful when fishing this beautiful lake

Lake of Vassivière

Location:	In the middle of France, about 20 miles from Aubusson
Type and Size:	Dammed river forming a huge lake of more than 2700 acres with a maximum depth of 100 feet
Carp Stock:	Well stocked with big fish to over 50lbs
Other Species:	All coarse fish with big pike to 40lbs
Permits:	Available from tackle shop in Royère. French national licence required
BK Rating:	Moderate
Comments:	Beautiful lake for spring holidays. Some English anglers have had tremendous success on this water with very big fish

Le Bourg

Location:	Neuilly s. Eure, a few miles north west of Chartres
Type and Size:	30 acre lake
How to Find:	South La Ferté Vidame to Neuilly s. Eure on the D8 road
Carp Stock:	Approximately 500 carp to 40lbs
Other Species:	Roach and tench
Permits:	On the bank
Cost:	£10 first 24 hours, £5 every 24 hours thereafter
Control:	Private
Restrictions:	Six anglers maximum except by mutual agreement. Reservations - Tel: (16) 33 73 96 10
Baits/Methods:	All conventional baits and methods work
BK Rating:	Easy
Comments:	All fish to be returned unharmed

Les Baillargeaux   A

Location:	Near Montpon, in the Dordogne; on the River Isle north east of Bordeaux
Type and Size:	Large lake
Carp Stock:	Well stocked with twenties and thirties to 37lb
Category:	Not known - probably some other coarse fish
Permits:	Only for those who book accommodation - Jenette and Roger Gaunt, Les Baillargeaux, 24700 Montpon, France. Tel: (010 33) 53 80 08 729 (cheaper after 8pm and weekends). English spoken
BK Rating:	Not known
Comments:	Full board or bed and breakfast in the farmhouse. Permit to fish waters in the Dordogne costs about £13 and applies to all public waters. Numerous other carp lakes in area; the one quoted offers special rates to guests, at an extra cost for fishing of £3.50 per day. B and B £70 weekly per person; full board £140; half board £125. Reduced rates for children

Les Ormes   A

Location:	Near Dinan, Brittany
Type and Size:	Small pit of less than 10 acres
Carp Stock:	Heavily stocked with doubles, and the occasional twenty
Permits:	On site, but only for those who stay at the camp site
BK Rating:	Easy
Comments:	Ideal family venue, busy at times

L'Étang de Catus

Location:	In the dept of Lot, between Cahors and Gourdon
Type and Size:	Attractive 15 acre lake
Carp Stock:	Well stocked with carp to at least 20lbs
Category:	Mixed Fishery
Other Species:	Tench, perch and trout
Permits:	Day, weekly and annual permits from the Fed départementale des APP, 40 Boulevard Gambetta, 46000 Cahors
BK Rating:	Moderate
Comments:	Smaller than many French carp lakes. Some information from the Town Hall (Mairie). Tackle shop Amat, 87 Rue Joffre; Boiyssou, Cahors

L'Étang d'Helfaut

Location:	Pas-de-Calais, near Saint Omer, east of Boulogne
Type and Size:	Four lakes totalling 18 acres
Carp Stock:	Well stocked with carp to 20lbs
Category:	Mixed Fishery
Other Species:	Tench, bream, bleak, pike and perch
Permits:	Season and annual permits; try the APP, 2 Résidence de France, Rue Émile-Zola 62400 Béthune
BK Rating:	Not known

Les Étangs de la Forêt de Rambouillet

Location:	Rambouillet, south west of Versailles near Paris
Type and Size:	Three attractive forest lakes of 7 to 15 acres each
Carp Stock:	Very well stocked with carp, sizes not known
Category:	Mixed Fishery
Other Species:	Bream and perch
Permits:	AAPP des Yvelines, 19 Rue du Docteur-Roux, 78520 Limay, or try the tackle shop in Rambouillet-Pommier, 27 Rue Felix-Faure
BK Rating:	Easy
Comments:	Public place with lots of people, but this is a good carp fishery near Paris

Les Étangs de l'Hirondelle, Becquerel et Grand Marais

Location:	Pas-de-Calais, east of the town of Arras, at d'Ecourt-St-Quentin
Type and Size:	Three lakes of 120 acres, up to 17 feet in depth
Carp Stock:	Very well stocked with carp, numbers and sizes not known
Category:	Mixed Fishery
Other Species:	Tench, pike, perch and eels
Permits:	Day and annual permits from the Town Hall (Mairie)
BK Rating:	Easy
Comments:	There are rowing boats on these lakes

Les Étangs du Stock et de Gondrexange

Location:	About 7 miles from Sarrebourg along the canal of Houllières about 60 miles east from Nancy
Type and Size:	1775 acres for the étang of Stock and 1400 for the étang of Gondrexange. The maximum depth for the two lakes is about 18 feet
Carp Stock:	Heavily stocked with many thirties and a good number of forties. A Dutch angler caught a 47lb in 1991, but bigger fish are living in these two lakes
Other Species:	Bream, roach, perch and big pike over 35lbs
BK Rating:	Easy to Moderate
Comments:	The carp are mirrors, heavily scaled. Possibility to fish also the nearby canal of Houillières which holds a good stock of carp

Les Quis

Location:	45 miles south east of Paris, in the Seine Valley. The lake is near Montereau, at Bray-Sur-Seine
Type and Size:	13 acre sandpit, 35 years old
Carp Stock:	Heavily stocked with twenties to 35lbs, and little fished
Category:	Carp Water
Permits:	Fish-In-France, 90 Grove Park Road, Mottingham, London SE9 4QB. Tel: 081-851 8868
Cost:	On application
Restrictions:	Six anglers only on lake; three rods each allowed
BK Rating:	Not known
Comments:	Legal night fishing allowed. Attractive tree-lined lake about 10 feet deep close in. Big fish only. A Fisherman's Lodge is planned. 3½ hours drive from Calais and 40 minutes from Euro-Disney

Les Sablieres de Les Planches

Location:	Châteauroux (Indre)
Type and Size:	Little 2 acre lake
Carp Stock:	Heavily stocked with carp
Category:	Mixed Fishery
Other Species:	Roach, bleak, tench, zander
Permits:	Day tickets from AAPP de Chateauroux, 19 Rue des Etats-Unis, 36000 Châteauroux
Comments:	The smallest French water we have been able to find!

Lyon Canal

Location:	In the big city of Lyon
Type and Size:	Large canal used by huge barges and tankers
How to Find:	The Lyon ring road passes over this canal which runs from the River Saone to the River Rhone
Carp Stock:	Heavily stocked and although the full potential is unknown, many thirties are caught
Permits:	French national licence from tackle shops in Lyon
BK Rating:	Easy
Comments:	This is a water for the adventurous, who don't mind boat traffic and human beings. Location is easy, as the carp congregate in groups and some very big fish can be seen

Marcillac la Croisille

Location:	25 miles east of Tulle
Type and Size:	A dammed river forming a large lake in excess of 600 acres
How to Find:	A little south of the main E70 road which runs from Tulle to Clermont Ferrand
Carp Stock:	Moderately stocked with carp to at least 50lbs
Permits:	Normal French national licence required
BK Rating:	Moderate
Comments:	This water definitely holds big carp but little else is known about it. Lots of potential for the pioneering type angler

Merceuil

Location:	Four miles south of Beaune, between Dijon and Chalon-sur-Saone
Type and Size:	Gravel pit of about 40 acres
How to Find:	Turn off the A6/E15 motorway at Beaune, and head east on the D970. Follow signs to Bligny-les-Beaunes. The lake is alongside the motorway about 4 miles out of Beaune
Carp Stock:	Lightly stocked with carp to over 35lbs
Permits:	Available from Jackie Greset's shop in Chalon-sur-Saone (alongside the river a little downstream of the road bridge). French national licence required
BK Rating:	Fairly Hard
Comments:	Mussels and crayfish a problem. The old river course in the centre of the lake is productive. Very hard boilies (such as KM Maestros) necessary to beat the crayfish

Mimizan

Location:	Mimizan, close to the west coast, 60 miles south west of Bordeaux
Type and Size:	Dammed river forming a lake of more than 200 acres
Carp Stock:	Quite well stocked with long, lean commons to over 30lbs, with plenty of 20's
Permits:	Local tackle shops; French national licence
BK Rating:	Moderate
Comments:	Strictly controlled, as it is near an air force base, and so is patrolled at night

Parcours de Pêche

Location:	Domaine des Forges, near Montmirail off the RD33 between Paris and Chalons sur Marne, and east of Paris
Type and Size:	There are three lakes, not large, on the fishery, but the carp are in the Étang du 'Bois Joli'
Carp Stock:	Heavily stocked with carp from 16-25lbs, though forty pounders are claimed
Category:	Mixed Fishery
Other Species:	Some coarse fish
Permits:	Domaine des Forges, Les Forges 51270 Talus St. Prix; Tel: 26 80 39 29
Cost:	Day - 150 francs; 48 hours - 250 francs; week - 1,500 francs
Restrictions:	Night fishing allowed for carp only
Comments:	There are two other lakes on site: one is a trout lake, the other contains catfish to 100lbs and big pike. Separate permits and prices for these. The owners will book local accommodation if required

Pareloup

Location:	Between Rodez and Millau
Type and Size:	Dammed streams which form a huge reservoir, several miles across, and 1,800 acres in extent
How to Find:	The lake is about 3 miles to the south of the 911 road between Rodez and Millau - take the D993 towards Salles Curan
Carp Stock:	A good head of low doubles, some 20's, 30's and 40's and a reported 57 pounder
Permits:	French national licence from the tackle shop in Millau

Rating: Moderate
Comments: Location is of paramount importance - don't bother to fish until you spot carp; mussels and crayfish a bit of a problem. Boat recommended - an ideal water for the pioneering big fish man

Reservoir de Chazilly

Location: Chazilly/Ste-Sabine, north west of Beaune (Côte d'Or)
Type and Size: Very deep reservoir of 200 acres
Carp Stock: Well stocked with carp
Category: Mixed Fishery
Other Species: Pike, perch, roach, tench and bream
Permits: APP. 'La Gaule de l'Auxois' at the village of Ste-Sabine; Fed Departementale, 6 rue Charles-Dumont, 21000 Dijon
Comments: Annual permits; boat fishing allowed. No other water sports apart from fishing. Also smaller reservoir nearby, Reservoir du Tillot, 50 acres and very attractive; well stocked with carp

River Auvezere

Location: At Perigeux. One of the best areas is at Le Change about 10 miles upstream of Perigeux
Type and Size: A medium sized river averaging 40 metres in width. Slow flowing
Carp Stock: Reasonably well stocked with carp to at least 40lbs
Permits: Normal French national licence required
Rating: Moderate
Comments: Lots of potential. Carp to 40lbs have been caught but much bigger fish are said to exist

River Charente

Location: This excellent carp water is more than 100 miles long and runs into the Atlantic Sea at Rochefort. This river runs through Cognac and Saintes
Type and Size: A medium sized river, slow flowing and very deep in some areas
Carp Stock: Well stocked with big carp to over 45lbs
Other Species: All coarse fish
Permits: French national licence from tackle shops at Rochefort, Saintes or Cognac
Rating: Easy to Moderate
Comments: Beautiful carp river in French holiday area, with good places for carp fishing not far away from the Atlantic coast

River Cher

Location: This river is about 70 miles long and runs into the River Loire at Tours
Type and Size: A medium sized river, slow flowing and varying depths
Carp Stock: Heavily stocked with big carp to over 45lbs
Other Species: All coarse fish and big zander to 30lbs
Permits: From tackle shops at Vierzon, Romorantin or Chenonceaux
Rating: Easy
Comments: Good results with particle baits

Paul Regent with a 'boatfull' of French carp; a 30 and two 20's, part of a huge haul of fish taken on KM Maestro Ultra Birdspice boilies

River Dordogne

Location: This big French river is more than 100 miles long and runs through Bort les Orgues, Bergerac and Libourne into the Garonne, about 20 miles north of Bordeaux

Type and Size: The river is dammed in several sections around Bort les Orgues and Argentat, after which it is a beautiful river with considerable depths in some areas

How to Find: Very good areas for carp fishing around Bergerac

Carp Stock: Heavily stocked in some areas

Other Species: All coarse fish, especially big zander to 30lbs and big pike to 40lbs.

Big wels catfish have been caught in some areas

ermits: French national licence required

K Rating: Moderate

omments: The possibility to catch a very big carp is real. A French carp angler caught a brace of 51lb and 53lb mirrors in the same day on this river!

River Doubs

ocation: This carp water is more than 100 miles long and runs into the River Saône at Verdun sur le Doubs

ype and Size: A medium sized river with considerable depths. Good places in the Besançon area

arp Stock: Well stocked with big carp to over 55lbs

ther Species: All coarse fish

ermits: French national licence required

K Rating: Easy to Moderate

omments: Good places in Besançon area. A big catfish of 150lbs was caught in the 70's

River Garonne

ocation: The Garonne runs from the Toulouse area through Moissac, Agen and Marmade, and out to the Gironde about 10 miles north of Bordeaux

ype and Size: A big French river about 130 miles of good carp fishing, quite fast flowing and slow flowing in other places

arp Stock: Well stocked with very big carp over 55lbs. One of the best carp rivers in France

ther Species: All coarse fish, especially very big zander and big pike

ermits: French national licence from tackle shops in Moissac, Agen or Marmande

K Rating: Moderate

omments: Beautiful river in the south of France. Good places for carp fishing in Agen or Moissac areas

River Lay

ocation: In the French département of Vendée (85), on the west French coast

ype and Size: This good carp river is about 30 miles long and runs very slowly into the Atlantic sea on a very touristic French coast

ow to Find: From La Roche Sur Yon, take the D746 to Mareuil sur Lay

arp Stock: Well stocked with a lot of common carp

ermits: French national licence

K Rating: Easy to Moderate

omments: Very beautiful common carp

River Loire

ocation: The Loire runs from the Lyon area northwards through Roanne and Nevers, and then west through Orleans (60 miles south of Paris), Tours, Angers, and out to the sea at Nantes

ype and Size: A medium-sized river about 400 miles in length, quite fast flowing, and fairly shallow in places, especially in its upper reaches. There are several power stations on the banks

Carp Stock:	Most areas contain carp. The best part of the river is the 150 miles stretch from Decize to Blois. Carp bigger than 30lbs are often caught from the Decize, Fourchambault, St. Laurent and Gien areas
Other Species:	Most European species, including catfish to more than 100lbs
Permits:	French national licence from tackle shops
BK Rating:	Easy - once the fish are located
Comments:	The areas near the power stations, especially at Gien and St. Laurent des Eaux, produce a lot of good fish over 30lbs. Unlike most French rivers, boilies are readily acceptable by the Loire carp. It is worth noting that one or two of the lakes alongside the river hold carp of over 40lbs

River Lot

Location:	This excellent carp water is more than 100 miles long and runs into the River Garonne about 45 miles south of Bordeaux
Type and Size:	The river is dammed in several sections, and water levels vary considerably
How to Find:	There are many good areas on this river, but one of the most popular is near St. Geniez d'Olt - follow the signs to Cabanac village
Carp Stock:	Very heavily stocked with carp including many big commons. Plenty of doubles, twenties and thirties, and certainly some fish over 40lbs
Permits:	French National licence from local tackle shops, such as Serges, 4 Place du Marche, St. Geniez
BK Rating:	Easy to Moderate
Comments:	Often the carp form in large groups so location is important. Large beds of boilies and cooked particles have been very successful. A boat is recommended, and these can be hired in Cabanac. The Lot is featured in two videos: Dave Plummer's 'French Carp Fishing' and Mick Hall's film

River Maine

Location:	In the town of Angers
Type and Size:	Formed by the junction of three big French rivers: Sarthes, Loire and Mayenne. Only 10 miles long, runs slowly into the river Loire through Angers
Carp Stock:	Very well stocked with mirrors and commons
Other Species:	All coarse fish
Permits:	French national licence from tackle shop at Angers
BK Rating:	Easy to Moderate
Comments:	A lot of thirties with a good number of forties and fifties. The biggest fish caught in a French competition were caught in this river in 1990 with a mirror carp of 50lbs (22.8kg). Very hard boilies to beat the small catfish

River Rhône

Location:	This excellent carp river is more than 200 miles long and runs through Lyon, Valence, Orange and Avignon and out to the Mediterranean Sea about 30 miles west of Marseille
Type and Size:	Big French river with several power stations
Carp Stock:	Well stocked with big fish over 55lbs
Other Species:	All coarse fish and big catfish to over 60lbs

Permits:	French national licence required
BK Rating:	Moderate to Easy
Comments:	More and more catfish are being caught in this good carp river in the south of France

River Saone

Location:	From just north of Dijon to Lyon, at its confluence with the Rhone
Type and Size:	River about 100 miles long and 200-400 yards wide; slow flowing with depths of 20-25 feet in the middle
Carp Stock:	Good stock of singles, doubles and twenties along the whole length. Carp to over 60lbs have been caught, and it is believed that this river holds a French record
Category:	Mixed Fishery
Other Species:	Most European coarse fish, including many catfish to 150lbs
Permits:	Local tackle shops; French national licence
BK Rating:	Moderate
Comments:	For big fish, location is vitally important. One of the best areas is in the town of Chalon-sur-Saone, close to the islands and barge moorings. Here many large carp well over 50lbs have been caught. Boilies not successful at first, and you need to bait heavily with sweetcorn and other multiple baits, whilst introducing boilies. Large barges frequent this river, but don't present a problem. Serious approach and commitment needed for success on this river. The Saone was one of the areas fished during the making of the video 'Cat Fever', featuring Kevin Maddocks and Bob Baldock

River Seille

Location:	This river is about 40 miles long and runs into the River Saone at Tournus, between Chalon and Macon
Type and Size:	A medium-sized river which in its lower reaches is some 30 yards wide, with an average depth of about 10 feet
Carp Stock:	Heavily stocked with mid-doubles and a good sprinkling of thirties. The river record is supposed to be 59lbs, but the largest authenticated fish we know of is 42lbs
Other Species:	Most European species, and catfish to well over 100lbs
Permits:	French national licence from tackle shops
BK Rating:	Moderate
Comments:	One of the best stretches is between the Pont Seille and Ratanelle road bridges, especially in the areas of fallen trees. This river is very susceptible to flooding so always have another water you can fish so you don't go all the way there for nothing

River Seine

Location:	Runs from Troyes, through Paris, and out to the sea at Le Havre
Type and Size:	Very large river up to a quarter of a mile wide, with varying depths
Carp Stock:	Carp are found almost anywhere in the Seine, but certain areas produce the bigger fish. Fish of over 80lbs have been caught, and the French record came from the river, near the River Yonne - a common of 81½lbs!
Permits:	French national licence from local tackle shops

Permits: French national licence from local tackle shops
BK Rating: Moderate
Comments: For big fish local knowledge must be sought - carp of 50-60lbs are not uncommon in some areas. Heavy baiting with particles at first whilst boilies are introduced is recommended, as many of the fish have never seen boilies; the river carries a lot of boat traffic. A good spot is at Fault Yonne near Monteraux. There are several warm water outlets here, and the winter fishing is quite good

A magnificent 63 pound common from the River Seine

River Vezere

Location: Runs from Brive westwards
Type and Size: A medium sized river averaging 40 metres in width and slow moving
Carp Stock: Well stocked with carp. Good head of twenties with the chance of fish up to at least 45lbs
Permits: Normal French national licence required
Baits/Methods: Both particles and boilies work well
BK Rating: Moderate
Comments: This river is said to hold huge carp especially in the areas near Larche. Areas of bankside (or fallen) trees most productive

Marc Ponsot, presenter of Clean River's *French Carping 1: The 'Royal' River Seine* video with a 57 pound common from the Seine

Sennecey

Location:	Between Chalon-sur-Saone and Tournus
Type and Size:	The lake is over 40 acres in size, and is the largest of a group of three lakes
How to Find:	Turn off the A6/E15 motorway at Chalon. Head south along the N6, which runs parallel to the motorway, to the town of Sennecey. The lakes are clearly signposted in the town
Carp Stock:	Lightly stocked with carp to over 40lbs
Permits:	Available from Cafe de Laives near the church in Laives; day and year permit available
BK Rating:	Difficult
Comments:	Became well known some years ago and subsequently received a lot of angling pressure. One English angler had three forties in a weekend, but nowadays it is not much fished. Crayfish and mussels a problem

Sorigny

Location:	About 8 miles south of Tours
Type and Size:	Natural lake of about 40 acres
How to Find:	Take the N10 road heading south from Tours to the village of Sorigny. As you leave town follow the sign for camping/caravan site - the lake is part of the site
Carp Stock:	A reasonable head of commons and mirrors averaging nearly 20lbs. There are quite a few twenties with the occasional thirty
Permits:	Permission must be obtained from the camp site
BK Rating:	Moderate
Comments:	Water sports take place, but this doesn't spoil your chances of catching. At one time you could only obtain a permit if you were staying on the site, but this rule has now been relaxed

Richard Tring with
a 35.8 mirror from
one of the lakes at
Chalon-sur-Saone
(Tailly)

Tailly

Location: 4 miles south of Beaune, between Dijon and Chalon-sur-Saone
Type and Size: Two gravel pits of about 30 acres and 10 acres
How to Find: Turn off the A6/E15 motorway at Beaune, and head south on the D970. The lakes are either side of the road about 4 miles from Beaune, just past the Meursault turn
Carp Stock: The larger lake has a very good head of carp to 47lbs, including many twenties; the smaller lake contains fewer carp to just over 20lbs
Permits: French national licence from Jackie Greset's tackle shop at Chalon-sur-Saone
BK Rating: Moderate
Comments: Local anglers have been moving fish around these lakes to confuse visitors! Hard boilies needed to beat the numerous crayfish. The small lake has many snags. The large lake is shallow at one end, with a small island at the deeper end, and the island shelf is most productive

Ville Franche   A

Location: Near Montpon, 40 miles east of Bordeaux
Type and Size: Two lakes of 30 acres and 5 acres
How to Find: Leave the E70 road, which runs from Bordeaux to Perigeux, at Montpon, then south to Ville Franche. The lakes and camp site are clearly signposted as you enter the village
Carp Stock: The small lake is well stocked with small carp to mid-doubles. The larger lake is lightly stocked with fish up to 40lbs

Permits: Day tickets from the camp site
BK Rating: Small lake - Easy; larger lake - Difficult
Comments: Ideal place to take a family and also enjoy some carp fishing. Boats and swimming allowed on the larger lake, where there is a man-made beach. Very busy at times

Paul Booth with a 38 pounder caught on his first ever visit to France. Successful bait was KM Maestro Honey Necta 20mm boilie

GERMANY
by Sven Heininger

Ahlbacher Weiher

Location:	Westerwald, the Germans call it Mittelgebirge, near the river Rhein and the town Koblenz
Type and Size:	Five small lakes and one trout lake with fish to 6lbs
How to Find:	From Ahlbach only 12 kilometres to the lakes, follow the signpost from the fishing club
Carp Stock:	A lot of carp to 36lb
Other Species:	Trout to 18lbs, pike to 24lbs, zander to 15lbs and catfish to 28lbs
Permits:	At the car park at the lake, you can buy baits, food and drinks there too
Cost:	Not known
Control:	Fishing Club
Restrictions:	You can only fish on Wednesdays and Saturdays from 7am to 5pm
Baits/Methods:	Normal baits and methods for carp fishing
BK Rating:	Easy
Comments:	German national licence essential

Aggerstausee

Location:	Near the town of Gummersbach
Type and Size:	Big, river dammed lake
How to Find:	Take the A4 to Kölm-Olpe and leave the motorway at the town Bergmeustadt
Carp Stock:	A few carp to 20lbs
Other Species:	Small eels, zanders and pike, a lot of perch, trout and roach
Permits:	Fishing Club, Jahnstr. 12, Gummersbach-Dümmlinghausen
Cost:	Two day ticket 90 marks and the week 270 marks
Control:	Water Police
Restrictions:	No fishing from boat, special fishing permission from tourist department is necessary
Baits/Methods:	Boilies and particle
BK Rating:	Difficult
Comments:	It is not easy to get permission for the water!! German national licence essential

Altmühl

Location:	South Germany, Bavaria near Nürnberg
Type and Size:	Very small river in old mature farm
Carp Stock:	Well stocked with wild and common carp to 15lbs
Other Species:	Pike, bream, tench and eel
Permits:	Tackle shops
Cost:	30 marks per day ticket
Control:	Water Police
Restrictions:	Only two rods. No night fishing. No lifeboats
Baits/Methods:	Sweetcorn and boilies
BK Rating:	Moderate to Difficult for the bigger ones
Comments:	German national licence essential

A superb 29 pounder caught by top German carp angler Sven Heininger, who wrote this section of the book

Altmühlsee

Location:	In the south of Germany, Bavaria, near the towns of Gunrenhausen and Herrieden
Type and Size:	Big lake, not very deep
How to Find:	The lake is between München and Nürnberg, take the A9 to München, A3 to Nümberg
Carp Stock:	Well stocked with carp to 30lbs
Other Species:	Pike, tench, bream and roach
Permits:	From the tackle shop in Hervieden, Vogteiplace 1
Cost:	30 marks per day
Control:	Water Police
Restrictions:	No night fishing. Special German fishing permission is necessary
Baits/Methods:	Long range fishing, a lot of baits
BK Rating:	Very Easy - small fish to 16lb; Difficult - big fish
Comments:	It is necessary to walk long distances with all your gear. Not recommended for lazy anglers! In summer a lot of camping and swimming. German national licence essential

Alt-Rhein

Location:	In the Rhein-Main area, near Frankfurt and Damstadt
Type and Size:	Small part of the huge river Rhine
How to Find:	From Frankfurt take the A5 to Grozs-Gerau, then change to the motorway to Erfelden/Riedstadt
Carp Stock:	Well stocked with wild carp to 16lbs, some big mirror carp to 50lb
Other Species:	Pike, eel, bream, roach, zander, perch - very big ones to 8lbs. 1992 an angler caught a grass carp of 16lbs and the water police have found a dead catfish of 176lbs
Permits:	From all tackle shops at the river
Cost:	90 marks for the year
Control:	Water Police
Restrictions:	Only two rods. Please use the car parks
Baits/Methods:	Normal baits and methods, best are boilies at 24mm size, they are big enough to catch only carp
BK Rating:	Easy to moderate
Comments:	To many good swims you must walk long distances. You need a lot of baits because there is a lot of ship traffic. The bream cause problems as they like the carp baits. Some swims are very snaggy. Best places are deep holes in the river. German national licence

Bille

Location:	In the centre of Hamburg, north Germany
Type and Size:	Very small river with a lot of fish, not very deep
How to Find:	You can find the water on all town maps of Hamburg
Carp Stock:	Heavily stocked with small wild carp to 12lbs, some big ones
Other Species:	Eel, zander, bream, roach and pike
Permits:	From the tackle shops
Cost:	Not known
Control:	Water Police
Restrictions:	Only two rods. No night fishing
Baits/Methods:	Normal baits and methods
BK Rating:	Easy
Comments:	German national licence essential

Bostalsee

Location:	Between Hunsruck and Pfalz, in Saarland, south west Germany
Type and Size:	Huge gravel pit of 350 acres
Carp Stock:	Some carp from 10 to 18lbs
Other Species:	Perch, tench, eels, trout, zander and other coarse fish
Permits:	German national licence and day and weekly ticket on bank
Cost:	£3 per day and £14 per week
BK Rating:	Difficult
Comments:	Two rods only; no fishing from December 15th to January 31st. Very busy with campers and swimmers

Brombachsee

Location:	Near Gunvanhausen, Bavaria, south Germany
Type and Size:	Huge lake, only four metres deep
How to Find:	The lake is about 10 miles east of Gunvanhausen
Carp Stock:	Some carp to 30lbs
Other Species:	Pike, trout, perch
Permits:	Tackle shop: Baumann-Sonntag, Breitis Angtertreft Am Lindermer 1, 8820 Unterwurmbach
Cost:	30 marks per day ticket
Control:	Water Police
Restrictions:	No night fishing. Only two rods
Baits/Methods:	Bent hook rig, heavy leads
BK Rating:	Difficult
Comments:	German national licence essential

Dechsendorfer Weiher

Location:	Between Nürnberg and Erlangen, in Bavaria, South Germany
Type and Size:	Large pit, about three quarters of a mile in length
How to Find:	Off the A3 Nürnberg to Wurzburg road
Carp Stock:	Well stocked with carp, most of which are under 10lbs
Category:	Mixed Fishery
Other Species:	Tench and perch
Permits:	Sportamt Erlangen, Fahrstree 18, Erlange. Tel: 09131 86590
Cost:	£4 per day
Restrictions:	Two rods only
BK Rating:	Easy
Baits/Methods:	Boilies best at present

Diemel-Talsperre

Location:	Between Hessen and Nordreihnwestfalen, near the town Korbach
Type and Size:	Huge river dam
How to Find:	Take the A4 to Olpe, the B55 to Meschede, change to B7 to Messinghausen, then follow the signs 'lake'
Carp Stock:	Many carp between 7lbs and 15lbs and some to 30lbs
Other Species:	Catifsh to 80lbs, eels, pike, zander, roach, trout, tench, bream and perch
Permits:	From the tackle shops, Forest office and from some restaurants
Cost:	Two day ticket 30 marks; week 75 marks, and year 360 marks
Control:	Water Police
Restrictions:	Only two rods, no live baits

Baits/Methods: Normal methods, boilies best bait for big carp
BK Rating: Moderate
Comments: No closed season. Difficult to find a good swim, use a boat. German national licence

Donau

Location: South Germany, the river flows from Donaueschingen to the Austrian border. Towns on the river: Regensburg, Passau, Ulm
Type and Size: Huge European river
How to Find: Take A8 or A7 to Ulm, then you can drive parallel to the river
Carp Stock: Well stocked with carp to 50lbs possibly
Other Species: Catfish to 150lbs, sturgeon, pike, eels, chub, perch, roach, bream, tench, grass carp, mirror carp, zander
Permits: Tackle shops near the water
Cost: Not known
Control: Water Police
Restrictions: Only two rods. In some areas no night fishing
Baits/Methods: Huge size boilies necessary
BK Rating: Difficult to find the carp
Comments: A water with a lot of species of fish in a nice surrounding. German national licence essential

Duisburg Harbour/River Rhein

Location: West Germany, near the Dutch border, the Germans call the area the 'Ruhrgebiet' in the centre of Duisburg
Type and Size: Huge harbour
How to Find: At the A2/A3 take the A2 from Venlo to Duisburg
Carp Stock: Few carp, but very big ones, record carp of 51lbs
Other Species: Pike, zander, eel, roach, bream and perch
Permits: Tackle shop Gervasi, Sternstr. 51, 4150 Krefeld. Tel: 02151 615341
Cost: 30 marks
Control: Water Police
Restrictions: Two rods only
Baits/Methods: Hard fished water by German carp fishers, modern baits and methods are best at present
BK Rating: Moderate to Difficult
Comments: A difficult water with a chance of a very big fish. German national licence essential

Dümmer

Location: Take the B51 from Osnabruck to Diepholz, near Niedersachen, North Germany
Type and Size: Very big lake, several miles square, and only about five feet deep
Carp Stock: Not many, but some very big ones
Category: Few Carp
Other Species: Perch to 6lbs, pike to 36lbs, a few tench and many eels
Permits: The tackle shop Bödeker/Hüde, or Friedrich Kemper, Steinstreet 19, 2840 Diepholz. Tel: 05541 3329
Cost: £3 per day

BK Rating: Super-Difficult
Comments: The best chance is boat fishing and boats can be hired for £3 an hour. Only for the dedicated specialist carp hunter as the fish are few and very hard to locate

Edertalsperre

Location: Hessen, in the middle of Germany, near the towns Kassel and Korbach
Type and Size: Huge river dam
How to Find: Take the A7 or A44 to Kassel, then change to B251 to Korbach, then take B252 to Herhousen
Carp Stock: Well stocked with small mirrors to 10lbs and some big ones to 40lbs
Other Species: Main fish are pike to 45lbs and zander, bream, roach, tench, eels and perch
Permits: From all tackle shops at the lake
Cost: 30 marks a day, 75 marks a week
Control: Water Police
Restrictions: Only two rods. No night fishing
Baits/Methods: Huge size boilies for carp essential, because the big bream eat the small boilies
BK Rating: Moderate to Difficult, because it's not easy to find the carp (use a boat)
Comments: German national licence essential. Best place to fish for carp is the Niederweber Bucht

Eider

Location: North Germany, near the town of Wrohm
Type and Size: Small river
How to Find: Take the B203 from Heide to Rendsburg
Carp Stock: Well stocked with carp to 30lbs
Other Species: Bream, eel, perch, zander, roach and pike
Permits: Tackle shop Mickan, Hauptstreet 44, 2241 Wrohm
Cost: Not known
Control: Water Police
Restrictions: Not known
Baits/Methods: Normal carp fishing baits and methods
BK Rating: Moderate
Comments: German national licence essential

Elbe-Havel-Kanal

Location: North east Germany, near Berlin and Brondenburg
Type and Size: Canal
How to Find: Take A2 to Madel
Carp Stock: Some carp
Other Species: Perch, bream, eels and roach
Permits: Tackle shops
Cost: Not known
Control: Water Police
Restrictions: Only two rods. No night fishing
Baits/Methods: Normal baits and methods
BK Rating: Difficult, because there are only a few carp
Comments: German national licence essential

Elchinger Gravel Pits

Location: South Germany, Badenwürttenberg, near to the towns of Unterelchingen and Ulm
Type and Size: Some nice gravel pits
How to Find: Take A7/A8 to Ulm, change at motorway to Ober and Unterelchingen
Carp Stock: Huge carp to 40lbs
Other Species: Pike, eel, zander, perch, roach, bream, chub, tench
Permits: Elchinger Tackle Shop, 7915 Unterelchingen. Tel: 07308/6161
Cost: Day ticket 60 marks
Control: Club
Restrictions: Not known
Baits/Methods: Boilies best bait for the big ones
BK Rating: Moderate
Comments: German national licence essential

Ellertshäuser Reservoir

Location: Unterfranken, between Würzbürg and Schweinfurt
Type and Size: Huge reservoir
Carp Stock: Well stocked with carp to 20lbs
Category: Mixed Fishery
Other Species: Tench, zander and trout
Permits: Bernd Müller, Zum See 10, 8721 Fuchstadt, Unterfranken
Cost: £5 per day
BK Rating: Insufficient information
Comments: The best water in Unterfranken, and a very pleasant area

Erlenholsee

Location: Westerforrest, Mittelgebirge, north of the town Montabaur, West Germany
Type and Size: Small lake
How to Find: Take A3 (Köln-Frankfurt)
Carp Stock: Well stocked with small carp
Other Species: Coarse fish
Permits: Tackle shop in Montabaur
Cost: Not known
Control: Club
Restrictions: Only two rods
Baits/Methods: Bent hook rigs and boilies are the best
BK Rating: Difficult, very hard fished water
Comments: German national licence essential

Falkenhagener See

Location: Near Berlin-Spandau, East Germany
Type and Size: A nice lake in a nice surrounding
How to Find: Take A2 to Berlin
Carp Stock: Carp water, paradise for carp anglers with many fish to 35lbs
Other Species: Pike, tench, rudd, roach, eel and perch
Permits: Tackle shops in Berlin-Spandau
Cost: 24 marks for day ticket; 90 marks for week
Control: Club

Restrictions:	Only two rods
Baits/Methods:	Hard fished with boilies, a lot of snags
BK Rating:	Easy to Difficult
Comments:	A lot of lilies and fields. German national licence essential

Fulda

Location:	Hessen, near the towns Fulda and Kassel, in the centre of Germany
Type and Size:	River
How to Find:	Take A7 or A49 to Kassel
Carp Stock:	Many carp to 10lbs, but some big ones to 30lbs
Other Species:	Bream to 9lbs, chub to 6lbs, eels, trout, barbel, pike to 26lbs and perch
Permits:	Tackle shop near the water
Cost:	Day ticket 21 marks, week 120 marks and month 130 marks
Control:	Water Police
Restrictions:	Only two rods
Baits/Methods:	Most fish are caught by float and leger fishing with sweetcorn and boilies
BK Rating:	Moderate
Comments:	German national licence essential

Gamensee

Location:	East Germany, Brandenburg
Type and Size:	Big reservoir
How to Find:	Take motorway Berlin-Blumberg, then change to B158 to Dannenberg
Carp Stock:	Very well stocked with carp to 20lbs
Other Species:	Eel, bream, roach, pike, tench and some zander
Permits:	Tackle shop
Cost:	30 marks per day
Control:	Water Police
Restrictions:	Not known
Baits/Methods:	Boilies and modern carp fishing rigs are best at present
BK Rating:	Difficult, very hard fished water
Comments:	The many bream and roach are a problem as they take the baits. German national licence essential

Godelheimer Seen

Location:	North of Germany, near the towns of Godelheim and Höxter
Type and Size:	Five gravel pits
Carp Stock:	Well stocked with mirror and common carp to 30lbs
Other Species:	Catfish to 60lbs, pike to 25lbs, zander to 18lbs, eels to 5lbs and tench to 7lbs
Permits:	Tackle shop Müller in Godelheim
Cost:	30 marks
Control:	Fishing club and Water Police
Restrictions:	Not known
Baits/Methods:	Standard rigs, boilies, particle baits and floater fishing
BK Rating:	Easy
Comments:	The fishing ticket is for all lakes! German national licence essential

Grafenwöhr

Location:	Between Amberg and Bayreuth
Type and Size:	Some of small river and three lakes
How to Find:	Take the motorway B299 to Grafenwöhr
Carp Stock:	The lakes are well stocked with carp to 28lbs
Other Species:	Pike to 35lbs, bream, roach, eel, barbel, chub, tench, zander and a few catfish
Permits:	Tackle shop Weiden, Holunderweg 1, 8480 Weiden
Cost:	Day ticket 36 marks and the week 120 marks
Control:	Club
Restrictions:	Only two rods. No night fishing. In lakes only leads to 10gms
Baits/Methods:	Particle baits and boilies are very successful because nobody has fished the water with these baits before
BK Rating:	Easy
Comments:	German national licence essential

Griebnitzsee

Location:	In the middle of Berlin
Type and Size:	Large town lake
Carp Stock:	Many commons and mirrors to 25lbs
Category:	Carp Water
Other Species:	Bream, roach, eels and pike
Permits:	Tickets from the fishing club Schöneberg, Islandrellistret 56, 1000 Berlin 46
Cost:	£15 for 6 months
BK Rating:	Easy
Comments:	Two rods only; German national licence essential

Griesäcker Gravel Pit

Location:	South Germany, near the town Ulm, Baden Württenberg
Type and Size:	Small gravel pit
How to Find:	Take A7 to Ulm, then change at motorway to Aislingen
Carp Stock:	Stocked with carp to 38lbs
Other Species:	Big pike and all coarse fish
Permits:	Erwin Zaboch, Hauptstreet 26, 7923 Königsbronn/Ochsenberg
Cost:	Day ticket 60 marks, year 600 marks
Control:	Club
Restrictions:	No night fishing. Two rods and no live baits
BK Rating:	Easy to Moderate
Comments:	German national licence essential

Hammerweiher

Location:	Near the town of Bodenwöhr, Bavaria, South Germany
Type and Size:	Small lake
Carp Stock:	Stocked with carp to 36lbs
Other Species:	All coarse fish
Permits:	Petrol station Kraus, 8465 Bodenwöhr. Tel: 09434/2606
Cost:	150 marks per week; 300 marks per month
Control:	Club/Water Police

Restrictions:	Not known
Baits/Methods:	All advanced baits and rigs, boilies are the best baits. Not hard fished by boilie fishers
BK Rating:	Easy to Moderate

Happurger Reservoir

Location:	Abbochtal, between Deckersberg, Houbirg and Reicheneck in the Franken area of Bavaria, South Germany
Type and Size:	150 acre reservoir
Carp Stock:	A few carp to 18lbs
Category:	Few Carp
Other Species:	Tench, zander, big trout, roach and eels
Permits:	From the Town Hall in Happurg
Cost:	£5 per day
BK Rating:	Difficult
Comments:	Much sailing and windsurfing in summer

Henne-Talsperre

Location:	In the industrial area of Ruhr-Gebiet, near the town Meschede
Type and Size:	Huge reservoir about 200 hectares
How to Find:	Take the motorway 55 to the town Meschede
Carp Stock:	Some carp to 25lbs
Other Species:	Pike, trout, eel, perch, zander, tench, bream and roach
Permits:	Day ticket water from tackle shop Bischoff, Zeughausstreet 12, 5778 Meschede. Tel: 6488
Cost:	24 marks for day
Control:	Water Police
Restrictions:	Two rods only
Baits/Methods:	Worms, particles and boilies. Standard rigs are very successful
BK Rating:	Moderate
Comments:	The best places to catch carp are Horbach-Bucht and Enkhausen. German national licence essential

Hohenwarte-River-Dam

Location:	East Germany, near the towns of Neidenberga and Saulthal
Type and Size:	Huge river dam
Carp Stock:	Some carp to 38lbs
Other Species:	Pike to 45lbs, zander, tench, perch, eel, roach, bream
Permits:	Tackle shop Posselt, Hohenwarter Street, 0-6801 Kaulsdorf
Cost:	Day ticket 30 marks
Control:	Water Police
Restrictions:	No live baits. Only two rods
Baits/Methods:	Flat places are the best swims for carp fishing. Normal baits and methods
BK Rating:	Difficult, because it is not easy to find the fish
Comments:	Good chances to catch a very big carp if you have enough time to find the fish. German national licence essential

Hopfensee

Location:	Hopfen am See, Bavaria, South Germany
Type and Size:	Big lake about half a mile across
Carp Stock:	Well stocked with carp to 40lbs
Category:	Mixed Fishery
Other Species:	Tench, bream, roach, pike, zander, perch and eels
Permits:	German fishing permit, and a £3 day ticket from the Hanpt tackle shop nearby
BK Rating:	Difficult
Baits/Methods:	Most fish are caught by float fishing with sweetcorn
Comments:	Very snaggy water with island. Boat needed to catch the carp; a very pleasant lake

Kamneder See

Location:	Off the A43 motorway between Witten Herbede and Hattingen, in Nordrheinwestfalen, North Germany
Carp Stock:	Not many carp
Category:	Few Carp
Other Species:	Bream, roach, pike, zander and perch
Permits:	ASV Bochum, Ruhr 1935; the tackle shop simmerman Bochum, Herner Street 363. Tel: 0234 551679
Cost:	£2 per day
BK Rating:	Difficult

Kölner Seen-Platte

Location:	Off the A4 from Aachen to Köln (Cologne), Nordrheinwestfalen, North Germany
Type and Size:	Huge lake
Carp Stock:	Well stocked with commons to 18lbs
Category:	Mixed Fishery
Other Species:	Perch, pike to 33lbs, tench and grass carp
BK Rating:	Very Difficult
Comments:	You will need to enquire locally how to get permits to fish this lake, as we were not able to find out

Krumme See

Location:	East Germany, Brandenburg, near the town of Krummersee
Type and Size:	Nice huge gravel pit
How to Find:	Drive from Königs-Wusterhausen to Mittenwold and drive left to Schenkendorf, now follow the signs to the lake
Carp Stock:	Well stocked with mirror and common carp to 30lbs
Other Species:	Bream, roach, pike, zander, eel and perch
Permits:	Tackle shop and town office
Cost:	Not known
Control:	Club/Water Police
Restrictions:	Only two rods
Baits/Methods:	All advanced baits and methods
BK Rating:	Easy
Comments:	German national licence essential

Lahn

Location:	Middle Germany, Hessen, near the towns of Wetzlar and Limburg
Type and Size:	Small river
How to Find:	Take A3 to Limburg or A45 to Wetzlar
Carp Stock:	Well stocked with carp to 25lbs
Other Species:	Pike, trout, barbel, chub, few tench and catfish, perch, eel, roach, bream and zander
Permits:	Tackle shops and private
Cost:	Day ticket 30 marks
Control:	Club/Water Police
Restrictions:	Not known
Baits/Methods:	Normal carp fishing methods and baits
BK Rating:	Easy
Comments:	German national licence essential

Landgrafenweiher

Location:	Fichtilgebirge, near Warmensteinach
Type and Size:	Large gravel pit
Carp Stock:	Quite well stocked with carp which average 6-8lbs. Some bigger fish to about 20lbs
Category:	Mixed Fishery
Other Species:	Grass carp, pike, zander, bream and catfish
Permits:	From the house at the lake in Warmensteinach
BK Rating:	Easy
Restrictions:	No baiting with boilies, fish food or particles

Leine

Location:	Near the town of Hannover, North Germany
Type and Size:	Small river which flows into the Aller (flow very fast)
How to Find:	Take A2 from Bielefeld to Hannover
Carp Stock:	Carp to 24lbs
Other Species:	Pike, eel, trout, roach and bream
Permits:	FV Hannover, Hildesheimer Street 112, 3000 Hannover 1. Tel: 0511 880054
Cost:	60 marks per week; 240 marks per month
Control:	FV Hannover
Restrictions:	Not known
Baits/Methods:	Normal carp fishing baits and methods
BK Rating:	Moderate
Comments:	German national licence essential

Mahnig-See

Location:	East Germany, district of Brandenburg
Type and Size:	Small lake
How to Find:	From Buchholz to Halbe-Teupitz
Carp Stock:	Carp to 28lbs
Other Species:	All coarse fish
Permits:	Club, tackle shop and forest office
Cost:	Not known
Control:	Club
Restrictions:	Only two rods. No night fishing

Baits/Methods: Normal carp fishing methods and boilies as bait
BK Rating: Easy
Comments: German national licence essential

Main

Location: In the middle of Germany, near the towns of Frankfurt, Hanau, Wümburg and Aschaffenburg
Type and Size: Huge European river with many sluices
Carp Stock: Many carp to 20lbs, some to 40lbs
Other Species: Pike, eel, catfish to 150lbs (German record), zander, roach, bream, barbel
Permits: From all tackle shops near the river
Cost: 90 marks for year
Control: Water Police
Restrictions: Only two rods
Baits/Methods: A lot of bait, strong line, heavy leads. 24mm size boilies are very successful as bream cannot take them
BK Rating: Easy, if you are in the right place
Comments: Some English carp fishermen have fished the river and caught carp to 40lbs

Mossandl-Weiher

Location: Between Mamming and Dingolfing, near Regensburg in Bavaria, South Germany
Type and Size: Gravel pit of about 60 acres
Carp Stock: Well stocked with mirrors and commons to about 20lbs
Category: Mixed Fishery
Other Species: Pike and zander
Permits: Restaurante Fischwirt, 8388 Mamming, and Dingolfing tackle shop, Obere Stadt 52, Dingolfing. Tel: 08731 2404
Cost: £10 per week
Restrictions: No night fishing, but boat fishing is allowed
BK Rating: Moderate

Mosel

Location: Nordrheinwest Falen, West Germany, between the towns of Koblenz and Trier
Type and Size: River, which flows into the Rhein
How to Find: Take the B416/B49 from Trier to Koblenz
Carp Stock: Well stocked with carp to 44lbs
Other Species: All coarse fish
Permits: From tackle shops at the river
Cost: Not known
Control: Water Police
Restrictions: Only two rods. Do not park your car anywhere
Baits/Methods: Huge size boilies otherwise you will only catch bream, chub and barbel
BK Rating: Easy to Moderate
Comments: German national licence essential

Naab

Location:	South Germany, Bavaria
Type and Size:	Small river
Carp Stock:	Big mirrors to 30lbs
Other Species:	All coarse fish and catfish to more than 100lbs. Jurgen Paul and his friends have this year caught pike and catfish to 26lbs
Permits:	Tackle shops
Cost:	180 marks a week
Control:	Club/Water Police
Restrictions:	Only two rods
Baits/Methods:	Snag leader fishing in some swims essential
BK Rating:	Easy to Moderate
Comments:	A well stocked water in a nice nature area. German national licence essential

Neckar

Location:	Near Heidelberg and Heilbronn
Type and Size:	River with a lot of ship traffic and sluices
How to Find:	Take the A5 from Frankfurt to Heidelberg, then the motorway parallel

Sven with another big common, which weighed forty pounds

	to the river to the town Mosbach/Heilbronn
Carp Stock:	Heavily stocked with carp to 55lbs, best German carp water
Other Species:	Chub, barbel, roach, bream, eels, some pike, a few zander and catfish to 60lbs
Permits:	From all tackle shops near the river
Cost:	150 marks for the year, no day tickets
Control:	Water Police
Restrictions:	No night fishing. Two rods. No returning of fish
Baits/Methods:	Fish mix. Fixed lead and short hooklength
BK Rating:	Easy
Comments:	Very snaggy, rods to 2½lb, sometimes only 1½lb, leads between 2oz and 4oz, big reels for example Baitrunner 4500 with 15lb line, snagleader very useful. Best fishing before and after a sluice. Not only the carp like boilies so do big barbel and chub. Make 24mm size boilies if you want to catch carp only. A good water to catch your dream carp. A water with a lot of carp between 20lbs and 30lbs. The best times for carp fishing are spring/autumn and sometimes early winter. German national licence essential

Niedermooser See

Location:	Hessen, in the centre of Germany, between Giessen and Fulda
Type and Size:	90 acre gravel pit
Carp Stock:	Heavily stocked with commons to about 20lbs, and mirrors to 25lbs
Category:	Mixed Fishery
Other Species:	Tench, pike, eels, zander, trout and most other coarse fish
Permits:	From the Campingrestaurante at the lake
Cost:	£4 per day; £24 per week
Control:	ASV Lauterbock, Lindenstrasse 4, 6420 Lauterbach
BK Rating:	Moderate
Comments:	A big lake also used for sailing

Niederwaldsee

Location:	Near Frankfurt, between Nauheim and Gross Gerau
Type and Size:	Big gravel pit
How to Find:	Take the A67 from Frankfurt to Darmstadt, then the road to Gross Gerau
Carp Stock:	Well stocked with small commons to 15lbs, and mirrors to 30lbs
Category:	Mixed Fishery
Other Species:	Pike, tench, chub, roach, bream, perch, eels and zander
Permits:	Day tickets should be purchased from the tea shop at the lake. The tickets only cover 12 hours - night fishing not allowed
Cost:	£3 per day
Control:	Club
BK Rating:	Small fish - Easy; big ones - Very Difficult
Baits/Methods:	Advanced carp fishing rigs, methods and bait are needed at this lake for the big carp. Boilies and sweetcorn are very successful
Restrictions:	No night fishing, two rods only
Comments:	Restaurant and disco at the lake; camping in summer; car park

Op Finger See

Location:	South Germany, near the town Freiburg
Type and Size:	Gravel pit of about 34 acres
How to Find:	Take the motorway Basel-Karlsruhe
Carp Stock:	Many doubles to 38lbs
Other Species:	Perch, pike, zander, tench, eel, roach, bream and a few trout
Permits:	From all tackle shops in Freiburg
Cost:	Day tickets only, 45 marks
Control:	Water Police and Club
Restrictions:	Two rods only. Special fishing licence necessary
Baits/Methods:	Carp tactics and baits, including sweetcorn and float fishing
Comments:	In the hot months a lot of camping and swimming, difficult to get a ticket. German national licence essential

Rappbodetalsperre

Location:	Asthorc, near the town of Wernigerode
Type and Size:	Huge river dam
Carp Stock:	Some carp to 40lbs and a lot of crucian carp
Other Species:	Big perch to 7lbs, pike, eel, zander and all coarse fish
Permits:	From the fish growing station at the lake
Cost:	Day ticket 45 marks and week 90 marks
Control:	Water Police
Restrictions:	Not known
Baits/Methods:	All the most advanced baits, rigs and methods needed for this hard fished water. Some swims are very snaggy and you must use strong line, heavy leads and hooks of between sizes 6 and 2
BK Rating:	Moderate to Difficult
Comments:	German national licence essential

Rhein-Herne-Canal

Location:	Canal between Duisburg, Bochum and Herne, canal flows into the river Rhein
Type and Size:	Canal, 5 to 8 metres deep and 30 metres wide
How to Find:	Near Gelsenkirchen and Duisburg, take A2 from Venlo to Duisberg, change to A59 and in Hamborn change to A42 to Herne
Carp Stock:	Many carp, the biggest caught weighed 36lbs
Other Species:	Eels, roach, bream and zander
Permits:	Reko Fishing Tackle, Kahrstreet 71, 4300 Essen
Cost:	15 marks day ticket
Control:	Water Police
Restrictions:	Two rods only
Baits/Methods:	Advanced carp fishing rigs, methods and baits are needed at the lake for the big carp. German carp fishermen use sweetcorn and boilies
BK Rating:	Easy to Moderate
Comments:	German national licence essential

River-dam Quitrdorf

Location:	Sachsen, near Dresden, on the Polish border in what used to be East Germany
Type and Size:	Huge reservoir of about 2,000 acres

Carp Stock:	Well stocked with commons and mirrors; water record is 38lbs
Category:	Mixed Fishery
Other Species:	Grass carp, tench and zander
Permits:	Permits from the camping area in Kollm
Cost:	£4 per day; £12 per week; boat hire £2 per day - two rods only
BK Rating:	Moderate

River Lahn

Location:	Hessen, between the towns of Marburg and Gießen
Type and Size:	Small river with a lot of snags
How to Find:	Take the B3 from Kassel to Marburg or the motorway Frankfurt-Gießen
Carp Stock:	Carp to 39lbs
Other Species:	Eel, barbel, chub, bream and roach
Permits:	Tackle shops in Marbug and Gießen
Cost:	30 marks per day
Control:	Water Police
Restrictions:	Two rods. No night fishing
Baits/Methods:	Advanced baits and methods would be needed, snag leader fishing
BK Rating:	Moderate
Comments:	German national licence essential

River Rhein

Location:	West Germany, near the French border
Type and Size:	Huge European river
Carp Stock:	Many carp under 10lbs, but the record is 60lbs
Category:	Mixed Fishery
Other Species:	Pike to 35lbs, zander to 30lbs and big catfish
Permits:	German national rod licence *and* a weekly permit, bought locally
Cost:	£10 per year
Control:	Water police
BK Rating:	Easy, if you can locate the fish
Baits/Methods:	Boilies catch the big fish. You need powerful rods, heavy leads, and line of 15lb breaking strain - and at least 200 metres of it, in case you hook one of the big catfish
Comments:	Not a river for beginners to fish

Schnackensee

Location:	Near the town of Gunzenhausen, Bavaria, South Germany
Type and Size:	Eight acre lake
How to Find:	The lake is about 25 miles south of Nürnberg
Carp Stock:	Well stocked with plenty of doubles, and some bigger fish. Lake record is 44lbs
Category:	Mixed Fishery
Other Species:	Many catfish to 150lbs (see Kevin Maddocks' book 'Catfish'), grass carp to 70lbs, pike, zander and 'Mamur Carp' to 70lbs
Permits:	Day ticket on bank
Control:	Private - Werner Vogel
BK Rating:	Easy
Cost:	£8 for 2 rods; £6 per day for caravans and £3 for tent or bivvy

Baits/Methods:	Modern, advanced rigs, methods and baits needed
Comments:	A pleasant, heavily stocked water producing hundreds of carp each week; can be very busy at weekends. Night fishing not allowed

In between carp sessions you can have a try for the famous Schnackensee catfish. Here Kevin Maddocks supports a medium-sized fish of 54 pounds - his best from this small fishery is 113 pounds

Schwalm

Location:	Between Knüllgebirge and Kellerforest, Hessen in the middle of Germany
Type and Size:	Small river
Carp Stock:	Some carp to 20lbs
Other Species:	Pike, perch, chub, trout, tench, bream and lot of barbel to record size
Permits:	From the village office in Schwolmstadt
Cost:	Day ticket 30 marks
Control:	Water Police
Restrictions:	Only two rods. No night fishing
Baits/Methods:	Big size boilies, if not you will only catch barbel
UK Rating:	Moderate to Difficult
Comments:	Not a water for beginners or for big catches. German national licence essential

Sieg

Location:	Between the two towns of Bonn and Siegburg, in the west of Germany on the left side of river Rhein
Type and Size:	Small river which flows into the river Rhein
How to Find:	Take the A565, A59 or A3 to Bonn
Carp Stock:	Well stocked with carp to 30lbs
Other Species:	Barbel, pike, trout, chub, small catfish
Permits:	Fishing clubs: ASV Obere Sieg, ASV Köln-Nord, ASF Eitdorf, ASF Stein-Stadt Blankenburg
Cost:	35 marks for day ticket
Control:	Fishing Clubs
Restrictions:	Two rods, sometimes only one rod, no live bait fishing
Baits/Methods:	In some areas very snaggy, snag leaders fishing, heavy lead
BK Rating:	Moderate
Comments:	Not easy to get a licence. German national licence essential

Silbersee

Location:	At the town of Neuss and near Düsseldorf
Type and Size:	Big gravel pit
How to Find:	Take the motorway to Düsseldorf and change to Neuss
Carp Stock:	Heavily stocked with a lot of carp to 40lbs
Other Species:	Tench, pike, zander, roach, bream
Permits:	Tackle shop Holger Menne, Bannerstr. 60, 4040 Neuss/Grimlinghausen
Cost:	18 marks for day ticket
Restrictions:	Two rods. Small carp must be returned
Baits/Methods:	Boilies and modern rigs
BK Rating:	Easy to Moderate
Comments:	Crayfish attack the boilies and other baits. One carp fishermen caught 50 carp between 20lbs and 30lbs. German national licence essential

Spree

Location:	In the centre of Berlin
Type and Size:	Small river
How to Find:	In the middle of Berlin
Carp Stock:	Few carp to 24lbs
Other Species:	Main fish are zander, roach, bream, pike and eel
Permits:	From tackle shops in Berlin, day tickets
Cost:	Not known
Control:	Water Police and Clubs
Baits/Methods:	Modern specimen hunting methods and baits
BK Rating:	Difficult
Comments:	A problem to find an angling place because the river is in the centre of the town. German national licence essential

Stichkanal

Location:	Off the A2/A39 near Braunschweig
Type and Size:	Big canal much used by boats
Carp Stock:	Well stocked with carp to 35lbs
Category:	Mixed Fishery
Other Species:	Most coarse fish, including pike and zander

Permits:	In advance only from Restaurant Gerhard Dolsner, Weinberg 8, 3303 Vechelde
Cost:	£4 per week - three rods
BK Rating:	Moderate
Baits/Methods:	Best method is a fixed lead with a pop-up hair rigged bait such as dog food

Storkower See

Location:	The lake is south of the motorway Berlin-Frankfurt, near the Berlin Urstromtals, in Berlin
Type and Size:	Lake of about 100 acres
How to Find:	Take the B248 or the motorway Berlin-Frankfurt
Carp Stock:	Well stocked with carp
Other Species:	Roach, bream, zander, pike and eel
Permits:	From the fishing club Storkow
Cost:	Year; for carp fishing 450 marks, for pike fishing 510 marks; per day 30 marks
Control:	Fishing Club
Baits/Methods:	Nobody has fished with boilies before
BK Rating:	Moderate
Comments:	Camping area at the lake. German national licence essential

Talsperre-Bautzen

Location:	In the middle of Germany, near the town Bautzen
Type and Size:	Huge reservoir, which is dammed by the river Spree
Carp Stock:	Many carp (up to 60lbs) and tench
Other Species:	Zander, eel, perch, roach, bream and grass carp
Permits:	Tackle shop Wadewitz in Bautzen
Cost:	30 marks per day; 105 marks per week
Control:	Water Police
Restrictions:	Two rods only. No live baits for pike fishing
Baits/Methods:	Sometimes it is necessary to fish at long range
BK Rating:	Easy, if you find the right fishing place
Comments:	Around the lake are lots of car parks. Night fishing is permitted. German national licence essential

Twislesee

Location:	West Germany, Hessen near the town Arolsen
Type and Size:	Huge lake
How to Find:	Take A44 to Diemelstadt, change to B252 to Arolsen
Carp Stock:	A very well stocked fishery, with some very big carp
Other Species:	Pike, trout, roach, bream, chub, perch, zander and eel
Permits:	Tackle shop, petrol station, restaurants
Cost:	Not known
Control:	Water Police
Restrictions:	Only two rods
Baits/Methods:	Fixed lead, short hook length and boilies. Dutch fishermen have caught carp to 40lbs with two boilies on the hair, pop-up
BK Rating:	Difficult, not easy to find the fish
Comments:	German national licence

Unteres Oderbruch

Location:	East Germany, near the Polish border
Type and Size:	Canal
Carp Stock:	A few carp
Other Species:	Chub, zander, roach, bream, eels and a lot of perch
Permits:	Not known
Control:	Water Police
Baits/Methods:	Normal rigs and baits
BK Rating:	Difficult, because there are only a few carp
Comments:	German national licence essential

Werbellinsee

Location:	East Germany, near the town Neuruppin in Brandenburg
Type and Size:	Huge gravel pit
Carp Stock:	Well stocked with carp to 30lbs
Other Species:	All coarse fish
Permits:	Club and tackle shop
Cost:	Not known
Control:	Club
Baits/Methods:	Nobody has fished the water with boilies
BK Rating:	Easy
Comments:	German national licence essential

Werrastalsperre

Location:	Between the towns of Eschwege, Kassel and Gottingen, in Hessen, central Germany
Type and Size:	Huge gravel pit
How to Find:	Take the A7 from Salsgitter to Kassel and then the B7 to Eschwege
Carp Stock:	Carp to 20lbs
Category:	Mixed Fishery
Other Species:	Zander, rudd, bream and roach
Permits:	Fremden Verkelswerein (FVV) Eschwege - 3440 Eshwege
BK Rating:	Moderate
Comments:	Float fishing is the best method here

THE BEEKAY GUIDE TO 1500 BRITISH & EUROPEAN CARP WATERS	**Is YOUR Water listed? If so, are the details correct?** If you spot omissions, inaccuracies, or know of any changes, please let us know by filling in the Waters Questionnaire at the back of this guide and return it to us at: FREEPOST Beekay Publishers Withy Pool Henlow Camp Bedfordshire SG16 6EA

HOLLAND

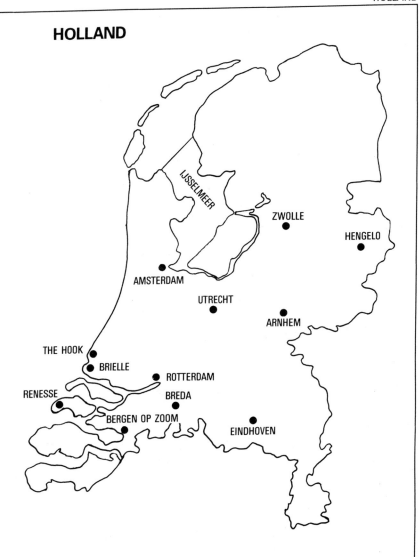

ZWOLLE

HENGELO

AMSTERDAM

UTRECHT

ARNHEM

THE HOOK

BRIELLE

ROTTERDAM

RENESSE

BREDA

BERGEN OP ZOOM

EINDHOVEN

IJSSELMEER

Amstelveense Poel

Location:	Near town of Amstelveen
Type and Size:	Big lake
Carp Stock:	Many carp but not easy
Other Species:	Several
Permits:	National Licence and Licence Amsterdamse Hengelsport Vereniging
Control:	Amsterdamse Hengelsport Vereniging
Baits/Methods:	Difficult water, so use modern rigs
Comments:	Nice place to fish

Barge and Jetty Lake and Complex

Location: Knieuwkoop, about an hour's drive from the Hook of Holland

Type and Size: Barge and Jetty Lakes about 1½ acres each. The main complex is about 150 acres, made up of many small lakes

Carp Stock: Jetty Lake is heavily stocked with carp from 15 to 30lbs, including some big commons. Barge Lake also heavily stocked with carp to mid-twenties

Permits: In advance only from: Carp Fishers Abroad, Rose Cottage, Roddington Heath, Shrewsbury, Shropshire SY4 4RB. Tel: 0952 770771

BK Rating: Easy to Moderate

Comments: Carp Fishers Abroad have a secure clubhouse with washing and toilet facilities. The small lakes immediately adjacent to the clubhouse are heavily stokced with carp to 30lb and are pretty easy. The complex is a mass of natural lakes interconnected by small canals. Access around these is by boat. The lakes are very productive especially in early season. We have a local guide who knows the area very well and will put you straight onto the fish. The Carp Fishrs Abroad package inlcudes ferry tickets, local directions, licences, boats, use of the clubhouse and preferential access to the best island swims in the complex (a chance for real isolation!). Night fishing is no problem in the summer months

Brielle Moat

Location: 15 miles west of Rotterdam, very near the coast

Type and Size: Moat around the old town of Brielle

Carp Stock: Quite heavily stocked, including several 20lb commons

Permits: Available from 'local bar' or tackle shops

BK Rating: Moderate

Comments: A very well known fishery, which is heavily fished at times

Damse Vaart

Location: Between Sluis (Holland) and Brugge (Belgium)

Type and Size: Small canal

Carp Stock: Carp up to 30lbs

Other Species: Many

Permits: National Licence and a licence from local tackle dealers in Sluis

Restrictions: Night fishing allowed

Baits/Methods: Modern

BK Rating: Very Difficult

De Bosbaan

Location: Not far from Amsterdam

Type and Size: Large lake

Carp Stock: Enormous population of carp with fish up to 50 pounds. Plenty of thirties

Permits: Normal 'Sportvisakte' required

Restrictions: No groundbait and no free offerings

Baits/Methods: Good rigs needed as fish only ever encounter hookbaits!

BK Rating: Moderate

Comments: Heavily fished

De Kleiputten of Esbeek

Location:	Near the village of Esbeek (Hilvarenbeek) about 5 miles south of Tilburg
Type and Size:	Small clay pit, very attractive
How to Find:	At the end of a sand track out of the village of Esbeek
Carp Stock:	Plenty of doubles and a few twenties
Category:	Easy
Permits:	Normal 'Sportvisakte' required
Restrictions:	No night fishing
Baits/Methods:	Standard baits and rigs work well
Comments:	A good place for regular runs!

Het Apeldoornskanaal

Location:	A channel that goes from Apeldoorn till it ends in the River Ijssel. From the Hook you drive to Den Haag, take the A12 to Utrecht. Take the A28 to Amersfoort. In Amersfoort you take the A1 to Apeldoorn. Leave the road at Apeldoorn-zuid, go left and the first right, you'll find it there
Type and Size:	18 miles long
Carp Stock:	There is an interesting stock of carp in the channel. Not really very many but up to 34lbs
Category:	Mixed Fishery
Other Species:	Most European coarse fish
Permits:	Government and local permit which you can get at the local tackle shop in Apeldoorn. Address - Marktstraat 5 Apeldoorn
UK Rating:	Easy to Moderate
Comments:	Night fishing only from 1st June to 31st August

Het Kinselmeer

Location:	Near the dam of Ijsselmeer, the huge inland sea in the north of Holland
Type and Size:	Huge lake, beautiful and quiet
Carp Stock:	A reasonable sprinkling of huge carp
Permits:	Normal 'Sportvisakte' required
UK Rating:	Difficult
Comments:	Location is important. Has produced some huge carp to persistent anglers

Het Nijkerker Nauw/Het Eemmeer

Location:	A water next to the N301 between Nijkerk and Zeewolde. From the Hook you drive to Den Haag, take the A12 to Utrecht. In Utrecht you take the A28 to Amersfoort, in Amersfoort you stay on the A28 to Nijkerk. Leave the road at Nijkerk/Zeewolde. Now you are on the N301, go in the direction of Zeewolde. After about 1 mile you cross the river
Type and Size:	About 8 miles long and an average of half a mile wide
Carp Stock:	Not really known, but there are a lot of carp. Professional fishermen have found carp up to 50lbs in their nets
Category:	Mixed Fishery
Other Species:	Most European coarse fish, very large pike and zander
Permits:	Government permit only
UK Rating:	Moderate to Difficult
Comments:	A lot of day trips and watersports on the water. Night fishing only from 1st June to 31st August

Hoge Vaart

Location:	Between Lelystad and Almere
Type and Size:	Small river
Carp Stock:	Many carp to 20 pounds
Other Species:	Big bream
Permits:	National Licence and a permit from D G Cornelissen, Archipel 15-27 te Lelystad
Control:	Club
Restrictions:	Night fishing allowed in June, July and August
BK Rating:	Easy
Comments:	No close season

Lage Vaart

Location:	Between Lelystad and Almere
Type and Size:	Small river
Carp Stock:	Many carp to 20 pounds
Other Species:	Big bream
Permits:	National licence and a permit from D G Cornelissen, Archipel 15-27 te Lelystad
Control:	Club
Restrictions:	Night fishing allowed in June, July and August
BK Rating:	Easy
Comments:	No close season

Little Melanen

Location:	Bergen op Zoom, 20 miles west of Breda
Type and Size:	Town lake of about 8 acres
How to Find:	In the town of Bergen op Zoom
Carp Stock:	Very heavily stocked with some twenties
Permits:	From the tackle shop in the town, or at the camp site nearby
BK Rating:	Very Easy
Comments:	An ideal water to take the family; several camp sites nearby

Molengat and Ovensgat Lake

Location:	Rossum, near Utrecht
Type and Size:	Two lakes of about 7 acres
How to Find:	Take the A2 and the N322 to Rossum (between Utrecht and den Bosch)
Carp Stock:	Carp to at least 35 pounds
Permits:	Available from cafe named 'Waalzicht' in Rossum, cost approximately 5 guilders per day and 60 guilders for a year
BK Rating:	Moderate
Comments:	Very nice waters with potential of some very big fish. The nearby river also holds carp

Molenwiel

Location:	Near Nederasselt, between Wychen and Druten
Type and Size:	6 acre lake
Carp Stock:	Fish to at least 35 pounds, quantity unknown

Permits:	Day tickets available from grocer's shop 'Van der Stappen' in Nederasselt, cost: 3 guilders, or 60 guilders per year
BK Rating:	Moderate
Comments:	A good quality water holding some very big carp - full potential unknown

Nieuwkoopse Plassen

Location:	About 4 miles north east of Alphen aan de Rijn, which is 20 miles north of Rotterdam
Type and Size:	A huge complex of shallow lakes
Carp Stock:	Fairly well stocked with carp of all sizes
Permits:	Normal 'Sportvisakte' required
Baits/Methods:	Simple baits and rigs work
BK Rating:	Moderate
Comments:	Location is of prime importance on this large water and then holding the fish is sometimes difficult. A boat is essential. Great potential for the serious carp angler

Noord-Hollands Kanaal

Location:	Runs from Amsterdam to Den Helder
Type and Size:	Big river
Carp Stock:	Plenty of carp and other species, up to at least 30lbs
Permits:	National licence and from the Amsterdamse Hengelsport Vereniging
Control:	Amsterdamse Hengelsport Vereniging
Restrictions:	Ask the angling club
Comments:	Difficult water to locate the carp but once found, they are easy to catch

Oisterwijkse Vennen

Location:	About 5 miles north east of Tilburg
Type and Size:	A combination of several waters but the only good one is the Belvertsven Lake of about 25 acres. Very deep in the middle
Carp Stock:	Some doubles and twenties with a sprinking of thirties
Permits:	Normal 'Sportvisakte' required
Baits/Methods:	Advanced rigs and baits required
BK Rating:	Moderate
Comments:	Spring and summer sees many holidaymakers in the region but very quiet in the autumn

Othense Kreek

Location:	In the town of Terneuzen
Type and Size:	Very big lake
How to Find:	East part of the small town
Carp Stock:	Carp to 30lbs, lots of twenties
Other Species:	Many
Permits:	National licence at any post office
Control:	Local eel angler
Restrictions:	No close season. No night fishing
BK Rating:	Very Easy
Comments:	A good place to fish

Renesse

Location:	30 miles south west of Rotterdam, on the coast
Type and Size:	5 acre lake
Carp Stock:	Well stocked with carp, and lots of twenties
Permits:	Available on site at £6 per year
BK Rating:	Very Easy
Comments:	A good place to take the family; many camp sites close by

Rijnkanaal

Location:	Amsterdam area, where there are many other canals, all containing carp
Type and Size:	If you thought the Twente was big, you ought to see this one!
Carp Stock:	Heavily stocked with plenty of big carp
Category:	Mixed Fishery
Other Species:	Most coarse fish
Permits:	Compulsory Sportvisakte, the national licence obtainable from Post Offices; you MUST NOT fish in Holland without this licence - no other permit required. Covers two rods for a year at low cost
BK Rating:	Difficult, unless the fish can be located when it is quite easy
Comments:	No close season. Many big fish lost when line is cut on freshwater mussels, so you need line heavy enough and of the right type to combat this problem. NB. The new Dutch record of 52lbs was caught from a river, and most of the biggest carp are found in rivers and canals; for this reason we strongly recommend anglers to fish these and not the lakes, which often are private and do not contain the biggest carp. Night fishing only allowed in June, July and August

River De Eem

Location:	A not very long river. The most interesting part for carp fishermen is the part from highway A1 to the end in the Eemmeer. From the Hook you drive to Den Haag, take the A12 to Utrecht. In Utrecht you take the A27 to Hilversum, stay on this road till you can take the A1 to Amersfoot. Leave the road at Baarn. The road you come on now is next to the river
Type and Size:	14 miles long
Carp Stock:	You won't catch 10 carp a day, but there are plenty of nice fish up to 35lbs
Category:	Mixed Fishery
Permits:	Government and at most parts you need a local permit too
BK Rating:	Moderate to Difficult
Comments:	Night fishing only from 1st June to 31st August

River Ijssel

Location:	Runs through Zwolle which is about 50 miles east of Amsterdam
Type and Size:	A medium sized river with not too much flow
Carp Stock:	Heavily stocked with many twenties and thirties
Permits:	Normal 'Sportvisakte' and local permits are required
Cost:	About £15 a year
Baits/Methods:	Advanced rigs and baits very effective
BK Rating:	Moderate
Comments:	The stretch near Kampen has produced several huge commons. Lots of potential for the serious carp fisher

River Maas

Location:	Runs from Liege heading north to Nijmegen, then west and out to sea below Rotterdam
Type and Size:	A large river with considerable flow at times and regularly used by boats
Carp Stock:	This river yielded the latest Dutch record of about 50lbs in 1991. Tremendous potential
Permits:	Normal 'Sportvisakte'. A permit from a local tackle shop at a cost of about £15 a year is required to fish one of the attached sand pits
BK Rating:	Difficult
Comments:	There are numerous sand pits connected to this river and the ones near the towns of Roermond and Echt are prolific carp venues

Sloterplas

Location:	Amsterdam
Type and Size:	Big lake
How to Find:	East part of Amsterdam
Carp Stock:	Many carp up to well over 30lbs
Other Species:	Many
Permits:	National licence at any post office. Licence from Amsterdamse Hengelsport Vereniging
Control:	Members Amsterdamse Hengelsport Vereniging
BK Rating:	Difficult
Comments:	A very well known fishery

The Ijsselmeer

Location:	North Holland, north of Amsterdam
Type and Size:	Huge inland sea, once salt water, 40 miles long and about 25 miles across and separated from the sea only by the Afsluitdijk, a 12 mile dam built by the Dutch and one of the world's greatest engineering feats
Carp Stock:	Very well stocked with carp, most of which are huge and immensely long wildies which go to well over 20lbs
Category:	Mixed Fishery
Other Species:	Most European coarse fish
Permits:	You must have the official Government licence, the Sportvisakte, obtained from Post Offices at low cost, and valid for two rods for a year. No other permits needed
BK Rating:	Very Difficult, though some huge catches have been made when the fish are located
Comments:	No close season. Best areas are around Amsterdam and Flevoland. Try to get help from someone who knows the area, and may know where carp are caught. When I stood at the middle of the dam, two years ago, the waves on this 'lake' were several feet high, with spray breaking over my head

Gary Delyster with a Dutch common of 36 pounds

The Lakes van het Gooi

Location: Ankeveense plassen; Loenerveense plas; Loosdrechtse plassen; Breukeleveense plassen; Maarseveense plassen; Vinkeveense plassen These are the waters you find in the square Amsterdam-Hilversum-Utrecht-Amstelveen

Carp Stock: There have been catches over 50lbs and there are plenty of carp in the lakes, but the lakes are big

Category: Mixed Fishery

Permits: Government and there are a few places you need a local permit, but you better ask around

BK Rating: Difficult

Comments: Night fishing is not allowed everywhere and not on every place the year round. These water are heavily controlled so best behaviour is a must

T. Luytelaar

Location: Mariahout, near Eindhoven

Type and Size: Lake of about 3 acres

How to Find: Take the N266 and N272 to Lieshout and from there to Mariahout

Carp Stock: Heavily stocked with carp to 30 pounds, mainly commons

Other Species: Big grass carp

Permits: Day tickets available in the village of Mariahout and the address and directions are explained on a signpost at the lake

BK Rating: Easy

Comments: A very peaceful and quiet place to fish

Twentekanaal

Location: Hengelo area, by the warm water outlet
Type and Size: Huge canal, about 80 metres across
Carp Stock: Heavily stocked with many big carp to nearly 40lbs
Category: Mixed Fishery
Other Species: Most coarse fish
Permits: You will need a Sportvisakte, which is a national licence — you *must* not fish in Holland without this licence, which can be bought at all Post Offices and most tackle shops. The licence is annual, covers two rods and costs only about £4 for a year - there is no close season in Holland. You can fish most other Dutch waters with this licence, and no other permits, the exceptions being where a club has the rights, which is usually indicated by the sign 'Verpacht Viswater'
BK Rating: Very Difficult
Comments: This is one of the most famous and pressurised fisheries in Europe, especially as it fishes so well in the winter, due to the warm water. It is wide and very deep, and the boats are of ocean-going size, and will disturb your swim for half an hour after they pass. Best fishing is at night, and the most sophisticated methods and rigs are needed - PM had a blank here too - though nothing at all was caught during the day whilst he was there, although a number of good fish were taken during the night.. after he had left for England! Night fishing only allowed in June, July and August. Steam rises from the water in winter!

Wilhelminakanaal

Location: Tilburg
Type and Size: A long canal which eventually runs out into the sea below Rotterdam
Carp Stock: Sparsely stocked with carp of a good average size
Permits: Normal 'Sportvisakte' required
Baits/Methods: Advanced rigs and baits an advantage
BK Rating: Moderate
Comments: Once one of Holland's top carp waters but not so good nowadays

Zeumerse Plas

Location: A water next to the A1 highway between Amersfoort and Apeldoorn. From the Hook you drive to Den Haag, take the A12 to Utrecht. In Utrecht you take the A28 to Amersfoort. In Amersfoort you take the A1 to Apeldoorn. Leave the road at Voorthuizen, turn left and immediately to the right, now you drive straight to the water

Type and Size: 15 acres

Carp Stock: A lot of commons up to 18lbs

Category: Mixed Fishery

Other Species: Most European coarse fish except zander

Permits: Goverment and local permit, information from: Zevenbergjesweg 27, 3781 NV Voorthuizen

BK Rating: Easy to Moderate

Comments: No baiting, night fishing only from 1st June to 31st August. Very deep water, not under 20 feet, good plumbing necessary. Control every day so keep the place clean

Zuiderdiep

Location: Near the town of Stellendam on the west coast about 15 miles south of the Hook of Holland

Type and Size: A dammed stretch of canal with a soft bottom

Carp Stock: Well stocked with upper doubles and twenties with the occasional thirty pounder

Permits: Normal 'Sportvisakte' and a local permit

Cost: About £15 a year

BK Rating: Easy

Comments: A magnificent water offering high class fishing and only a few minutes drive from the nearest ferry port

---

THE
BEEKAY
GUIDE
TO
1500
BRITISH
& EUROPEAN
CARP
WATERS

Is YOUR Water listed? If so, are the details correct?

If you spot omissions, inaccuracies, or know of any changes, please let us know by filling in the Waters Questionnaire at the back of this guide and return it to us at:

FREEPOST
Beekay Publishers
Withy Pool
Henlow Camp
Bedfordshire
SG16 6EA

SPAIN
by Norman Smith

LA CORUNA

SANTANDER

PORTO

PORTUGAL

LERIDA

SALAMANCA

ZARAGOZA

BARCELONA

MADRID

LISBOA

BADAJOZ

VALENCIA

PORTIMAO

CORDOBA

MURCIA

FARO

SEVILLA

MALAGA

Barragem de Santa Clara   A

Location:	About 70 kms north of Portimao on the N266 road (PORTUGAL)
Type and Size:	Huge attractive reservoir
Carp Stock:	Reputed to hold carp to very large size
Category:	Mixed Fishery
Other Species:	Black bass, barbel, very large catfish
Permits:	Enquire at Tourist Office in Portimao
BK Rating:	Insufficient information
Comments:	Has a Pousada or state run hotel on its banks

Conde de Guadalhorce   A

Location:	62 kms north of Malaga, near the village of Ardales
Type and Size:	Reservoir for irrigation water. Approximately 1350 acres
Carp Stock:	Many carp to double figures. Best fish reported was 25 kilos but bigger fish very few and far between
Category:	Mixed Fishery
Other Species:	Barbel, black bass. Unusually for a southern Spanish fishery, there are also a few pike
Permits:	Licence from IARA office in Malaga - Edificio de Usos Multiples, Avenida de Andalucia

Restrictions: No night fishing. Two rods. Strictly speaking no boats or swimming allowed but pedaloes at campsite and swimming does take place
BK Rating: Easy, except for the few very big fish
Comments: 2000 place municipal campsite on bank. Very popular picnic spot at weekends and on Fiesta days

Embalse Alcantara 2 Jose Maria de Oriol

Location: 48 kms north of Caceres on the N630 road
Type and Size: Largest capacity reservoir in Spain at nearly 30,000 acres
Carp Stock: Large stock of carp, mainly commons to unknown size
Category: Mixed Fishery
Other Species: Barbel, black bass and tench
Restrictions: Two rods. No night fishing
BK Rating: Insufficient information
Comments: Made difficult due to its size, it would take a lifetime to explore it

Embalse de Arcos

Location: 35 kms east of Jerez on the N342
Type and Size: Small reservoir of approximately 80 acres
Carp Stock: Heavily stocked but carp rather small
Category: Mixed Fishery
Other Species: Barbel and black bass
Restrictions: Two rods. No night fishing
BK Rating: Easy
Comments: Fun fishing

Embalse de Azutan

Location: Turn off the N5 Madrid-Badajoz highway at Talavera de la Reina
Type and Size: Reservoir of approximately 3000 acres
Carp Stock: Heavily stocked with mainly wild carp
Category: Mixed Fishery
Other Species: Barbel, tench and black bullhead catfish
Permits: Licences from ICONA office in Toledo
Restrictions: Two rods. No night fishing
BK Rating: Easy
Comments: Fished very little by non-Spanish anglers

Embalse de Bornos

Location: 50 kms east of Jerez de la Frontera to the south of the N342 highway
Type and Size: Reservoir of more than 6000 acres
Carp Stock: Heavily stocked with carp, maximum size not known
Category: Mixed Fishery
Other Species: Barbel, black bass
Restrictions: Two rods. No night fishing
BK Rating: Easy
Comments: Little fished by non-Spanish anglers

Norman Smith with one of his many Spanish carp

Embalse de Buendia

Location: East of Madrid. To the south of the N320 Guadalajara - Cuenca road
Type and Size: Fourth largest reservoir in Spain. More than 20,000 acres
Carp Stock: Carp to 60lbs and more reported
Category: Mixed Fishery
Other Species: Barbel, black bass, pike
Restrictions: Two rods. No night fishing
BK Rating: Difficult, due to size of water

Embalse de Castrejon

Location: 45 kms south west of Toledo
Type and Size: Large reservoir, dammed section of River Tajo. Approximately 1900 acres
Carp Stock: Very large, 90% commons
Category: Mixed Fishery
Other Species: Barbel, tench and black bullhead catfish

Permits: Licences available in ICONA office in Toledo
Restrictions: Two rods. No night fishing
BK Rating: Very Easy for fish up to double figures
Comments: Potential unknown. Very lightly fished

Embalse de Cerro Alarcon

Location: 45 kms west of Madrid
Type and Size: Small reservoir approximately 60 acres
Carp Stock: Heavily stocked with fish of modest size
Category: Mixed Fishery
Other Species: Barbel and black bass
Permits: Licences from ICONA office in Madrid at Calle de Jorge Juan 39
Restrictions: Two rods. No night fishing
BK Rating: Very Easy
Comments: Water reported to be good for fishing and swimming. Lake's prime purpose is recreation. Will get very crowded weekends and fiesta days

Embalse de Chira (Canary Islands)

Location: South of the centre of the island of Gran Canaria 58 kms from Las Palmas
Type and Size: Small irrigation water reservoir of approximately 28 acres
Carp Stock: Good stock of carp to 50lbs plus
Category: Carp Fishery
Permits: ICONA office in Las Palmas
Restrictions: Two rods. No night fishing
BK Rating: Moderate
Comments: Access by difficult mountain roads

Embalse de Cornalbo

Location: 60 kms east of Badajoz
Type and Size: Reservoir of approximately 100 acres
Carp Stock: Holds carp but stock uncertain
Category: Mixed Fishery
Other Species: Not known, but probably barbel and black bass
Permits: This is a special fishing preserve or Coto and an additional permit may be required
Restrictions: Two rods. No night fishing
BK Rating: Easy

Embalse de Cubillas   A

Location: 7 kms north of Granada on N323 Madrid road
Type and Size: Irrigation water reservoir approximately 500 acres
Carp Stock: Very many small to medium sized carp and a few bigger ones to about 20lbs
Category: Mixed Fishery
Other Species: Barbel, black bass and a few pike
Permits: From campsite office or bar San Isidro in nearby village of El Chapparal
Restrictions: Two rods. No night fishing

BK Rating: Very Easy for smaller carp, bigger fish difficult to find
Comments: Very friendly family run campsite at waters edge. Yacht club and windsurf club on opposite bank to campsite

Embalse de Cuevas de Almanzora

Location: To the east of the N340 road just north of the town of Vera
Type and Size: Reservoir of approximately 1400 acres
Carp Stock: Plenty of carp up to double figures
Category: Mixed Fishery
Other Species: Barbel and black bass
Permits: Licence from IARA office in Almeria
Restrictions: Two rods. No night fishing
BK Rating: Moderate
Comments: The driest area of Spain. Water level often low

Embalse de Ebro

Location: 65 kms south of Santander on N623
Type and Size: Huge reservoir of approximately 16,000 acres
Carp Stock: Heavily stocked with carp to 20lb, potential for larger fish not yet explored
Restrictions: Two rods. No night fishing
BK Rating: Insufficient information
Comments: This water boasts an Olympic rowing course

Embalse de Encinarejo

Location: 30 kms north of Andujar in the province of Jaen. Turn off the NIV main Madrid-Cadiz highway
Type and Size: Reservoir of approximately 400 acres
Carp Stock: Some good fish to 35lbs plus
Category: Mixed Fishery
Other Species: Many black bass to good size, also barbel and gudgeon
Restrictions: Two rods. No night fishing
BK Rating: Insufficient information
Comments: Few places where access to water possible due to very steep sides

Embalse de Grena

Location: 50 kms north west of Caceres. Not far from border with Portugal
Type and Size: Small reservoir of about 30 acres
Carp Stock: Holds carp but size and numbers uncertain
Category: Mixed Fishery
Other Species: Barbel and black bass
Restrictions: Two rods. No night fishing
BK Rating: Easy
Comments: Water reported to be rather coloured but providing good fishing. Rarely fished by non-Spanish anglers

Embalse de Guadalhorce

Location:	74 kms north of Malaga on the Campanillas/Alora road
Type and Size:	Irrigation water reservoir of approximately 1800 acres
Carp Stock:	Good stock of carp to double figures, better fish hard to find
Category:	Mixed Fishery
Other Species:	Barbel and black bass
Permits:	From IARA office in Malaga, Edificios de Usos Multiples, Avenida de Andalucia
Restrictions:	No swimming. No motor boats. Two rods. No night fishing
BK Rating:	Easy for fish to double figures. Difficult to find bigger fish
Comments:	Carp respond well to floating crust

Embalse de Guadalteba

Location:	74 kms north of Malaga on the Campanillas-Alora road
Type and Size:	Irrigation water reservoir of approximately 2000 acres
Carp Stock:	Good head of carp to double figures, larger fish exist but hard to find
Category:	Mixed Fishery
Other Species:	Barbel and large black bass
Permits:	Licence from IARA office in Malaga. Edificio de Usos Multiples, Avenida de Andalucia
Restrictions:	No swimming. No motor boats. Two rods. No night fishing
BK Rating:	Easy for smaller fish. Larger carp hard to find
Comments:	Carp respond well to floating crust

Embalse de Iznajar

Location:	Turn off N342 Malaga - Granada road on to C334 to Rute
Type and Size:	Ninth largest reservoir in Spain at approximately 7000 acres
Carp Stock:	Large number of fish to large size
Category:	Mixed Fishery
Other Species:	Barbel and black bass
Permits:	IARA office in Granada
Restrictions:	Two rods. No night fishing
BK Rating:	Easy for smaller fish. Big fish Very Difficult to locate

Embalse de Jandula

Location:	35 kms north of Andujar in the province of Jaen. Turn north off the N4 highway
Type and Size:	Large reservoir of 2,250 acres
Carp Stock:	Numbers uncertain but fish to 30lbs plus
Category:	Mixed Fishery
Other Species:	Large numbers of black bass plus barbel and gudgeon
Restrictions:	Two rods. No night fishing
BK Rating:	Insufficient information, but good potential

Embalse de la Concepcion

Location:	To the west of Marbella, turn north off the N340 towards Istan
Type and Size:	Drinking water reservoir
Carp Stock:	Carp to double figures
Category:	Mixed Fishery

Other Species: Barbel
Permits: Licence from IARA office in Malaga - Edificio de Usos Multiples,
Avenida de Andalucia
Restrictions: No swimming. No motor boats. Two rods. No night fishing
BK Rating: Easy
Comments: Access to water difficult due to very steep sides

Embalse de la Vinuela

Location: North of Velez Malaga to the west of the C335 road
Type and Size: Reservoir of approximately 1500 acres
Carp Stock: Plenty of small carp, potential for bigger fish unexplored
Category: Mixed Fishery
Other Species: Barbel and black bass
Permits: Licence from IARA office in Malaga, Edificio de Usos Multiples,
Avenida de Andalucia
Restrictions: Two rods. No night fishing
BK Rating: Easy

Embalse de los Bermejales

Location: 44 kms south west of Granada, turn south off N342 towards Alhama
de Granada
Type and Size: Reservoir, approximately 175 acres
Carp Stock: Plenty of carp to double figures. Otherwise unknown
Category: Mixed Fishery
Other Species: Barbel and black bass
Permits: Licences available from IARA office in Granada
Restrictions: Two rods. No night fishing
BK Rating: Easy for smaller fish
Comments: Potential unknown. Little fished

Embalse de los Hurones   A

Location: 100 kms east of Jerez on the C344
Type and Size: Drinking water reservoir of approximately 2250 acres
Carp Stock: Many carp up to 5lbs or so, larger fish difficult to find
Category: Mixed Fishery
Other Species: Barbel and black bass
Restrictions: No swimming. No motor boats. Two rods. No night fishing
BK Rating: Easy
Comments: This fishery has a Parador (government run luxury hotel) close by

Embalse de Mequinenza

Location: 45 kms south west of Lerida
Type and Size: Fifth largest reservoir in Spain, nearly 20,000 acres
Carp Stock: Good stock of fish to 40lbs, although the average is less than 10lbs
Category: Mixed Fishery
Other Species: Catfish to 100lbs plus, large black bass and barbel
Restrictions: Two rods. No night fishing

BK Rating: Moderate for good fish
Comments: A water with enormous potential for anyone with the time to explore it. This water boasts an Olympic rowing course. Most of the larger carp caught have taken a dead fish

Embalse de Proserpina

Location: 5 kms north of Merida just off the N630 road
Type and Size: Small, very old reservoir of about 20 acres
Carp Stock: Uncertain but known to exist
Category: Mixed Fishery
Other Species: Barbel
Permits: Additional permit may be required as this is a special fishing preserve or Coto
Restrictions: Two rods. No night fishing
BK Rating: Easy
Comments: Fishing reported to be very good but used as a recreation area so best avoided at weekends

Embalse de Santillana

Location: 48 kms north of Madrid turn off N1 highway to Colmenar Viejo
Type and Size: Irrigation water reservoir approximately 2400 acres
Carp Stock: Good stock of carp to huge sizes, fish of 60lbs plus reported and even bigger fish seen. Mainly commons
Category: Carp Fishery
Permits: This is a nature reserve and permits are difficult to come by. They are issued together with the licences from the ICONA office at Calle de Jorge Juan 39, Madrid
Restrictions: Two rods. No night fishing
BK Rating: Moderate
Comments: A major fish kill was reported from this area in 1991. It is not known how this has affected the stocks

Embalse de Sau

Location: 28 kms west of Gerona
Type and Size: Drinking water reservoir of approximately 1850 acres
Carp Stock: Reputed to hold very big carp
Permits: From ICONA office in Gerona
Restrictions: No swimming. No motor boats. Two rods. No night fishing
BK Rating: Insufficient information
Comments: Water reported to be dirty looking

Embalse de Soria (Canary Islands)

Location: To the south of the centre of the island of Gran Canaria. 58 kms from Las Palmas
Type and Size: Modest sized reservoir approximately 170 acres
Carp Stock: Plenty of good sized fish to 50lbs plus
Category: Carp Fishery
Permits: From the ICONA office in Las Palmas
Restrictions: Two rods. No night fishing
BK Rating: Moderate
Comments: Approached by difficult mountain roads

Another upper
double for Norman
Smith from Spain

Embalse de Susqueda

Location: 29 kms west of Gerona
Type and Size: Drinking water reservoir of approximately 1300 acres
Carp Stock: Reputed to hold very large carp
Permits: From the ICONA office in Gerona
Restrictions: No swimming. No motor boats. Possible other restrictions regarding angling. Enquire when buying licence. Two rods. No night fishing
BK Rating: Insufficient information

Embalse de Valdajos

Location: Turn north off the N400 Ocana - Taracon road at Sta Cruz de la Zarza
Type and Size: Small irrigation water reservoir of approximately 10 acres. Dam constructed 1530
Carp Stock: Large head of carp to 5lbs; bigger fish exist but hard to find
Category: Carp Fishery
Other Species: Barbel and tench
Permits: ICONA office in Toledo
Restrictions: Two rods. No night fishing
BK Rating: Easy

Embalse de Valdecanas

Location: 10 kms south of Navalmoral de la Mata. Turn off main N5 Madrid-Badajoz highway
Type and Size: Sixth largest reservoir in Spain at more than 20,000 acres
Carp Stock: Large head of carp, mainly commons

Category:	Mixed Fishery
Other Species:	Barbel, tench, black bass and spiny catfish
Restrictions:	Two rods. No night fishing
BK Rating:	Easy
Comments:	Rarely fished by non-Spanish anglers. Potential unknown

Embalse de Valmayor

Location:	29 kms west of Madrid
Type and Size:	Drinking water reservoir of approximately 1900 acres
Carp Stock:	Good stock of carp to 20lbs plus
Category:	Mixed Fishery
Other Species:	Pike, barbel and sun bass
Permits:	From ICONA office in Madrid, Calle Jorge Juan 39
Restrictions:	No swimming. No motor boats. Two rods. No night fishing
BK Rating:	Moderate
Comments:	Very popular water with the locals. Heavily bailiffed. It is possible that extra permits are required. Enquire when buying licence

Embalse de Vellon

Location:	45 kms north of Madrid, turn off N1 highway towards Guadalix de la Sierra
Type and Size:	Irrigation water reservoir of approximately 1000 acres
Carp Stock:	Heavy stock of mainly common carp to 40lbs plus. Fish of 60lbs reported by Spanish press
Category:	Carp Fishery
Other Species:	Pike and tench
Permits:	Licence from ICONA Calle de Jorge Juan 39, Madrid
Restrictions:	Two rods. No night fishing
BK Rating:	Easy for carp to 20lbs; Moderate to 35lbs
Comments:	Yacht club and windsurf club. Banks very busy weekends and fiesta days. Stocks now rather uncertain since partial draining in 1989

Ribeira de Arade (Portugal)

Location:	Town of Silves, about 38kms inland from Portimao
Type and Size:	Small attractive river, looks almost like a chalk stream
Carp Stock:	Large numbers of carp to double figures
Category:	Mixed Fishery
Other Species:	Large numbers of grey mullet to good size
Permits:	Enquire at Tourist Office in Portimao
BK Rating:	Easy
Comments:	Bottom baits only due to the mullet taking anything presented on the surface or midwater

Rio Ebro

Location:	Countless good fishing areas including Amposta, Tivenys, Tortosa, Mesquinenza etc, almost anywhere on this river will fish well
Type and Size:	Huge river that runs right across Spain and empties into the Mediterranean about halfway between Tarragona and Castellon
Carp Stock:	Enormous numbers of small common carp but some of a very large size especially in the river's many reservoirs

Category: Mixed Fishery
Other Species: Catfish to 100lbs plus, barbel, black bass, chub, dace and pike
Permits: This river flows through many different licensing areas
Restrictions: Two rods. No night fishing
BK Rating: Easy
Comments: It would take a lifetime just to visit all the fishing areas on this river and a book the size of the Bible to detail them all

David Maddocks with a typical Ebro common carp. Fish of this size are typical of the Ebro, where carp spawn several times a year and tend to over-populate

Rio Fluvia

Location: Flows west/east about 40 kms north of Gerona
Type and Size: Smallish river
Carp Stock: Mainly wildies with a few mirrors
Category: Mixed Fishery
Other Species: Barbel, rudd and borgue
Restrictions: Two rods. No night fishing
BK Rating: Easy
Comments: Due to improvements now flows underground in places

Rio Guadalquivir

Location: Cordoba
Type and Size: Major river running from Jaen to San Lucar de Barrameda
Carp Stock: Many carp to 5lbs plus can be seen clearly from the bridges crossing the river within city limits
Category: Mixed Fishery
Other Species: Barbel
Permits: IARA office in Cordoba
Restrictions: Two rods. No night fishing
BK Rating: Easy
Comments: This river is an important trout fishery in its upper reaches but is badly polluted as it passes through Jaen by olive oil producing factories. Easy access within the city of Cordoba, cars can be driven to water's edge during summer months

Rio Tajo

Location:	Flows round three sides of the city of Toledo
Type and Size:	Huge river. Flows right across Spain and empties into the sea in Portugal
Carp Stock:	Almost paved with carp up to double figures
Category:	Carp Fishery
Other Species:	Barbel, tench and black bullhead catfish
Permits:	Licences from ICONA office in Toledo
Restrictions:	Two rods. No night fishing
BK Rating:	Very Easy
Comments:	Carp respond well to floating crust

Rio Teba

Location:	Turn off the C341 Ronda Campillos road at Teba, signposted to Ardales
Type and Size:	Very small, rather muddy river
Carp Stock:	Small head of carp to low double figures
Category:	Carp Fishery
Permits:	Licence from IARA office in Malaga, Edificio de Usos Multiples, Avenida de Andalucia
Restrictions:	Two rods. No night fishing
BK Rating:	Easy
Comments:	Not worth a special trip as access is limited to area either side of the road bridge but if you are in the area fishing one of the reservoirs it is worth a try for an hour or two. It is often possible to take one or even two decent fish

Rio Ter

Location:	Rises inland and flows through Gerona into the sea near Torroella de Montgri
Type and Size:	Good sized river; the flow varies a lot, not only with the season but due to various improvements
Carp Stock:	Mainly wild carp to 7lb plus
Category:	Mixed Fishery
Other Species:	Barbel, rudd and borgue
Restrictions:	Two rods. No night fishing
BK Rating:	Easy
Comments:	Polluted in region of Gerona

Tranco de Beas   A

Location:	Within the National Park of La Cazorla (Jaen)
Type and Size:	Reservoir of approximately 4500 acres
Carp Stock:	Many carp to unknown size, possibly quite large
Category:	Mixed Fishery
Other Species:	Barbel and black bass
Permits:	Enquire at control points at entrance to park
Restrictions:	Two rods. No night fishing
BK Rating:	Easy
Comments:	Many hostels and campsite within park limits

Index

EUROPEAN WATERS

Waters Questionnaire

Please insert name of contact...
Tel (............) .... who can verify details

Name: ....

Location: ....

Type and Size: ....

How to Find: ....

Carp Stock: ....

Other Species: ....

Permits: ....

Control: ....

Cost: ....

Restrictions: ....

Baits/Methods: ....

Comments: ....

Please insert name of contact...
Tel (............) .... who can verify details

Name: ....

Location: ....

Type and Size: ....

How to Find: ....

Carp Stock: ....

Other Species: ....

Permits: ....

Control: ....

Cost: ....

Restrictions: ....

Baits/Methods: ....

Comments: ....

Please return to:

FREEPOST Beekay Publishers
Withy Pool
Henlow Camp
Bedfordshire
SG16 6EA